Earth Science

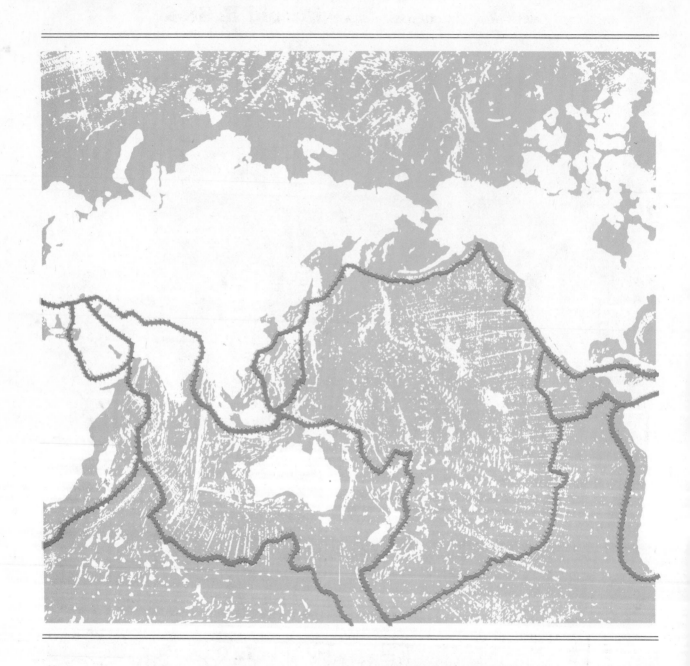

AMERICAN BOOK COMPANY

Samuel N. Namowitz
with the editorial assistance of **Donald B. Stone**

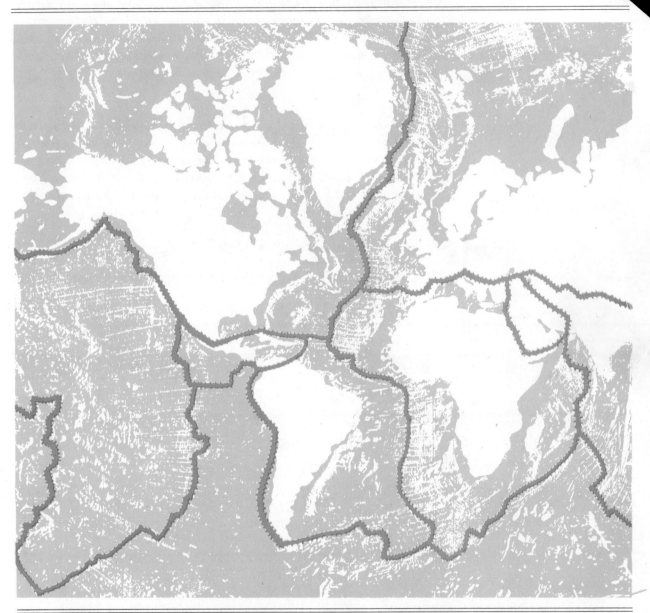

Earth Science

N. Namowitz

Formerly Principal, Charles Evans Hughes High School, New York City. Has been actively teaching earth science as a teacher in public high schools for over 25 years, and an instructor in geology and earth science at the college level, as well as at NSF Summer Institutes. He has written numerous articles for professional journals and The Book of Knowledge. He has also presided over or been a member of several New York City and New York State Earth Science Committees.

Donald B. Stone

Formerly lecturer in earth science, Russell Sage College, Troy, New York. Has taught earth science at both the high school and college level for many years; has also taught earth science teaching methods at several NSF Summer Institutes. He has written many articles for professional journals and co-authored other educational materials. He is presently lecturer in earth science at Union College, Schenectady, N.Y.

Illustrations: Audrey Namowitz

Cover Art: Jerome Kresch

AMERICAN BOOK COMPANY

New York   Cincinnati   Atlanta   Dallas   San Francisco

Copyright © 1978 by Litton Educational Publishing, Inc.

ISBN 0-278-47400-4

5   7   9   11   12   10   8   6

Preface

In this edition of EARTH SCIENCE every effort has been made to simplify the language of the text while maintaining the treatment of the subject at the same high level as in the preceding editions. Emphasis on scientific inquiry has been continued and expanded. Students begin with inquiries on their own from every chapter. Then students are introduced to the questions and problems that challenge the earth scientist. Throughout the text students devise and conduct simple inquiries of their own into problems of the earth sciences.

New Text Materials

In Chapter 1, students are introduced to the theory of plate tectonics, a growing area of geology that attempts to describe the structure of the earth and the origin of the continents. This new chapter presents both the theories and the supporting evidence. Plate tectonics is treated in greater detail in Chapters 12 and 13. There are further references at appropriate places throughout.

Unit 4 on the oceans has been revised to keep pace with oceanographic research, tools, methods, and data. Unit 5 on the earth and the universe has been updated in both stellar astronomy and the solar system, exploring space, and our moon.

Metric units are used exclusively throughout the text except in the chapters on Atmospheric Science. There, topics use the system of the U.S. National Weather Service for the most part. The Appendix contains tables on measurement and metric units based on SI—the International System of Measurement.

Learning Aids

In addition to the features just described, this edition retains many of the learning tools teachers have found so helpful in previous editions. These include:

1. Illustrative Materials. Full-color and black-and-white photographs, including many color photos of rocks and minerals, two-color line drawings, and tables and charts are used to introduce, reinforce, and extend concepts. New line drawings and carefully selected new photographs, mostly in full color, have been added to maintain the high standard of illustration throughout the text.

2. Topic Questions. Numbered Topic Questions at the end of each chapter direct students to the main ideas covered in the same-numbered topic within the chapter.

3. General Questions. These questions at the end of the chapter call for student application of concepts to new problems. Some questions require students to tie together the main ideas of several topics.

4. Student Activities. These activities at the end of the chapter suggest practical investigations and projects related to the work of the chapter.

5. Topographic Sheets. Suggestions and references for topographic maps pertinent to chapter content are listed at the end of the chapter.

6. Vocabulary and Pronunciation Guides. Key vocabulary words are printed in bold-face type within the text. The phonetic pronunciation of difficult or unfamiliar words is provided within the text following the first appearance of the word.

7. Appendix. At the end of the book is an appendix that includes a chapter on topographic maps, measurement tables, a table of the chemical elements, a simple key to the identification of minerals, and a table listing the properties of the common minerals.

8. Glossary and Index. At the end of the book there is an extensive glossary and an exhaustive index.

Components

TEACHER'S EDITION helps the teacher manage an earth science program that has both variety and appropriateness for different classrooms. A three-track Outline of Topics covered in the basic text shows how topics may be assigned for students of various ability levels. The Guide is organized by lessons, and the topics to be covered in each lesson are indicated; concepts and suggestions for each lesson are provided. Answers to all the General Questions at the end of the chapter are included. The TEACHER'S EDITION also includes sources of visual aids, specific suggestions for films and film-strips, a list of supply houses and sources of materials, and a bibliography.

Annotated Student Text Pages. This feature helps the teacher reinforce major earth science concepts, provides additional information, and suggests additional activities for the student. Over-printed references to experiments from the ACTIVITIES book are given at appropriate places in the text.

ACTIVITIES IN EARTH SCIENCE is a laboratory manual providing "hands-on" learning experiences. It contains a variety of investigations for classroom, laboratory, and the field. Detailed instructions enable students to work on their own or in small groups. The Activities book may be used to supplement the basic earth science program, or it may be used alone to build concepts and process skills in a laboratory-oriented program. An annotated Teacher's Edition is available.

TESTS FOR EARTH SCIENCE is a self-scoring set of chapter tests on spirit duplicating masters. Each chapter of the basic text is covered in a test, and answers are provided on the front of each master in nonreproducing form.

Acknowledgments

The authors wish to acknowledge the assistance given by a number of people at various stages in the evolution of this edition. Critical reviews of units in their areas of specialization were made by Professor Maurice Rosalsky of the Department of Geology, Professor Richard Rommer of the Department of Meteorology and Oceanography, and Dr. Robert Wolf, Chairman of the Department of Physics, all at the City College of New York. Dr. Donald Fisher provided a critical reading of the Earth History Unit. Last, but not least, the authors wish to thank the many correspondents, both teachers and pupils, whose helpful suggestions with respect to previous editions have resulted in many subtle refinements in the language and illustrations of the text.

S.N.N., D.B.S.

Contents

unit one   Structure of a Dynamic Earth   *x*

1   The Origin of the Earth   2
Origin of the solar system; how the oceans, atmosphere, and rocks are formed.

2   The Earth's Shape, Dimensions, and Internal Heat   15
What shape, how big?; how heavy, how hot?

3   Atoms to Minerals   22
What rocks are made from; elements, atoms, and isotopes; compound minerals; minerals that are crystals.

4   How to Know the Minerals   36
Identifying minerals; descriptions of rock-forming minerals.

5   How Our Rocks Were Formed   50
Igneous rocks; sedimentary rocks; metamorphic rocks.

unit two   Forces That Attack the Surface   74

6   Weathering and Mass Movement   76
Weathering; mass movement; soils.

7   Water Moving Underground   92
Fresh water on the earth; wells and springs; temperature of ground water; caverns and mineral deposits.

8   Running Water   110
Stream erosion and transportation; the river valley; waterfalls; river deposits; the flood plain and floods.

9   Glaciers   130
Ice Age; types of glaciers; glacier movement; deposits by glaciers; the Ice Age.

10   Erosion by Winds   151

11   Erosion by Waves and Currents   161
Waves in the sea; features formed by waves and currents; shoreline: corals.

unit three   Forces That Raise the Surface   178

12   **Volcanism and Plate Tectonics**   *180*
Volcanic eruption and plate tectonics; materials erupted from volcanoes; classes of volcanoes: famous eruptions; igneous intrusions.

13   **Earthquakes and Plate Tectonics**   *197*
How earthquakes originate; locating and measuring earthquakes; plates and the earth's interior.

14   **The Origin of Mountains**   *209*
The rocks move; faulting, plateaus, and mountains; mountains and plate tectonics.

unit four   The Oceans   222

15   **The Composition and Temperature of Ocean Waters**   *224*
Early research: minerals in sea water; heat, gases, and life in the sea.

16   **The Ocean Floor and Its Sediments**   *235*
Features of the ocean floor; sediments of the ocean floor.

17   **Ocean Currents**   *251*
Currents under the surface; surface currents.

unit five   The Earth and the Universe   262

18   **Studying the Heavens**   *264*
How telescopes work; radio waves; the spectroscope.

19   **Stars and Galaxies**   *275*
What stars are like; stars and their brightness; life history of stars; galaxies and the universe; how the stars look from earth.

20   **The Sun and the Solar System**   *296*
The sun; the planets and Kepler's laws; describing the planets; other parts of the solar system.

21   **Our Moon**   *322*
Studying the moon; the moon's surface features; the moon's motions; sun, moon, and tides.

22   **The Earth's Motions**   *346*
Revolution and rotation; daylight, night, and the seasons.

23   **Location, Navigation, and Time**   *357*
Latitude and longitude; navigation; time and date.

viii   *Contents*

unit six Atmospheric Science 370

24 **The Heating of the Atmosphere** 372
Composition and structure; heating of the atmosphere; measuring air temperature.

25 **Atmospheric Pressure and Winds** 389
Studying air pressure; studying winds.

26 **World Wind Belts** 402
Origin of world wind belts; other winds and wind shifts.

27 **Evaporation and Condensation** 415
Evaporation; relative humidity and condensation; forms of condensation.

28 **Precipitation** 431
From clouds to rain; where and when it rains.

29 **Air Masses and Fronts** 440
Air masses; fronts.

30 **Storms and Weather Forecasts** 449
Middle latitude lows; tropical storms; tornadoes and thunderstorms described; lightning and thunder.

31 **Factors that Control Climate** 467
Climate and temperature controls; factors that control rainfall.

32 **A Matter of Ecology** 477

unit seven Earth History 484

33 **The Rock Record** 486
Eras, periods, and fossils; measuring geological time.

34 **Precambrian Through Paleozoic** 501
Precambrian time; the Paleozoic era.

35 **Mesozoic Through Cenozoic** 514
The Mesozoic era: Age of Reptiles; the Cenozoic era: Age of Mammals.

Appendix 533
Topographic Maps 533
The Metric System and SI Units 542
The Chemical Elements 543
Properties of Some Common Minerals 544
Mineral Identification Key 546
Glossary 547
Index 559

Since people have
been in space, we have been able to
see photographs of the earth as a whole, as
shown on the page opposite. Actually, this photo
shows only one quarter of the earth. The far side is not
seen, of course. Why can't you see all of the near side?
What does this tell you about the position of the sun with
respect to the earth when the picture was taken from Apollo 10?

Apollo 10 was one of the United States missions to the moon. The part of the earth that can be seen in this photograph includes Europe, Asia, and parts of Africa. These large land masses appear in the photograph almost as a single giant continent. The continents you can't see are separated from these by many kilometers of ocean. It would be easy to suppose that Europe, Asia, and Africa are joined underwater as one continent, and that the other continents have always been separate. Scientists now believe, however, that all the continents and parts of the continents are riding on separate chunks of the earth's crust. The African "chunk," or plate, is separate from the plate that includes Europe and part of Asia. These plates are moving with respect to one another.

It is believed that, at one time in the distant past, the plates containing the continents had moved so that they were all together. All the land was in one place and the rest of the earth was a vast ocean.

Here you see the earth as a ball floating in space, with no
neighbors nearer than the moon. Its crust is composed of
rocks and minerals, much of it covered by oceans.
The earth's atmosphere is filled with clouds
of water vapor. All of this, and more,
forms the subject matter of
earth science.

Structure of a Dynamic Earth

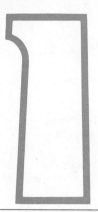

The sun and other stars are very hot. The earth's interior is also hot. Where did this heat come from? Some sources are suggested in the following investigations.

1. Blow up a balloon. Let the air escape against the back of your hand from only a couple of centimeters away. Is the air hotter or colder than the surrounding air? What caused the difference in temperature?

In this case the change in temperature is caused by expansion of the gas. What do you think will happen if you compress a gas? Try it. Take a bicycle pump and quickly pump up a bicycle tire. Now feel the tire and the valve. Was your prediction correct?

2. Hammer a large nail into a board quickly. When the nail is almost in, stop and feel the nail and the face of the hammer. Is there a temperature change? If so, this change was caused by hitting, or impact.

The Origin of the Earth

Origin of the Solar System

Earth science is the study of the earth. It includes *geology,* which is the study of rocks and land, *oceanography,* which is the study of the oceans, and *meteorology* and *climatology,* the study of the atmosphere.

Earth science is also interested in our neighbors in space. So it also includes the science of *astronomy.* Where shall we begin our earth science—land, oceans, atmosphere, sky? Perhaps a good place is where the earth begins—the origin of the earth itself.

Of course, the earth is only one member of a family of planets belonging to the sun. This family is the *solar system.* All of the planets in the solar system probably had their origin at the same time.

We picture our solar system this way.

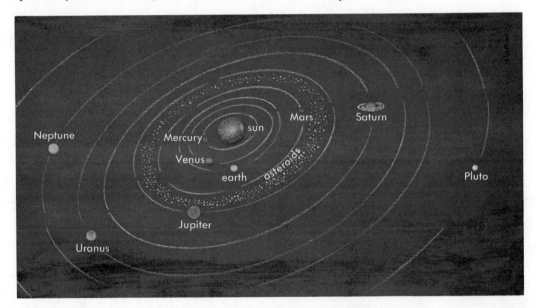

2. **Facts about the Solar System**

Many explanations, or *hypotheses,* have been proposed for the origin of the solar system. All of them have had to consider these facts:

1. All of the planets *revolve* around the sun in the same direction (counterclockwise as viewed from above our North Pole).
2. The paths, or *orbits,* of the planets around the sun are all nearly circular.

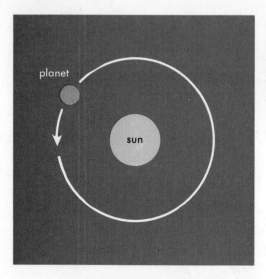

All planets revolve around the
sun in long paths.

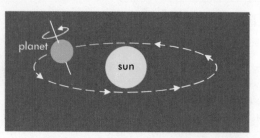

**All planets rotate around
an imaginary line
through their centers.**

3. The orbits of the planets are all in nearly the same flat surface,
   or *plane.*
4. The sun turns on its axis (*rotates*) in almost the same plane as
   the planets, and in the same direction as they revolve.
5. Most of the planets rotate in the same direction as the sun.
6. Six planets have moons. Most of these revolve around the
   planets in the same direction as the planets revolve around the
   sun.
7. The sun's rate of rotation is slower than expected by scientists.

Let us see how a few famous hypotheses have tried to explain
these observed facts.

Encounter Hypotheses

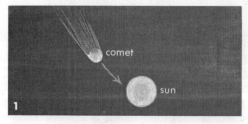

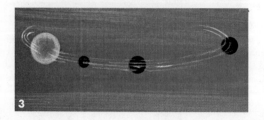

Most hypotheses of the solar system origin fall into two groups: encounter hypotheses and nebular hypotheses.

All of the **encounter hypotheses** state that our solar system began
nearly five billion years ago, with our sun already in existence. Let us
imagine back to that time; the sun is just an ordinary star whirling
through space. Then an extraordinary event takes place. Another
heavenly object—usually a star—passes very close to the sun.

The first scientist to suggest an encounter hypothesis was Count
Buffon of France in 1749. In Buffon's version, the sun's encounter is
not with a star. Instead, a great comet collides with the sun!

The collision throws many great streams of gas from the sun.
These streams all move in the same direction around the sun. After
millions of years they shrink into ball-shaped bodies. The largest
streams become *planets.* Smaller streams become moons, or *satellites,*
of the planets. Still other streams fail to shrink and remain as *comets.*

In 1895 the American scientists Chamberlin and Moulton proposed their *planetesimal hypothesis.* This hypothesis avoids a collision

**Buffon thought that a comet and the sun collided,
throwing out streams of gas from the sun.**

Structure of a Dynamic Earth

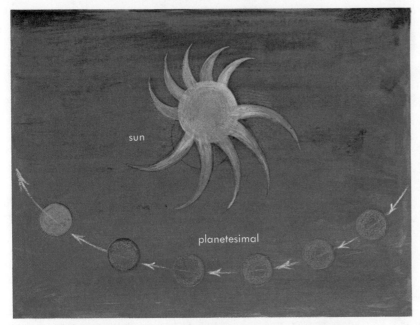

Chamberlin and Moulton suggested that a passing star pulled gas from the sun. The gas then shrank into planetesimals.

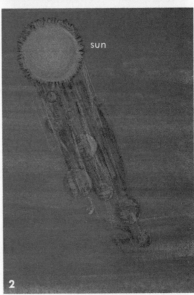

by using the force of gravity to pull the planets from the sun. Gravity pulls stars together just as it pulls a thrown stone and the earth together.

There is an encounter between the sun and another star, and great quantities of gas flow from the sun into space. The other star's gravitational attraction pulls gas from the sun. The gas shrinks into cold, solid rocklike masses called *planetesimals*. These "grow" together by gravitational attraction and collisions to form the planets and their moons.

Still another hypothesis was the *tidal hypothesis* proposed by the Englishmen Jeans and Jeffrey in 1917. In this explanation, the encounter between the sun and another star is so close that gravitational attraction causes a great tidal bulge in the sun. This bulge splits off and breaks up to form the planets.

What are the weaknesses of encounter hypotheses?

First, the close meeting of two stars (that such hypotheses require) is extremely unlikely.

Second, if planets were formed after stars encountered each other, they should be much closer to the sun than they are.

Third, some of the hypotheses fail to explain why the sun rotates so slowly.

Finally, they have difficulty accounting for the moons of the planets.

Jeans and Jeffrey proposed a tidal bulge that was caused by the sun's encounter with another star. The bulge formed into planets.

The Origin of the Earth **5**

Nebular hypotheses begin with the sun not yet in existence. A huge cloud of gas, much larger than the entire solar system today, rotates slowly in space. Millions of years pass. The great cloud, or *nebula*, cools and shrinks. The shrinking makes it spin faster. This happens for the same reason that spinning skaters spin faster when they fold their arms. The increased speed causes the nebula to throw off a ring, then another, until nine rings form, one inside the other.

Meanwhile the cloud at the center of the rings has shrunk greatly. But shrinking causes compression, and compression causes heating. (Feel the valve when you pump up a tire!) The cloud at the center of the ring becomes fiery hot, "burning" in the same way as a hydrogen bomb burns, but with enough hydrogen fuel to last it for many billions of years. It has become the star we call the sun.

While this takes place, the nine rings split open and shrink into planets and their moons. Sun, planets, and moons are all spinning in the same direction as the nebula from which they were formed.

A nebular hypothesis was first suggested by the German scientist Kant in 1755. Kant's idea was slightly changed by the Frenchman Laplace in 1796.

Critics of the nebular hypothesis have pointed out two major weaknesses in it. First, the "rings" could not have contained enough matter to condense into planets. Second, it too fails to explain why the sun rotates so slowly.

The nebular hypothesis of Laplace was a popular theory for many years. As a great cloud spins, it throws off nine rings that form the planets.

Even today we have no complete explanation of the origin of the solar system. The hypothesis most in favor now is the **protoplanet hypothesis.** It was first proposed about the year 1944 by the German astronomer von Weizsacker.

Like the nebular hypothesis, the protoplanet hypothesis begins with a great cloud of gas and dust. The cloud shrinks under the pull of its own gravitation. Most of its material gathers around its center, becoming hot enough by compression to form the sun. Unlike the nebular hypothesis, however, no separate rings are formed. About 10 percent of the matter in the cloud forms a single disk around the sun. The disk rotates slowly with the sun. Friction within the disk causes most of its material to collect in several huge whirlpool-like *eddies.* These shrink into more compact masses called *protoplanets,* and later into planets and moons. Some "uncollected" materials still remain as comets, meteors, and planetoids.

How does this modern hypothesis overcome the objections to the nebular hypothesis? First, it replaces the unlikely rings with more likely eddies. Second, it suggests an explanation of the sun's slow rotation.

Why do modern hypotheses favor a nebular origin over a star-encounter origin? The answer lies in the low probability of stars' meeting. Although there are millions of stars, they are very far apart. Star encounters are the rarest of happenings at best.

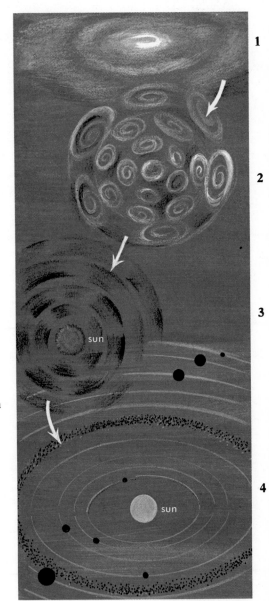

1   The protoplanet hypothesis is favored today. It, too, begins with a cloud of dust and gas.

2   Gravity causes the cloud to shrink. As it does, eddies form in the cloud.

3   The eddies also shrink, forming the masses that become the planets.

4   Finally the protoplanets change into the planets and moons we know today.

How the Oceans, Atmosphere, and Rocks Are Formed

Origin of the Oceans 6.

Scientists now agree that when the earth first formed, it had neither oceans nor atmosphere. But as the protoplanet Earth changed to the planet Earth, it grew hotter and hotter. There were three sources of heat: compression, radioactive minerals, and bombardment by showers of meteors. Radioactive minerals are natural substances that give off energy, which becomes heat. Meteors produce heat both by friction and by impact. (Feel a nail that has been hit hard several times with a hammer!)

When the earth became hot enough, volcanoes erupted, bringing hot liquid rock (*lava*) and hot gases to the surface. The gases contained vast amounts of steam, which turned into the water that slowly filled the oceans. This was fresh water. The salt we now find in ocean waters was carried into them by rivers over billions of years. The rivers dissolved the salt from the rocks over which they flowed.

Origin of the Atmosphere 7.

The atmosphere that surrounds the earth today includes about 78% nitrogen and 21% oxygen. These gases are *free;* they are not combined with other elements. The remaining 1% is mostly the gases argon, carbon dioxide, and helium. (Water vapor is in the atmosphere, too; but it varies in amount with weather and climate.)

This present mixture is very different from what scientists think the earth's original atmosphere must have been. They believe that the original atmosphere came from volcanoes and was like the mixture of gases that now erupts from volcanoes. This mixture usually is more than half water vapor, with large amounts of carbon dioxide and sulfur gases. But it contains *no free oxygen!*

Almost all forms of life on the earth today need free oxygen. Where, then, did it come from? Scientists think the atmosphere's first free oxygen came from the breakup of water molecules by sunlight in the upper atmosphere. Water is a particular combination of hydrogen and oxygen. Then as simple green plants came into existence, they added more and more free oxygen to the atmosphere by *photosynthesis.* In this process, green plants manufacture sugars and starches from carbon dioxide and water in the presence of sunlight. But more than half of the oxygen in the carbon dioxide and water is left over. This is released into the atmosphere as free oxygen.

Geologists today have a fairly clear picture of the earth's structure from its surface to its very center. Since the center is nearly 6400 kilometers from the surface, most of this picture of the earth is obviously based on indirect evidence. This evidence will be discussed when you study earthquakes.

As for now, look at the "earth model" that geologists describe. It has a spherical **inner core** 2575 kilometers in diameter, made of *solid* iron and nickel. Surrounding this is an **outer core** 2175 kilometers thick made of *liquid* iron and nickel. Then comes a 2900 kilometers thick layer of heavy rocks rich in compounds of iron, magnesium, and silicon. This layer is called the **mantle.** It reaches almost to the earth's surface. The mantle is covered by a layer of lighter rocks called the **crust.** The crust ranges in thickness from about 10 kilometers to about 65 kilometers. Mines and wells go deep into the crust, but none has ever reached the mantle.

Was the earth layered like this when it formed more than four billion years ago? Not at all. If we believe the protoplanet hypothesis, the surface of the earth then looked very much like the moon does today. And below the surface, the earth was probably composed of the same kind of rock all the way to its center.

How then, did the earth develop its layers of core, mantle, and crust? Many geologists think that as the newly formed earth heated up, large quantities of iron and nickel in its rocks melted. Then these great streams of hot heavy liquids flowed downwards towards the earth's center. On their way down they melted lighter rock materials and forced them up to the surface. There the light rock became solid and formed the earth's crust. The mantle formed between the crust and the core.

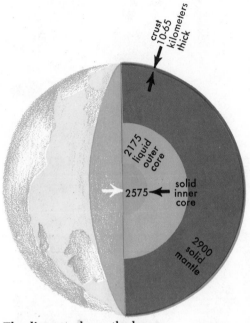

The diagram shows the layers that form the solid earth.

9. How the Continents Formed

One hypothesis suggests that when the melted iron and nickel sank into the earth's core, it forced out enough light rock to form an immense single continent. Another suggestion is that the continents were formed from great flows of lava that erupted from volcanoes over a period of hundreds of millions of years. In either case, today's continents are quite different from those that first formed on the earth's surface. In the billions of years following their origin, the continents have undergone many changes. We shall see in the succeeding chapters how these changes occurred.

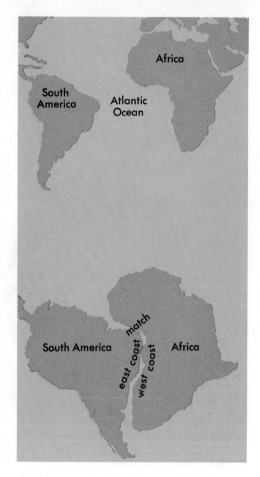

Can continents really "drift" on the earth's surface? In 1915 a German scientist named Alfred Wegener proposed his **hypothesis of continental drift.** Wegener was impressed by the way the east coast of South America matches the west coast of Africa. He also noted the somewhat less perfect fit of the east coast of North America with the west coast of North Africa and Europe. To explain these "jig-saw puzzle" fits, Wegener suggested that all the present continents came from a single vast *protocontinent* which he called Pangaea.

Pangaea, said Wegener, split up several hundred million years ago into continent-size pieces that had moved slowly apart. The split between America and Europe formed at the mid-Atlantic Ridge. This is a huge undersea mountain chain that stretches from Iceland almost to Antarctica. North America and South America moved westward, the other continents moved eastward, and the Atlantic Ocean opened between them.

Wegener's picture of drifting continents was attractive. It "solved" a global jig-saw puzzle. It also explained why rocks and certain remains of ancient plants and animals from mountains in South Africa and Argentina—a whole ocean apart—were so much alike. But Wegener could not explain what made his protocontinent split and move. Neither could Wegener produce any direct evidence that the continents were moving.

Wegener noticed that the coasts of South America and Africa could be fit like pieces of a puzzle. He developed the notion of an original supercontinent he called Pangaea, from which the present continents split and drifted apart.

Although the coastlines of Africa and South America fit, the split is at the Mid-Atlantic Ridge.

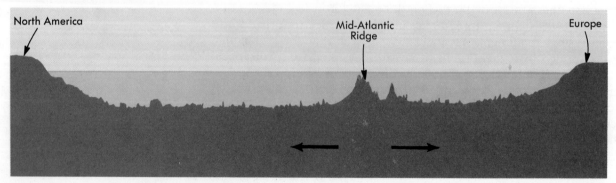

When Wegener died in 1930, few scientists believed in continental drift. By 1969, however, geologists had discovered strong evidence that slow steady movements of the earth's crust take place at under-sea ridges such as the Mid-Atlantic Ridge. The top of this ridge—16,000 kilometers long—is split by a deep depression, or *rift valley*. In it are many active volcanoes and openings in the rock. As the ocean floor splits away from both sides of the rift, hot liquid lava erupts through the enlarged openings. The lava solidifies into new sea-floor rock on both sides of the ridge. The movement of the sea floor is called **sea-floor spreading.** Its rate is slow—only from 1 to 10 centimeters a year. But even 2 centimeters a year is 1 kilometer every 50,000 years. In 100 million years, this equals 2000 kilometers.

What evidence for sea-floor spreading have geologists found?

1. The sea-floor rocks closest to the Mid-Atlantic Ridge (and other undersea ridges) are very young. Apparently, they were formed recently. As distance from the ridge increases, the age of the rocks increases.

2. The oldest sea-floor rocks are only about one-tenth as old as the oldest land rocks.

3. At different distances from the ridge, magnetic minerals in the sea-floor rocks are magnetized differently (the "North Poles" face in different directions). These differences match on both sides of the ridge. Each pair of matching directions apparently indicates a separate period during which lava flowed out of the spreading rift.

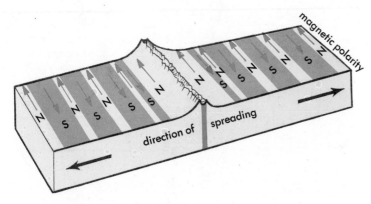

Bands of reversed magnetic polarity on either side of the Mid-Atlantic Ridge are good evidence of sea-floor spreading.

If the floor of the Atlantic Ocean is still spreading out from its middle and forming new rock, does that mean that North America and Europe are still moving apart? It does—at the rate of about 2 centimeters every year! The Atlantic Ocean is getting wider, while on the opposite side of the globe the Pacific Ocean is getting narrower.

If new rock is being formed, why isn't the earth's crust simply expanding? Records of deep earthquakes show that at many continental margins the ocean crust is moving downward into the mantle under the continent. Where this happens, deep ocean valleys called *trenches* are formed, such as those that border the coasts of western America and Japan. And that brings us to the hypothesis of plate tectonics.

Plate Tectonics 12.

After studying the evidence for sea-floor spreading, scientists became convinced that Wegener's "drifting continents" were not far from fact. Apparently the earth's solid crust *does* move, though not exactly as Wegener thought. Geologists have now proposed an explanation of how and why the solid crust moves.

In this new *hypothesis of plate tectonics*, the earth's surface is *not* covered by an unbroken shell of solid rock. Instead, the outer rock shell is split in many places to a depth of 70 kilometers or more. This depth includes some of the mantle as well as the crust. The entire

Geologists now believe that the earth's crust is split into six large plates and a number of subplates that fill in the gaps.

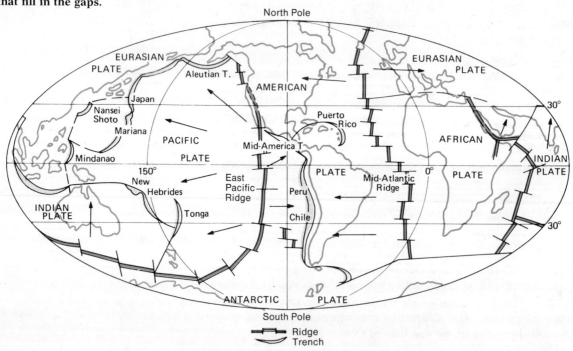

70-kilometer layer is called the **lithosphere.** Because it is split, it consists of a number of vast blocks, or **plates,** of rock. The plates are irregular in shape and unequal in size. Six of them—the major plates—cover most of the surface. The spaces between them are filled by smaller **subplates.**

The six major plates are the American, African, Eurasian, (Europe and Asia), Indian, Pacific, and Antarctic plates. Unlike Wegener's "drifting" continents, plates may include ocean floor as well as continents, and they extend deep into the earth's mantle. The American Plate, for example, extends westward from the Mid-Atlantic Ridge all the way to the Pacific Ocean. Its eastern half is all sea floor, but its western half carries an "upper deck" of continental crust 20 to 50 kilometers thick.

How do plates move? They may move away from each other as the American and Eurasian plates do at the Mid-Atlantic Ridge. They may move toward each other, as the Eurasian and Indian plates do. They may slide alongside each other, as the Pacific and American plates do.

What makes plates move? Many geologists believe the answer lies in the convection currents caused by heat in the earth's mantle. In places where convection currents rise to the surface, plates are pushed apart. Where convection currents sink into the mantle, plates are pushed together or slide past each other. The plates move or slide on a partly melted layer of the mantle called the *asthenosphere*. This lies just below the lithosphere.

In succeeding chapters we shall see how the hypothesis of plate tectonics helps us to explain the origin of mountains, the causes of earthquakes and volcanic eruptions, the occurrence of ice ages, and many other problems in the geologic history of the earth.

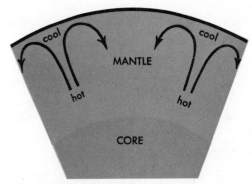

As hot molten rock rises, cooler molten rock sinks. This causes the currents that move the plates.

Each topic question refers to the topic of the same number within this chapter.

TOPIC QUESTIONS

1. Which sciences are included in earth science?

2. State at least three facts about the solar system that are usually explained by assuming an original great spinning mass.

3. (a) Explain briefly how an encounter hypothesis accounts for the origin of the solar system. (b) What are the weaknesses of most encounter hypotheses?

4. (a) Explain briefly how a nebular hypothesis accounts for the origin of the solar system? (b) What are two of the weaknesses of a nebular hypothesis?

5. (a) Briefly describe the protoplanet hypothesis. (b) How does it overcome the weaknesses of the nebular hypothesis?

6. Explain how our oceans were formed.

7. (a) Explain how our present atmosphere differs from the atmosphere we think the earth started out with. (b) How did our present atmosphere acquire its oxygen?

8. (a) Give a brief description of the structure the earth is believed to have. (b) How were the core, the crust, and the mantle believed to have formed?

9. Describe two ways by which the continents may have formed.

10. (a) What was Wegener's hypothesis of continental drift? (b) What could Wegener not explain in his hypothesis?

11. (a) Explain what sea-floor spreading is. (b) List two evidences for sea-floor spreading. (c) Why isn't the earth's surface expanding?

12. (a) Explain how plates and subplates are related to the lithosphere. (b) How do plates differ from Wegener's "drifting" continents? (c) How do plates move? (d) What makes them move?

2

1. Do you live near the ocean or near a large lake? If you do, you can see for yourself the evidence of the earth's curvature shown in the drawing on the next page. Go to the shore and carefully observe a ship that is moving away from you until it disappears from sight. Which part of the ship disappears first? Which part of a ship that is coming into view appears first?

2. If you do not live near a large body of water, or prefer not to wait until you go there, try this: Get a large globe, a basketball, or any large round object to represent the earth. Sit or stand so that your eye level is just even with the top of the globe. This level is your "horizon line." Use a block of wood, a piece of chalk, or even your finger to represent a ship. Start the "ship" at an "out-of-sight" position over the horizon. Bring the "ship" up toward you slowly until you see all of it. Which part appears first?

The Earth's Shape, Dimensions, and Internal Heat

What Shape, How Big?

The Earth Is Spherical

Is the earth flat or round? Until 1522 most people believed the earth was flat. In that year one of Magellan's ships completed the first trip all the way around the earth. Long before Magellan, however, early scientists believed the earth was shaped like a ball. In geometry the ball shape is called a *sphere*, so the early scientists believed that the earth is *spherical*.

They based this belief on such evidences as these:

1. The mast of a ship was the first part to appear over the horizon. It was the last part to disappear. The traditional cry of the lookout in a sailing vessel is, "I see a *mast*."

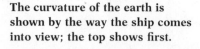

The curvature of the earth is shown by the way the ship comes into view; the top shows first.

2. When ships sailed north or south, sailors observed that the nighttime sky changed in appearance. The North Star rose higher in the sky as they sailed northward. It sank in the sky as they sailed southward. The change in the North Star's position was so even that it could only be explained in one way. The ship was sailing on a spherical surface. When ships sailed far enough south, constellations such as the Big Dipper could no longer be seen, but new ones such as the Southern Cross appeared in the sky. Would this be true on a flat earth?

3. An eclipse of the moon occurs when the earth's shadow falls on the moon. During an eclipse of the moon, the edge of the earth's shadow as it moved across the moon was always the arc of a circle. But only a sphere always casts a circular shadow, no matter what position it is in.

The evidences listed above are, of course, still visible today, although a lookout is much more likely to see a smokestack than a mast.

From the surface of the moon, you can see that the earth is round.

Gravity provides further evidence that the earth is a sphere. The weight of an object is simply a measure of the force with which gravity pulls it towards the earth's center. The weight changes if the object's distance from the earth's center changes. But a given object weighs *almost* the same everywhere on the earth's surface. What does this mean? It means that all of the earth's surface is *almost* equidistant from the earth's center. And this means that the earth is *almost* spherical.

Why almost? Careful measurements show that the weight of an object is not *exactly* the same all over the earth. An object that gives a reading of 195 kilograms on a spring scale at sea level at the earth's North Pole or South Pole loses weight as it approaches the Equator, where it gives a reading of only 194 kilograms. What does this mean? For one thing, the object must be nearer the earth's center at the Poles than at the Equator. In other words, the earth is not a perfect sphere. It is flattened at the Poles, and it bulges at the Equator. We call this shape an *oblate spheroid*. The flattening is caused by the earth's rotation.

How do you measure the distance around the earth?

In principle, the method is simple. Take two points a substantial distance apart on the earth, with one directly north of the other. The line joining these points will be part of the circle that goes around the earth through the North Pole and South Pole. Measure the distance between the two points. Find out what part of the whole circle that part is (we shall see how in a moment). Then multiply the measured distance by the number of parts needed to make the whole circle. This gives us the north-south distance around the earth. This distance is called the *circumference of the earth.*

The first scientific measurement of the earth's circumference was probably made by the Greek astronomer Eratosthenes (er uh TOS thuh neez) more than 2000 years ago. Eratosthenes, who lived in Alexandria, heard of a famous well in the city of Syene in southern Egypt. Once a year, at noon on the longest day of the year, the sun shone straight down to the bottom of this deep vertical well. This meant that the sun was directly overhead in Syene at that moment. But at noon on the same day in Alexandria, the sun was 7.2° below the overhead point. Since Alexandria was supposed to be directly north of Syene, this meant that Syene and Alexandria were separated by

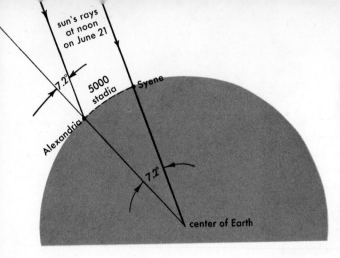

shadow at noon

Alexandria
June 21

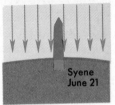
Syene
June 21

no shadow at noon

The diagram of facts Erathosthenes had to work with shows how he used the angle of the sun's rays to find the distance around the earth.

7.2° on a circumference of the earth. But 7.2° is one-fiftieth of the whole distance (360°) around the earth. So Eratosthenes multiplied the distance between Syene and Alexandria by 50, and obtained his answer for the earth's circumference.

What was Eratosthenes' answer? The distance between the two cities was 5000 stadia (a *stadium* was about 185 meters). Multiplied by 50, this gave a circumference of 250,000 stadia, or 46,250 kilometers. Despite a number of inaccuracies in his assumptions, Eratosthenes had come remarkably close to the real size of the earth's circumference (about 40,000 kilometers). If you look at a map of Egypt, you may discover one—perhaps two—of Eratosthenes' errors. (Syene is now called Aswan.)

The Earth's Dimensions

The method used by Eratosthenes is still used today to measure the earth's circumference. But, modern instruments allow us to get much more precise answers. Here are a few of the important dimensions of the earth (remember, the earth bulges at the Equator, and is flattened at the Poles):

Circumference at Equator	40,076 kilometers
Circumference at Poles	40,008 kilometers
Diameter at Equator	12,756 kilometers
Diameter at Poles	12,740 kilometers

The total surface area of the earth is about 510 million square kilometers. Of this, about 149 million square kilometers stand above sea level as continents and islands. The remaining 361 million square kilometers are covered by oceans. Thus the percentage of land is only about 29 percent, while that of water is about 71 percent.

How Heavy, How Hot?

The element mercury (the silvery liquid in many thermometers) is a very heavy substance. It has a *specific gravity* of 13.6. What does this mean? It means that it is 13.6 times as heavy as water. To find the **specific gravity** of any object, compare the object's weight with the weight of an equal volume of water.

How do scientists determine the specific gravity of the earth? The law of gravitation makes it possible to calculate the earth's weight from the force with which it attracts objects to its surface. The volume of the earth can be calculated from its dimensions. Comparing the earth's weight with that of an equal volume of water, we get the earth's specific gravity. This turns out to be about 5.5.

How does this number fit the geologist's picture of the earth's interior? It supports it. The earth's crust has an average specific gravity of about 3.0. Therefore the interior would have to have a specific gravity well above 5.5 in order for the whole earth to average 5.5. In the geologist's model, the core is made largely of iron and nickel. The specific gravity of iron is just under 8; that of nickel is a little over 8.

Did you ever visit a big underground cave? In summer, caves are pleasantly cool. But do you know that deep caves stay at about the same temperature all year? Neither the sun's heat nor the winter cold penetrates the earth below about 20 meters. At this depth, the temperature usually remains equal to the average yearly temperature of the particular place—except in areas of hot springs and volcanoes.

From 20 meters or so downward, however, the temperature of the ground rises. Thousands of measurements have been made of this temperature rise in mines, tunnels, water wells, and oil wells. Thousands more have been made in the sea floor by instruments lowered from ships on scientific expeditions. The increase in temperature differs from place to place, but for the outer crust it averages about 1° Celsius every 40 meters downward.

The rate of 1° C in 40 meters is very high. If that rate continued all the way to the earth's center, the inner core would have a temperature of about 150,000° C. But geologists believe that the inner core is probably no hotter than 5000° C. Obviously, therefore, if the geologists are correct, the rise in temperature must slow down greatly somewhere past the first few miles of the earth's crust.

What Makes the Crust Hot? 7.

A radioactive atom may release three different kinds of energy.

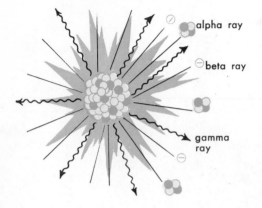

alpha ray

beta ray

gamma ray

If the crust gets hotter with increasing depth, there must be some source of heat in the rocks. Most of the heat appears to come from radioactive elements. These elements include uranium, thorium, and a form of potassium. Some heat undoubtedly comes from the original heat of the earth's interior. Another possible source of heat is the friction involved in the movements of the earth's plates.

Rocks are poor conductors of heat. This is why the earth loses its interior heat so slowly to outer space. However, some rocks conduct more heat than others. Rocks also differ in the percentage of radioactive minerals they contain. This is why different amounts of heat from the earth are measured at different places.

What explains the presence of hot rock near the surface in regions of volcanoes and hot springs? One explanation is that the rock is excessively heated in these places by unusual concentrations of radioactive minerals.

One reason that we know the earth is hot is that hot steam escapes from it in some places.

Each topic question refers to the topic of the same number within this chapter.

1. Explain two of the evidences of the earth's spherical shape that were known even thousands of years ago.

2. (a) Explain how gravity tells us the earth is almost spherical. (b) How does gravity tell us the earth is oblate?

3. Explain how Eratosthenes measured the earth's circumference.

4. (a) Which is larger, the polar diameter or the equatorial diameter? Why? How much? (b) Examine a globe or map of the world. Which hemisphere has most of the earth's land area? Which is largely ocean?

5. (a) How is the earth's specific gravity determined? (b) What does it mean to say that the earth's specific gravity is 5.5?

6. (a) Why is an underground cave cool in summer and warm in winter? (b) What is the average rate at which temperature rises with depth in the crust?

7. (a) Where does the heat in the earth's crust appear to come from? (b) What may be the cause of the hot rocks in areas of volcanoes and hot springs?

3

What is soil *(also known as earth or dirt) made of?*

Study one or more samples of soil to see what kinds of materials you can identify. Get samples from several places—a park, an empty lot, a garden, a field, the beach, a flower pot. From each place take enough soil to test it in several ways.

Spread a spoonful of each sample on a sheet of paper. Examine the soil carefully with a hand magnifying glass. Feel some of each sample. Then find out how a magnet affects each sample. Record what you learn.

Most soil is made of several different materials. What materials do you find that were once living? Can you find glassy bits (quartz), shiny flakes (white mica and black mica), or black grains (magnetite)? How can you differentiate between the nonliving and the once-living materials? Which materials are you unable to identify?

Atoms to Minerals

What Rocks Are Made From

In many parts of the earth the solid outer crust is hidden by a cover of loose rock, sand, or soil. This cover may take the form of the sands of deserts and beaches, the boulders and gravels at the bases of cliffs, the soils of farm and forest, the muds and clays of a swamp, or the slimes and oozes of lake and sea floors. Beneath this loose material, however, there is always unbroken solid rock. This solid rock that seems to be firmly attached to the entire mass of the earth is called **bedrock.** It is the outer part of the earth's crust. This bedrock is not to be confused with the unattached blocks of rock known as **boulders,** however large the boulders are.

In most places the bedrock is covered with a layer of soil. Where it is not covered, it is called an outcrop. Large pieces of rock not attached to the bedrock are boulders.

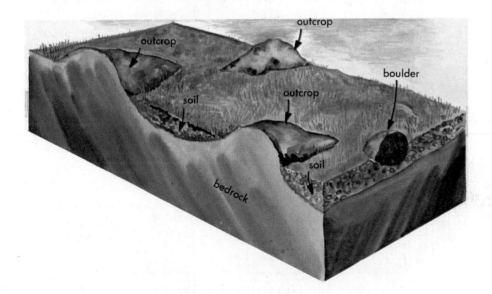

How deep is the loose rock or soil that covers the bedrock? In some places it may be hundreds of meters thick. In other places there may be no cover at all, and the bedrock can be seen at the surface in *outcrops.* Outcrops are more likely to appear in hilly and mountainous regions than in level regions. Where a road cuts through rocky hills, both the bedrock and its cover are likely to be visible.

Granite is made from crystals of different minerals. Conglomerate is made from pebbles and sand grains held together by cement.

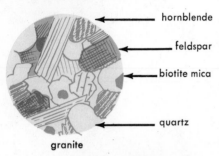

hornblende

feldspar

biotite mica

quartz

granite

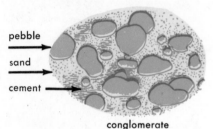

pebble

sand

cement

conglomerate

Bedrock is likely to be of the same rock over a large area. The bedrock may be granite, shale, limestone, sandstone, or something less familiar. Close inspection shows that it is composed of one or more definite substances called **minerals.**

The minerals may be quartz, mica, calcite, magnetite, or many others. Minerals range from tiny grains to pebble-size crystals and seem to be cemented or melted together to form the rock. Some varieties of rock have only one kind of mineral in them. Most varieties of rock contain two or more different minerals. To illustrate: the rock *limestone* may consist only of the mineral *calcite;* the rock *granite* always contains quartz, feldspar, and at least one other mineral.

Rocks may be compared to gelatin with fruit. The rock is the whole dessert; the minerals are the pieces of pear, peach, grape and other fruits, and the particles of sugar and gelatin. The pieces of fruit represent mineral crystals large enough to be seen with the unaided eye. The sugar and gelatin represent minerals whose crystals can be seen only under a microscope. Just as pears and peaches may be found in many different flavors of gelatin, so the same minerals may be found in many different kinds of rocks.

Geologists define **rocks** as masses or "aggregates" of minerals. But what are minerals? Minerals are elements or compounds that occur naturally in the earth's crust in solid, crystalline states. Let us explain this further.

Minerals
May Be Elements 3.

An **element** is a substance that cannot be broken down into simpler substances by ordinary chemical means. (Atomic fission is not considered ordinary chemical means.) The names of many elements are familiar to us.

Oxygen and nitrogen, which are important in the atmosphere;

gold, silver, iron, tin, copper, lead, zinc, mercury, aluminum, and uranium, which are important metals;

sulfur and carbon, which are nonmetals.

In all the earth no more than 92 different elements occur naturally, although chemists have created artificial elements that are not found in the earth.

The elements that exist in nature occur in very different amounts. Two of the elements, oxygen and silicon, compose nearly 75 per cent of the total weight of the outer crust. The ten most common elements together make up more than 99 per cent of the weight of the outer crust.

**The Ten Most Common Elements
in the Earth's Crust**

Name	Chemical Symbol	Percent by Weight
Oxygen	O	46.60
Silicon	Si	27.72
Aluminum	Al	8.13
Iron	Fe	5.00
Calcium	Ca	3.63
Sodium	Na	2.83
Potassium	K	2.59
Magnesium	Mg	2.09
Titanium	Ti	0.40
Hydrogen	H	0.14
	Total	99.13

These ten elements are almost always found combined with other elements. For example, oxygen and silicon are combined in the common mineral quartz; aluminum, silicon, hydrogen, and oxygen are combined in common clay.

Some elements do exist uncombined in the crust in substantial amounts. These elements include gold, silver, platinum, copper, sulfur, carbon, and a few others.

Gold is one of the few elements found uncombined in the crust.

Elements, Atoms, and Isotopes

What an Atom Is 4.

More than 150 years ago the English chemist John Dalton stated his belief that each element is made of tiny particles called atoms. Dalton defined the **atom** as *the smallest part of an element that has all the properties of that element.* Today we know that the atom itself is made from three kinds of still smaller particles. Furthermore, all atoms—from every kind of element—are made of the same kinds of particles! Let us see how this is possible.

Picture of an Atom 5.

How does one picture an atom? Imagine clouds of particles spinning at high speeds around a central *nucleus* (plural, nuclei). The orbiting particles are *electrons.* Each one carries a tiny charge of electricity.

In the nucleus of the atom are particles called *protons* and *neutrons.* Each proton has a charge of electricity, also. The electric charge of the proton is different from that of the electron, however. Scientists call the electron's charge *negative* and the proton's charge *positive.* The amount of the proton's positive charge is exactly equal to the amount of the negative charge of an electron. The proton, however, is 1836 times as heavy as the electron.

The neutron carries no electricity, but is slightly heavier than the proton.

The atom is a tiny thing. An atom of oxygen, for example, is about 25 billionths of a centimeter in diameter. But most of this is empty space! The diameter of the nucleus is, on the average, about one hundred thousandth of the diameter of the space in which its electrons spin. More than 99.9% of the weight of an atom is in its nucleus.

Today we believe that every element—solid, gas, or liquid—is made from tiny particles called atoms.

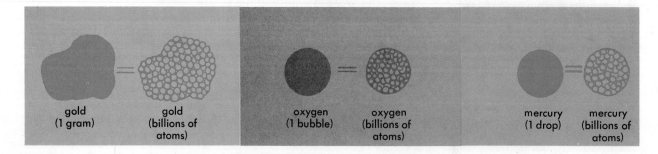

gold
(1 gram)

gold
(billions of
atoms)

oxygen
(1 bubble)

oxygen
(billions of
atoms)

mercury
(1 drop)

mercury
(billions of
atoms)

The simplest and lightest of all atoms is the atom of ordinary *hydrogen*, the symbol for which is *H*. Ordinary hydrogen has a nucleus of just one proton. (It is the only atom without neutrons.) Around this nucleus spins a single electron. Electrically the atom is neutral, since protons and electrons have equal but opposite charges. Scientists have found that *all atoms are, like the hydrogen atom, electrically neutral*. This means that every atom must have as many electrons outside the nucleus as it has protons in the nucleus.

The next lightest of the elements is *helium, He*. This atom has a nucleus of two protons *and two neutrons*. Balancing the two positive charges, two electrons spin around the nucleus. The space in which these electrons spin is called a *shell*. Notice in the diagram that the nucleus of helium contains two neutrons. These approximately double its weight but do not increase its electrical charge.

The next lightest element is *lithium, Li*. The lithium atom has three protons in its nucleus, and three electrons spinning around the nucleus. The nucleus also includes four neutrons. Two of lithium's three electrons spin around the nucleus in a shell like that of the helium atom, *but the third electron lies beyond the first two in a shell of its own.*

This scheme of atomic structure continues through the natural elements—adding one proton at a time for each new element, until 92 elements are formed. Each additional proton calls for an additional electron. As the number of electrons increases, new orbit shells come into existence, but in every atom the number of electrons equals the number of protons.

The largest number of electron shells in any atom is seven. The number of electrons differs from shell to shell, but the innermost shell never holds more than two electrons, and the outermost shell of any atom never holds more than eight. Other shells may hold as many as 32 electrons.

With each change in the number of protons and electrons, there is a change in the properties of the atom, and a new element is born. The heaviest of the natural elements, *uranium, U,* has 92 protons in its nucleus. Its 92 electrons are distributed in its seven shells as follows: 2, 8, 18, 32, 21, 9, 2. Do they add up to 92?

You can picture atoms as in these diagrams, but real atoms are three-dimensional. No one knows what atoms really look like.

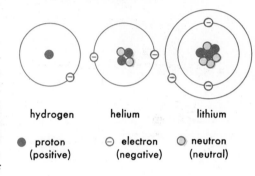

hydrogen　　helium　　lithium

● proton (positive)　　⊖ electron (negative)　　○ neutron (neutral)

7. Atomic Number and Atomic Weight

The **atomic number**—the number of protons in an atom—of hydrogen is 1; of helium, 2; of lithium, 3; of uranium, 92. Knowing the atomic number, you can easily picture the atom of any element.

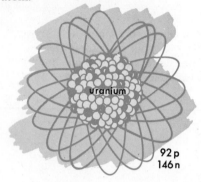

This diagram suggests the three-dimensional nature of an atom.

uranium

92 p
146 n

For example, the atomic number of oxygen is 8. The oxygen atom therefore has 8 protons in its nucleus and a cloud of 8 electrons—2 in the first shell and 6 in the second—spinning around the nucleus.

But how many neutrons are there in a nucleus? There is no simple rule relating the number of neutrons to the number of protons. However, the **atomic weight** of the element tells you approximately the number of protons and neutrons combined in an atom. To find the number of neutrons in an atom, then, you simply subtract the atomic number (number of protons) from the atomic weight.

For example, the atomic number of sodium is 11; its atomic weight is 23. The sodium nucleus therefore contains 11 protons and 12 (subtracting 11 from 23) neutrons. How many electrons spin around the nucleus? Since the number of electrons must equal the number of protons, the answer is 11 electrons.

One more illustration: If uranium, atomic number 92, has an atomic weight of 238, its atom must include 92 electrons, 92 protons, and 146 neutrons. Check this.

Isotopes

The identity of an atom depends only on the number of protons it has, and not on the number of neutrons. Can a particular element have atoms with different numbers of neutrons? Many elements do. These "different" atoms are called *isotopes*. **Isotopes** are *atoms of the same chemical element with different atomic weights.*

Hydrogen has three isotopes. The most common one, ordinary hydrogen, has one proton and *no* neutrons in its nucleus. Its atomic number is 1; its atomic weight is also 1. But hydrogen has a second isotope with 1 proton and 1 neutron in its nucleus. Its atomic number is 1, but its atomic weight is 2. This isotope is known as "heavy hydrogen" or *deuterium* (du TEER ee um). It is much less common than ordinary hydrogen. The third isotope of hydrogen is very rare indeed. Known as *tritium* (TRIT ee m), it has an atomic weight of 3, with a nucleus of 1 proton and 2 neutrons.

Almost everyone has heard of "carbon 14." This is a heavy isotope of carbon. Ordinary carbon atoms have an atomic number of 6, an atomic weight of 12. Each ordinary atom of "carbon 12," therefore, has a nucleus of 6 protons and 6 neutrons. But "carbon 14" atoms (atomic weight 14) have nuclei with 6 protons and 8 neutrons. Carbon 14 is important in the dating of events of very recent geologic time.

Uranium has a number of isotopes. Ordinary uranium, described in Topic 7, has atomic weight 238, with 146 neutrons in its nucleus. Uranium 235 (atomic weight 235), however, has only 143 neutrons in its nucleus. All isotopes of uranium must, of course, have 92 protons in the nucleus.

The three isotopes of hydrogen are different only in the number of neutrons in the nucleus.

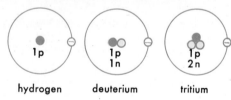

1 p

1 p
1 n

1 p
2 n

hydrogen   deuterium   tritium

Carbon 12 is ordinary carbon. Carbon 14 is radioactive.

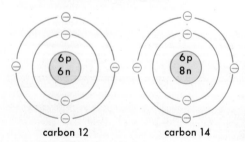

6 p
6 n

6 p
8 n

carbon 12   carbon 14

Compound Minerals

So far we have been talking about elements. But most minerals—and in fact, most substances—are compounds. A **compound** is a substance consisting of two or more elements chemically combined.

Unlike a mixture, a compound has new properties entirely unlike those of the elements of which it is composed. For example, water is a compound formed from hydrogen and oxygen. Water is certainly different from a mixture of hydrogen and oxygen. For example, at room temperature water is a liquid, but hydrogen and oxygen are both gases. Another example is salt, which is a compound of the elements sodium and chlorine. Both sodium and chlorine are poisonous, but most people eat salt safely with their food.

Still other examples are the mineral *quartz*, of which most sand is composed, and the mineral *galena*, an ore of lead. Quartz is a compound of the elements silicon and oxygen. Galena is a compound of lead and sulfur.

In a **mixture** of chemical elements the individual elements keep their own properties and can usually be recognized by color, odor, taste, and so forth. The elements in a mixture may be present in any proportions. They can usually be separated easily by "physical means"—picking them apart, separating light from heavy, dissolving the one that is soluble, or by using a magnet to remove magnetic elements.

In a compound, however, the elements lose their individual properties. Each element is present in a definite ratio to the other elements by weight. (This is known as the Law of Definite Proportions.) The elements in a compound can only be separated by "chemical means." For example, water and salt can be decomposed into their individual elements by passing a strong electric current through each. The lead in galena can be separated from the sulfur by heating.

Dalton said that an atom is the smallest part of an element. But the smallest part of a compound consists of at least two atoms. These are combined to form a molecule. A **molecule** *is the smallest part of a compound that has all the characteristics of that compound.*

What makes the atoms of different elements unite to form the molecules of a compound? For one major kind of compound, the answer lies in electrical attraction.

In its normal state each atom is electrically neutral. It has an equal number of protons and electrons. If an atom *gains* one or more electrons, it becomes negatively charged. If an atom *loses* one or more electrons, it becomes positively charged. *An atom in a charged condition, either negative or positive, is called an* **ion.** (Groups of atoms may also form ions.)

Since opposite charges attract each other, ions of opposite charges may unite to form compounds. For example, *a positively charged sodium ion* can unite with a *negatively charged chlorine ion* to form a molecule of the compound *sodium chloride,* a common salt.

When a sodium ion and a chlorine ion unite, they form sodium chloride, the compound we know as ordinary table salt.

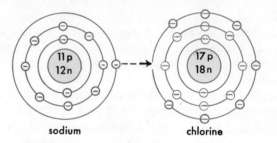

sodium   chlorine

How do atoms lose or gain electrons to become ions? This may happen in many ways. When some compounds dissolve in water, their molecules split up into ions. For example, a molecule of sodium chloride will form a positive sodium ion and a negative chlorine ion (also called a chloride ion). When the water evaporates, the ions reunite to form solid sodium chloride.

Here are some other common ways ions form: Friction between materials may rub electrons off atoms and create what is called static electricity. This happens when you rub rubber with fur. High temperatures in furnaces or in the interiors of stars will separate electrons from atoms to form ions. The impact of cosmic rays may convert atoms of oxygen and nitrogen into ions in the upper atmosphere.

Elements that lose electrons easily and form positive ions are classed as **metals.** They include gold, silver, iron, copper, lead, aluminum, sodium, potassium, calcium, zinc, magnesium, and many others.

Elements that gain electrons easily and form negative ions are classed as **nonmetals.** They include nitrogen, oxygen, fluorine, chlorine, phosphorus, and sulfur.

Some elements—such as helium, neon, and argon—never gain or lose electrons, never form ions, and so can never form compounds naturally. They are described as **inert elements.**

Definite Chemical Composition: Formulas

Since minerals are elements or compounds, *every mineral has a characteristic chemical composition*. If the mineral is an element, it is composed entirely of that one substance. If it is a single compound, it follows the Law of Definite Proportions with each element of the compound present in a definite proportion by weight.

In Topic 10 you learned that *the molecule is the smallest part of a compound that has all the characteristics of that compound*. To represent a single molecule, the chemist uses a *formula* showing the elements in the molecule and the number of atoms of each kind in it. For example, the formula for water is H_2O. This means that one molecule of water consists of two hydrogen atoms and one oxygen atom. One oxygen atom (atomic weight 16) is 16 times as heavy as one hydrogen atom. But since the water molecule includes two hydrogen atoms, the weight ratio of oxygen to hydrogen is 16:2 or 8:1. Therefore water is a compound with the *definite composition by weight* of 8 parts oxygen to 1 part hydrogen. In other words, if 9 pounds of water were completely decomposed into oxygen and hydrogen, the products would be 8 pounds of oxygen and 1 pound of hydrogen.

 ## How Minerals Were Formed

Early in the earth's history, while the earth was still very hot and molten, all of the elements were already present as ions. Remember that ions are formed by great heat. Because of the high temperature, these ions were prevented from combining with other ions.

But as the earth cooled, many ions with opposite charges drew together to form compounds. Not all of the ions entered into combinations with other elements. The inert gases, unable to combine by natural processes, remained as elements. A small number of other elements were able to do both—some of their ions entered into combinations as compounds, while others remained uncombined as elements. These included the metallic elements copper, mercury, gold, silver, and platinum, and the nonmetallic elements sulfur and carbon. (Where these occur as uncombined elements in the earth's crust, they are spoken of as "native gold, native copper," etc.) With few exceptions, the other elements occur in the earth's crust only as parts of compounds.

Minerals are often found in the form of beautiful *crystals*. These crystals have regular geometric forms featured by smooth surfaces, or *crystal faces*. The crystal forms are different for different minerals, but each mineral always has the same crystal form. In quartz crystals the form is that of a regular six-sided prism. The crystals of halite (sodium chloride), pyrite (iron sulfide), and galena (lead sulfide) are cubes. Diamond crystals are eight-faced, like two four-sided pyramids fitted base to base.

Mineral crystals occur in definite shapes for each mineral.

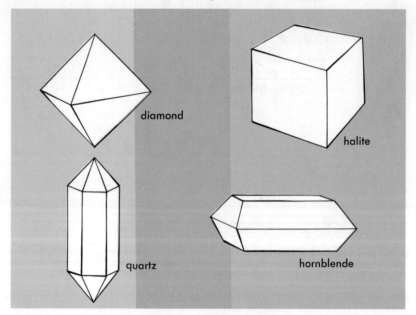

diamond

halite

quartz

hornblende

Here are two ways to picture the arrangement of atoms in a crystal of sodium chloride. The smaller spheres are sodium ions; the larger spheres are chlorine ions.

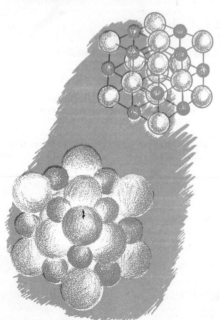

Mineralogists reasoned that the crystal form of a particular mineral was probably the result of a regular geometric arrangement of its ions or atoms. In 1912 X-rays were first used for studying the internal structure of crystals. These X-ray photographs showed the arrangement of the ions or atoms in crystals of the various minerals.

Consider the alternating arrangement of sodium and chlorine ions in a crystal of halite. The *regular arrangement of the ions is called* **crystalline structure.**

When large numbers of ions are free to arrange themselves during the growth of the mineral, large perfect crystals may form. More often, however, the conditions of growth in the earth's crust are too crowded. Crystals are hemmed in by other crystals while they are all still tiny and imperfect. The magnifying glass or microscope can reveal crystal faces not apparent to the unaided eye.

Not all crystals are compounds. In crystals such as those of diamond, sulfur, or gold, atoms that are all of one kind share electrons with each other in regular geometric arrangements. In diamond, for example, carbon atoms are arranged in a pattern. Each atom shares one electron with each of four other atoms.

14. The Silica Tetrahedron

More than 90% of the minerals in the earth's crust are members of a family called *silicates*. These are compounds made of the elements silicon and oxygen, plus one or more metallic elements, such as aluminum or iron. In all silicates, the silicon and oxygen atoms are bound together in an arrangement known as the **silica tetrahedron.**

A tetrahedron is a four-cornered, four-sided pyramid. In the silica tetrahedron, a positively charged silicon ion is located inside the pyramid at its center. The four corners of the pyramid are occupied by four negative oxygen ions.

Metallic ions such as iron, magnesium, aluminum, and calcium may attach themselves to the oxygen ions. Furthermore, the tetrahedrons may be arranged in many different regular patterns. The results are hundreds of different minerals that use the silica tetrahedron as the basic building block. The best known of these minerals are quartz, feldspar, mica, hornblende, and olivine.

Silicon and oxygen ions form the silica tetrahedron.

silica ion (positive)

oxygen ion (negative)

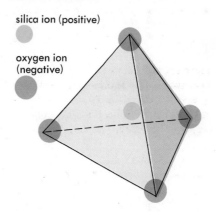

15. Crystals and Physical Properties

The orderly arrangement of the atoms or ions in a mineral helps to explain other properties of the mineral besides its crystal shape.

A mineral is *solid* because of the close packing together of its ions or atoms, and the resulting strong electrical attractions among them. When heat weakens the bonds between particles, solids melt into the loose groups of molecules that make up a liquid, or they evaporate into a gas in which individual molecules are far apart.

The *hardness* of a mineral depends on the arrangement of its ions or atoms and the resulting electrical forces among them. A good example of this is seen in the element carbon. In one arrangement it forms diamond, the hardest natural mineral. In another arrangement carbon forms graphite, one of the softest minerals.

The *cleavage* of a mineral is its tendency to split easily or to separate along flat surfaces. When a mineral has such tendencies, the planes of separation represent directions of weak bonds among the ions or atoms.

Remember that the specific gravity of a mineral is the ratio of its weight to that of water. This depends on the weight of the ions or atoms of the mineral, but it also depends on how closely they are packed together. The specific gravity of the loosely packed mineral graphite is about 2.3, but that of the closely packed diamond is 3.5. Both are pure carbon.

Hardness, cleavage, specific gravity, and other *physical properties* of minerals are discussed in greater detail in the next chapter.

Summary: What Is a Mineral? 16.

Let us now summarize the principal characteristics of a mineral as we have described them in this chapter:

1. A mineral is an element or compound found in nature.
2. Its ions or atoms usually are arranged in regular patterns that give it a crystalline structure and make it a solid.
3. It has a characteristic chemical composition.
4. It has definite physical properties.

In the following chapters important rock-making minerals will be described.

TOPIC QUESTIONS

Each topic question refers to the topic of the same number within this chapter.

1. Explain the difference between boulders and bedrock.

2. (a) Using specific examples, explain the relation between rocks and minerals. (b) Define a mineral.

3. (a) Define *element*. (b) Name eight familiar elements. (c) Give the name and approximate percentage by weight of the four most abundant earth elements. In which common minerals are they found?

4. What is an atom? Who was John Dalton?

5. Name and describe the three kinds of particles of which atoms are made.

6. (a) Describe the structure of the atoms of hydrogen and helium. (b) In what way do the 92 different elements resemble one another in atomic structure? (c) In what ways do they differ in atomic structure?

7. **(a)** What is the atomic number of an element? **(b)** What is the atomic weight of an element? **(c)** Explain how to determine the number of protons, neutrons, and electrons in a sodium atom.

8. **(a)** What is an isotope? **(b)** Describe two isotopes of hydrogen, carbon, or uranium.

9. **(a)** What is a compound? a molecule? **(b)** How does a compound differ from a mixture? **(c)** What is the Law of Definite Proportions?

10. **(a)** What is an ion? **(b)** How are ions formed? **(c)** How do ions form compounds? **(d)** Define metals. **(e)** Define nonmetals. **(f)** Define inert.

11. Why does a mineral have a "characteristic chemical composition? **(b)** How does the formula H_2O tell us water is 8 parts oxygen to 1 part hydrogen by weight?

12. According to the hypothesis described in Topic 12, account for the origin of **(a)** the mineral elements, **(b)** the mineral compounds.

13. **(a)** What is crystalline structure? **(b)** Explain why some mineral crystals are large and perfect, while others are small and irregular.

14. **(a)** What are silicate minerals? **(b)** How are the ions arranged in a silica tetrahedron? **(c)** Why are there so many different silicate minerals?

15. How does the crystalline structure of a mineral explain its **(a)** solid state, **(b)** hardness, **(c)** cleavage, **(d)** specific gravity?

16. Summarize the characteristics of a mineral.

HOW DO YOU KNOW THAT...?

1. Which is harder, slate or chalk? When chalk rubs off against a slateboard, does this answer the question? When a piece of slate is rubbed against a piece of chalk, how does it show that the slate is harder than chalk? (See Topic 3 for the answer.)

Using these techniques (of rubbing one material against the other), compare the hardness of a copper penny, a nickel, a glass plate, and a steel nail file or nail.

2. Collect four or five different kinds of rocks in your neighborhood. Get ones that are as smooth as possible. Using the same scratch tests as for the first activity, compare the hardness of the rocks.

Are all rocks equally hard? Are rocks harder or softer than such materials as glass and steel? Use scratch tests again to find answers to these questions.

Rock surfaces that have been exposed for a long time are weathered. Were any of your rocks weathered? How did the weathered surfaces compare in hardness with fresh surfaces?

How to Know
the Minerals

Identifying Minerals

Over 2,000 minerals are known. Many of them—such as gold and diamond—are rare. About 40 minerals make up so much of the rocks of the crust that they are called *rock-forming minerals*. Ten of them are so common that they make up more than 90 per cent of the weight of the crust.

On a field trip, minerals are usually identified by their physical properties. These properties can be determined by inspection and simple physical tests. Simple chemical tests may also be used.

2. Identification by Inspection

The color, luster, and sometimes the crystal shape of a mineral may be seen simply by looking at the specimen with the unaided eye. This is called *inspection*.

The **color** of a mineral often helps to identify it, but very few minerals can be identified by color alone. One reason is that many different minerals have similar colors. A few minerals that are easily identified because their color is always distinct are cinnabar, a red ore of mercury; malachite, a green ore of copper; sulfur, a bright yellow crystal or powder.

The color of a mineral is important in identification.

Cinnabar

Sulfur

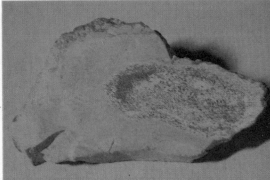

Malachite

A second reason is that even a trace of "impurity" (another element, usually a metal) in an otherwise colorless mineral such as quartz or calcite may make it pink, green, blue, violet, gray, or some other color. Amethyst, for example, is quartz that includes a tiny amount of the metallic element *manganese*. The manganese dissolved in the quartz when the quartz was still liquid.

A third reason is that some minerals change color, or tarnish, quickly on exposure to air. Sometimes this helps to identify the mineral, as with the peacock-purple color of tarnished *bornite*, an ore of copper. But for most minerals one must be sure to inspect a fresh surface to determine its color.

The **luster** of a mineral is the kind of "shine"—or lack of "shine"—that it has. Luster depends upon the way in which the surface of the mineral reflects light. All lusters are either *metallic* or *nonmetallic*. If a mineral sample shines like polished metal, its luster is metallic. Otherwise, its luster is nonmetallic, which may be further described in a number of ways. A *vitreous* luster, shining like glass, may be seen in quartz. Mica has a *pearly* luster, like that of the pearl. The mineral sphalerite, an ore of zinc, shows *resinous* or *waxy* luster, like that of yellow wax. The mineral asbestos has *silky* luster. Other common lusters are *adamantine*, like the diamond; *greasy* or *oily*, *dull*, or *earthy*.

Quartz

Mica

Sphalerite

Another important way to identify minerals is by their lusters.

The **crystal shape** is sometimes helpful in identifying a mineral. If conditions were favorable when the minerals formed in the rocks, their atoms or molecules arranged themselves in patterns that made flat-faced, regularly shaped *crystals*. But more often the mineral grains seen in rocks are so small or so imperfectly crystallized that crystal faces are difficult to find.

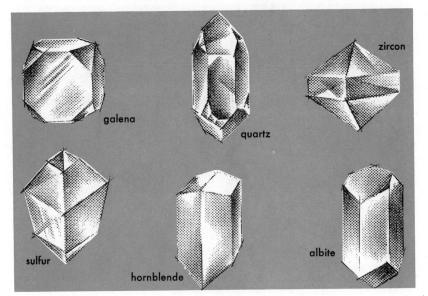

The shape of the crystals that make up a mineral are also used in identifying the mineral.

Identification by Simple Tests

The streak, cleavage, and hardness of a mineral can be tested very easily. The **streak** of a mineral is the color of its powder. For many minerals the streak is not the same as the color of a solid lump of the mineral. Iron pyrite crystals are brass-yellow, but their streak is always greenish-black. The streak is obtained by rubbing the mineral on the surface of an unglazed white tile called a *streak plate*. Although the color of a mineral may vary greatly, its streak rarely does. As a rule, the streak of a *metallic* mineral is at least as dark as the lump specimen. The streak of a *nonmetallic* mineral is usually colorless to white.

The **cleavage** of a mineral is its tendency to split easily or to separate along flat surfaces. Cleavage surfaces can be observed even on tiny mineral grains. This makes cleavage very useful for mineral identification. Mica splits very easily, always in the same direction,

The greenish black streak tells you it's iron pyrite, not gold.

streak plate

iron pyrite crystals

Because mica splits easily and in only one direction, you can break off flat pieces like those shown in the photograph. This is called "perfect cleavage." Cleavage is used in identification also.

39

Calcite splits "perfectly" in three planes slightly oblique to one another, forming flat-sided pieces called rhombs.

Feldspar splits at right angles, so it may be flaked into pieces with square corners.

and is said to have one "perfect" cleavage. Feldspar splits readily in two different directions, at or near right angles, and is said to have two "good" cleavages. Calcite and galena cleave in three directions.

Not all minerals have cleavage. When minerals break along other than cleavage surfaces, they are said to have **fracture.** *Conchoidal* (kon KOY dul), or shell-like, fracture can be seen in the mineral flint or the rock obsidian. The fracture surface is smoothly curved like the

Obsidian does not have cleavage. When a piece is broken off, it exhibits the pattern known to geologists as conchoidal fracture.

40

inside of a clam shell. *Fibrous* or *splintery* fracture leaves a jagged surface with sharp edges, as in native copper. *Uneven* or *irregular* fracture leaves a generally rough surface, as in the mineral serpentine.

The **hardness** of a mineral is its resistance to being scratched. The diamond is the hardest of all minerals because *it will scratch any other mineral against which it is rubbed.* On the other hand, talc is the softest of all minerals because all other minerals scratch it.

In order to give a specific measure to hardness, the mineralogist Friedrich Mohs devised a hardness scale. In this scale ten well-known minerals are given numbers from one to ten, arranged from softest (talc) to hardest (diamond). The differences in hardness between one grade and the next are about the same for all grades except the last. Diamond is very much harder than number 9, corundum.

From **Mohs' scale** you can find the approximate hardness of any common mineral with a copper penny, a knife blade or nail file, and a small glass plate. If a mineral is harder than number 5 but softer than number 6 in the hardness scale, it has a hardness of about 5½.

Hardness should not be confused with brittleness. Glass is a brittle substance that breaks easily when dropped, but it is much harder (resistant to scratching) than copper and many other metals.

In doing a scratch test for hardness, the powder *rubbed off* the softer mineral may look like a *scratch* on the harder mineral. For example, when calcite is rubbed against glass, the calcite may appear to have scratched the glass. Rub this "scratch" with your finger. If it proves to be powder that comes off and leaves the glass unscratched, the calcite is obviously softer than the glass. A real scratch can be felt with the fingernail.

Mohs' Scale of Hardness

Mineral	Simple Test
1. Talc	1. Fingernail scratches it easily.
2. Gypsum	2. Fingernail scratches it.
3. Calcite	3. Copper penny just scratches it.
4. Fluorite	4. Steel knife scratches it easily.
5. Apatite	5. Steel knife scratches it.
6. Feldspar	6. Steel knife does not scratch it; it scratches window glass easily.
7. Quartz	7. Hardest common mineral; it scratches steel and hard glass easily.
8. Topaz	8. Harder than any common mineral.
9. Corundum	9. It scratches topaz.
10. Diamond	10. Hardest of all minerals.

A mineral weighs less under water than it does in the air.

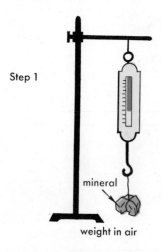

Step 1

mineral

weight in air

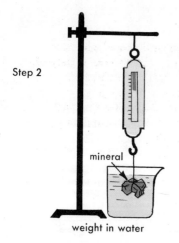

Step 2

mineral

weight in water

Specific gravity is another property that is helpful in identifying a mineral. It is the ratio of the weight of a mineral to the weight of an equal volume of water. In other words, the specific gravity of a mineral tells you how many times as heavy as water the mineral is.

Nearly all minerals are heavier than water, so their specific gravities are larger than 1. Typical nonmetallic minerals—such as quartz, feldspar, calcite, and talc—have specific gravities of a little less than 3. Typical metallic minerals—such as the iron ores hematite and magnetite—have specific gravities of about 5, but others are much heavier. Gold has a specific gravity as high as 19.3 when pure.

The specific gravity of a mineral is found as suggested by the definition. The weight of the mineral sample is found first simply by weighing it. Then the weight of an equal volume of water is found by any one of a number of methods described in physics textbooks.

In one such method the mineral sample is weighed again *while the specimen is fully submerged in water.* This second weighing indirectly gives the weight of an equal volume of water. The sample weighs less submerged because of the buoyant effect of the water. Archimedes' Principle tells us that this *loss in weight* is equal to the weight of the displaced water. But the displaced water is equal in volume to the mineral sample that displaced it. Thus,

$$\text{Specific gravity} = \frac{\text{Weight of sample in air}}{\text{Weight of equal volume of water}}$$

$$= \frac{\text{Weight of sample}}{\text{Loss of weight in water}}$$

For example, suppose a specimen weighs 50 grams in air and 30 grams in water. Its loss of weight is 20 grams. Then the specific gravity of the specimen is

$$\frac{50 \text{ grams}}{20 \text{ grams}} = 2.5.$$

In other words, the specimen is 2.5 times as heavy as water.

The Acid Test 5.

Calcite, the principal mineral in limestone and marble, is easily identified by a simple chemical test. Calcite is calcium carbonate, $CaCO_3$. If a drop of cold weak hydrochloric acid is placed on calcite, the drop of acid fizzes as bubbles of carbon dioxide gas are given off.

There are many other properties of minerals that are studied in courses in mineralogy. A few particularly interesting ones follow:

Some minerals are *magnetic* and can be picked up by a magnet. The best example is magnetite, an iron ore. Lodestone, a variety of magnetite, itself acts as a magnet.

Halite (rock salt) can be identified by its *taste*.

Fluorescence, or the state of glowing while under ultraviolet light, is shown by scheelite, some calcites, and many other minerals. The minerals willemite, sphalerite, and others continue to glow after the ultraviolet light is turned off. They are *phosphorescent.*

Some minerals, such as the uranium minerals carnotite and uraninite, are *radioactive.* They will activate a Geiger counter.

The mineral calcite splits light rays into two parts. One ray travels straight through the mineral. The other ray is bent. This causes two images to be seen when an object is viewed through a transparent specimen of calcite. This property is called *double refraction.*

The paragraphs that follow describe some important rock-forming minerals. Appendix Table 3 gives more information and lists other minerals.

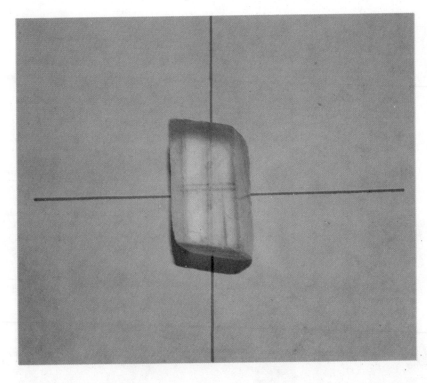

The mineral shown here is a colorless, transparent variety of calcite called Iceland spar. Because it splits light rays into two parts, it makes the single cross on the paper appear to be double.

Silicates: From Silica Tetrahedrons 7.

In Topic 14 of Chapter 3, we discussed the silica tetrahedron, nature's most important building block for minerals. All of the following minerals are made of the silica tetrahedron, either alone or combined with other elements.

(a) Quartz is made entirely of silica tetrahedrons bound tightly together. Quartz has the chemical formula SiO_2. Its chemical name is silicon dioxide. Quartz is number 7 in Mohs' scale of hardness. It is the hardest of the common minerals.

Pure quartz is colorless or white, but many colored varieties exist. Among these are pink *rose quartz*, purple *amethyst*, and brown or gray *smoky quartz*. Quartz has glassy or greasy luster. Its fracture is shell-like or irregular.

Quartz is the second most abundant mineral in the earth's crust. It is an important part of all granites and forms almost all of the sandstone and quartzite rocks. Most sands consist mainly of grains of quartz.

Some forms of quartz are semiprecious stones.

1 Rose quartz

2 Quartz crystals in geode

3 Smoky quartz

4 Amethyst

Orthoclase feldspar

Plagioclase

Orthoclase and plagioclase feldspar are chemically different. They can be identified by their cleavages.

(b) The **feldspars** are a family of silicate minerals in which the silica tetrahedrons have been joined by atoms of aluminum and other metals. Feldspars are number 6 in the scale of hardness and have two good cleavages. They are the most abundant of all the minerals. Like quartz, they occur in all granites. In granites they are easily identified by their colors—usually white, yellow, gray, or pink—and their smooth cleavage surfaces.

Orthoclase is an important feldspar in which atoms of aluminum and potassium have joined with the silica tetrahedrons. *Plagioclase* is another important feldspar in which atoms of sodium or calcium—or both—take the place of the potassium. In plagioclase, one of the cleavage surfaces usually shows fine parallel lines, or *striations*.

(c) **Mica** is a soft silicate mineral found in many rocks. Its flat shiny flakes are easily picked out of such rocks as granite and gneiss. *Muscovite mica*, also known as "isinglass," is silvery white. *Biotite* mica is dark brown or black. Both are soft—each has hardness of about 2.5. Each has one excellent cleavage.

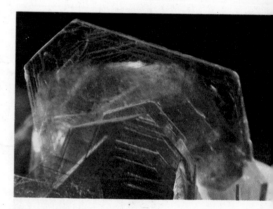

Muscovite mica

Muscovite mica is light colored and biotite mica is dark.

Biotite mica

Hornblende in calcite

Augite

(d) **Hornblende** is a complex silicate mineral containing atoms of iron and magnesium. Such silicates are called *ferromagnesian silicates*. They are always dark in color. Hornblende is dark green, brown, or black. It has two good oblique cleavages. Its long needle-like crystals are six-sided. Its hardness is 5 to 6.

(e) **Augite** (AW jyte), which resembles hornblende, is also a ferromagnesian silicate. It is dark green, brown, or black, has two good cleavages, and a hardness between 5 and 6. It can be distinguished from hornblende by

its poorer luster;

its short stout crystals;

cleavage surfaces that meet nearly at right angles.

Both hornblende and augite are common minerals in many dark crystalline rocks.

(f) **Olivine** is an olive-green ferromagnesian silicate found in dark crystalline rocks. It is glassy, shell-like in fracture, and very hard—about 6.5. It is found in some meteorites.

Olivine

Garnet

Garnets in schist

(g) **Garnets** may be dark red, brown, green, or black. They are very hard (from 6.5 to 7.5) and are much used as abrasives, as in garnet paper. Clear crystals are used as gems. Garnets are found in many crystalline rocks.

(h) **Talc** is our softest mineral—number 1 in Mohs' scale. It is white, gray, or greenish in color, has one good cleavage, and a soapy feel. Talcum powder is ground talc.

(i) **Kaolinite** or **kaolin,** is an aluminum silicate formed by the weathering of feldspar and other silicate minerals. It is the principal mineral in clay and in the rock called shale. Pure kaolin is white, but impurities usually change its color to yellow. Less often it is red, brown, green, or blue. It has an earthy (crumbly) fracture. Its hardness is between 1 and 2.5. It feels greasy, and, when breathed on, it gives off a typical earthy odor.

Talc

Kaolinite

Carbonate Minerals: Calcite and Dolomite 8.

Calcite is calcium carbonate, $CaCO_3$. Pure calcite is colorless or white, but impurities dissolved in it may make it almost any color. It has a hardness of 3. Its three perfect cleavages at oblique angles give it a very strong tendency to break into little flat-sided *rhombs* when dropped or struck. It is easily identified by the acid test described in Topic 5.

Colorless transparent calcite is called *Iceland spar*. Iceland spar's property of double refraction (see Topic 6) is important in the polarizing microscope used in optical analysis of minerals and rocks.

Calcite is the chief mineral—often the only one—in most limestones and marbles.

Dolomite is calcium magnesium carbonate. It has a hardness of 3.5 to 4. It cleaves like calcite. In the acid test, however, dolomite will not effervesce unless it is scratched or powdered or the hydrochloric acid is heated. Dolomite usually occurs as coarse or fine grains in "dolomitic" limestones and marbles.

Ferrous Minerals: Magnetite And Pyrite 9.

Magnetite is a black magnetic iron oxide. It has a hardness of 5.5 to 6.5. It occurs in many rocks in the form of small grains or crystals. Its name comes from the fact that it is attracted to a magnet.

Lodestone is a highly magnetic variety of magnetite. It is a natural magnet from which the first magnetic compass needles were made.

Pyrite is a pale brass to golden-yellow mineral. Its hardness is about 6. Because of its golden color and high metallic luster, it is sometimes mistaken for gold, and is known as "fool's gold." Pyrite is iron sulfide. It is the common sulfur mineral.

TOPIC QUESTIONS

Each topic question refers to the topic of the same number within this chapter.

1. How are minerals usually identified in field work?

2. (a) Why is it difficult to identify a mineral by its color alone? (b) What is luster? Name different types of luster and give examples. (c) Why is crystal shape not especially helpful in field identification?

3. (a) Explain what a mineral streak is, how it is obtained, and how the streak of metallic and nonmetallic minerals differs. (b) Using examples, explain what is meant by the cleavage of a mineral. (c) What is mineral fracture? Give examples of different types of fracture. (d) Explain what hardness is. How is it determined? (e) Name the 10 minerals in Mohs' scale of hardness. (f) What precaution must be taken in observing the results of a hardness test?

4. (a) What is specific gravity? (b) Compare, giving examples, the specific gravity of metallic and nonmetallic minerals in general. (c) Explain how to find the specific gravity of a mineral sample.

5. Describe the acid test for calcite.

6. Describe briefly four special properties of minerals. Give examples.

7. (a) Give brief descriptions of quartz, feldspars, and mica. (b) Compare hornblende and augite. (c) Compare talc and kaolinite. (d) Compare olivine and garnet.

8. Compare calcite and dolomite.

9. (a) Describe magnetite. Distinguish between magnetite and lodestone. (b) Describe pyrite.

GENERAL QUESTIONS

1. Make a chart listing 10 important rock-forming minerals and giving the following information for each: composition, color, hardness, cleavage or fracture.

2. In each pair, state which substance is harder and how you know: (a) tooth powder and tooth enamel, (b) chalk and slate, (c) diamond and glass.

3. With the minerals described in this chapter, how many half-steps can you add to Mohs' scale of hardness? (For example, mica's hardness is 2.5, placing it between gypsum and calcite in hardness.)

4. How can you distinguish: (a) talc from mica, (b) quartz from glass, (c) calcite from quartz, (d) calcite from talc (e) magnetite from hornblende?

STUDENT ACTIVITIES

1. Obtain the answers to General Question 4 by actual experiment.

2. Using the method described in Topic 4, find the specific gravity of talc, calcite, orthoclase, quartz, and hornblende.

3. Verify the statement made in Topic 3 with respect to the streak of metallic and nonmetallic minerals. Use at least three of each and record your results.

4. Try the acid test described in Topic 5 on as many carbonate minerals as possible, such as calcite, dolomite, azurite, malachite, and siderite. Record your results carefully, indicating whether scratching, powdering, or heat was necessary to get a reaction.

5. Using a copper penny, a penknife, and a square of ordinary window glass, show that the hardness of each of these minerals is about as indicated: (a) hornblende, 6; (b) mica, 2.5; (c) augite, 5.5; (d) garnet, 7.5; (e) kaolin, 1.5; (f) sphalerite, 3.5.

5

The rocks of the earth's crust formed over long periods of time in three principal ways. You can "model" two of these ways.

1. Put two heaping tablespoons of sand into a clean paper cup or cut-down milk container. Add a few small pebbles and one tablespoon of cement. Mix thoroughly. Slowly add cold water and stir until a thick mixture is formed. Let it stand until it hardens. The "rock" you get is a sedimentary rock like those described in Topic 11.

2. Put one teaspoon of para (paradichlorobenzine) flakes into a test tube or small bottle. Stopper the test tube tightly. Stand it in a beaker of very hot water until the para melts. Remove the test tube and allow it to cool. The "rock" that forms is an igneous rock, comparable to those described in Topic 3.

How Our Rocks Were Formed

Igneous Rocks

Modern geology is said to have had its real beginnings in 1795. In that year the Scotch geologist James Hutton explained his **doctrine of uniformity of process,** also called *uniformitarianism.* Before Hutton, most geologists believed that the physical features of the earth, such as mountains, canyons, and so forth, had been formed by sudden spectacular events, which they called *catastrophes.* In their view, these catastrophes caused the birth of mountains, the formation of canyons, the creation of waterfalls, and in general, the origin of almost all the landforms or "scenery" of the continents.

James Hutton

James Hutton's ideas were quite different. After years of field studies, he came to the conclusion that "the present is the key to the past." By this he meant that: (1) The geologic processes now operating on the earth were also active in the past; (2) The present physical features of the earth were formed by these geologic processes, operating over long periods of time.

According to Hutton, a canyon or a great river valley was not formed by sudden splitting of the earth's crust. Instead, it was formed by slow and steady wearing away of the land. This was done, said Hutton, by the very same river now running in the canyon, doing for thousands and thousands of years what it is still doing today.

2. **Three Families of Rocks**

Hutton's principles have been used by geologists to explain the origin of rocks. Geologists have noted, for example, that erupting lava hardens into rocks which are similar to rocks that have been found in many places on the earth. They have noted that sands and clays on sea and lake bottoms harden into rocklike materials. These resemble present-day sandstone and shale. They have noted that when hot lava flows over other rocks, it changes them. From many studies like these, geologists have concluded that all the rocks of the crust form in one of three general ways:

Igneous rocks are formed by the cooling and hardening of hot molten rock (**magma**) from within the earth's mantle.

Sedimentary rocks are formed by the hardening of layers of sediments. The sediments may consist of rock fragments, plant and animal remains, or chemicals that form on lake and ocean bottoms.

{ **Metamorphic** rocks are formed when rocks that already exist are changed into new kinds of rock.

The solidified lava of a volcano is igneous; sandstone, formed of sand, is sedimentary; and marble, derived from the transformation of limestone, is a metamorphic rock.

Recognizing Igneous Rocks 3.

When hot liquid magma pours out of the earth's crust in a volcanic eruption and then becomes solid, it forms the kind of igneous rock called **extrusive** or *volcanic*. The geologist can see such rocks being formed. From them he can identify rocks formed in the same way in other times or places.

But igneous rocks are also formed from magmas that never reach the surface. Such igneous rocks are called **intrusive** because they have intruded into other rock masses. We see them only after the rock that covers them is worn away. Geologists have found several types of evidence in these rocks that indicate they were once liquid magma. They resemble extrusive rocks in mineral composition. Their crystal grains interlock as if they had been formed from a hot liquid.

If magma stops and hardens beneath the surface, intrusive rock is formed. If magma reaches the surface, extrusive rock is formed.

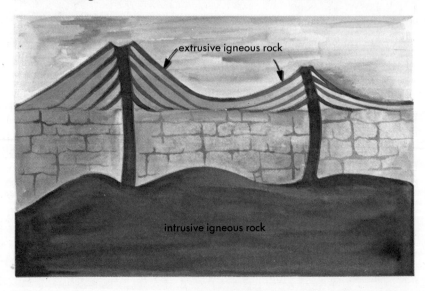

extrusive igneous rock

intrusive igneous rock

What is magma made of? Geologists have answered this question by studying volcanic lavas and other materials.

Magma is called *lava* when it reaches the earth's surface. Magma can be "made" by melting rocks like granite and basalt in the laboratory. When the geologist analyzes volcanic lavas and laboratory-made magmas, he finds that they fall into two main types. Both types are hot solutions of silicates, with temperatures ranging from about 600° C to 1200° C. But they differ in chemical composition. One type has a high percentage of silica (SiO_2) and not much of the calcium, iron, and magnesium that form dark-colored minerals. This *high-silica* or *acid* type of magma is relatively thick and slow flowing. When it hardens, it forms mainly light-colored minerals, such as quartz and orthoclase feldspar, and light-colored rocks, such as granite. Most intrusive rocks are of this type. Most of the rock that forms the continents is of the high-silica type.

The second main type of magma has a much lower percentage of silica and a high percentage of calcium, iron, and magnesium. This *low-silica* or *basic* type of magma is hotter and more fluid than the acid type. When it solidifies, it forms mainly dark ferromagnesian minerals, such as hornblende, augite, and black mica, and dark-colored rocks, such as *basalt*. Most extrusive rocks are of this type. Geologists believe the earth's mantle consists of low-silica rock.

Igneous rocks range from glassy-smooth rocks such as obsidian to coarse-grained rocks such as granite. The *texture* of the rock depends on the sizes, shapes, and arrangement of its grains or crystals.

The sizes of the grains seem to depend mostly on how fast the magma cools and solidifies. The longer the magma stays liquid, the larger the grains become. In the liquid state the ions are free to move together, which increases the size of the growing crystals.

Another factor favoring the growth of large crystals is the presence of a high percentage of dissolved gases in magma. This is because the gases keep the magma liquid longer.

Still another factor in texture is the order in which particular minerals crystallize from the magma. Those that crystallize first are likely to be larger and more regular in form. Those whose crystals form later have less time and less room to grow in.

Magmas that form deep within the earth's crust cool very slowly and solidify slowly. They form intrusive rocks with large mineral

Granite

Basalt

grains of fairly uniform size. These rocks are *granular*, or *coarse-grained*. The most familiar example is granite.

Magmas that cool on the surface harden more rapidly. They form extrusive rocks with tiny crystals usually too small to be seen without a microscope. These rocks are *fine-grained*. A good example is basalt.

In some cases magmas flowing onto the earth's surface harden so rapidly that there is no time at all for crystals to develop. The rocks that form then are as smooth as glass, and are said to have *glassy* texture. A good example is obsidian.

Obsidian

Feldspar crystals in a porphyry

A rhyolite porphyry

6. Porphyritic Texture

Some igneous rocks consist of two distinctly different textures. Large crystals are surrounded by a *groundmass* that is fine-grained or glassy. Such a rock is called a **porphyry** (POR fi ree).

One explanation of how a porphyry is formed involves two stages of cooling. In the first stage the magma is at great depth. Here it cools slowly enough so that large crystals of one mineral can form. The rest of the magma remains liquid. Then the magma moves upward, possibly breaking through overlying rock, until it comes close to the surface. Here the magma cools rapidly. The liquid hardens into a groundmass surrounding the first-stage crystals.

7. Families of Igneous Rocks

Geologists put the igneous rocks into families according to the minerals that form the rocks. Each family has its coarse-grained, fine-grained, and glassy member.

The **granite family** comes from high-silica magmas. All of the rocks in this family are made mainly of orthoclase feldspar and quartz. Other minerals likely to be present are plagioclase feldspar, mica, and hornblende. Since orthoclase and quartz are light in color, the rocks in this family are usually light colored. In this family *granite* is coarse-grained, *rhyolite* is fine-grained, and *obsidian* and *pumice* are glassy. But all have similar chemical composition.

Rhyolite

Diabase

Anorthosite gabbro

The **gabbro family** comes from low-silica magmas. The rocks in this family are made mainly of *plagioclase feldspar* and *augite*. Other likely minerals are olivine, hornblende, and biotite. Since all but the feldspar are the dark, heavy ferromagnesian minerals these rocks are generally very dark in color and heavier than the granites. In this family *gabbro* is coarse-grained, *basalt* is fine-grained, and *basalt glass* is glassy. Diabase lies between gabbro and basalt in texture.

The **diorite family** falls between the granite and gabbro families. (See the table of igneous rocks.)

Also of interest are three coarse, dark, heavy rocks that may be like the rock of the earth's mantle. *Pyroxenite* is nearly all pyroxene; *dunite* is almost all olivine; *peridotite* is a mixture of pyroxene and olivine.

Diorite

Descriptions
of Igneous Rocks

Granite is made from quartz, orthoclase feldspar, and at least one other mineral, such as mica or hornblende. The quartz grains look like little chips of cloudy or grayish glass. The feldspar crystals can be recognized by their smooth cleavage surfaces and by their color, usually white, gray, or pink. The mica flakes, usually black mica, can be chipped out with your fingernail or knife blade. Hornblende is also black or dark green. It comes in small chunks or sticks that cannot be removed so easily.

Granites range in color from light grays to medium grays and pinks, with the color of feldspar having the greatest influence on the overall color of the rock.

Granite is the most common of all igneous rocks. It can be seen in the Rockies, the Adirondacks, the Black Hills of South Dakota, the

The imposing faces of Mount Rushmore are carved in granite.

White Mountains of New Hampshire, and in many other mountainous areas. Since granite is intrusive, its presence at the surface shows that erosion has removed thousands of meters of overlying rocks.

Obsidian is formed by the rapid cooling of surface flows of lava. It is usually dark brown to black in color and glassy in texture. Obsidian is very hard but brittle. It breaks rather easily with a shell-like fracture. Obsidian splits easily and forms sharp edges. For these reasons, it was much used by primitive peoples for making knives, axes, arrowheads, and other tools.

Pumice is lava that hardened while steam and other gases were still bubbling out of it. This formed a rock that looks like a sponge with many small holes in it. Its air holes may make it light enough to float.

Basalt is the most common rock formed from flows of lava. It is fine-grained and ranges in color from dark green to black. Large areas of basalt occur in the lava flows of Iceland, the Hawaiian Islands, and in the Columbia Plateau in the western United States.

Pumice

Diabase

Diabase is like basalt in color and is made from the same minerals, but it is coarser in texture. Diabase is also known as *dolerite* and *trap rock*.

Summary Table: Common Igneous Rocks

Texture and Origin	Light-colored Rocks		Medium-colored Rocks	Dark-colored Rocks	
	Colors: white, tan, gray, pink, red *Minerals:* Feldspar (mostly orthoclase), quartz; also some mica and hornblende		*Colors:* gray, green *Minerals:* Feldspar (mostly plagioclase) hornblende, augite, biotite	*Colors:* dark green, dark gray, black *Minerals:* Plagioclase feldspar, augite; also olivine, hornblende, biotite	
	With Quartz	*Almost No Quartz*	*Without Quartz*		
Glassy: cooled quickly at surface of earth	Obsidian Pumice		Obsidian	Basalt glass Scoria	
Fine-grained: cooled more slowly at or near surface	Rhyolite	Trachyte (Felsite)	Andesite	Basalt Diabase	
Coarse-grained: cooled very slowly, usually at great depths	Granite Pegmatite	Syenite Granodiorite	Diorite	Gabbro	*No feldspar* Peridotite Pyroxenite Dunite

Sedimentary Rocks

9. Kinds of Sediments

There are three main sources for the sediments that form sedimentary rock.

Clastic sedimentary rocks are formed from fragments of other rocks, such as clay, sand, or gravel.

Chemical sedimentary rocks are formed from mineral grains that precipitate out of solution by evaporation or chemical action.

Organic sedimentary rocks are formed from the remains of plants and animals.

At one time the whole crust of the earth was igneous rocks. Today, however, sedimentary rocks cover about three-fourths of the continents. They also make up more than one-tenth of the total volume of the continental crust's outer sixteen kilometers.

Sedimentary rocks are rocks formed from layers of sediments. What are the different kinds of rock-forming sediments? Where do they come from? How do they become changed into rock?

10. How Clastic Rocks Form

The fragments that form clastic rocks come from the weathering of rocks already in existence. These fragments range in size from larger to smaller as follows: pebbles, gravels, sand, silt, and clay.

Rock fragments form wherever rock meets the air. The fragments are carried off by winds, waves, rivers, and glaciers and form in great layers of sediment. The largest amounts of sediment are formed and collected by rivers. The sediments are left by floods or at the river's mouth in a lake or in the ocean. In lakes and oceans the sediments are usually spread out by waves and currents for great distances in the shallow-water areas bordering the land. (The shallow-water areas that border the continents are called the *continental shelves.*)

When the sediments become hundreds of meters thick, the lower layers may harden into rock. How? In fine sediments such as silt and clay, the great pressure makes the particles stick together. In coarser sediments such as sands and gravels, the particles do not hold together unless they have been cemented. Ocean and lake waters contain dissolved minerals such as silica (from quartz), lime (from calcite), and iron compounds. These are natural cements. As they soak into the layers of sands and gravels, they cement the fragments into rocks.

Silica and lime cements are usually gray or white; iron cements are rust colored, brown, or reddish. Each gives the same colors to the rocks they cement.

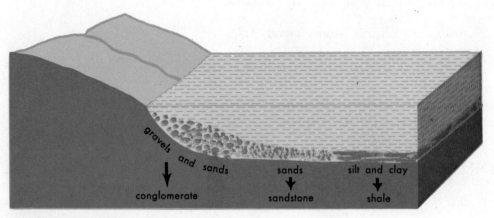

The kinds of sediment and rock in an ocean (or lake) floor change as you go out from the shore.

Sorting the Sediments 11.

When a river flows into the ocean (or into a lake) the river drops its sediment as it gradually loses its speed. The first sediments to be dropped are the heavy pebbles and gravels. These settle to the bottom in the shallow waters of the continental shelves nearest to shore. Next come the lighter sands, and finally the silts and clays.

The process of *sorting* does not produce perfect separation. Sand is found mixed with pebbles and gravels in shallow water, or with silts and clays in deeper water. Nevertheless, the sediments are fairly definite.

As the sediments become cemented together, the pebbles and gravels form a rock called *conglomerate,* the sands form *sandstone,* and the silts and clays form *shale.* Whether large or small, the particles are rounded as a result of their having been carried by running water.

Conglomerate is the coarsest of the clastic rocks. It is a cemented mixture of rounded pebbles and sand grains. The pebbles in conglomerate may be any rock material, but quartz is the most common because of its great durability.

Conglomerate

Sandstone

Shale

Most **sandstones** are made largely of grains of quartz. Although the grains are cemented together, the cement never fills all the spaces between the grains. So sandstones may have up to 30 per cent of air space in them and are *porous* (filled with small holes). Since water can pass through sandstones, they are *permeable*. Sandstones are rough, gritty, and durable.

The clays that make up **shale** are usually made from the mineral kaolin.The spaces between the very small particles in shale are so tiny that water cannot pass through the rock. This makes shale *impermeable*. Shales are smooth, soft, and easily broken.

13. Sedimentary Rocks of Chemical Origin

Minerals often dissolve in sea, lake, swamp, or in underground waters. Chemical sediments are formed when these minerals are deposited from the water by evaporation or chemical action. The most

Rock salt

Limestone

Rock gypsum

common chemical sediments are limestone, rock salt, and rock gypsum.

Limestones of chemical origin are formed from tiny grains of calcite deposited from sea or lake waters. The most common ones are called *compact limestones*. They are usually gray or tan, dense in appearance, and smooth to the touch.

Rock salt is the natural form of common table salt (sodium chloride). It occurs as a sedimentary rock in thick layers in many parts of the world. It consists almost entirely of the mineral *halite*.

Rock gypsum, like rock salt, occurs in sedimentary layers and in veins of nearly pure mineral gypsum.

Both rock salt and rock gypsum are believed to have been formed by the evaporation of the waters of salt lakes or ocean bays cut off by sand bars.

Sedimentary Rocks of Organic Origin 14.

Organic sediments come from the remains of animals and plants. The most important rocks that come from organic sediments are *limestone* and *coal*.

The origin of organic limestone. The lime in these limestones is the mineral *calcite*. Calcite is dissolved out of rocks on land, carried to the ocean (or lakes) by streams, and taken from the water by lime-forming organisms.

Great numbers of lime-forming animals and plants live in the waters of the continental shelf. These include clams, mussels, oysters, sea snails, corals, microscopic algae, and many others. When they die, their lime shells—sometimes whole, often broken into fragments by the grinding action of the waves—pile up on the floor of the continental shelf. In time the shells become cemented together into limestones. The limestones that form near the shore may contain a good deal of clay. Those that form in deeper water may be almost pure lime.

Limestone (organic)

Since most limestones are composed of the mineral calcite, they can readily be identified by the acid test. (Chapter 4, Topic 5)

The story of coal. When ferns, mosses, twigs, and even tree trunks are buried in swamp waters, they undergo slow decay. At first they decay into **peat**, a brownish mass of mosses, leaves, and twigs. With further decay and compression, peat changes into a more compact material called **lignite**, or brown coal. Further change produces **bituminous coal**, commonly called soft coal. The entire transformation may take many thousands of years.

An average soft coal specimen consists of about 85 percent carbon, an element that is not lost in the transformation. During mountain formation, the crushing of beds of soft coal changes it into a coal that may be 90 to 95 per cent pure carbon. This is called *hard coal*, or **anthracite**. It is a metamorphic rock.

Coal is a valuable rock since it is used for fuel. But, careful safety precautions must be taken in mining coal. Here a miner tests for gas in a coal seam.

Bituminous coal

How Our Rocks Were Formed **63**

Oil and natural gas are also fuels. We get them by drilling into pockets in certain rock formations.

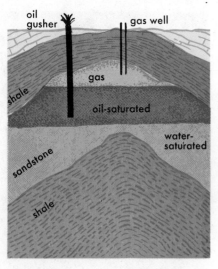

Petroleum, or oil, is not usually thought of as a rock. It is found mainly in sedimentary rocks, however, and is believed to come from living things in most cases.

Geologists generally agree that petroleum comes from the remains of certain oil-forming plants or animals or both. They think that large amounts of these remains were deposited in shallow coastal waters.

Just how the oil came from these deposits is not known. In any case, the oil appears to have somehow got in the pores of rocks such as sandstone or in the cracks and fissures of rocks such as limestone. If shale were present as a *cap rock*, it trapped the oil and prevented its escape. (Shale is an *impermeable* rock—through which liquids and gases cannot penetrate.)

So-called *oil pools*, or *reservoirs*, are simply oil-saturated areas of rock—usually sandstone or limestone. Where the rock is shaped like an upside down V, the oil is found at the top, sealed in above by shale, and below by water (usually salt water).

Natural gas is often found together with oil. It probably comes from the oil. When gas is present, it stands at the top of the rock formation, above the oil. If the gas pressure is high at the time a well is being drilled into the formation, the pressure of the gas causes a gusher. Otherwise the oil is pumped out.

Sedimentary Features: Stratification 16.

Sedimentary rocks show special features that help to identify them. One of these is **stratification**—arrangement in visible layers. How does stratification develop?

The layers of these rocks in Yugoslavia show stratification. The lines separating the layers show bedding planes.

You can see cross-bedding in this famous Navajo sandstone in Utah. Geologists believe these cross-bedded layers started in ancient sand dunes. Note the slanted bedding planes.

When any change occurs in the kind of sediments being laid down in one place, new rock layers are formed. For example, if a coarse clay is deposited on a fine one, layers of different shale will form, one on top of the other. If sand is deposited on clay, a layer of sandstone will form on a layer of shale. In this way sedimentary rocks become *stratified,* and their beds or layers are separated by **bedding planes.** Bedding planes are usually horizontal. *Cross-bedding* may develop when beds are deposited in inclined positions on sand dunes and deltas.

Sediments change for many reasons. For example, the river that brings the sediment to the ocean or lake may be wearing away new kinds of rock. It may carry larger quantities and more varieties of pebbles, sand and clay during flood times. It may carry its sediments farther out to sea than formerly. It may drop them closer to shore.

17. Fossils in Sedimentary Rocks

As sediments pile up on continental shelves, on lake bottoms, or on swamp floors, animals and plants that die there are buried by the sediments. The soft parts of the animals and plants decay. The hard parts may remain as **fossils** when the sediments turn to rock. The shells of clams, mussels, and snails are frequently found inside layers

When a fish dies, its body comes to rest on the ocean floor. Mud soon covers the fish. When the mud hardens into rock, any remains or impressions of the fish become part of the rock.

of sandstone, limestone, and shale. Sometimes the shells themselves disappear but leave impressions that can be seen when the rock layers are split apart. Fish skeletons also form fossils.

Plant remains or impressions are usually found in rocks that come from swamp sediments.

Fossils, therefore, are the remains, impressions, or any other evidence of the existence of plants or animals preserved in rock.

Ripple Marks; Mud Cracks 18.

Many sandstones show **ripple marks** on the surface of a bedding plane. Ripple marks are formed by the action of winds, streams, waves, or currents on sand. Many of them are preserved when the sand becomes sandstone. Ripple marks can be seen today on any sandy beach or stream bed.

The wavy lines in the sandstone at the right are ripple marks.

The intersecting lines in the sandstone below are mud cracks.

Mud cracks apparently develop when deposits of wet clay dry out and crack before hardening into rock. The cracks are preserved if they are filled with different materials by a later layer of sediment. Mud cracks can be seen wherever muddy roads or beds of clay dry after a rain.

Limestone often contains lumps of flint or other "foreign material." These are called **concretions.** The lumps may have been deposited from a solution, bit by bit, around a nucleus of fossil material trapped in the rock. Concretions often are the same mineral as that which cements the rock together.

The lumps of flint in this chalk are concretions.

Limestones sometimes include small, fairly round cavities lined with crystals of quartz or calcite. These **geodes** (JEE odes), like miniature caverns, are believed to have been formed by mineral-carrying waters. First they dissolved limestone to form the hollows. Later they deposited crystals in them.

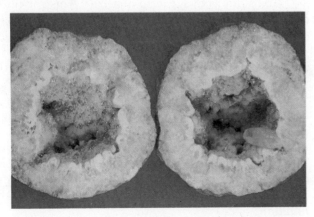

The little crystal-lined cave is a geode.

Metamorphic Rocks

What Metamorphic Rocks Are 20.

Marble, slate, gneiss, quartzite—these are rocks we have not yet described. They fail to fit into either of our first two classes, for they are not formed from either magma or sediment. Yet in many ways they are like members of our first two groups. Marble resembles some limestones, slate reminds us of shale, quartzite looks like crystallized sandstone, while gneiss contains minerals like those in granite.

These resemblances are not mere coincidence. The rocks in these pairs really are related. One actually comes from the other through changes produced by natural forces. These **metamorphic** (*meta*, change; *morph*, form) *rocks* are *rocks formed from existing bedrock by the action of heat, pressure, and chemicals.*

Dynamic Metamorphism 21.

One way in which metamorphism occurs is called **dynamic** (moving) **metamorphism.** During mountain formation, horizontal layers of sedimentary rock have very large squeezing *pressures* on them. Friction between the moving rock layers builds up vast amounts of *heat*. The combination of pressure and heat produces great changes in the rocks.

Let us take some examples.

Sandstone is changed to quartzite. This rock is still quartz mineral, but it is no longer porous like sandstone. It is also much more crystalline in appearance.

Limestone is changed to marble. Again, there is no change in minerals. Marble is all calcite, as limestone was. But marble, too, is a shiny crystalline rock.

Soft coal is changed to hard coal (*anthracite*). Anthracite is harder and shinier than soft coal and has a higher percentage of carbon.

When shale is metamorphosed, even more changes take place. New minerals, such as mica and hornblende form. The flakes of mica or the needles of hornblende become arranged in parallel layers along which the new rock splits easily. This new feature is called **foliation.**

Anthracite coal

Gray slate

Red slate

The first rock formed from shale during dynamic metamorphism is *slate*. In slate the foliation layers are microscopically thin. If metamorphism continues, a shiny rock called **phyllite** is formed. More intense metamorphism produces a flaky rock called **schist,** in which the foliation layers can easily be seen.

Schists can be formed from many different rocks, such as shales, impure sandstones, and basalt. The result is that there are many varieties of schist. These are usually named for their principal mineral. *Mica schist* consists of mica and quartz. Other varieties are talc schist and hornblende schist.

Gneiss is another metamorphic rock formed from a variety of rocks. These include shale, granite, conglomerate, and many others. Gneiss has the coarsest foliation of all the metamorphic rocks. Its minerals are arranged in cardboard-thick parallel bands. Light-colored minerals such as quartz and feldspar may alternate with dark minerals such as hornblende or biotite to form easily seen bands.

Phyllite

Mica schist

Biotite gneiss

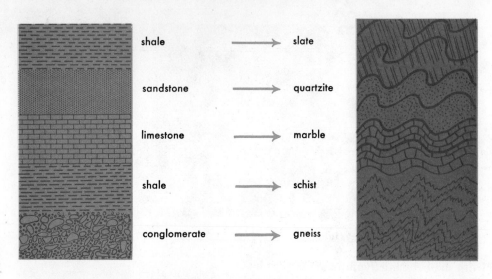

shale   →   slate

sandstone   →   quartzite

limestone   →   marble

shale   →   schist

conglomerate   →   gneiss

Look at the two columns. The rocks on the left turn into the rocks on the right during dynamic metamorphism.

Relation of Principal Sedimentary Materials, Sedimentary Rocks, and Metamorphic Rocks

Sedimentary Material	Sedimentary Rock	Metamorphic Rock
Pebbles, gravel, and sand	Conglomerate	Quartzite conglomerate Gneiss (also from granite and rhyolite)
Sand grains (usually quartz)	Sandstone	Quartzite
Clay (usually kaolin); silt	Shale, mudstone	Slate, phyllite, hornfels, schist
Lime (shells, fragments, or grains)	Limestone	Marble
Peat	Bituminous coal	Anthracite coal

Thermal Metamorphism 22.

A second way in which metamorphism occurs is called **thermal** (heat) **metamorphism.** This takes place when hot magma from the mantle forces its way into or between layers of overlying rock. The heat of the magma "bakes" the intruded rocks. In addition, hot liquids and gases enter the intruded rocks and react with its minerals. But these effects rarely extend more than a hundred meters into the intruded rock, so the changes are not nearly so great as in dynamic metamorphism. Foliation is never produced.

Classifying the rocks of the crust according to their origin shows how closely related they are. The igneous rocks may be thought of as the *primary*, or parent, rocks of the crust. As these are attacked by weathering and erosion, sediments form and harden into *secondary* rocks, the sedimentary rocks. If these rocks are buried beneath other sediments and are involved in movements of the plates of the crust, they may become metamorphic rocks.

As the theory of plate tectonics tells us, the plates bearing these rocks may gradually be forced deep into the earth's crust. There the rocks will be subjected to temperatures so high that they melt into magma. The magma may someday solidify into igneous rocks to complete a "rock cycle."

The rock cycle also has short cuts and detours. Igneous rock may be metamorphosed directly. Sedimentary rock may be weathered without being metamorphosed. Metamorphic rocks weather or may be metamorphosed a second time. The story of the rock cycle is outlined in the accompanying diagram. In brief form it is a large part of the story of geology.

Imagine that you're a rock, and put yourself on this wheel. Then follow the arrows to see what other rocks you can become.

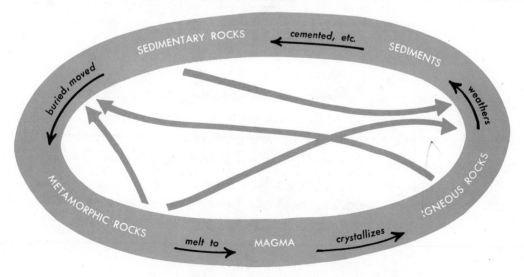

Each topic question refers to the topic of the same number within this chapter.

1. **(a)** Before James Hutton, how had geologists explained the origin of landforms? **(b)** What two principles are embodied in Hutton's "uniformitarianism"? **(c)** Compare Hutton's explanation of the origin of a canyon with that of a "catastrophist."

2. **(a)** Give two examples of the ways in which geologists apply Hutton's principles to learning the origins of rocks. **(b)** Define the three families of rocks.

3. **(a)** What are extrusive rocks? Why are they easy to recognize as igneous? **(b)** What are intrusive rocks? How do we know they are igneous?

4. **(a)** How can the geologists tell what magmas are made of? **(b)** Describe the acid type of magma. **(c)** Describe the basic type of magma.

5. **(a)** What determines the size of the mineral grains in an igneous rock? **(b)** Explain when a magma will form a coarse-grained rock, a fine-grained rock, or a glassy rock. **(c)** What other factors favor the growth of large crystals?

6. What is porphyritic texture? How does it develop?

7. **(a)** Describe the granite family of igneous rocks. **(b)** Describe the gabbro family of igneous rocks. **(c)** What is the diorite family?

8. Give brief descriptions of granite, obsidian, pumice, basalt, and diabase.

9. Define the three groups of sedimentary rocks.

10. Explain how sediments form rocks.

11. Explain how rock sediments are sorted when deposited in water. Name the rocks formed from each sediment.

12. **(a)** Explain why sandstone is permeable. **(b)** How does shale's composition explain its being impermeable?

13. **(a)** How are chemical sediments formed? **(b)** How do limestones of chemical origin form? **(c)** How are rock salt and gypsum formed?

14. **(a)** Explain the origin of organic limestones. **(b)** How is peat formed? How are lignite and bituminous coal formed? **(c)** How is anthracite coal formed from bituminous?

15. **(a)** Describe the probable origin of petroleum. **(b)** Describe the rock structures in which petroleum is usually found. **(c)** What makes an oil gusher?

16. What is stratification? How does it develop in sedimentary rocks?

17. What are fossils? How do they form in sedimentary rocks?

18. How did ripple marks and mud cracks form in sedimentary rocks?

19. What is a concretion? How does it develop? What is a geode? How is it formed?

20. Define metamorphic rocks. Name four examples.

21. **(a)** Explain what dynamic metamorphism is. **(b)** What changes does metamorphism cause in sandstone? In limestone? In soft coal? **(c)** What is foliation? **(d)** What rocks are formed from shale as metamorphism progresses? **(e)** Describe gneiss.

22. (a) What makes thermal metamorphism occur? (b) How do its effects compare with those of dynamic metamorphism?

23. Describe the rock cycle briefly either in words or by a simple diagram.

GENERAL QUESTIONS

1. Why are fossils more likely to be formed in shale and sandstone than in conglomerate?

2. Can fossils ever be formed in igneous rocks? Explain.

3. Why are fossils less likely to be found in metamorphic rocks than in the rocks from which they are derived?

4. Explain several ways of distinguishing white marble from white quartz.

STUDENT ACTIVITIES

1. Using the acid test, hardness tests, and any other means you have learned, differentiate the following rocks: (a) white limestone, white marble, and white quartzite; (b) dark gray limestone and basalt; (c) gray sandstone and gray limestone; (d) red shale and red sandstone; (e) schist and gneiss.

2. Pair off the following metamorphic and sedimentary rocks, and then make a list of the similarities and differences you can observe in them: (a) shale and slate, (b) bituminous coal and anthracite, (c) limestone and marble, (d) conglomerate and gneiss, (e) sandstone and quartzite.

3. Heat a small quantity of crushed soft coal in a pyrex test tube or metal dish. Do the same with hard coal. Which coal gives off more liquids and gases? If you heat the coal until no more gases are given off, what will remain?

4. With the aid of a hand magnifier, examine specimens of coarse granite, gabbro, marble, and conglomerate. Make a list of the minerals you can identify in each rock.

5. Make your own collection of igneous, sedimentary, and metamorphic rocks.

6. Take the following "field trips" to see how many different kinds of rock you can identify: (a) to your own school building (look at window sills, staircases, and the ornamental stone in lobbies, the auditorium, the front of the building, etc.); (b) to other public buildings in your town or vicinity; (c) to local parks and other outdoor areas; (d) to a monument works or graveyard.

unit two

The crust of the earth
is shaped by wind, wave, water, ice,
and other agents of erosion. What forces do
you think are responsible for shaping the forms
found in the Colorado National Monument, shown on
the page opposite? Certainly these forms are not like those
found in most of the United States. How would you describe
the rock and soil formations that occur near where you live?
Have they been shaped by wind, by water, or by ice? Or by some
combination of the three? Can you account for the differences
between your region and this desert region in Colorado?

Here is some information you can use to decide what forces shaped your
region. In wet regions, the actions of air and water tend to produce
rounded forms. They attack surfaces with some frequency and from a
variety of directions. In drier regions, when there is any water at all, there is
usually a lot of it. Dry gulches suddenly fill with rivers formed by
cloudbursts. These rivers tend to follow the same paths, producing the
steep cliffs you see in the photograph. Desert winds, which often contain
more dust than winds from a moister region, do their share of erosion,
also. Sand carried by these winds near ground level acts as a cutting
agent, further shaping the rock.

Other agents of erosion also leave characteristic forms. That
is how we know that much of the earth was once covered
with ice. Markings on rocks, the position of rocks, the
shapes of hills and mountains, and the shapes of
lakes are all clues. What kinds of clues
would you expect a river of ice to
leave behind?

Forces That Attack the Surface

1. *Rocks containing iron are easily changed by certain conditions. Try the following experiment to identify the conditions.*

   Take two dry pads of steel wool (soapless preferred, but not essential). Wet one thoroughly with water. Keep the other dry. Let them "weather" overnight in an open dish. Compare their appearance. If one has changed more than the other, explain why. Is the rusting of iron an example of chemical action or physical action? Why? In what way does rusting change the steel wool physically?

2. *In Chapter 5, Student Activity 6, you were asked to take a "field trip" to such places as your own school building, other public buildings, parks, and graveyards. The purpose was to identify different kinds of rocks.*

   Go to these places again. But now look for signs of change or weathering in these rocks. Compare fresh surfaces with surfaces that have weathered. See how they differ in appearance and hardness. What caused the changes? What substance can you recognize that is formed by the weathering of the rocks?

Weathering and Mass Movement

Weathering

The Palisades of the Hudson are the nearly vertical cliffs that form the west walls of the lower Hudson River Valley. The Palisades are made of diabase, a hard, tough crystalline rock. Like all rocks, diabase is changed by the weather. As time passes, its smooth, dark-gray surface turns brown and crumbly. Cracks form on the face and top of the cliff and spread inward and downward. Eventually material breaks away from the cliff. The material is in the form of brown claylike powder, rock chips the size of sand grains and pebbles, and occasional boulders. These changes are called **weathering.** Weathering is the *breakup of rock mainly from exposure to atmosphere and weather.*

What happens to the newly formed clay, sand, pebbles, and boulders? The heavy boulders and pebbles may fall all the way to the base of the cliff, where they continue to weather. The sands and clays may lodge in the rock temporarily part of the way down. They reach bottom some days or weeks later after being washed down by rain or melting snow. Finally, someday some of this material will fall or be washed into the river.

What next? The sediment washed into the river is carried to the sea. The river wears down or *erodes* its valley and carries off rock sediment. The river is an agent of erosion. **Erosion** *is the breakup and removal of rock by moving natural agents.* In addition to rivers, the other common agents of erosion are glaciers (ice in motion); winds (air in motion); waves and currents (water in motion).

Weathering and erosion have shaped this cliff. (Yellowstone National Park)

Sandstone crumbles into sand. Shale is shattered into thin fragments. Flakes of black mica in schist and gneiss turn golden brown and fall away. Dark basalts are stained reddish brown. All these evidences of *weathering* can be seen in exposed bedrock.

Weathering includes many processes, but they are usually classed under two headings. **Mechanical weathering,** or *disintegration,* takes place when rock is split or broken into smaller pieces of the same material without changing its composition. The breaking of a *granite* cliff, for example, into boulders and pebbles of *granite* is mechanical weathering. **Chemical weathering,** or *decomposition,* takes place when the rock's minerals change into different substances. The crumbling of dark gray diabase rock into rusty brownish clay is an example of chemical weathering.

Mechanical Weathering 3.

These boulders used to be part of the solid bedrock in a mountain. Water melting and freezing in the cracks split the rock into pieces.

Rocks are weathered mechanically mainly as a result of weather changes.

Effects of temperature change. The change in day and night temperatures of bare rocks in mountain and desert areas is very large. Temperature changes cause different minerals in a rock to expand and contract at different rates. Therefore, day and night changes in temperature *might* be expected to loosen the mineral grains until they fall apart. Laboratory tests, however, fail to produce such effects. Temperature change alone apparently does little to weather rock.

Frost action. Water expands by about 10 percent of its volume when it freezes into ice. This expansion exerts a tremendous force on the walls of any container in which the water may be held, whether that container is a water pipe or a crack in a rock. In climates where the temperature goes below freezing, the freezing of water may be the most damaging of all weathering processes. This is especially true in porous rocks or rocks that are already cracked.

The more often the ice melts and refreezes, the more often will this *frost action,* or *wedgework of ice,* be able to split the rock. Mountain tops are particularly subject to frost action. The surface of a mountain above the tree line may be covered by large sharp-cornered boulders in *boulder fields.*

Exfoliation. In humid or moderately humid climates one may see rocks that look as though layers have been stripped away from their surface. The rocks are usually unstratified coarse-grained rocks, such as granite and gabbro. They usually contain feldspars or other minerals that weather into clay.

This *peeling,* or *scaling off,* of the outer layers is called **exfoliation.** Exfoliation's effects range from thin flakes of rock weathered from small boulders to enormous sheets of rock that split away from cliffs and mountain tops.

On a small scale, exfoliation results when rainwater gets into tiny cracks in the rock. The water combines chemically with grains of feldspar just below the surface. This causes the feldspar to swell and to expand. The expansion splits off a thin flake or shell of the rock.

Weathering is fastest at corners and edges because of their greater exposure. This results in a rounding off of the rock. If a rock mass contains many cracks that run both vertically and horizontally, exfoliation may carve the rock into a large number of *rounded knob-like forms.* Those that break off become *rounded boulders.*

On a large scale, gigantic slabs of fresh rock may split away from the tops of exposed mountain peaks of granite. Granite is an intrusive rock formed far below the earth's surface. It is believed that when great weights of overlying rock are removed by erosion, the granite expands. This expansion causes long curved breaks, or **joints,** to appear in the rock *parallel to the surface* and at various depths. It is along these joints that exfoliation occurs. The rounded peaks formed by the process are called *exfoliation domes.*

In the United States, many spectacular exfoliation domes occur in Yosemite National park, California. Stone Mountain, Georgia, and Sugar Loaf Mountain, near Rio de Janeiro, are other famous granite domes.

This rock used to have sharp edges. Water in the cracks near the edges made the minerals swell. Then the edges peeled off.

Exfoliation splits off whole layers of rock on some mountain peaks, making them dome-shaped.

Simple plants called lichens can grow on rock and make it crumble.

Action of plants. Tiny plants, such as simple lichens (LYE kens) and green mosses, grow on rocks. Small as they are, these plants help to split and decay the rock. One way is by wedging their hairlike roots into the tiny pores of the rock. A second way is by the formation of rock-dissolving acids in the roots. Trees and shrubs may grow through cracks in boulders that lie on top of soil, or many send rootlets into cracks in the bedrock.

Action of animals. Earthworms, ants, woodchucks, and other burrowing animals dig holes in the soil. The holes let air and water seep down to the bedrock and weather it.

Chemical Weathering 4.

Chemical weathering of rock results chiefly from the action of *rainwater*, *oxygen*, and *carbon dioxide*. Let us see how these chemical agents work.

The chemical union of *water* with other substances is called **hydration.** Common minerals that undergo hydration include feldspar, hornblende, and augite. When these minerals are exposed to water, they unite with it slowly. At first they swell up, and then they crumble into powdery clay.

The chemical union of *oxygen* with other substances is called **oxidation.** The minerals most easily attacked by oxygen are compounds of iron. These include magnetite, pyrite, and the dark-colored ferromagnesian minerals hornblende, augite, and biotite. Oxidation of these minerals forms iron rust, just as the oxidation of an iron nail does. If the iron combines with oxygen alone, the rust found is the red iron oxide *hematite*. When water is also present, rusting is much faster and the brown rust *limonite* is formed. The hematite and limonite formed by weathering are usually responsible for the reddish and brownish colors of soils and weathered rocks.

The chemical union of *carbon dioxide* with other substances is called **carbonation**. Alone, carbon dioxide gas has almost no effect on minerals. Carbon dioxide dissolves readily in rainwater and ground water, however, to form a weak acid called **carbonic acid.** This is the same acid as in carbonated soft drinks. Carbonic acid attacks many common rock-forming minerals, such as feldspar, hornblende, augite, and biotite mica. Its effect is to *leach* out (dissolve) such elements as potassium, sodium, magnesium, and calcium. When this happens, the original mineral crumbles into clay.

Carbonic acid is even more effective with calcite than with the minerals mentioned above. It dissolves calcite completely. Unless the calcite is impure, no clay is left over. The same thing happens to gypsum and salt, both of which will dissolve slowly but surely. The dissolving action of carbonic acid has hollowed out the great underground caverns of the world from limestone bedrock, which is composed almost entirely of calcite.

Carbonic acid created this cave by dissolving limestone bedrock. (Luray Caverns, Virginia)

Acids formed by the decay of plants and animals are dissolved by rainwater and carried down to the bedrock. Like carbonic acid, these acids attack rock minerals.

People cause environmental changes that affect chemical weathering. In industrial regions, carbon dioxide and sulfur compounds are released into the air in large quantities. The amount of carbonic acid and sulfuric acid is increased in rainwater. Consequently, the amount of weathering is increased. Similarly, mining often produces hills of acid-forming materials as waste. Water running off these heaps of waste contains more acid, and so it attacks rocks more readily.

As we have seen in the preceding paragraphs, water is very important in chemical weathering. Furthermore, heat speeds up all chemical action. Thus, chemical weathering goes on faster in a hot rainy climate.

Which Minerals and Rocks Resist Most? 5.

Let us look at the over-all effects of weathering on the main rock-making minerals and their rocks.

Quartz is almost completely unchanged by water and acids, so it is practically immune to chemical weathering. Its hardness makes it resist mechanical weathering as well. It weathers very slowly, forming pebbles or sand grains that are still pieces of quartz.

Feldspar, hornblende, mica, augite, calcite, and gypsum are all subject to chemical weathering as well as to mechanical weathering. Mechanical weathering breaks them into large fragments. Chemical weathering eventually turns the fragments into fine clays. Calcite and gypsum are also carried off in solution.

Most of the igneous rocks and many of the metamorphic rocks weather much more rapidly in wet climates than in dry ones. This is because they contain minerals that are easily attacked by chemical weathering. The first products of the weathering of these rocks are boulders, pebbles, sands, and clays. In time even the boulders crumble to clay. Pebbles and sands remain only if the rocks contain quartz or some other chemically resistant mineral.

Sandstones, quartzites, and quartz-pebble conglomerates are only as durable as the cements that hold them together. When the rocks break up, however, their quartz fragments remain as boulders, pebbles, and sands. Quartzites and well-cemented sandstones and conglomerates (with silica cement) are among the most lasting of all rocks.

Shales, weakest of the sedimentary rocks, split easily between layers. In time they crumble into the clays from which they were formed.

Marbles and limestones are fairly resistant to mechanical weathering, but their calcite undergoes slow attack by acids in water. This makes them generally less durable in moist climates than quartzites or sandstones. In dry climates, however, limestones may be among the most durable of rocks.

6. Weathering Is a Slow Process

Under average conditions, weathering is a very slow process. This is especially true for any individual weathering agent. For example, it is estimated that even in wet climates the *rate of solution* of limestone may be only one-twentieth of a centimeter in a hundred years. At this rate it would take 60 million years to dissolve a 300 meter layer of limestone from the earth's surface by this process alone. At the same time, however, other weathering processes would remove far more rock.

7. Cleopatra's Needle

The rate at which weathering takes place depends upon many factors. The most important are the kind of rock and the climate.

An interesting example of the effect of climate on weathering is seen in the case of the granite monument called Cleopatra's Needle. In 1880 it was taken from the dry, hot, Egyptian climate where it had stood almost unchanged for 3,000 years. It was moved to the wet hot-and-cold climate of Central Park in New York City. Chemical weathering and frost action attacked the granite. The hieroglyphics provided places that water could occupy. Frost action in such openings caused more damage in a few years than in as many centuries in Egypt.

Cleopatra's Needle looked new for 3000 years in hot, dry Egypt. Look at the damage caused by weather in only 100 years in New York City's Central Park.

Weathering and Mass Movement

Mass Movement

Mass Movements Caused by Gravity

Wherever the ground slopes, gravity may cause rock fragments to fall, slide, or move at invisibly slow speeds to lower levels. Such downslope movements of large masses of loose rock material are called **mass movement.** Mass movement is usually divided into rapid movements and slow movements. Let us see what some of the more important types of mass movement are.

Rapid Movements

A **landslide** is the sudden movement of a mass of bedrock or loose rock down the slope of a hillside, mountain, or cliff.

Large masses of bedrock may become separated from underlying layers and slide down steep mountainsides or valley walls. Such a slide took place in 1925 in the valley of the Gros Ventre River southeast of Grand Teton National Park. A large mass broke off from the side of Sheep Mountain, slid down, and crossed the valley. The slide dammed up the river to form a lake five miles long.

Before a 1925 landslide, the debris in the valley was rock and soil on the mountain. The dotted lines show this.

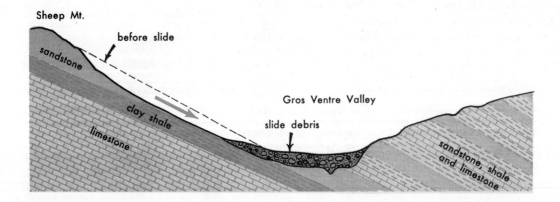

Another famous rock slide occurred on the slopes of Turtle Mountain in Alberta, Canada, in 1903. It destroyed the mining town of Frank located at the base of the mountain.

Landslides are likely to occur on slopes made very steep by erosion or by mining activities. Small landslides are common on cliffs and steep hillsides bordering highways. All landslides, both large and

small, are most likely to occur after heavy rains or spring thaws. Landslides are frequently triggered by earthquakes.

A **mudflow** is a rapid movement of a large mass of "mud" formed from loose earth and water. Mudflows occur most often in the normally dry canyons of desert regions when heavy thunderstorms suddenly flood the canyons. As the water washes down the loose rock of the canyon walls and floor, rock and water mix to form the mudflow, which sweeps down the canyon to its mouth. Such flows cause considerable erosion in their paths.

Talus is an accumulation of rock fragments of all sizes at the base of a cliff. Boulders are most prominent in talus, but continued weathering of the boulders produces pebbles, sand, and clay as well. Talus hides the lower part of the cliff, resting against it at an angle as high as 40°. *Talus slopes*, as they are called, are common wherever there are cliffs.

The pile of rocks slanting down the mountainside looks like a river of rocks. The pile is called a talus slope.

Creep is a slow, invisible, downslope movement of the soil. Creep can be detected by its effects. It causes fence posts, poles, tree trunks and other objects fixed in the soil to lean downhill. Soil water probably helps gravity in causing this movement.

A rock glacier is a ridge or series of ridges of loose rock material that extends down mountain valleys. The "glacier" moves slowly downslope in the manner of glaciers of ice.

Note how the top layer of soil is being pulled downhill. This movement is known as creep.

Gravity Aids Weathering 11.

Soil that lies on top of bedrock provides the bedrock with partial protection against the atmosphere. Such protection slows down the rate at which the bedrock weathers. On steep slopes, however, gravity tends to remove loose earth. This keeps the bedrock continually exposed. Gravity, then, is an aid to weathering. It is largely responsible for the fact that steep slopes weather more rapidly than gentle ones.

Results of Weathering 12.

Weathering has attacked the rocks of the earth's surface since the beginning of geological time. It has helped to wear down mountains and to shape countless landforms in this and past ages. It has provided materials for sedimentary rocks and valuable mineral deposits. Most important, it has been chiefly responsible for forming a priceless resource—the earth's life-supporting soil.

Without soil there could be no life on land. **Soil** is loose weathered rock material in which plants with roots can grow. Soil always contains some organic material. Soil is made of three recognizable parts: sand, clay, and silt.

The material from which a soil is weathered is called its **parent material.** This may be the underlying bedrock. In such a case the soil is said to be **residual.** But in many areas the bedrock has been covered over by deposits transported there by winds, rivers, or glaciers. Soils derived from such materials are called **transported soils.**

The soil of the famous Blue Grass region of Kentucky is a residual soil because its parent material is the underlying limestone bedrock. The soils of New England are transported soils. Their parent material is the loose rock deposited in New England by glaciers during the Ice Age.

14. What Determines Soil Makeup

Soils differ in many ways. They differ in color, mineral composition, and amount of organic material. They differ in texture because they have different percentages of sand, silt, and clay. All this is to be expected, for soils come from many different parent materials.

But soil scientists have learned that *climate* is more important than parent material in soil development. For example, the soil formed from a granite in a wet tropical climate is very different from that formed in a desert.

There is an even more important relationship between soil and climate. Soil scientists have found that nearly all soils in a particular climatic region strongly resemble each other, regardless of their parent materials! We shall discuss this further in Topic 16.

Soils are exceedingly precious materials. It takes thousands of years for fertile soils to form from most parent materials. A fully developed soil is said to be *mature.* Such a soil is described in Topic 15.

15. A Mature Soil Profile

Scientists who study soils dig through layers of soil until they reach the parent material. The cross section of earth exposed by the digging is called the **soil profile.** In most mature soils, three distinct zones, or

SOIL PROFILES   ACTUAL SECTIONS 500 FROM THE GROUND

These soil profiles show the top-bottom arrangement of soil layers from topsoil, subsoil to weathered parent bedrock.

Compare the diagram below to the picture at the left.

A–horizon: topsoil
Gray to black, sandy, contains humus.

B–horizon: subsoil
Reddish, brownish, or yellowish; clayey; contains iron oxides and soluble carbonates

C–horizon:
weathered bedrock

unweathered bedrock

horizons, can be seen in the soil profile. These are named the A, B, and C horizons. Beneath them is the parent material.

The A-horizon is *topsoil*. It is darker than the B-horizon, because it contains organic material, or *humus*, from decayed plant and animal materials. Its color is generally gray to black. It is likely to be sandy, because some of the clay formed in it by chemical weathering has been washed by rain into the B-horizon. The B-horizon begins with the *subsoil*. It contains more clay than the topsoil. It is likely to be reddish or brownish in color. The color comes from iron oxides formed in the A-horizon. The B-horizon may contain soluble minerals such as calcium and magnesium carbonates.

The C-horizon includes slightly weathered parent material, such as rock fragments. Near the bottom, these fragments change slowly into the unweathered bedrock.

Most of the continental United States is fairly typical of the temperate climate regions of the world. In general, only two main types of soil have developed in the United States regardless of parent materials.

In the eastern half of the United States, rainfall exceeds 65 centimeters a year. Here the soils are of a type called **pedalfers.** The name pedalfer is made up of *ped* for soil, *al* for aluminum, and *fer* for ferrum or iron. These soils are rich in clay, iron oxides, and quartz fragments. They are poor in soluble minerals, such as calcium carbonate, which are leached out by the rain.

In the western half of the United States (except the Pacific Coast region) rainfall is less than 65 centimeters a year. Here the soils are **pedocals.** The name comes from *pedo* for soil, *cal* for calcium. Pedocals are rich in calcium carbonate, because the amount of rainfall is not enough to wash the calcium carbonate out of the B-horizon and the soil. They also include less clay than the pedalfers.

Each topic question refers to the topic of the same number within this chapter.

1. Distinguish between weathering and erosion.

2. (**a**) Mention a few examples of weathering. (**b**) Define mechanical weathering and give an example. (**c**) Define chemical weathering and give an example.

3. (**a**) Explain how rocks are weathered by: (1) temperature change, (2) frost action, (3) exfoliation, (4) plants and animals, (**b**) What is a boulder field? an exfoliation dome?

4. (**a**) What substances cause chemical weathering? (**b**) In what type of climate is chemical weathering most active? least active? Why? (**c**) Explain the weathering action of (1) oxygen, (2) water, (3) carbon dioxide, (4) acids of plant and animal decay, (5) acids caused by the actions of humans.

5. (**a**) Explain how weathering affects each of the principal rock minerals. (**b**) Explain how weathering affects the common rocks.

6. Discuss the length of time involved in weathering processes.

7. Under what conditions do rocks weather most rapidly?

8. What is mass movement?

9. (**a**) What is a landslide? (**b**) Where and when do landslides occur? (**c**) What is a mudflow? (**d**) What is talus?

10. (**a**) What is creep? (**b**) What is a rock glacier?

11. How does gravity aid weathering?

12. What are the overall results of weathering?

13. Define soil. Distinguish between residual and transported soils. Give an example of each.

14. (a) In what characteristics do soils differ?   (b) Cite two examples showing that climate is more important in soil development than parent material.

15. Briefly describe the three horizons of a mature soil.

16. (a) Define *pedalfers*. Explain why pedalfers are found in the wet eastern part of the United States.   (b) Define *pedocals*. Explain why they develop in the dry western part of the United States.

GENERAL QUESTIONS

1. Why is frost action likely to damage sandstone more than limestone?

2. In what respects does the weathering of a bare mountain peak differ from the weathering of the bedrock under the soil of a forest?

3. Sandstones cemented by lime usually weather much more rapidly than those cemented by silica. Why?

4. In parts of Bermuda where the limestone bedrock consists almost entirely of white calcite, with a small percentage of iron-containing minerals, the residual soil is a fine red material. How is this explained?

5. What should be the content of residual soil formed in a humid climate from a granite composed of quartz, feldspar, and black mica?

6. Why are the pavements of streets and highways damaged so much more in the winter months than in the summer months in most of the United States? (Compare the processes of weathering between the two seasons.)

STUDENT ACTIVITIES

1. "Rocks are known to split and break if heated strongly enough." See if you can verify this by the following procedures: (a) strongly heat small samples of such rocks as obsidian, granite, sandstone, shale, slate, and schist in the flame of a Bunsen burner. Observe and note your results after comparison with unheated specimens of the same rocks.   (b) Repeat the procedure of (a), but this time plunge your heated rock samples into cold water.

2. Use the acid test (1 or 2 drops of dilute hydrochloric acid) on samples of different varieties of sandstone to determine which of them contain lime cements.

3. Place samples of limestone, shale, sandstone, granite, and other rocks in a beaker of dilute hydrochloric acid and let stand for at least 10 minutes. Remove the samples, wash carefully in cold water, and inspect for signs of "chemical weathering." Compare with fresh samples.

1. *Landslides:* Red Rock, Washington; U.S.G.S., 15 minute series.

2. *Landslides:* Frank, Alberta (shows Turtle Mt. Landslide of 1903; obtain from Map Distribution Office, Ottawa, Canada).

3. *Exfoliation domes and cliffs:* Yosemite Valley, California; U.S.G.S., scale 1:24,000.

7

Fill a plastic or glass container to the top with coarse gravel or marble chips. Why isn't the container really full? Estimate what fraction of the space in the container is air space. Now check your estimate. Fill a same-size container to the top with water. Then pour the water into the container with the gravel until it can hold no more water. Compare your estimate with your observation. Now carefully pour the water out of the gravel and back into the water container. A piece of screen over the gravel will help to keep the gravel from spilling. Why doesn't all the water return from the gravel?

This simple experiment is a model of the way the earth stores the underground water that feeds springs, wells, rivers, lakes, and all growing plants between rains.

Water Moving Underground

Fresh Water on the Earth

1. All the World's Water

How much water is there on and in the whole earth? Scientists estimate the answer to be about one and a third billion cubic kilometers. The number is so large that it is difficult to picture. How much of the earth's water is salt water, how much is fresh water? This question is of importance because most of our uses for water require fresh water. With the advance of industry and the growth of population the need for fresh water becomes more and more critical.

More than 97 percent of all the earth's water is in the oceans. Of course it is salt water. So less than three percent is fresh water. But more than two-thirds of that—a little over two percent of all the earth's water—is frozen into the glaciers of Greenland, Antarctica, and the high mountain regions.

Now you are left with about one half of one percent of all the earth's water that is usable *fresh liquid water.* And where is that? A tiny part of it flows on the surface in the form of rivers. About 100 times as much is stored in lakes and swamps. But most of the fresh liquid water is in the ground. The amount of *ground water* is more than 50 times as much as all the water in rivers and lakes! It is thousands of times as much as in all the earth's rivers at any given moment.

2. The Water Cycle

Fresh water is being used every day by living things—people, animals, and especially the plants in fields, swamps and forests. Where does the fresh water come from? How is it replaced after use?

The answer to these questions lies in the **hydrologic cycle,** or **water cycle,** shown in the labeled diagram. The cycle is a never-ending circle. The salt waters of the oceans supply fresh water to the continents over and over again.

Sunlight provides the energy that evaporates water from the surface of the earth. Most of the water vapor comes from the oceans, but some comes from the continents. Winds carry the water vapor over the continents. Part of the water vapor condenses into clouds, and falls as rain or snow.

Some of the rain returns to the ocean from rivers and streams as *runoff.* Some seeps into the ground to become the *ground water.* Some returns to the air by *evaporation* from the ground or by *transpiration.* (Transpiration is the way leaves of plants give off water

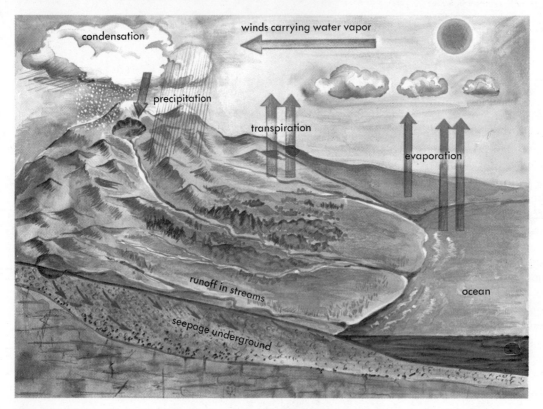

Imagine a drop of water. Follow the arrows to find how it travels the water cycle.

vapor.) Hydrologists usually combine evaporation and transpiration under the name **evapotranspiration.**

When the runoff from the continents returns to the oceans, one "route" of the water cycle is completed. Other shorter "routes" are shown in the diagram.

The Water Budget 3.

A *budget* is a statement of expected income and expected outgo, or expenditures. In a balanced budget, income and outgo are equal. In a water budget, the income is rain or snow. The outgo includes water lost by runoff and by evapotranspiration.

Let us examine the water budget of the continental United States. Its "income" is an average yearly rainfall (melted snow included) of about 75 centimeters. About 70 percent of this (52 centimeters) returns to the air by evapotranspiration. About 30 percent (23 centimeters) runs off into the oceans.

Water Budget

Income	Outgo	
average yearly rain and snow 75 cm	evapotranspiration	52 cm
	ocean water vapor	23 cm
		75 cm

Notice that the United States receives more water from the air as rain (75 centimeters) than it returns to the air (52 centimeters). The difference (23 centimeters) is made up by water vapor from the ocean. It is returned to the ocean as runoff.

 Individual Water Budgets

The water budget given in Topic 3 is based on averages for the entire United States. But annual rainfall is as little as 5 centimeters in the Mojave Desert of California and as much as 250 centimeters in the Olympic Mountains of coastal Washington. Each locality or region has its own water budget. What factors determine the percentage that runs off and the percentage that evaporates? What determines how much rainwater enters the ground to become ground water?

One important factor is *climate.* In the hot dry air of the Mojave Desert, for example, nearly 100 percent of the rainfall evaporates. By contrast, only about 25 percent evaporates in the cool moist air of the Olympic Mountains.

Another factor is the *distribution of the rainfall.* The percentage of runoff is usually much higher in a heavy downpour than when the same amount of rain falls slowly and steadily. Other factors include the *steepness* of the slope, the *kind of soil or rock,* and the cover of *vegetation.* Runoff will be higher on steep, bare rock surfaces. It will be lower on level porous soils covered by plants.

The percentage of water entering the ground in a particular region depends on all of the above factors. Some of these factors may also vary from season to season.

 Can Rocks Hold Water?

Pores in rocks are simply the spaces between the crystals or grains of the rock.

In sedimentary rocks the pores are the spaces between grains of sand, clay, etc. that have not been filled with cement. The amount of

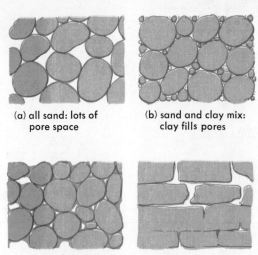

(a) all sand: lots of
pore space

(b) sand and clay mix:
clay fills pores

(c) sandstone: cement
reduces pore space

(d) limestone cracks
are pores

These diagrams show why some materials have more pore space than others.

such space differs greatly, especially in sandstones. Large deposits of gravel, sand, or clay, having little or no cement between grains may be nearly half pore space. The percentage of pore space is greatest where the particles are round and all of the same size (*well sorted*). Where the material is poorly sorted, as in a mixture of sand and clay, small particles fill the spaces between large particles, and this greatly reduces the total pore space.

Water is often retained in rocks that have a large percentage of pore space. The relationship between pore space and water is considered further in the next topic.

Can Rocks Transmit Water?

The **porosity** of a rock tells us how much of its volume is open space. No matter how porous a rock is, water will not pass through the rock easily if the pores are tiny, as they are in clays and shales. On the other hand, water passes readily through sediments or rocks with large pores, as in sands, gravels, and many sandstones. Thus to the geologist, the permeability of rock material is at least as important as its porosity. **Permeability** is the ability of the rock to transmit water or other liquids. It is of great importance in the origin of springs, wells, and other ground water features.

Materials—such as sand, gravel, and sandstone—through which water passes easily are said to be *permeable*. Materials—such as clay, shale, and most igneous and metamorphic rocks—through which water does not pass easily are *impermeable*.

Remember that a material may be highly porous and yet be impermeable. On the other hand, nonporous rocks, such as limestone and some lavas, often become permeable because of the formation of cracks through which water can pass.

7. Forming the Water Table

When rain falls on the ground, it enters the pores in the soil and sticks to the mineral particles. If enough rain enters the soil, some of the water continues downward until it reaches impermeable material such as clay or shale. Here the water fills the pores at the bottom of the permeable material. The water in the ground rises higher and higher as the rain continues and forms the **zone of saturation.** The zone of saturation is the part of the ground that can hold no more water. The upper surface of the zone of saturation is called the **water table.**

From the water table to the surface, the ground can still hold more water. This section is called the **zone of aeration.** It includes three parts. Just below the surface is the *belt of soil water*, where films of water stick to the grains of topsoil. Just above the water table is the *capillary fringe*, where water from the water table rises in porous material the way water will rise in a ball of cloth or a sponge laid on a puddle. Between the two is a dry *intermediate belt*.

The water table separates the zone of saturation from the zone of aeration.

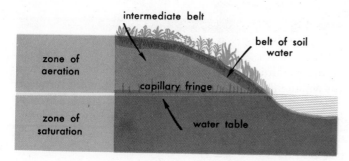

intermediate belt

belt of soil water

zone of aeration

capillary fringe

zone of saturation

water table

How far under the surface is the water table? This depends on many things—the amount of rainfall, the season, the slope of the ground, the thickness of the soil, the climate, the time between rains, and others.

In some places—swamps, lakes, rivers—the water table is at the surface. In desert regions it may be hundreds of meters below the surface. In woods, fields, and farmland it is likely to be within a few meters of the surface. In hilly country it is generally nearer the surface in valleys than in the hills.

**The water table feeds this lake.
(Sylvan Lake, South Dakota)**

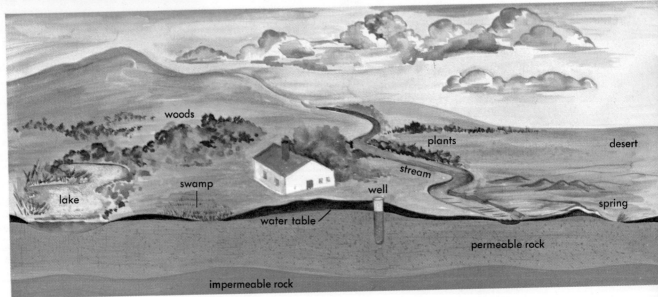

From the water table down to the impermeable rock, the ground is saturated with water that feeds a lake, swamp, well, stream, and spring.

The water table is important in several ways. The seepage of water from the water table is what keeps streams flowing between rains and maintains the water levels of swamps and lakes. Through the capillary fringe, the water table supplies water to growing plants. And by means of springs and wells, the water table provides people with drinking water.

Wells and Springs

Ground water is naturally filtered by the earth through which it seeps and is usually perfectly clear. Dissolved substances, however, may be present in it. Its freedom from harmful materials depends on whether or not the ground through which it passes has been contaminated by human or animal wastes or poisonous minerals.

In places where the water table does not reach the surface, the ground water may be reached by digging or driving wells into the ground. If these wells are to provide water in all seasons they must go below the lowest level to which the water table is likely to fall in dry weather. A well of this type, known as an **ordinary well,** contains water from its bottom up to the level of the water table. As the water table rises and falls with weather changes, so does the level of the water in the well.

On hillsides where the water table cuts the surface, ground water may flow to the surface as **hillside springs.**

10. Artesian Formations

In many parts of the world, permeable beds are near the surface on hillsides and mountainsides, then dip underground between impermeable beds. This "sandwich" of permeable and impermeable rocks is known as an **artesian formation.** Rain that enters the permeable bed is confined in it by the impermeable beds above and beneath.

The upper impermeable layer, usually shale or clay, is the **cap rock.** The permeable layer, usually sandstone or sand, is the **aquifer** (water bearer). The water trapped in the aquifer follows its sloping course underground under the pull of gravity.

One of the best known artesian formations in the United States carries water hundreds of miles underground from the Rocky Mountains to the Great Plains. Its aquifer is a porous sandstone more than 100 feet thick, called the Dakota sandstone. Its cap rock is shale.

Both the soil layer above the shale cap rock and the sandstone layer below it are filled with water. The water trapped in the sandstone is under pressure.

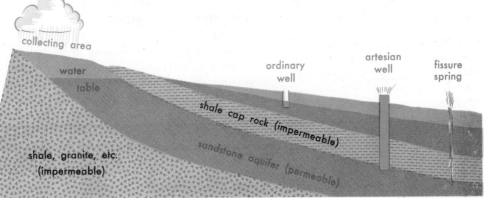

collecting area

water table

ordinary well

artesian well

fissure spring

shale cap rock (impermeable)

sandstone aquifer (permeable)

shale, granite, etc. (impermeable)

Other important artesian formations occur in the Atlantic Coastal Plain states, New York's Long Island, Florida, and the Los Angeles area. Long Island's aquifer is unconsolidated sandy material. Florida's is a limestone full of cracks and fissures.

Artesian Wells and Springs 11.

Great quantities of water may enter the aquifers of artesian formations where they outcrop at the surface. Like the water in a great sloping pipe, this water is under pressure. When wells are drilled into the aquifers at lower levels, even hundreds of miles away from the outcrops, water rises in the wells. It may even spout into the air if the water pressure is sufficient.These are **artesian wells**—wells in which the water comes from aquifers below an impermeable layer.

Artesian wells differ greatly in depth. As a rule, the greater the distance from the source of the water, the deeper the aquifer. On the Great Plains, wells that are hundreds of kilometers from the mountains may go down more than a thousand meters to reach the aquifer.

Artesian formations may be broken naturally by cracks in the cap rock called *fissures. Artesian springs*, or **fissure springs,** rise through these cracks. Such a spring may form an oasis in the desert.

Conserving Ground Water 12.

Ground water supplies are not limitless. The amount of water returned to the ground in a given area must be at least equal to that removed from its wells and springs. If it is not, the water table will drop. Wells and springs will shrink accordingly. In some artesian areas, so many wells have been drilled and so much water has been pumped that the water table has dropped steadily. Near the sea coast the lowered water table may allow salt water from the ocean to seep into wells.

How is the ground water restored or "recharged"? Rains and melting snow must provide most of the replacement for the water drawn out of wells and springs. Where this is not enough, artificial recharge methods are used.

The principle is simple. As much used water as possible must be returned to the ground instead of being poured off into sewers. This can be done by running or pumping the water into **return wells,** or into large shallow ponds, or directly onto the ground. Many states now require large commercial users of water and all commercial air-conditioning installations to do this. (Commercial air conditioning uses a lot of water.) In many cases the waste water must be purified before it is returned to recharge the ground water.

Temperature of Ground Water

13. Ground Water Is Usually Cool.

At a depth of about 15 meters under the surface, protection from weather changes is quite complete. The ground at that depth stays at nearly the same temperature throughout the year. This temperature is the *average yearly temperature of its location.* In most parts of the United States this is somewhere between 5 and 15 degrees Celsius. The water of an ordinary well or spring has practically the same temperature as the ground from which it comes. This explains why the water is comparatively cool in summer and does not freeze in winter.

Since spring or well water is close to the average temperature of its locality, such water is obviously colder in a cool climate like that of Maine than in a warm climate like that of Florida. In polar regions, where the average temperature is below freezing, there can be no wells or springs, for the water in the ground is always frozen. This permanently frozen ground, which may be hundreds of meters deep, is called the **permafrost.**

14. Hot Springs, Geysers, and Fumaroles

Below the 15-meter depth, heat from the earth's interior raises the earth temperatures at the rate of about 1° C every 40 meters down. Water from deep artesian wells or springs may therefore be much warmer than water from ordinary wells or springs. Fissure springs that originate thousands of feet deep may be *warm springs* or even *hot springs,* such as those at Warm Springs, Georgia, or Hot Springs, Arkansas.

Ground waters may be hot without coming from great depths. In many regions of recent volcanic activity, lava rock near the surface is still hot enough to boil water. In such places the ground water may come to the surface as boiling hot springs. Here and there in Yellowstone National Park and other volcanic regions, hot springs emerge through sticky colored clays formed by the weathering of the volcanic rocks. These sputtering hot springs are called *paint pots* or *mud volcanoes.*

This paint pot is formed by hot water that comes up through the colored clay.

A geyser erupting is like extra steam and water escaping through a safety valve in a hot-water boiler. (Castle Geyser, Yellowstone National Park)

Fumaroles are like spouts on a boiling tea kettle. Steam constantly escapes from them.

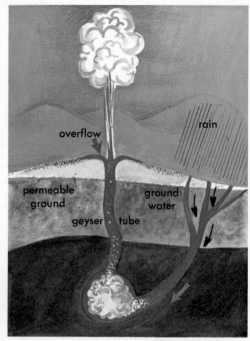

Before a geyser erupts, hot water flows out of the geyser tube. Then the water below turns into steam and erupts.

Boiling hot springs that erupt from time to time as gushers of hot water and steam are called **geysers.** There are only a few places in the world where geysers occur. The most important ones are in Yellowstone National Park in Wyoming, North Island in New Zealand, and Iceland. Old Faithful in Yellowstone is famous for both its height and its frequency. Its average time between eruptions is now about 66 minutes, though the time may be as short as 35 minutes or as long as 80 minutes. An eruption lasts several minutes and usually reaches a height of 45 meters or more.

Geyser eruption is like the explosion of a hot water boiler or pressure cooker. The "boiler" is a fissure, or *geyser tube,* that extends many meters down into the hot rock. At the bottom of this tube, ground water, under pressure of the water above it, is "superheated" to a temperature far above water's normal boiling point. The heated water expands. This causes the water above it to overflow onto the surface. This lowers the pressure at the bottom of the tube. The superheated water can now boil. It explodes into steam. The water above the steam rushes forth in the form of a geyser eruption.

Fumaroles (FEW meh roles) are holes or fissures in the ground from which steam and hot gases escape. They are found in volcanic regions where relatively recent eruptions have occurred. The high pressure steam from fumaroles is used commercially to generate electricity, in Italy, Japan, Iceland, New Zealand, Mexico, the Soviet Union, and the United States.

15. The Minerals in Ground Water

Rain water is water that has been "naturally distilled" by the heat of the sun. When water evaporates, it leaves impurities behind. Therefore rainwater has no dissolved mineral matter in it. When rainwater seeps into the ground, however, the situation changes. As ground water passes through the subsoil or bedrock it dissolves minerals. The kind and quantity of mineral matter that water contains depend largely on the kind of rock through which it passes, the distance it travels underground, and its temperature.

Dissolved minerals that contain ions of calcium, magnesium, or iron make water **hard**. Of these, calcium (from calcite) is the most common cause of hardness. The dissolved minerals in hard water interfere greatly with its use. In laundering they react with soap to form sticky lumps instead of suds. In boiler tubes and hot water pipes they form deposits of *boiler scale.*

Artesian water is usually harder than ordinary ground water. This is because it travels farther and may be warmer, so it can dissolve more mineral matter. Ordinary ground water is almost always harder than river water. In regions where the bedrock is limestone, practically all the water is hard, since limestone is largely calcite, $CaCO_3$.

16. Mineral Springs

A spring whose water contains so much dissolved mineral that it cannot be used for ordinary drinking or washing purposes is called a **mineral spring.** The high mineral content of the water may be due to:
1. its passage through very soluble rock (such as the salt beds of Michigan);
2. the fact that it contains large quantities of acid-forming gases such as carbon dioxide (example: Saratoga Springs, N.Y.) or hydrogen sulfide (example: White Sulphur Springs, W. Va.); or
3. the fact that it is very hot (example: Hot Springs, Arkansas).

Many such mineral spring areas have become *spas,* or health resorts. In desert regions, however, *alkali mineral springs* may be poisonous.

How Caverns Form   17.

Road workers cut through this limestone, exposing the joints. Rain and ground water dissolved the rock around the joints and made them wider.

This sink hole used to be a deep, narrow crack which filled with water to form a sink-hole pond.

Limestone is not a porous rock. But limestone formations are frequently split by fissures that run down from the surface and by cracks that run horizontally between the beds. Ground water always contains carbonic acid, formed by dissolved carbon dioxide from the air. As ground water runs through the cracks and fissures in limestone, its carbonic acid slowly dissolves and removes limestone and carries it away.

After thousands of years, the vertical fissures may grow into large, circular, surface openings. At the same time the cracks between the beds may form networks of underground tunnels many kilometers in length and hundreds of meters high in places. The surface openings are called **sink holes,** or *sinks.* The tunnels are called **caverns,** or caves. Sink holes also form when parts of cave roofs fall in. Water in sink holes that are below the water table forms **sink-hole ponds** or *lakes.*

When a large section of a cave roof falls and a middle section is left standing, a **natural bridge** may be formed. Natural bridges may also be formed when a surface river disappears into a fissure in the bedrock, runs underground a short distance, and then gushes out on the face of a cliff. As the fissure is enlarged, the area between it and

This Natural Bridge in Utah was formed by the action of a river on the rock.

the cliff is left as a natural bridge. The famous Natural Bridge of Virginia is believed to have been formed in this manner.

Limestone is a common surface or near-surface bedrock, so limestone caverns are found in many parts of the world. Some of the best-known caverns in the United States are Carlsbad Caverns in New

Calcite deposits from water dripping down build up these rock icicles. (Luray Caverns, Virginia)

This diagram shows a natural bridge in the center. A sink is on the right corner. Many caverns can be seen from the sides. The rock is limestone.

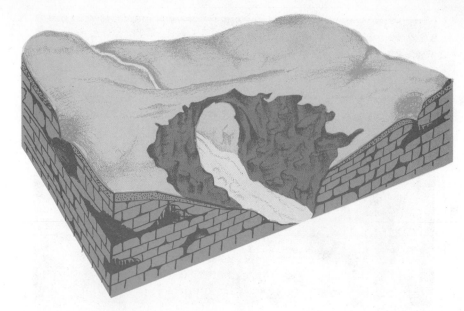

Mexico; Mammoth Cave in Kentucky; Luray Caverns in Virginia; Howe Caverns in New York; Oregon Caves in Oregon; and Wind Cave in South Dakota.

Karst Topography 18.

In regions of caverns, almost all of the rain water enters the ground through sink holes and fissures. There are very few surface rivers. **Lost rivers** are formed when surface streams disappear underground and flow out of caves miles away. Regions characterized by sinks, sink-hole ponds, lost rivers, and underground drainage are said to have **karst topography.** This name comes from the typical Kars Plateau region of Yugoslavia. The Mammoth Cave region of Kentucky has karst topography. Other karst regions in the United States are found in Florida, Tennessee, and Indiana.

Mineral Deposits by Ground Water 19.

The minerals dissolved in ground water are deposited by it in a variety of ways. Where ground water drips from the roof of a limestone cave, it very slowly deposits some of the calcite. Deposits shaped like icicles hang from the roof along the lines of the dripping water. These slender calcite formations are called **stalactites.** On the floor below the stalactites, blunt, rounded masses called **stalagmites** are formed.

When stalactites and stalagmites meet, *columns* or *pillars* are made. All three are examples of **dripstone**, calcite deposits from dripping water in caverns. Dripstone can form only when a cave is *above* the water table, where water can evaporate.

Calcite deposits around mineral springs are called **travertine** (TRAV er tin). Among the most famous such deposits are the delicately colored travertine terraces of the Mammoth Hot Springs in Yellowstone National Park. Here the hot water pours out of long hillside fissures in limestone bedrock, depositing some of its dissolved calcite as it cools. Tiny plants, called *algae* (AL jee), grow on the moist terraces, producing a variety of beautiful colors.

Around the openings of geysers, a white porous substance called **geyserite** is deposited. Geyserite is silica dissolved from the hot igneous rock through which the geyser waters pass on their way to the surface.

Hot ground water often deposits **veins** of minerals in cracks and fissures in bedrock. These may contain quartz, calcite, gold, and silver. **Petrified wood** is formed when minerals dissolved in ground water replace the decaying wood of buried trees. As each microscopic particle of wood is replaced by a grain of mineral matter, many details of the wood structure are reproduced. The petrified trees of Arizona and Yellowstone National Park, which originated in this way, consist of silica.

Perhaps the most important ground water deposit is the *cement* that binds together the sand grains and pebbles of sedimentary deposits to form sedimentary rocks. While calcite is the most common cementing mineral, silica and iron oxides are used in this way, too.

These hot springs come out of cracks in a hill of limestone. As they cool, they slowly form terraces of calcite deposits. (Minerva Terrace, Yellowstone National Park)

Each topic question refers to the topic of the same number within this chapter.

1. **(a)** Compare the percentage of salt water and fresh water on the earth. **(b)** Describe the distribution and amounts of fresh water on the earth.

2. **(a)** With the aid of a simple diagram, briefly describe the water cycle. **(b)** What is evapotranspiration?

3. **(a)** What is a water budget? **(b)** Explain the water budget of the United States.

4. Briefly name and explain the factors that determine how much rain becomes ground water.

5. **(a)** Why do rocks have pores? **(b)** What determines the amount of pore space in sedimentary materials?

6. Distinguish between porosity and permeability. Give examples.

7. **(a)** Explain what the water table is and how it forms. **(b)** Describe the zone of aeration.

8. **(a)** Explain why the depth of the water table varies. **(b)** How deep is it in swamps, lakes, deserts, farmland?

9. **(a)** Explain what an ordinary well is. **(b)** Explain what a hillside spring is.

10. **(a)** With the aid of a diagram explain what an artesian formation is. **(b)** Define the aquifer and the cap rock.

11. **(a)** What is an artesian well? How does it originate? **(b)** How deep is an artesian well? **(c)** What is a fissure spring?

12. **(a)** Why is the water table dropping steadily in some areas? **(b)** What special problems arise in connection with artesian wells in coastal regions? **(c)** What is a return well? **(d)** Describe one other method of recharging ground water.

13. **(a)** Why does spring water or well water seem so cold in summer? **(b)** Why doesn't well water freeze in winter? **(c)** Explain why well water is warmer in Florida than in Maine. **(d)** What is the permafrost?

14. **(a)** Why is the water of deep artesian wells *warmer* than ordinary well water? **(b)** Explain the source of the heat of boiling hot springs and geysers. **(c)** What is a geyser? **(d)** Where do geysers occur? **(e)** Explain the action of a geyser. **(f)** What is a fumarole?

15. **(a)** What factors determine the amount and kind of mineral matter dissolved in ground water? **(b)** What is hard water? **(c)** Compare the water of ordinary wells, artesian wells, and rivers in hardness. Explain. **(d)** Why is all the water hard in a limestone region?

16. Describe the different kinds of mineral springs.

17. **(a)** Explain how ground water forms sink holes, caverns, natural bridges, and sink-hole ponds. **(b)** Name several of the great limestone caves of the United States. **(c)** Why are limestone caves so common?

18. **(a)** What is a lost river? **(b)** What is karst topography? Give examples.

19. **(a)** Explain how stalactites and stalagmites are formed. **(b)** What is dripstone? **(c)** Explain the origin of travertine, geyserite, mineral veins, and petrified wood.

1. In regions of cold climates less water enters the ground during winter than in any other season. Why?

2. What advantages and disadvantages may artesian water have as compared with ordinary well water?

3. Is a rainy climate necessary for the formation of limestone caves? Explain.

4. Why cannot dripstone form when a cave is below the water table? (See Topic 19, paragraph 1.)

5. In some regions petrified wood is composed of silica, a form of quartz. In other regions it is composed of calcite. Why?

1. Fill 3 test tubes (or small beakers, cups, tumblers, etc.) with gravel, sand, and clay respectively. By pouring water from a graduated cylinder or small test tube, measure the quantity of water needed to "saturate" the material in each test tube.

2. Compare the permeability of gravel, sand, and clay by putting each material into a funnel (lined with filter paper) and then noting the time required to pour a given amount of water through the material.

3. Make a plaster or clay model of an artesian formation or of the water table.

4. Make a working model of an artesian well.

5. Compare the amount of dissolved mineral matter in samples of well water, lake water, river water, etc., by evaporating to dryness equal volumes of each.

6. Compare the hardness of different kinds of water (distilled water, tap water, lime water, river water, spring water, salt water, etc.) by using the following method:

   (a) Take a small test tube. Mark it, with tape or glass marking crayon, about 2 centimeters from the bottom. Fill it to this line with distilled water. Add liquid soap, 1 drop at a time, and shake vigorously. Count the number of drops needed to make lasting suds. This number will be your *standard of soft water.*

   (b) Repeat the procedure with your other samples. Be sure to use the same volume of water each time. Do you need more or less soap than in (a)? Is there any cloudiness in the water? Compare the hardness of your samples.

   Remember, the more soap needed, the harder the water.

(15-minute series, unless otherwise stated)

1. *Sink holes and karst topography:* Mammoth Cave, Kentucky (also in 7½-minute series); Garfield, Kentucky, 7½-minute series; Crystal Lake, Florida.

2. *Springs:* Thousand Springs, Idaho, 7½-minute series.

8

Pour enough clay into a tall clear container to form a layer 2 or 3 centimeters deep. Cover this first with the same depth of sand, then with 2 or 3 centimeters of coarse gravel or marble chips. Cover all of these with about 15 centimeters of water. With a stirring rod, mix all the materials together until the sediment layers have completely disappeared. Stop stirring. Observe the order and arrangement of the sediments as they settle. Which materials settle first? Which settle last? Why? Why is there considerable mixing of the materials? Would a taller container and more water improve the separation? Try it.

Stir the mixture again, but this time do not disturb the gravel. How can you manage this? Again change your stirring speed until only the clay remains in suspension. When you stop stirring, where is the clay? What does this experiment show about the relation between the speed of moving water and the size of material it can carry?

Running Water

Stream Erosion and Transportation

1. Running Water and Its Energy

Of all the agents of erosion, running water is the most effective in wearing down the surface of the earth. **Running water** includes all the water that falls onto the earth as rain or snow and then moves downhill under the pull of gravity. It begins with drops of water moving down hillsides. It grows until it forms great rivers such as the Mississippi and the Amazon.

Like the other agents of erosion, running water gets its energy from the sun. The sun lifts water from the surface of the oceans by evaporation. Winds created by the sun's heating of the atmosphere carry the water vapor over the continents. When the water falls as rain or snow and runs back to the sea, it is using the sun's energy to erode the lands.

2. Running Water Attacks Bedrock

Like all agents of erosion, running water wears down the land in two ways. It breaks up bedrock. It removes weathered and eroded rock materials.

Running water attacks bedrock chiefly by *mechanical* means. Using sand, pebbles, and even boulders as its cutting tools, running water grinds and hammers away at its bed. The grinding action is called **abrasion.** Abrasion works both ways, of course. The cutting tools are worn down, too, especially at their corners and edges. In time this produces the rounded boulders, pebbles, and sand grains found in the beds of streams and rivers.

Cutting tools are very important for stream erosion. But even clear water can break up the rock of a stream bed if it runs fast enough. When running water strikes cracks in the bedrock, it causes a **lifting effect** that splits off chunks of the rock.

Running water's **chemical** attack on bedrock consists mainly of dissolving soluble minerals. Limestone, marble, and sandstones with lime cements are the chief rocks affected in this way. Rivers flowing over such rocks form pits and holes in the river bed.

Note the different levels in this mountain stream. The fast water carves the bedrock unevenly.

When rain runs down even the gentlest of slopes, it carries some weathered rock material with it. Eventually this reaches a larger and more permanent body of running water—perhaps a tiny brook. The brook, small as it may be, is probably part of some river system. And so the sediment carried by the brook will find its way through larger and larger streams of water until it reaches the main stream. Once in the main stream, it will be carried down to the sea or to a lake.

Streams bring rock and soil from the mountains.

Rivers carry rock material in three ways. Some mineral matter is carried in solution. Most of this comes to the river in the ground water that seeps into it. The most common minerals carried in solution are compounds of calcium and magnesium, especially in limestone regions.

When river water looks muddy, it is carrying rock material in suspension. Suspended material includes clay, silt, and fine sand. Although these are heavier than water, they are stirred up and kept from sinking by the *turbulence* of stream flow. Turbulence means swirls and eddies resulting from friction between the stream and its bed and banks. The faster the stream flows, the more turbulent—and muddy—it becomes. A rough bed also increases turbulence.

Sand, pebbles, and boulders that are too heavy to be carried in suspension may be carried as bed load, especially during floods. Boulders and pebbles roll or slide on the river bed. Large sand grains are pushed along in jumps and bounces, like grains of sand in a sandstorm.

Geologists estimate that the rivers of the United States carry about one-fourth of their load in solution, about one-half in suspension, and about one-fourth as bed load.

The labels on the far right name the material carried at different depths of a river. On the left, the labels tell how each rock material is carried.

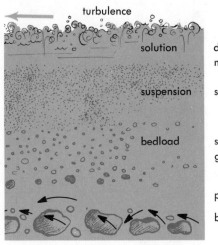

turbulence

solution — dissolved minerals

suspension — silt, clay

bedload — sand, gravel

pebbles

boulders

4. Carrying Power and Load

The carrying power of a stream depends on its volume (how much water) and its velocity (how fast it runs). The larger the stream and the faster it runs, the more it can carry.

The velocity of a stream depends mainly on the steepness, or *gradient*, of its bed. Velocity also increases with increased volume and depth. During floods the volume and depth of a river increase tremendously. Since this also increases its speed, its carrying power may be hundreds of times as great in flood stage as normally. For this reason, a river does much of its erosion at such times. If it can remove all the sediment from its bed during a flood, it can dig deeper into its bedrock floor.

When the speed of a river doubles, it far more than doubles its power to carry large heavy objects. At normal times the lower Mississippi River may carry nothing heavier than silt in suspension. In flood it may tear bridges from their foundations.

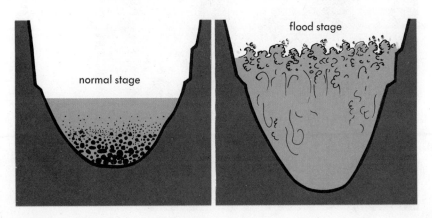

normal stage

flood stage

When a river floods, it goes much faster. It picks up the sediment on the bottom and digs into the rock underneath.

113

Note the parallel black lines going from front to back. They show the original banks of the river.

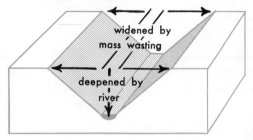

widened by mass wasting

deepened by river

This young river flows fast. So, its valley floor wears down much faster than its sides. (Aare Gorge, Switzerland)

Early in its life history, the valley carved out by a river is likely to be V-shaped in cross section. This is especially true in regions of mountains and high plateaus. In such places a river runs fast and cuts down rapidly into its bed. At the same time, the valley is being widened by weathering and erosion. The upper valley walls are widened the most because they are the first to be exposed to weathering. The result is a V-shaped valley.

Valleys with very steep, almost vertical sides are features of scenic interest. In the arid regions of the United States they are called **canyons**. The greatest of these is the Grand Canyon of the Colorado River. Elsewhere they may be called *gorges,* such as the Royal Gorge of the Arkansas River in Colorado, or *chasms,* such as Ausable Chasm in New York.

How long does it take a river to make a canyon? This depends on the kind of rock it must cut, its supply of water and cutting tools, the climate, and other factors. The Colorado River is believed to have taken millions of years to cut its mile-deep canyon into the tough rocks of the Colorado Plateau. Other rivers may have needed much less time to cut their canyons into softer rock in rainier climates.

A stream cannot cut its bed any lower than the level to which it flows. This level is called its **base level.** For streams that flow into the ocean, base level is sea level. But base level may also be the level of a lake or river into which the stream flows.

The deeper a stream cuts into its valley, the closer it approaches its base level. Its slope and speed decrease, and so it cuts down more slowly. The main stream also attacks its valley walls more than before because its slower flow is more easily pushed sidewards. Meanwhile, however, the valley walls continue to be attacked by weathering, erosion, and tributary streams. The result is a much wider valley with a broad floor and gentler valley walls.

The walls of this valley are just starting to erode more than its floor. (Yellowstone National Park)

115

Erosion causes these gullies to get deeper and longer.

When a hillside is stripped of its trees and shrubs, it loses its protective covering. Then even a single heavy rain may erode a miniature stream valley on its surface. This valley, too, is likely to be V-shaped and to have "tributaries" running into it. When the rain ends, the "river" may disappear, but the tiny valley remains. Such a valley is called a **gully.**

Gullies grow in length, width, and depth every time it rains. The term *headward erosion* is used to mean the wearing away of the land at the source, or head, of the gully, or of any stream valley. Headward erosion makes the gully longer.

As a gully grows in length and depth, it may cut below the water table and become a permanent stream. Its tributary gullies may do the same, and in time a "river system" may be born. Most of the world's river systems probably originated in similar fashion.

Even in deserts it rains sometimes. When it does, it may rain very hard. Desert cloudbursts in regions of soft clay beds cause many gullies to form. Early explorers found these regions so hard to travel through that they called them **badlands.** Among the best known badlands in the United States are those in South Dakota, North Dakota, and Nebraska.

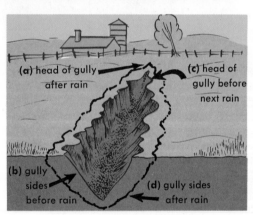

(a) head of gully after rain
(c) head of gully before next rain
(b) gully sides before rain
(d) gully sides after rain

The outline shows how large the gully will be after the next rain.

Sudden, heavy rainstorms formed the many intersecting gullies. (Badlands National Monument)

The "high land" that separates one gully from the next, or one river valley from the next, is called a **divide**. A river and all its tributaries is called a *river system*. The **drainage basin**, or *watershed*, of a river includes all the land whose rainfall runs into the river, either directly or through its tributaries.

Let us take a few examples. The Rocky Mountains form the major divide in the United States. They are known as the Continental Divide. Rain falling east of the Rockies eventually flows into the Atlantic Ocean. Rain falling west of the Rockies flows into the Pacific Ocean.

The largest single drainage basin in the United States is that of the Mississippi. Its western divide is the Rockies. Its eastern divide is the Appalachians. On the north in Wisconsin and Minnesota a low divide separates it from land sloping toward the Great Lakes and the Arctic Ocean. Within these three divides lies two-fifths of the area of the United States (excluding Alaska and Hawaii).

9. Stream Piracy

Stream piracy, or *stream capture*, is an interesting result of the lengthening of a river by headward erosion. In the diagram, two rivers are shown separated by a divide. As headward erosion continues, their headwaters get longer. Eventually the headwaters of river A wear through the divide and capture the headwaters of B. River A has grown larger and extended its drainage basin at the expense of its neighbor.

Does this happen often? Geologists believe that stream capture has been an important factor in the early growth of great river systems.

At first, one stream starts at B and another stream starts at A. Then the land between A and B erodes; the right stream steals the upper part of the left stream.

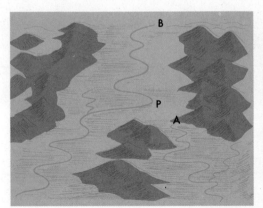 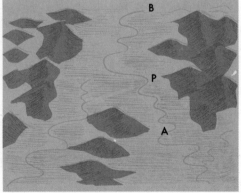

As a river cuts down into its valley, it may meet an unusually resistant rock formation. As time passes, this formation will wear away much more slowly than the surrounding rock. It will form a ridge through which the river runs in a narrow cut called a **water gap.** An example is the famous gap cut by the Delaware River through the Kittatinny Mountain ridge in New Jersey and Pennsylvania.

The rock around the narrow part of the river erodes more slowly than the rest of the valley. (Delaware Water Gap)

In regions where water gaps occur, an occasional one is found without any river in it. Such an abandoned water gap is called a **wind gap.** It is believed to have formed when its river was captured by one of its neighbors.

Waterfalls; River Deposits

A stream running over an irregular bed develops little whirlpools in many places. As sand, pebbles, and small boulders swirl around in the whirlpools, they grind out oval or circular basins. These are called **potholes.**

Potholes come in all sizes. Very large ones called **plunge pools** are found at the base of great waterfalls such as Niagara Falls.

When the river flooded, whirlpools formed these potholes in the rock.

12. Waterfalls and Their Recession

Streams running through steep mountain regions flow over ever-changing slopes. At places the river bed may be steep enough to form "white water" rapids. Here and there it may level out into a lake or pond. At other points the stream may plunge over a cliff to form a waterfall.

The steep slopes and cliffs of rapids and waterfalls form in many ways. Most are formed by earthquakes, volcanic action, and especially unequal erosion by glaciers and by rivers themselves. When a river runs from hard rock to softer rock, it forms steps or cliffs in its bed. These become rapids or waterfalls. The two great falls of the Yellowstone River in Yellowstone National Park were formed in this way.

As we saw in Topic 11, waterfalls often have plunge pools at their bases. The whirlpools in these great potholes erode the bottom part of the cliff. Such **undermining** causes the top of the cliff to overhang. From time to time, pieces break off from the top. Each time this happens, the waterfall is left a little farther upstream. To describe this, we say the waterfall *recedes*.

Undermining and recession are fastest in waterfall cliffs made of horizontal layers of rock. This is especially true if the layers being attacked by the whirlpool are soft, weak rocks such as shale.

Niagara Falls is the world's most famous receding waterfall. Its horizontal rock structure includes a 20-meter thick top layer of tough dolomite rock. But the rocks underneath this layer are almost all thin beds of shale. Shale is rapidly eroded, and the undermined cap rock breaks off at a rate now averaging about 1.5 meters a year at the Canadian Falls.

Niagara Gorge stretches about 11 kilometers from Lewiston to Niagara Falls. It was formed in only 10,000 years by the recession of Niagara Falls from Lewiston, where it began at the close of the Ice Age.

Whirlpools at the bottom attack the weaker rock. Without support from below, the top will fall down. (Niagara Falls, New York)

river

dolomite

shale

shale

This waterfall used to be at the cliffs near the bottom of the picture.

The Niagara River flows to the front. Niagara Falls used to be further downstream. The falls have eroded back to this point. (New York)

13. Meanders and Oxbow Lakes

In times of heavy rains, a river may overflow its banks and cover part of the valley floor. This part is called the **flood plain.** At first the flood plain is narrow, but as time passes it becomes wider. Why?

As a river cuts its bed lower and lower, its slope and speed decrease. Its course becomes more winding, and the river is more easily deflected sidewards. It erodes its banks and valley walls and widens the valley floor.

A river starts in a narrow valley. It begins winding when one side erodes faster than the other. The curves get larger because the river is faster on the outside of the curve. Note the flood plain formed.

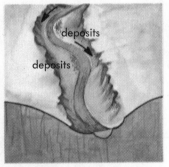
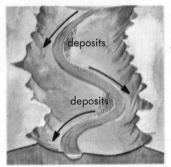

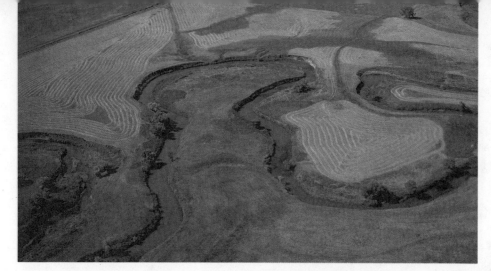

Note the parts of the river which will come together someday to form oxbow lakes. (South Dakota)

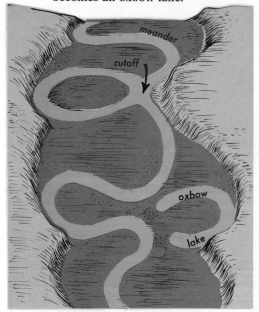

A meander pinches together to form a cutoff. Mud and silt are deposited on the meander side of the cutoff. The old meander becomes an oxbow lake.

When a river swings around a bend, its channel (deepest water) follows the outside of the bend. Erosion is most rapid here. At the inside of the bend the water is shallowest. Sediment is often deposited here. The result is to shift the river bed towards the outside of the bend. If one bend shifts to the right, the next bend shifts to the left. As this pattern continues, the river eventually forms a series of broad curves across a wide flood plain. The broad curves are called **meanders** (mee AN ders) after the River Meander in Asia Minor.

There is a limit to how large a meander can become. As it swings wider and wider, the curve becomes a loop that the river breaks through. The breakthrough is called a *cutoff*. Then the river drops mud and silt at the ends of the abandoned meander. In time the deposits completely separate the meander from the river. It becomes an **oxbow lake.**

Deep canyons with meandering courses (**entrenched meanders**) are found cut into some high plateaus. These are believed to have formed when the area was raised high above sea level after the meanders had developed on a flood plain.

A meandering river on a high plateau can create spectacular scenery. (Utah)

122

The faster a river runs, the more sediment it can carry. The slower it runs, the less it can carry. This is the simple key to understanding deposits made by a river.

The Mississippi, the Nile, and other great rivers have left level, fan-shaped deposits at their mouths. These deposits are called **deltas**. Deltas form when the river flows into a quiet body of water—a lake, a gulf, or an inland sea. Its waters come almost to a standstill. Most of its sediment drops at its mouth. The river splits around its own deposits and drops more sediment. As the deposit grows in size, it may resemble the shape of the Greek letter Δ (delta). A river flowing over its delta divides into branches called *distributaries*.

Rivers that flow into the open ocean do not form deltas. This is because strong waves and currents carry the sediment away as fast as the river delivers it.

Follow the diagrams from the left to the top and then to the bottom. They show the growth of a delta.

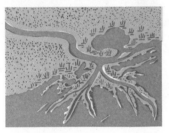

The diagram at the left shows the Mississippi delta. The area circled in white is shown in the photograph below. (*Note:* River flows south toward the top of the map.)

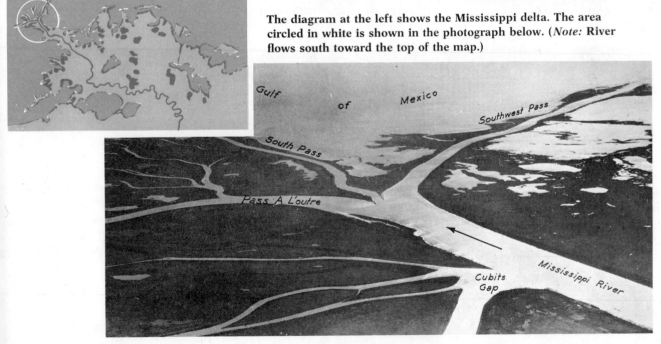

When a steep swift mountain stream reaches more level land at the base of the mountain, it slows down greatly. As a result, it drops a large part of its sediment load, and a fan-shaped deposit forms where the stream ends.

The deposit differs from a delta in several respects. It is formed on land, not in water. Its sediments are coarse sands and gravels, rather than silts and clays. Its surface is sloping, not flat. Very steep deposits are called *alluvial cones.* Gentler ones are **alluvial fans.** They are most common in desert or semi-desert regions. In the United States, many occur at the foot of the Rocky and Sierra Nevada Mountains.

The sand and gravel were left by a stream slowing down as it reached more level land. They show how the stream fanned out.

This colorful alluvial fan shows the fall colors of tundra.

The Flood Plain and Floods

At flood times great rivers such as the Mississippi carry large amounts of sediment. When such a river overflows onto its flood plain, it slows down. Most of its sediment is dropped. The biggest loss of speed occurs right at the banks. More sediment is dropped here than farther back. Not only is the amount greater, but the materials are coarser, too. Because of this, thicker deposits are built up along the banks. These deposits form low ridges called *natural levees.*

Beyond the levees the flood plain is lower and the sediments are finer. Since the flood plain slopes away from the river, *back swamps* may form on it. **Yazoo streams** may also form. These are tributaries that flow through the back swamps. They may flow many miles, more or less parallel to the main stream, before they cut through the levees to join the main stream.

Flood plains are among the most fertile of agricultural areas. The fertility of a flood plain is partly due to the new soil that each flood deposits on the valley floor. Flood plains in arid regions, such as that of the Nile in Egypt, were of the greatest importance in the early development of civilization.

Note the height of the flood plain as you go from the river. The land rises, then falls.

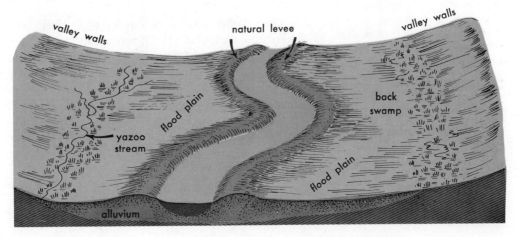

River floods can be destructive as well as constructive, so the causes and control of floods are of great interest.

Most river floods result from heavy or long-lasting rains, the rapid melting of winter snows, or both. A single cloudburst may cause

Where two rivers come together, cities often develop as transportation centers. But, they suffer great damage if the rivers flood. (Paducah, Kentucky, on the Ohio and Tennessee Rivers)

a **flash flood.** This is especially true when the cloudburst hits the narrow valley of a young mountain stream. Towns at the bases of such valleys suffer severely when hit by flash floods.

Large rivers such as the Ohio, the Missouri, and the Mississippi never have flash floods. Their floods result from many days of steady rainfall over large parts of their vast drainage basins. In winter and early spring, thaws (warm spells that melt snow) may add a good deal of runoff. This is especially true when the ground is still frozen. Frozen ground has its pores filled with ice. This keeps the melted snow from soaking into the ground.

The floods of a large river move downstream. As they do, they may flood areas far removed from the sources of the flood waters.

Other Causes of River Floods 18.

When a dam forms across a river, it floods the valley above the river up to the height of the dam. People build dams to create reservoirs. But dams also form naturally.

A common type of natural dam is the *ice jam.* An ice jam may form when a frozen river breaks up in spring or winter thaws. Other natural dams may result when a volcano erupts and pours lava across streams. Dams caused by landslides are even more common.

Many bad floods have been caused by the failure of reservoir dams. The famous Johnstown, Pennsylvania, flood of May 31, 1889, happened when a dam made of earth collapsed after days of heavy rain. The dam had been built to make a reservoir on the Conemaugh River two miles above Johnstown. When the dam broke, the water in the entire reservoir burst down on the sleeping city. More than 2200 people drowned.

In 1963 a massive landslide poured into a reservoir in the Alps in Italy. The dam held, but a surge of water swept over the dam and destroyed the town of Longarone, drowning nearly 3000 people.

19. Preventing Floods

Can floods be prevented? As we saw in Topic 18, the causes of floods are largely natural. The removal of natural vegetation—trees, shrubs, grass—however, usually increases runoff. This makes floods more likely. In areas where this has happened, the replanting of trees (reforestation) and other natural vegetation helps to prevent floods. This is most important in the headwater parts of a river's drainage basin.

Let us move downstream a bit. The flood waters are already swelling the river's tributaries. Can they be contained before they overflow the main stream? To do this, dams are built across head-waters and tributaries. Excess runoff is stored in reservoirs. An outstanding example of this method of flood control is seen in the Tennessee River system, where 26 dams have been built to control the river.

Move downstream farther—to the lower waters of a great river such as the Ohio, the Missouri, or the Mississippi. To overflow, the river must rise above its natural levees. Here the usual method of flood control is to build up the levees. *Artificial levees* are made by placing sand bags or other materials—even concrete walls—on top of the natural levees.

The Mississippi River forms natural levees. Often people build the levees higher with sand bags to help prevent floods.

What can be done near the river's mouth? On the lower Mississippi, **spillways** are used. These are channels that run through the back swamps parallel to the main stream and then into the Gulf of Mexico. At certain points on the flood plain, water is guided into these spillways to relieve the flooding in the Mississippi itself.

Flood problems are, in general, becoming more severe because more land is being cleared of natural vegetation and "developed." It is essential, therefore, that lakes, ponds, swamps, flood plains, and other natural storage areas for rain water *not* be filled in or used for building purposes. To preserve these *wetlands* and to regulate their use, many states have set up wetland agencies.

TOPIC QUESTIONS

Each topic question refers to the topic of the same number within this chapter.

1. (a) What is meant in earth science by "running water?" (b) Explain how "running water gets its energy from the sun."

2. How does running water attack bedrock (a) by abrasion; (b) by a lifting effect; (c) by chemical means?

3. Explain briefly how rock material is removed from the land.

4. (a) What determines the carrying power of a stream? (b) Why does a river erode its bed so much during flood times?

5. (a) Explain why a river should have a V-shaped valley. (b) What is a canyon?

6. (a) What is a river's base level? (b) Why does a river valley widen?

7. (a) What is a gully? (b) How are gullies related to river systems? (c) What are badlands?

8. (a) What is a divide? Why are the Rocky Mountains a divide? (b) What is a drainage basin? Describe the drainage basin of the Mississippi River.

9. Explain what stream piracy is.

10. (a) What is a water gap? How does it form? (b) What is a wind gap? How does it form?

11. (a) How do potholes form? (b) What is a plunge pool?

12. (a) Explain how a plunge pool makes a waterfall recede. (b) Why does Niagara Falls recede? (c) How was Niagara Gorge formed? (d) How were the Yellowstone Falls formed?

13. (a) What is a flood plain? (b) Why does a flood plain get wider? (c) What is a meander? How does it develop? (d) How does an oxbow lake form? (e) How does an entrenched meander form?

14. (a) What makes a river drop its sediment? (b) Explain how a delta forms. (c) Which rivers do not form deltas? Why?

15. (a) How is an alluvial fan formed? (b) How does it differ from a delta?

16. (a) How do natural levees form? (b) How do back swamps form? (c) What is a yazoo stream? (d) Why are flood plains fertile?

17. (a) What is a flash flood? (b) What causes floods in large rivers such as the Missouri?

18. What kinds of natural dams are formed?

19. Explain how each of the following helps to prevent floods: (a) reforestation; (b) building of dams; (c) artificial levees; (d) spillways.

GENERAL QUESTIONS

1. Why should the Niagara River upstream from Niagara Falls have less eroding power than downstream, even where it flows at equal speeds?

2. The rock layers of Niagara are not perfectly horizontal, but dip into the earth toward Niagara's source. How will continued recession change the height of Niagara Falls? Explain.

3. Under what conditions may a river be able to build a delta along an open sea coast?

4. Can a tributary form a delta in its main stream? Explain.

5. Alluvial fans are made of more permeable sediments near the mountains than farther away. Why?

6. Why is a meandering river like the Rio Grande a very unsatisfactory boundary between the United States and Mexico?

STUDENT ACTIVITIES

1. Make a plaster or clay model of a canyon, a water gap, a meandering river and its flood plain, an entrenched meander, a waterfall, a delta, an alluvial fan, or any other feature described in this chapter.

2. Make a series of models showing the development of (a) an oxbow lake, (b) a wind gap through stream piracy.

3. Take a field trip to observe the features of a stream valley in your vicinity and the activities of the stream.

4. Observe the formation of small gullies, alluvial fans, etc., in local parks, etc., after a heavy rainfall.

TOPOGRAPHIC SHEETS

(15-minute series)

1. *Canyon:* Bright Angel, Arizona.
2. *Waterfalls:* Niagara Gorge, New York.
3. *Alluvial fans:* Cucamonga, California.
4. *Meanders and flood plain:* St. Louis, Missouri.
5. *Natural levees and flood plain:* Donaldsonville, Louisiana.
6. *Delta and distributaries:* East Delta, Louisiana.
7. *Young valley:* Fargo, North Dakota.
8. *Mature valley:* Charleston, West Virginia.
9. *Water gaps:* Harrisburg, Pennsylvania.
10. *Stream Piracy:* Kaaterskill, New York.
11. *Entrenched meander:* Rural Valley, Pennsylvania.

1. *Glaciers form from snow that builds up in mountain regions above the snow line. To see how solid ice can form from snow, take a handful of snow or crushed ice and squeeze it between your hands. Repeat a few times.*

What does the squeezing seem to do to the separate grains of snow or ice? What seems to happen when the squeezing stops? How can you explain the effect on the snow or ice? This effect is called packing. *What would cause packing of snow in mountain regions?*

2. *Glaciers move downhill in mountain regions. Their movement may be partly due to sliding. They usually move faster in summer than in winter. Why?*

Set up a slope. This may be a board, large pan, ruler or any flat-surfaced object at least 50 centimeters long. One end rests on the table. The other end is held and raised to any angle.

Begin with a small angle. Place an ice cube at the held end. Slowly raise this end until the ice cube just begins to slide slowly down the slope. Note the height of the held end, or the angles the plane makes with the table. What makes the ice cube slide?

Repeat the experiment. As the ice cube melts, does it slide at a lower angle? Why?

Ice Age; Types of Glaciers

Geologists tell us that continental ice sheets, like those in Greenland and Antarctica, covered nearly all of Canada and much of northern United States until about 11,000 years ago. They tell us that this "Ice Age" probably lasted about a million years. We accept these statements because they are backed up by sound scientific evidence. But the concept of an Ice Age was not generally accepted by geologists until the middle of the 1800's.

In the early 1800's, European geologists noted that many rock outcrops in northern regions had polished and scratched surfaces, unlike rock outcrop surfaces of more southern regions. Giant boulders were different from the bedrock on which they rested. The boulders could sometimes be traced to outcrops many miles north. Pebbles and other sediments were strange to the locality in many places.

Geologists agreed that these "foreign" materials could not be explained by stream action. Many geologists, particularly the British, believed all this had happened in one great flood. They thought flood waters had carried the boulders, scoured the bedrock, and deposited sediments over a wide area. Because they believed water had moved the "foreign" materials, the British called all such material **drift**, a name still in use.

Meanwhile, however, another explanation was being offered. Students of glaciers in the Alps saw how bedrock is attacked by glacial erosion. They also saw how boulders and soils are carried downslope. Sometimes they found such happenings miles down the valley from the glacier front or high above the glacier on the valley walls. In those cases, they reasoned that not too long before the glacier had been longer and thicker. A number of geologists then used this reasoning to explain the "drift" that covered so much of northern Europe. They concluded that great ice sheets had covered the drift area during a long ice age.

The man who is known for this idea is the famous Swiss naturalist, Louis Agassiz (AG ah see). Agassiz did much research to prove his theory, and he worked hard to publicize it.

2. What Is a Glacier?

Imagine a steep valley high in the Alps of Switzerland. No river runs in this valley. Instead, the entire valley floor is covered by a thick mass of snow-covered ice. This mass of ice reaches for hundreds of meters

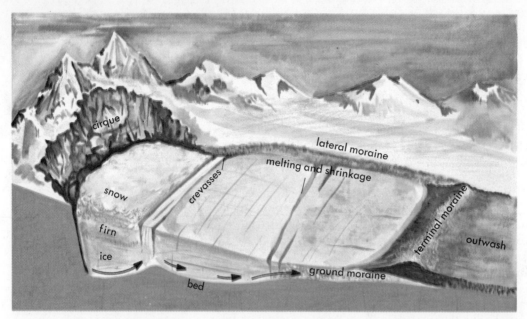

The glacier is formed at the left. Firn is snow made icy by the weight of the snow on top—like a packed snowball. Weight also turns the firn at the bottom into solid ice. The ice moves downhill as a glacier.

up the valley walls. It can be followed up the valley for kilometers. The mass of ice begins in huge fields of ice and snow just below the very highest peaks.

Careful study would show that the ice moves downhill at the rate of several meters a day. At the lower part of the valley, the ice thins out and suddenly ends. Milky colored water runs out from beneath the ice and flows down the open valley. This long, slow-moving wedge-shaped stream of ice is a **valley glacier.**

Glaciers in Switzerland flow down the Alps.

Imagine a great land mass in the polar latitudes of the far north or south. The climate is so cold that only snow falls. For thousands of years snows have been falling, building up, and changing to ice. Almost the whole land mass, thousands upon thousands of square kilometers of lowland, hill, valley, and mountain, is covered by a thick mass of ice. Only the highest mountain peaks reach above the ice.

The ice is thousands of meters thick, and it moves outward from its center in all directions—north, south, east and west—toward the sea coasts. In some places it reaches the sea through low valleys. Here great chunks of ice break off to float away as icebergs. This moving mass of ice, far larger than a valley glacier, is called an **ice sheet.**

3. The Snow Line

Glaciers are born in areas always covered by snow. These are areas where each year more snow falls than melts. Some snow is always left over to add to the build-up of previous years. Climates cold enough to cause such conditions may be found in any part of the world. This is because air temperatures drop with greater height above sea level and with distance from the Equator.

Even in equatorial areas, then, permanent snows may be found on high mountains. Farther from the Equator the mountains need not be so high. In the polar areas, permanent snows may be found even at sea level. The lowest level that permanent snows reach in summer is called the **snow line.** A mountain that is completely covered with snow in winter, but from which the snows are all gone by summer, has no snow line.

Imagine a line at the bottom of the snow. This is the snow line. There is always snow above it.

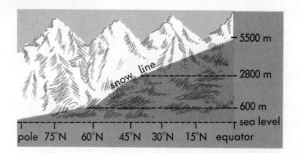

Choose a mountain on a map. Find its latitude at the bottom of this diagram. Then go up to the snow line. Read the height of the snow line at the right.

The snow line is highest near the Equator and lowest near the poles. As climates become colder with greater latitude (distance from the Equator), less height is needed to reach a snow line. The position of the snow line also changes with the total yearly snowfall and the amount of exposure to the sun. Thus the height of a snow line for each latitude varies.

Going north from the Equator through South America, Central America, and North America to the North Pole, the snow line drops as follows: Andes Mountains at the Equator, 5500 meters; Mexico, 4600 meters; Rocky Mountains in the United States, 2800 meters; southern Greenland (60°N), 600 meters; North Pole, sea level.

Birth of a Glacier

Except for bare rock cliffs, the mountain above the snow line is buried in snow. Great basins below the highest peaks are filled with snows hundreds of meters in thickness. In these huge *snow fields*, freshly fallen snows melt and freeze. Then they become compressed into a rough granular ice material called **firn.**

The granules of firn are no larger than fine buckshot. The firn is like the ice of a packed snowball. As the thickness of the firn grows, the lower layers change to solid ice. When this ice begins to flow downward or outward because of the weight of the overlying firn and snow, it has become a **mountain glacier.**

Where Valley Glaciers Occur

The two major types of glaciers are those described in Topic 2. *Valley glaciers* are also known as *Alpine glaciers.* They occur in all parts of the world where mountains stretch above the snow line. This includes all continents except Australia.

The smallest valley glaciers may be only 2 kilometers long, a few hundred meters wide, and less than a hundred meters deep. The largest may be 120 kilometers long, several kilometers wide, and hundreds of meters thick. The world's largest valley glaciers are in southern Alaska. Here mountains with a snow line at about 1500 meters reach to heights above about 6000 meters. The world's highest mountains, the Himalayas, also have very large glaciers.

Snow fields gradually build up to form glaciers.

6. Where Ice Sheets Occur

Ice sheets form in polar areas where the snow line is close to sea level and wide areas are above the snow line. Ice sheets are roughly circular or oval in shape. Small ice sheets called **ice caps** are found in Iceland, Baffin Island, Spitzbergen, and other large islands of the Arctic Ocean. An ice cap may have an area of several thousand square kilometers.

The much larger ice sheets of Greenland and Antarctica are called **continental glaciers.** The Greenland glacier is about 1,700,000 square kilometers in area and up to 3 kilometers thick. It covers all of Greenland except a narrow part of the coast.

The Antarctic glacier covers an even larger land mass with an area of about 12.5 million square kilometers. Here the ice reaches a thickness of nearly 5 kilometers. Along the coast the ice may descend more than 1.5 kilometers below sea level. Farther inland great mountain peaks called **nunataks** project through the ice.

The Greenland ice sheet covers almost all of the earth's largest island.

Glacier Movement

How Glaciers Move 7.

This crevasse is shown in a close-up. (British Columbia)

Geologists have studied the movement of glaciers by driving rows of stakes into the ice from one side of the valley to the other. They then observe the positions of the stakes at regular intervals. They have learned that small valley glaciers may move only a few centimeters a day. However, parts of the Greenland glacier may move as rapidly as about 30 meters a day. They have learned that glaciers move more rapidly in the center than at the sides. At the sides friction with the valley walls holds them back. They have seen that glaciers move faster after winters of heavy snowfall, faster on steep slopes than on gentle ones, and faster in summer.

Gravity causes glaciers to move, but the exact manner of motion is not known. One explanation is that the bottom ice melts under pressure and rolls forward a bit as water. Then it refreezes.

Another explanation is that the ice, at depths of more than about 30 meters, flows like wax under pressure. Studies have shown that the upper ice of a glacier, approximately 30 to 60 meters in thickness, is brittle. The bottom layers of ice, however, can flow slowly. In the "brittle zone" the ice cracks wherever it moves faster in one part than in another. The cracks are called **crevasses.** They may extend across the whole width of a glacier.

How Far Glaciers Move 8.

An Alpine glacier flows slowly downhill. As it moves into lower, warmer levels, the glacier shrinks steadily because of melting and evaporation. As long as the ice moves faster than it melts, the glacier continues to move forward, or **advance.** Most glaciers extend far below the snow line. The glacier reaches its lowest limit at the level *where the ice melts as fast as it moves.* Here at its *ice front* the glacier ends.

The glacier itself always moves forward. But as long as the rates of movement and melting are equal, the ice front is **stationary.** After a winter of heavy snows, which add pressure to the bottom ice, the glacier may move faster than normal, and advance beyond its usual limit. In very warm summers, on the other hand, it may melt faster than normal, causing the ice front to move back, or **recede.**

In regions such as Alaska and Greenland the snow line is close to sea level. Many glaciers reach the sea. Even at sea level they do not melt as fast as they move. As they extend into the water, great blocks break off to become **icebergs.** This is called *calving.*

These icebergs have broken off from Portage Glacier in the background. (near Anchorage, Alaska)

In Antarctica, where the snow line is at sea level, the ice sheet reaches the coastline almost everywhere. In a number of places the ice sheet extends beyond the coast far into the sea in huge *ice shelves*. The largest of these, the Ross Ice Shelf, is hundreds of kilometers wide and about 300 meters thick at its sides. The icebergs that break off from an ice shelf are tremendous. One such iceberg was about 65 kilometers long.

9. Glaciers Transport Loose Rock

Like rivers, glaciers remove loose rock from the valleys through which they move. All rock material carried by a glacier is called **moraine** (moh RAYN). There seems to be almost no limit to the size and amount of material carried by a glacier. Particles ranging in size from fine powder to giant boulders are picked up by the glacier from its valley floor. Often rocks fall into the glacier from the valley walls. Other material may be brought to it by tributary glaciers.

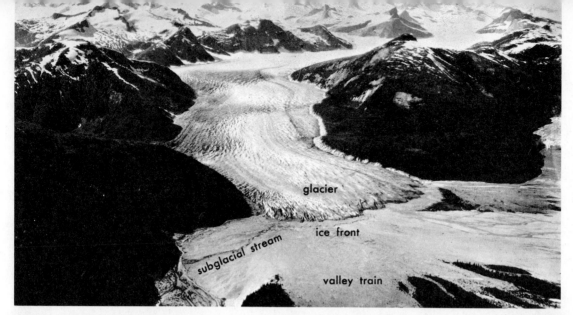

The front of this glacier is far below the snow line. (Norris Glacier, Alaska)

Note the various features of a typical glacier.

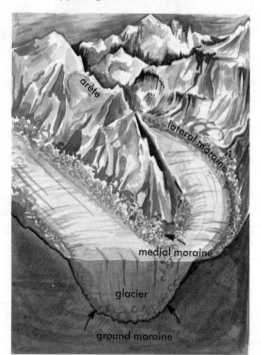

Rock flour is a mixture of fine sand and silt formed by the crushing of rock under the glacier. The meltwater pouring out of a glacier is likely to be filled with suspended rock flour. This gives the water a milky gray color and the name *glacial milk*.

Large buildups of rock pieces frozen into the bottom of the glacier are known as the *ground moraine*. The two long lines of rock pieces that pile up along the valley sides of the glacier are called *lateral (side) moraines*. Sometimes two glaciers come together to form a single larger glacier. Then their inside lateral moraines join to form a *medial (middle) moraine*. At the ice front, rock pieces brought forward by the glacier's motion build up as the ice melts. These pile up as a *terminal (end) moraine*, which may grow very large if the ice front does not move for a long time.

Compare this photograph of a Swiss glacier to the features shown in the diagram at the left.

138

Glaciers erode the bedrock largely through the use of pieces of rock as cutting tools. These pieces are dragged over the bedrock by the forward movement of the glacier. Particles of fine sand, acting like sandpaper, smooth and **polish** the bedrock. Coarse sand, pebbles, and sharp boulders leave long parallel scratches called **striations.** These scratches plainly show the general direction of ice movement. If the bedrock is soft, pebbles and small boulders may dig in so deeply as to leave long parallel **grooves.** The pebbles and boulders carried by the glacier show signs of wear, too, becoming flattened and scratched.

This rock was dragged under a glacier. The lines show the direction.

A glacier left this ridge grooved and polished.

11. Shaping the Bedrock

Glacial erosion shapes the bedrock into many new forms. Outcrops of bedrock become smooth and polished on the side from which the glacier comes. The opposite side may be left steep and rough where the glacier freezes and plucks away loose blocks of rock. Such outcrops are called **roches moutonnées** (rosh moo toe NAY), meaning sheep-rocks, because they look like resting sheep. *Potholes* are ground out beneath glaciers in whirlpools formed by meltwater falling into crevasses.

Look at the three cirques at the top. They enlarge toward each other and form the sharp peak.

Frost action and glacial erosion at the head of the glacier wear away the mountain peak walls it rests on. This forms a semicircular basin at the head of the glacial valley, called a **cirque** (SERK).

When two cirques are formed next to each other on a peak, the divide between them may become extremely narrow and sharp. It is then called an **arête** (ah RET), or knife-edge ridge. When three or more cirques cut into the same mountain peak, they may cut away so much that a spectacular pyramid-shaped peak is left. Such peaks are called **horns,** or **matterhorns,** after the famous Matterhorn in Switzerland.

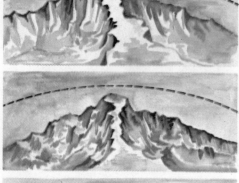

The famous Matterhorn was formed from several cirques.

Glacial Valleys Can Be Recognized 12.

A river touches only a small part of its valley floor. A valley glacier, on the other hand, touches the entire valley floor and a large part of the valley walls as well. As it moves through its valley, the valley glacier scours away the rock until it flattens the entire valley floor and makes the valley walls nearly vertical. The result is a **glacial trough**—a glacial valley that is roughly U-shaped up to the point on the valley walls reached by the ice.

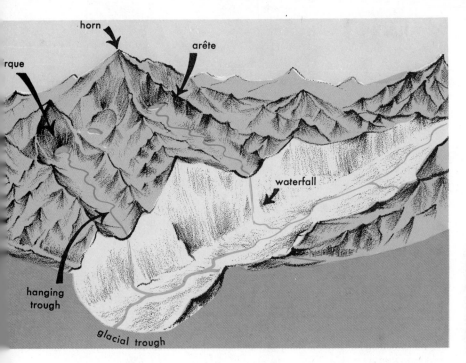

Labels on image: horn, arête, rque, waterfall, hanging trough, glacial trough

Compare the depths of the three glacial troughs. They show that the glaciers from the left fed into the glacier from the right.

The river above Bridal Veil Falls is in a hanging trough. The cliff behind the falls is the wall of the main glacial trough. (Yosemite National Park, Calif.)

Main valley glaciers are usually much thicker than their tributary glaciers. Therefore they erode their valleys much more powerfully. This can be seen in regions where a change of climates has caused glaciers to disappear. The main valleys are found to be much deeper than their tributary valleys. The tributary U-shaped valleys are called **hanging troughs.**

The rivers that now run in the hanging troughs plunge over the cliffs into the main river below. They are said to form *hanging-trough waterfalls.* Glacial troughs, hanging troughs, and hanging-trough falls are common in all glaciated mountains. A famous hanging-trough fall is Yosemite Falls in California.

13. What Continental Glaciers Do

Like alpine glaciers, continental glaciers remove loose rock and soil. They smooth, striate, and groove bedrock. They form roches moutonnes, and leave potholes. But their erosion of mountain areas differs from the erosion of alpine glaciers in a few ways. A continental glacier deepens and widens only those valleys that run in the same direction as its direction of travel. Since it covers most mountain tops, it grinds down the peaks and leaves them polished and rounded, rather than sharpened. In alpine areas, however, glaciers sharpen mountain peaks.

How Was It Deposited? 14.

In time, most of the rock material carried by glaciers is deposited by melting. All glacial deposits are called **drift.**

Drift is divided into two kinds. Deposits dropped right where the glacier melts are called **till.** Till deposits are *unstratified,* because the moraine materials simply pile up on top of each other as the ice melts. Deposits made by streams of glacial meltwater are called **outwash.** Unlike till, outwash is *stratified.*

Glaciers Leave Moraines 15.

Till is deposited by the glacier itself. Outwash is deposited by glacial streams.

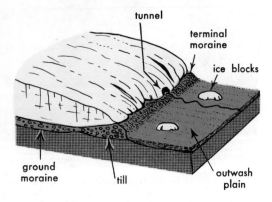

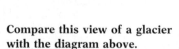

When a glacier melts, it leaves its moraines in nearly the same places as they were in the glacier. The *ground moraine* forms a thin, fairly even deposit over the whole area. *Lateral* and *medial* moraines form ridges running in almost the same direction as the one in which the glacier moved.

The *terminal moraine* forms a ridge along the ice front. The longer the ice front stays in one place, the larger the terminal moraine becomes. When a receding ice front stops in new places for any length of time, new "terminal" moraines are formed behind the main one. These are called **recessional moraines.**

Even a "stationary" ice front moves back and forth slightly with the seasons. So terminal moraine deposits are spread over a broad belt in front of a glacier. Furthermore, no two parts of the ice front

Compare this view of a glacier with the diagram above.

Forces That Attack the Surface

deposit exactly the same amount of material. For these reasons, terminal and recessional moraines are likely to be made up of irregular hills and hollows rather than a single straight ridge. Terminal moraines of continental glaciers may be hundreds of kilometers long, several kilometers wide, and a hundred meters high.

The materials of the moraines range from boulders to clays. They are mixed in widely varying amounts, and are always unstratified. Large glacial boulders are called **erratics,** because they are different from the underlying bedrock.

The glacial boulder on top protects the ice below from melting.

16. Drumlins

Drumlins are long, smooth, canoe-shaped hills made up of till. They usually are found in swarms of hundreds of drumlins. They all point in the direction of glacier movement. A typical drumlin may be 400 meters long, 100 meters wide, and 25 meters high.

Drumlins were probably formed when an advancing glacier ran over earlier ground moraine, sweeping it into long strips. Swarms of drumlins are found in southeastern Wisconsin, in New York State south of Lake Ontario, and near Boston, Massachusetts.

These long, smooth, canoe-shaped hills point in the direction of glacier movement.

Outwash Plains 17.

Glacial meltwater pours out at the ice front in streams filled with rock flour, sand, and gravel. These streams form gently sloping stratified deposits that may reach for miles beyond the terminal moraine. The deposits look like alluvial fans. In front of large glaciers they overlap and form broad flat areas called **outwash plains.**

Winding Hills Called Eskers 18.

Much of the water of a melting glacier falls to the bottom of the ice through crevasses. Here it forms *subglacial streams* that run in tunnels beneath the ice. They come out at the ice front. The winding tunnels of these streams become partly filled with roughly stratified sands and gravel. When the glacier disappears, the deposits slump down at the sides and are left as long winding ridges called **eskers.**

Eskers are found in the glaciated states of the Mississippi Valley, the north central states, central New York, and Maine. Eskers usually run in just about the same direction as the direction of ice movement.

Note the different kinds of deposits left by a glacier.

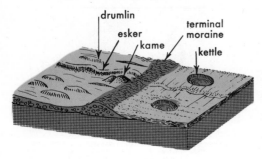

The raised ridge of rock in this picture is formed by deposits left by streams under a glacier.

Kames (KAYMS) are small cone-shaped hills of stratified sand and gravel. They are formed when streams from the top of the glacier deposit their sediments. These pile up in heaps at the ice front or at the bottom of circular holes in the glacier.

Kettles are circular hollows found on terminal moraines and outwash plains. They are formed in two steps. First, moraine or outwash deposits bury large blocks of ice left as the glacier recedes. Then the ice melts, leaving the kettles.

When glacial streams empty into lakes at or beyond the ice front, **deltas** are formed. These are made up largely of layers of gravel and coarse sand. Fine sands and clays may be spread evenly over the whole lake floor.

Glaciation of an area usually leaves many new basins or depressions in the land surface. If these basins are permanently filled with water, they form lakes, ponds, or swamps, depending on how large and deep they are. Three important types of lakes that come from glaciation are *cirque lakes*, *kettle lakes*, and *moraine-dammed lakes*.

Cirque lakes are formed when water fills the rock-floored cirque basins left by alpine glaciers. Cirque lakes and rock-basin lakes are also called **tarns.** A famous example is Lake Louise in the Canadian Rockies.

Kettle lakes form in large numbers in the kettle holes of moraines and outwash plains. They are common in Minnesota, Wisconsin, New York, and New England.

Moraine-dammed lakes are formed where river valleys are blocked by glacial moraines. The river rises to the height of the moraine dam and floods its valley to form a long, usually narrow lake. Many of the larger lakes of northern United States came about in this way. Examples are Lake George in New York and Long Lake in Maine.

In many cases lakes were formed by both glacial erosion which scoured out river valleys and deposition that dammed the rivers. The *Finger Lakes* of central New York State—Lakes Seneca, Cayuga, Canandaigua, and others—were formed in this way. Many of their former tributary valleys were left as hanging troughs high above the main troughs. The Great Lakes have a more complicated history. However, they, too, lie in river valleys that were deepened and then dammed by glacial moraines.

The Ice Age

About a million years ago it was as cold in much of northern North America and northern Europe as it is today in Greenland. Great ice sheets moved down from central and eastern Canada and northern Scandinavia. In North America the ice sheets reached about as far south as where the Ohio and Missouri rivers and central Long Island are now. Much of the northcentral and northeastern part of the United States was covered by ice. In Europe the ice sheets covered most of Scandinavia, the British Isles, Denmark, Belgium, northern France, and the Baltic countries, and reached far into Germany and Russia.

In North America there were three centers in which the snow and ice were thickest. From them the ice spread out in all directions. These **centers of accumulation** were the *Labrador center* east of Hudson Bay, the *Keewatin center* west of Hudson Bay, and the *Cordilleran center* in the Canadian Rockies.

From the Labrador center came the ice that covered eastern Canada and the northeastern United States. From Keewatin came the

The entire area in white was covered by ice sheets in the Ice Age. Note the uncovered area south of Lake Superior.

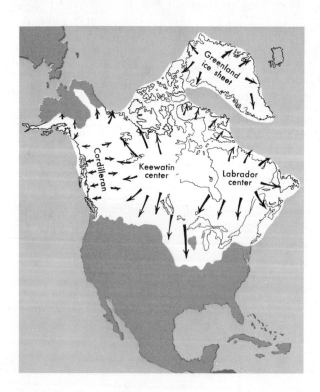

ice that covered central Canada and the northcentral United States. The Cordilleran ice sheet covered the Canadian Rockies down to their foothills, but did not move south. At that time there were valley glaciers in the mountains of the western United States, but they were far larger than they are today.

The ice sheets advanced and receded four times during the million year period as the climate changed from cold to warm and back again. The last recession took place about 11,000 years ago. Many geologists think we are now in a warm, or *interglacial*, period that will be followed by a return of the ice sheets in perhaps 20,000 years. Others think that this warm period will last millions of years.

22. Ice Age Evidence

Proof that there was an Ice Age is given in the many glacial features that have been described. The southern limit reached by the ice sheets is marked by terminal moraines. One of these is the Long Island, New York, moraine that extends almost 225 kilometers from Brooklyn to Montauk Point. Others stretch from New Jersey through Pennsylvania, Ohio, Indiana, Illinois, and westward to Puget Sound. South of the terminal moraines, outwash plains are found in many places.

Almost all of the United States and Canada north of the moraines is covered by drift. There are large numbers of glacial boulders in the ground moraine soils. Exposed bedrock is striated, grooved, and polished, even on mountain tops. North-south valleys are shaped into glacial troughs. East-west valleys are partly filled with drift. Kames, eskers, drumlins, and recessional moraines are found in many places. Lakes and swamps are far more common than in the unglaciated areas to the south.

In the Rockies and the Sierra Nevadas, glacial markings are found high upon the valley walls. This shows that much larger glaciers filled these valleys during the Ice Age.

Small cone-shaped hills of glacial deposits, swamps, and lakes are common in glaciated areas.

23. Causes of Glacial Climates

To explain why the earth was cold enough to have the recent Ice Age, one must account for certain facts:

1. This Ice Age began about a million years ago and included *four advances* of the ice sheets.
2. Warm *interglacial periods* came after each advance. We may now be in an interglacial period.

3. Other ice ages have occurred from time to time in the past 600 million years.

4. During the last Ice Age glaciers advanced and receded at the same time, not only in North America and Europe, but also in the Southern Hemisphere.

Geologists have proposed the following hypotheses to account for ice ages:

North America and Europe were higher, and therefore colder, during the Ice Age. Greater height does make a colder climate. However, our continents would have had to rise and fall four times in the past million years to account for the four advances of the glaciers. Geologists think that this is unlikely, and there is no evidence that it happened.

Melting of the Arctic Ocean ice caused more snow to fall. Glaciers then formed in northern Europe and North America. One objection to this idea is that it does not explain how the great Antarctic glacier was formed without any ocean at the South Pole to provide snow. Another objection is that it does not explain why glaciation happened at the same time in both hemispheres.

Volcanic dust in the air, from great volcanic eruptions, reduced the amount of heat reaching the earth from the sun. But there is no evitence that there was great volcanic activity during the glacial advances.

The amount of heat given off by the sun changes. At times of least heat, glacial climates may happen. The sun's heat does change a little, but we do not know enough about how long these changes last to explain glaciation by them.

Recent research has improved our knowledge of the times and durations of the previous Ice Ages. We also have discovered evidence of many more Ice Ages in the distant past than were previously suspected. As a result, most geologists now believe the following hypothesis to be true.

Changes in the tilt of the earth's axis and the shape of its orbit might cause colder climates in some parts of the earth. Changes of this kind take place over and over again at regular periods in earth history. We now know that glaciation has happened at these regular periods. Furthermore, such changes can cause glacial climates in both hemispheres at the same time.

Interestingly, Wegener, who suggested that continents drift, was among the first to propose this hypothesis also.

TOPIC QUESTIONS

Each topic question refers to the topic of the same number within this chapter.

1. (a) What were the strange happenings that geologists of the early 1800's found hard to explain? (b) What explanation was offered by British geologists? (c) What explanation was offered by Louis Agassiz?

2. In your own words describe (a) a valley glacier, (b) an ice sheet.

3. (a) Define the snow line and explain its meaning. (b) Explain how the snow line changes with latitude and give examples.

4. Describe the beginning of a mountain glacier. What is firn?

5. (a) Where are valley glaciers generally found? (b) How large are valley glaciers?

6. (a) What is the difference between ice caps and continental glaciers? Give examples. (b) What is a nunatak?

7. (a) What has been learned from studies of rows of stakes driven into a glacier? (b) How is glacier movement explained? (c) Why do crevasses form?

8. (a) Why do glaciers reach below the snow line? (b) What decides how far a glacier can go? (c) Explain the conditions when the ice front is stationary, advancing, or receding. (d) When do glaciers reach the sea coast? (e) How are icebergs formed?

9. (a) Describe the kind, amount, and source of material carried by a glacier. (b) Explain what ground, lateral, medial, and terminal moraines are. (c) What is rock flour?

10. Explain the cause of polished, striated, and grooved bedrock and boulders.

11. Describe the cause of roches moutonnees, potholes, cirques, arêtes, and horns.

12. Describe the shape and cause of glacial troughs, hanging troughs, and hanging-trough waterfalls.

13. How does erosion by a continental glacier differ from that by alpine glaciers?

14. (a) Explain the words *drift* and *till*. (b) How do till deposits differ from meltwater deposits?

15. (a) Describe the appearance of the moraines of a glacier after they are deposited by the glacier. (b) What are recessional moraines? (c) Why are terminal moraines usually broad and irregularly hilly? (d) What are moraines made of? (e) What are erratics?

16. Describe the shape, size, and possible cause of drumlins and where they are found.

17. Describe the cause and structure of an outwash plain.

18. Describe the cause and appearance of eskers, and where they are found.

19. (a) What are kames? How are they formed? (b) What are kettles? How are they formed? (c) How is a delta formed?

20. (a) Name and describe three types of lakes resulting from glaciation. Give examples. (b) What part did glaciers play in the beginning of the Finger Lakes?

21. Describe the beginning, centers of accumulation, and the extent of the ice sheets in North America during the last Ice Age.

22. Classify the evidences of glaciation given in Topic 22, using two headings, (1) erosion and (2) deposition.

23. Describe the currently accepted theory of glacial climates.

1. How should the total yearly snowfall and the direction a mountainside faces affect the position of the snow line?

2. Why should glaciers move faster in warm weather than in cold weather?

3. Why can striations and grooves made thousands of years ago still be seen?

4. Many eskers go up and down hills. How is that possible?

5. Moraine-dammed lakes often have many irregular inlets and bays. Why?

6. How do scientists know where the centers of accumulation were during the Ice Age?

7. After the ice sheet retreated from New England, valley glaciers existed for some time in the White Mountains of New Hampshire. What evidence would show this?

**STUDENT
ACTIVITIES**

1. Make plasticene models of any of the following: an area of alpine glaciers, a glaciated mountain area showing a main trough and hanging troughs, terminal moraine and outwash plain topography, eskers and drumlins.

2. If you live in a glaciated part of the United States, take a field trip to an area in which you can see some of the features studied in this chapter. If you do not live in a glaciated area, do your "field tripping" by studying pictures and topographic maps.

**TOPOGRAPHIC
SHEETS**

(15-minute series)

ALPINE GLACIATION

1. *Alpine glaciers:* Chief Mountain, Montana: Mt. Rainier, Washington.

2. *Matterhorns, cirques, hanging valleys:* Chief Mountain, Montana; Mt. Whitney, California.

3. *Terminal moraine (alpine):* Fremont Park, Wyoming.

CONTINENTAL GLACIATION

1. *Terminal moraine:* Whitewater, Wisconsin.

2. *Terminal moraine, outwash plain:* Brooklyn, New York; Hempstead, New York.

3. *Drumlins:* Palmyra, New York; Oswego, New York; Sun Prairie, Wisconsin.

4. *Eskers:* Passadumkeag, Maine; St. Francis, Minnesota.

5. *Finger Lakes:* New York (Skaneateles, Auburn, Genoa, Canandaigua).

10

The photograph on the next page shows a dust storm arriving in Springfield, Colorado, on the Great Plains. The dust has been blown out of the soil in areas to the west of Springfield. It is being carried east by strong winds that blow steadily from west to east. Which soil materials are picked up by the wind as dust? What kind of weather in the region west of Springfield allows this to happen? Is this more likely to happen in land that has had trees or grass removed, or has been plowed, or where crops have been planted? Or, is it more likely to happen in land with natural vegetation? Why?

How does the photograph show that the winds are very strong?

Erosion by Winds

Where Erosion by Wind Occurs 1.

Like rivers and glaciers, winds are agents of erosion. But air is far lighter than water or ice. For this reason, wind causes much less erosion of bedrock or of soil covered by vegetation.

Winds are most effective where sands, silts, and clays lie loose and dry. These conditions are found in great deserts, such as the Sahara in Africa and the Mohave in the southwestern United States. On a much smaller scale, these conditions are found on the beaches of seas and large lakes. They also are found sometimes in semiarid regions, such as the Great Plains when droughts (long dry spells) have killed the soil's protective vegetation.

Where soil is loose, high winds create dust storms. This approaching storm kept Springfield, Colorado, in total darkness for half an hour one spring afternoon.

Rock Materials Carried by Winds 2.

The only rock materials carried by ordinary winds are clay, silt, and sand. Clay and silt form most of the dust that even light winds can carry. When strong steady winds lift great amounts of silt and clay from the topsoil, dust storms happen. The most destructive dust storms in our history took place on the Great Plains during the droughts of the 1930s. In some of these, dust was carried kilometers high in the atmosphere.

Sand grains are much larger and heavier than clay and silt particles. Experiments with sand grains show that winds of at least 18 kilometers an hour are needed to move them. The sand grains do not move in a steady stream above the ground. Instead, they rise and fall in short hops and bounces called **saltation.** Even in very strong winds, most of the sand is carried within 1 meter of the ground.

3. Abrasion by Wind-Blown Sediments

Silt and clay particles are too soft to wear away most rocks. However, sand grains are very abrasive, or wearing, especially if they are quartz. Most sand grains are quartz.

The sand grains driven by the wind act like a sand blast. They grind and scour anything they hit. In some desert areas, rock outcrops with soft lower layers are worn away close to the ground by sand blasts to form toadstool rocks.

Desert sand blasts also grind boulders into strange shapes called ventifacts. In a ventifact the side facing the steady wind direction has been worn into a smooth flat surface, or *facet.* A ventifact may have more than one facet. The diagram shows how one facet forms. How does a second form? One way might be through a seasonal change of wind direction. A second might be through the turning of the boulder by frost or other weathering action.

Look at each ventifact. Try to see the direction of the wind that shaped it.

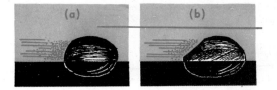

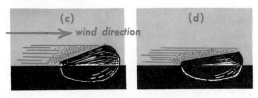

Note how the wind shapes this ventifact.

4. Erosional Effects: Deflation

Deflation is the geological term for the removal of loose rock particles by the wind. In many desert areas the sands and clays formed by weathering are blown out by the wind. Only pebbles and boulders are

This desert pavement has no sand or clay on the surface. (Arizona)

left at the surface. This pebble-and-boulder surface is a **desert pavement.** It protects the materials beneath from further deflation. Stony deserts of this type are common in the southwestern United States and in the Sahara.

In semiarid regions, such as the Great Plains, deflation has formed thousands of hollows, or **deflation basins.** Most of these are shallow and small, but some are kilometers long and perhaps 100 meters deep. If the bottom of the hollow reaches the water table, the wet ground stops further deflation. The growth of natural vegetation also stops deflation. Some of the oases of deserts such as the Sahara are located in deep hollows that were probably formed by deflation.

Sand Dune Regions; Dune Sands 5.

Sand dunes are hills of sand deposited by wind. They form when the sand piles up against shrubs, boulders, or other obstructions.

The right side of each dune is hit by the wind. It has a gentle slope with sand ripples. The left side of each dune is protected from the wind. Its slope is steep and smooth. (New Mexico)

Sand dunes are found wherever there are strong winds and there is plenty of loose sand. The largest stretches of land containing sand dunes are the great deserts such as the Sahara. Other large areas with sand dunes are sandy river flood plains in semiarid climates. The Columbia River in Washington has this kind of flood plain. Finally there are the sandy beaches of sea coasts and large lake shores.

Most sand dunes are made of quartz sands. But other sand-size grains may also form dunes. The dunes of White Sands National Monument in New Mexico are made of gypsum sands. The dunes of the Bermuda Islands are made of calcite sands eroded from the coral bedrock.

Wind abrasion gives dune sands a "frosted" look. Dune sands may also contain shiny flakes of mica and black grains of magnetite.

6. Shape and Size of Dunes

If the wind blows from a single direction, dunes will have a long gentle slope on the windy, or *windward*, side and a shorter steep slope on the sheltered, or *leeward*, side. For example, winds blowing steadily from the west form dunes with gentle slopes on their west sides. Steady winds of medium strength often form beautiful crescent-shaped dunes called *barchans* (BAR kans). Tiny sand ripples are often seen on the windward slopes of sand dunes.

The crescent-shaped dunes on the right show that a steady, medium wind blows from the left. (Columbia River, Oregon)

Dunes range in size from small beach dunes a few meters high to mountainous Sahara dunes more than 100 meters high and many kilometers long. Dunes occur in groups that may cover large areas. In the Sahara they cover about 800,000 square kilometers.

Each time the wind blows against the windward side of a sand dune, some of the surface sand is carried over the top. Then it falls down on the leeward side, also known as the **slip face.** As this process goes on, the whole dune is moved in the leeward direction. This **migration** may be as much as 30 meters a year.

Migrating dunes can bury towns, farms, and forests. But not all dunes migrate. In humid beach areas, grasses and shrubs may grow on the dunes. These keep the dunes from moving.

Shrubs and grasses hold back the migration of the sand dune.

Ancient Sand Dunes 8.

The sand grains of a sand dune may become cemented together. As a result, layers of sandstone form. This has happened many times in the geologic past. How does the geologist recognize these ancient sand dunes? How does he tell the difference between desert sandstones and sandstones formed under water?

The grains of dune sands are more uniform in size and generally better rounded than water-worn grains. They show the typical frosted surface. Furthermore, the layers of desert sandstones are tilted and cross-bedded.

This rock was formed from sand. The slanted layers show it was once a migrating dune. (Utah)

The tilted beds are believed to have begun as tilted layers of sand on the slip face of a migrating dune. According to this hypothesis, layers tilting in different directions and at different angles were formed when the wind changed its direction and possibly its speed. This caused a pattern of cross-bedding that remained when the sands were cemented into sandstones.

9. From Ancient Dust Storms

Large areas in China, northern Europe, and north central United States are covered by deposits of a fertile material called **loess** (LES or LOW ess). The loess ranges in thickness from about 1 meter to

This cliff is made of thick loess. (Vicksburg, Mississippi)

about 100 meters. It is made up of unstratified yellowish silt-sized particles of many different minerals and rocks.

Geologists believe that loess is a wind-carried sediment. The silt particles are the size carried by winds in dust storms. The main deposits of loess in the United States are found in the upper Mississippi and Missouri valleys.

The loess silts in the United States probably came from melting glaciers at the close of the recent Ice Age. Water and crushed rock from the glaciers drained into the Mississippi and Missouri rivers. The rivers overflowed, depositing the sediments on their flood plains. When the ice disappeared, the rivers shrank and their flood plains dried out. Then the silts were blown by great dust storms to their present locations.

Loess deposits in northern Europe are also believed to be of glacial origin. The loess of north China, however, is thought to have been blown eastward into China from the great deserts of Mongolia.

Wind as a Geological Agent

The landforms in desert areas are unmistakably different from those of humid areas. Nevertheless, even in desert areas, the wind is not the most important geological agent. The combination of weathering, mass wasting, and stream erosion is much stronger than the wind in eroding the desert and shaping its landforms. Most desert streams run only a short time when there is little rain. But desert rains are likely to be cloudbursts. This makes the streams raging torrents—short lived, but very powerful.

Mesas, Buttes, Natural Bridges

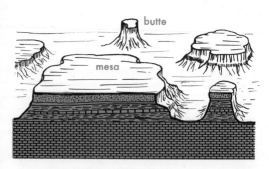

Mesas and buttes are striking features of the southwestern American desert. But they owe their beginning to the work of rivers, not winds. They form in plateaus capped by tough sandstone or limestone beds. The **mesa** is a flat-topped hill left between stream valleys. In humid areas the hill would be eroded and rounded by tributary streams. In the desert these tributary streams are missing. Narrow-topped mesas are called **buttes.** With their cliff-like walls, mesas and buttes stand high above the desert.

A mesa has a wide, flat top. The top of a butte is also flat but much smaller.

Once a high, flat plateau stood here. Erosion removed all of it except this butte. (Wyoming)

Rainbow Natural Bridge was formed when a river cut through its meander. (Utah)

Tall natural bridges are scenic features in southeastern Utah. They were formed when desert rivers cut through their entrenched meanders.

TOPIC QUESTIONS

Each topic question refers to the topic of the same number within this chapter.

1. In what kind of area is the wind most active as an agent of erosion?

2. **(a)** What rock materials are carried in dust storms? Where do they come from? **(b)** What is saltation? Explain how the wind carries sand.

3. **(a)** How does a ventifact form? **(b)** What are toadstool rocks?

4. **(a)** What is deflation? **(b)** How is a desert pavement formed? **(c)** How is a deflation basin formed?

5. **(a)** What are sand dunes? How do they form? Where are they found? **(b)** What minerals are dune sands made of? **(c)** Why are dune sands "frosted"?

6. **(a)** Describe the shape of a sand dune formed by steady winds. **(b)** What effect does wind direction have on the shape of sand dunes? **(c)** What are sand ripples? **(d)** How large are dunes?

7. (a) Explain the migration of a sand dune. What is the slip face of a dune? (b) Do all dunes migrate? Explain.

8. What things show the difference between beds of sandstone which were formed from ancient sand dunes and sandstones formed under water?

9. Describe the cause and characteristics of loess and where it is found.

10. Discuss the importance of wind as a geological agent.

11. (a) What is a mesa? How is it formed? (b) What is a butte? (c) How were Utah's natural bridges formed?

GENERAL QUESTIONS

1. Make sketches showing the windward and leeward sides of sand dunes for winds blowing steadily from (a) the north, (b) the south, (c) the east, (d) the west.

2. Topic 3 states that ventifacts may have been turned by frost or other weathering action. Explain how this could happen.

STUDENT ACTIVITIES

1. Obtain samples of dune sands from nearby beaches or other sources. Examine the sands with a hand magnifier or low power microscope. Can you identify grains of quartz, mica, feldspar, calcite, or magnetite? Do the grains appear frosted and rounded as described in Topic 8?

2. Examine sand grains rubbed from samples of sandstone. Analyze them as you did the sands in activity number 1.

3. If you live near an area of sand dunes, take a field trip to the dunes and observe: (a) the shapes of the dunes, (b) the relative steepness of their sides, (c) the materials of which they are made, (d) whether they are fixed or migrating, (e) their relation to the prevailing wind direction.

TOPOGRAPHIC SHEETS

15-minute series, unless otherwise noted)

1. *Sand dunes:* Yuma, California-Arizona; Yuma, East and Yuma, West 7½ minute series; Barnegat, New Jersey; Cape Henry, Virginia.

2. *Barchan dunes:* Sieler, Washington, 7½ minute series; Moses Lake, Washington.

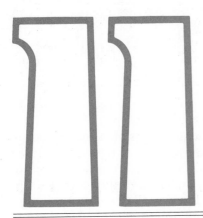

HOW DO YOU KNOW THAT...?

What kinds of minerals are beach sands made of? This question is discussed briefly in Topic 14. But see for your self, if you can.

Get a sample of beach sand. Spread it out on a sheet of white paper. Examine it with a hand magnifying glass. See if you can identify any of the following:

1. White glassy chips of quartz; 2. black grains of magnetite; 3. flakes of black mica; 4. flakes of white mica; 5. fragments of shells; 6. any other materials. Which mineral forms most of the sand? Are the quartz grains rounded and smooth, or sharp and rough? Why? Is clay present in your sample?

See if you can explain where each of the materials in your sample came from (the kind of rock, and so forth.)

Erosion by Waves and Currents

Waves in the Sea

Wind and Waves 1.

Streams, glaciers, wind, and waves—these are the agents of erosion. Each one has its "theatre of operations." Waves operate along shorelines where land meets water. How do the waves of the oceans begin?

An ocean wave is a rhythmic rise and fall of the water surface. The "ordinary" waves we see at the seashore are all made by the wind. Waves are sometimes made by undersea earthquakes also. The moon causes the rhythmic rise and fall we call the *tides*. Tides are a kind of wave, too, although you probably don't think of them as waves.

Wind-driven waves illustrate how the energy of the sun erodes the surface of the earth. The sun heats the atmosphere and causes winds. The winds blow steadily on the surface of oceans and lakes. Friction creates ripples. The ripples grow into waves that drive against the shore with the energy from the winds.

The size of waves depends on three things:

1. the *speed* of the wind;
2. the length of *time* the wind blows; and
3. the **fetch,** or length of open water over which the wind blows steadily.

Ocean waves rarely reach a height of more than 15 meters. But hurricane winds have created waves 30 meters high after blowing for hours with a fetch of 1500 kilometers. Because of shorter fetch, lake waves can never be as high as ocean waves.

A storm over the Pacific raised these waves above normal height. (La Jolla, California)

2. Features of Water Waves

When a wave passes through water the water surface rises and falls. The *height* of the wave is the difference between its high point, or **crest** and its low point, or **trough.** The **wavelength** is the distance from one crest to the next.

Strong winds make waves longer as well as higher. Storm waves often have wavelengths of more than 150 meters. On the average, the wavelength of an ocean wave is from 20 to 30 times its height. A wave 2 meters high would have a wavelength of between 40 and 60 meters.

The **period** of a wave is the time it takes one wavelength to pass a given point. Most ocean waves have a period of about two seconds to ten seconds. To find the speed of a wave, divide its wavelength by its period. For example, what is the speed of a wave 24 meters long, with a period of 4 seconds? The answer is 6 meters per second.

Wavelength is measured from crest to crest. Height is measured between top and bottom.

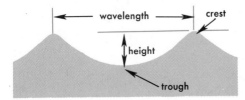

3. How Water Waves Travel

The passage of a wave through water is like the passage of a wave through a rope. When a rope is snapped, each bit of it rises in its turn to a crest. Then it falls into a trough. The wave has gone through the rope. But each bit of rope is still in the same place in the rope. All it has done is to rise and fall in a circular path.

The same thing happens in a water wave. Each particle of water at the ocean surface stays in its place and has a circular motion. This can be seen in the up-and-down bobbing of a floating object. But each moving particle passes its energy on to the next particle. So, the wave travels as far as its energy can carry it.

Wave motion takes place below the surface too. The water particles move in smaller and smaller circles as the depth increases. Finally the motion dies out at a depth equal to about half the wavelength.

Each water particle (black dots) has a circular motion in place. The water particles do not move toward shore either on the wave surface or below.

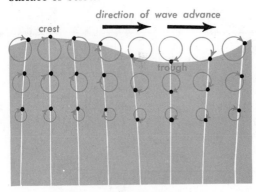

4. Whitecaps and Swells

When strong winds blow in gusts of changing speed and direction, choppy seas result. Each wave has a different height and length and may come from a different direction. As waves clash, and the wind tears their crests, foamy **whitecaps** are formed.

On calm days, the sea is likely to have a steady movement of smooth waves. These are smaller than the waves of stormy weather. They come at regular intervals of up to 10 seconds. How can there be waves without winds? These waves are called **swells.** They are waves caused by stormy winds far out at sea.

Swells get longer and lower with greater distance from their source. Their period increases. Swells with periods of more than 10 seconds are common on California beaches in summer. They are believed to come from Pacific Ocean storms thousands of kilometers to the west. On the Atlantic and Gulf of Mexico coasts, swells usually have shorter periods. The next time you go to the ocean beach, time the swells.

When swells from two different storm areas arrive together, very large waves may result.

Origin of Breakers 5.

Waves usually approach the shoreline smoothly until they reach water so shallow that the wave "feels the bottom." As explained in Topic 3, this happens where the depth is about half the wavelength. For example, a wave with a wavelength of 20 meters will scrape bottom at 10 meters.

As the wave trough scrapes bottom, the lower part of the wave slows down. Meantime, the upper part of the wave moves ahead. Finally the crest falls over and breaks into surf that washes up onto the beach. The line along which successive crests break is called the line of **breakers.** The depth of water there is one to two times the original height of the breaking waves.

Note the depth of water at the breaker. It is about the same as the original wave height.

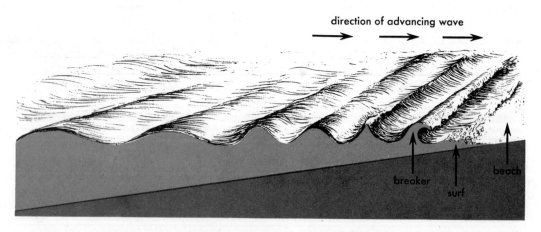

direction of advancing wave

breaker

surf

beach

A surfer starts up on the front slope of a breaker. (Hawaii)

The surf formed by breaking waves is a powerful agent of erosion. On rocky shorelines it pounds the rocks and cliffs and wears them down. On beaches it scours the bottom and moves sediments along the shoreline.

6. Undertows and Rip Currents

When waves break on a beach, large amounts of water are thrown above sea level. Most of the water runs back down the beach under the next wave. It continues along the bottom as a gentle **undertow** that carries sand with it to deeper water. It then dies out harmlessly before reaching the line of breakers.

Rip currents are more dangerous. They are strong surface currents that flow away from the beach. Since they reach speeds of up to 5 kilometers an hour, they are a real hazard for swimmers. It is believed that they form when the water from large breakers returns to sea through gaps in sand bars parallel to the shore.

7. Waves and Longshore Currents

Waves, like the winds that form them, may come from any direction. Therefore, most waves strike shorelines at angles.

As a wave breaks onto a beach, it pushes sand *diagonally* up the beach. Then as the water runs back, it drags the sand almost *straight down* the beach toward the sea. Each breaking wave repeats this process. The result is a zigzag movement of sand along the beach in the general direction of the waves.

The returning backwash from the waves forms a current running almost parallel to the shoreline. The current is called a **longshore current.** It is an important mover of sand and a maker of sand bars.

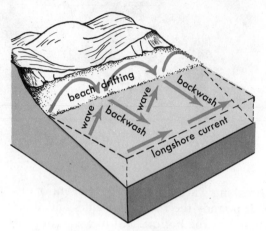

When backwash meets an incoming wave, a longshore current is formed.

Refraction of Waves

Most waves approach a shoreline at an angle. Yet when they reach shallow water, they tend to swing parallel to the shoreline. At that point they approach the shoreline head on. This bending of the wave is called **refraction.** How does refraction happen? As a wave comes in, the end closest to shore scrapes bottom first. This slows it down.

Land jutting out is hit hardest by a wave. It is hit first and on three sides.

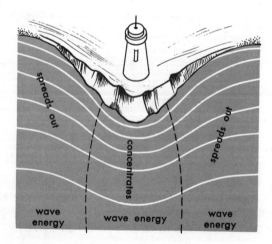

Waves hit the protruding rock hard and chip off pieces. The water then carries the rock pieces into the cove.

But the end that is still in deep water continues at its normal speed and tends to catch up. The result is a wavefront more nearly parallel to the shore.

Refraction of ocean waves helps to explain why an irregular shoreline with shallow water is worn away rapidly. The **headlands,** or the parts of the shore that stick out, are a target of waves. The waves reach shallow water sooner at the headlands. Therefore, they slow up sooner in front of the headlands. So the wave is bent nearly parallel to the headland, and strikes all three sides of the shore. However, the parts of the shoreline that indent, called bays or coves, are attacked much less. This is because they receive less water and less energy.

9. Long Waves

Waves with periods ranging from 5 minutes to 60 minutes are called **long waves.** The best known of the long waves is the *tsunami*, which is caused by an undersea earthquake. A typical Pacific Ocean tsunami may have a wavelength of about 150 kilometers and a period of 12 minutes! Dividing 150 kilometers by 12 minutes gives a speed of 12.5 kilometers a minute! When a wave like this reaches shore, it can do great damage.

Long waves may also be formed by great storms at sea. *Surf beats* are long waves that roll in to ocean shores at about 5-minute intervals. Their origin is unknown.

Features Formed by Waves and Currents

How Waves Erode Rock Materials

Breaking storm waves may strike rock cliffs with a force of thousands of kilograms per square meter. The breakers easily remove large masses of loose materials such as sand and clay. Bedrock is split into blocks by water driven into cracks and fissures. The bedrock is also scoured away by the grinding of sands and pebbles. Boulders that fall from rock cliffs are pounded into pebbles and sands.

Sea water also dissolves minerals from such rocks as limestone.

Erosion of Irregular Shorelines

When waves strike the headlands of a deep-water shoreline, they create landforms. The waves may cut away the rock up to high tide level to form *notches* in the headlands. If the rock materials are soft, the overhanging materials soon collapse. This forms a *sea cliff*. These cliffs wear back rapidly, in some cases as fast as a meter a year.

Erosion by waves creates many new landforms.

These sea stacks were once connected to the cliffs by arches. (Australia)

In harder rock materials, the notch may deepen until it becomes a *sea cave*, such as the famous Blue Grotto on the island of Capri. Waves may cut through the walls of sea caves to form *sea arches*. These may also be formed when waves cut through vertical cracks in narrow headlands. If the roof of a sea arch caves in, a tall narrow rock island called a *stack* remains.

All of these features can be seen on the coasts of California, Oregon, Washington, Maine, the Gaspé peninsula of Canada, and many parts of the Mediterranean Sea.

12. Attached Sand Bars

On irregular shorelines, longshore currents (Topic 7) carry away most of the sand and pebbles eroded from the headlands. As a longshore current passes across the mouth of a bay or cove, some of the sediment is carried inland by waves. There it may form a sand or pebble beach on the shores of the bay or cove.

Many times, however, the current carries enough sand to form a sand bar across the mouth of the bay. The bar seems to grow right out

Longshore currents pick up sand washed from the shore. These sand features are formed where the currents deposit the sand.

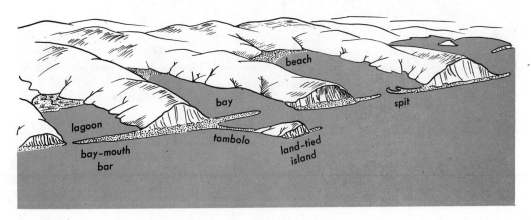

lagoon · bay-mouth bar · bay · tombolo · land-tied island · beach · spit

Erosion by Waves and Currents **169**

of the end of the headland. Such a bar, attached at one end, is called a **spit.** In time it may grow completely across the bay to become a **baymouth bar.** In some places bars form between islands and the mainland.

Waves and crosscurrents may drive the end of a spit towards the shore. Such a spit—with a curved end—is called a **hook.** Sandy Hook in New Jersey is a well-known hook. Others are Cape Cod in Massachusetts and Rockaway Beach on Long Island, New York. Although currents built them, they were raised above sea level by the action of waves and winds.

Sand bars usually protect the water behind them from strong winds and waves. The protected areas are called **lagoons.** As time passes, lagoons may fill with sediment and become *salt marshes.* Jamaica Bay, the lagoon behind the Rockaway Beach hook, is an important shelter for shore birds. So are many other lagoons.

Unattached Sand Bars 13.

Sand bars may form on coasts with straight shorelines, too. But these bars are not attached to the shoreline. Instead, they run parallel to it at some distance from the shore. They are called **offshore bars,** or *barrier beaches.* They are found along the coast of the United States from New York all the way to Texas.

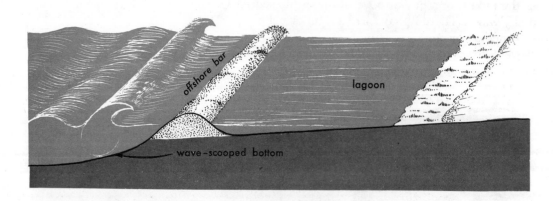

offshore bar

lagoon

wave-scooped bottom

When the ocean floor slopes gently, waves break far out. Off-shore bars often form.

Some well-known examples include Jones Beach and Fire Island in New York, and Atlantic City beach in New Jersey. One offshore bar, Padre Island, runs about 160 kilometers along the coast of Texas. Galveston, Palm Beach, and Miami Beach are also located on offshore bars.

Off-shore bars are very long compared to their width. Note the hooked end here. (Fire Island, New York)

Offshore bars are believed to be formed by the scraping action of breaking waves on smooth sandy sea bottoms. This action scoops up long piles of sand in the area of the breakers parallel to the shoreline. Shore currents may add sand to the growing bars. Wind and waves may raise them above sea level.

14. Beach Materials

According to geologists, a **beach** is the area between the high tide level and the low tide level. The gentler the sea floor, the wider the beach.

Beaches may be sandy, pebbly, or even rocky. If the sea floor is steep, sands and clays are washed out to sea by the undertows, and **pebble beaches** are left. But if the sea floor slopes gently, only clay is washed out, and **sand beaches** are formed. Beaches formed by long-shore currents are almost certain to be sand beaches, because sand is mainly what these currents carry.

Most beach sands are fragments of quartz. On coral islands such as Bermuda, however, the sands are mainly fragments of the coral, which is the mineral calcite. Other materials commonly found in beach sands are grains of black magnetite and flakes of mica.

Erosion by Waves and Currents **171**

Irregular Shorelines 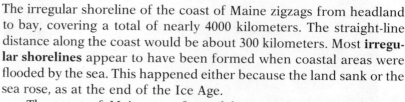 15.

The irregular shoreline of the coast of Maine zigzags from headland to bay, covering a total of nearly 4000 kilometers. The straight-line distance along the coast would be about 300 kilometers. Most **irregular shorelines** appear to have been formed when coastal areas were flooded by the sea. This happened either because the land sank or the sea rose, as at the end of the Ice Age.

The coast of Maine was formed by partial "drowning" of its mountainous land. The drowned main valleys became bays. The divides between the valleys became headlands. The drowned tributary valleys became branches of the bays.

The bays on the Maine coast are short and narrow with deep water near shore. Many hills were partly drowned and became islands. Some were completely drowned and became dangerous *shoals.* Other examples of this type of shoreline are the coast of Scotland and the northwest coast of Spain.

The rivers in the valleys between parallel mountains run to the sea.

Here, sinking of the land has drowned the valleys, forming bays and islands.

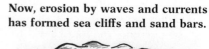
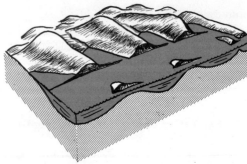

Now, erosion by waves and currents has formed sea cliffs and sand bars.

The more level land running along the Atlantic coast from New York to Florida is a *coastal plain.* Much of this, too, has an irregular shoreline formed by some drowning of the land. Because its river valleys were wide and gentle, its bays are wider and longer than the Maine coast bays. The water close to shore is not so deep. There are fewer islands.

The Hudson River cut through the land at the top. Later, sinking of the land allowed the sea to "drown" the valley. (West Point, New York)

Chesapeake Bay is the drowned valley of the lower Susquehanna River and its tributaries. New York Bay is the drowned valley of the lower Hudson River. Similarly, San Francisco Bay is the drowned valley of the lower Sacramento River.

16. Fiord Shorelines

During the Ice Age, glaciers in Norway, Alaska, and other near-polar regions came all the way to the sea. They scoured their glacial troughs below sea level. When the Ice Age ended, the sea flooded the below-sea-level parts of the troughs. This formed long, deep, steep-sided bays called **fiords.**

The tributary valleys of glacial troughs are the hanging troughs that were described in Chapter 9. Where they meet the main glacial trough, spectacular waterfalls drop down the walls of the fiord. Fiord shorelines are found in Greenland, Labrador, Chile, New Zealand, Norway, and Alaska.

A glacier cut through this coastal area in the Ice Age. When the glacier melted, the sea covered the part below sea level.

Erosion by Waves and Currents **173**

Almost the whole west coast of North America and South America—from Oregon to central Chile—has a fairly straight shoreline. Plate tectonics explains this. These shorelines are, for the most part, the boundary line between two sets of plates. As the heavier Pacific ocean plates meet the continental plates and plunge under them, mountains are raised and deep undersea troughs formed. Long lines of recently formed mountains run parallel to the coast. The ocean floor slopes steeply to great depths not far from shore. The coast is bordered in many places by sea cliffs and stacks.

This land has been lifted up by movement of tectonic plates. It used to be under the ocean.

Corals and Coral Reefs 18.

Corals are tiny sea animals that live in colonies. They remain fastened to rocky sea floors in warm, clear, fairly shallow water. In order for them to live, the water temperature must be from about 18° to 21° C. The depth must be no more than about 45 meters.

Since corals do not move, they depend on waves and currents to bring food to them. They make their shells from the lime in sea water. When corals die, their shells remain, and new corals grow above them. These large buildups of coral are called **coral reefs.** Corals grow only up to the surface of the sea. But as with sand bars, waves pile the coral shells above sea level. When coral shell fragments are cemented together they form coral limestone.

Coral colonies growing close to shore form **fringing reefs.** These can be seen in Florida and Bermuda.

Fringing reefs slowly move away from the shore. This is because a coral reef grows mainly on its ocean side. The ocean waves bring food to that side.

As a fringing reef grows oceanward, it becomes a *barrier reef*. The Great Barrier Reef of Australia is about 2000 kilometers long and up to 150 kilometers wide. The wide lagoon between it and the mainland is called the Inland Water Way.

Top row, left to right: **rose coral, many-pored coral, branching coral**
Bottom row, left to right: **brain coral, pink branching coral, organ-pipe coral, mushroom coral**

19. Coral Atolls

An **atoll** is a narrow ring-shaped island or chain of islands. Atolls are found mostly in open waters in the middle of the Pacific Ocean. Most atolls are made of coral limestone. What supports them? Holes bored through the coral show that each atoll has grown up from the slopes of a sunken volcano.

The top row shows the three stages of forming an atoll, as seen from an airplane. *Below each* is the same stage as seen from the side.

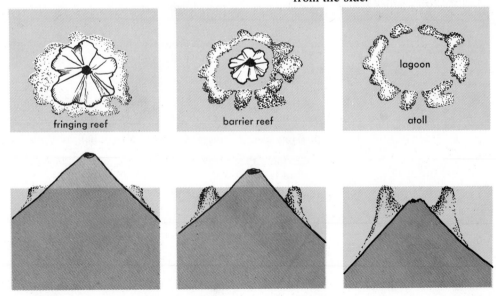

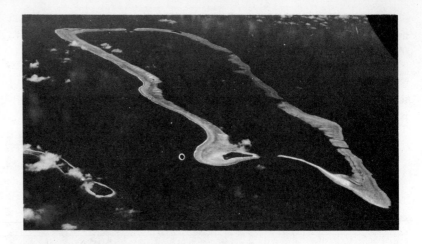

Note the small openings in this atoll. Boats go inside for protection from wind and waves outside.

The lagoon inside an atoll offers protection from winds and waves. For this reason large atolls such as Wake Island and Midway Island have become important refueling bases for trans-Pacific airplanes.

TOPIC QUESTIONS

Each topic question refers to the topic of the same number within this chapter.

1. (a) Explain how the sun makes water waves. (b) Name the things that determine the size of the waves. What is the fetch?

2. (a) Explain the meaning of wavelength, crest, trough, and period. (b) What is the usual ratio of length to height of ocean waves? (c) How can the speed of a wave be found?

3. (a) Explain the motion of the particles of water in a water wave. (b) At what depth does wave motion almost die out?

4. (a) What are whitecaps? (b) What are swells? How do they begin?

5. (a) How do breakers and surf begin? (b) Why is the surf important geologically? (c) How deep is the water at the line of breakers?

6. (a) How does an undertow form? (b) What are rip currents? How do they form?

7. (a) Explain the zigzag motion of sand along a beach. (b) How does a longshore current form?

8. What is refraction of waves? How does it happen? What is its effect on a headland?

9. What are "long waves"? Name three sources of long waves.

10. How do waves erode rock?

11. Describe the features caused by wave erosion on irregular shorelines.

12. How does a spit originate? a baymouth bar? a hook? What is a lagoon?

13. What is an offshore bar? How does it begin?

14. (a) Define beach. (b) How does a pebble beach form? (c) How does a sand beach form? (d) What minerals are beach sands made of?

15. (a) How were most irregular shorelines formed? (b) How were headlands formed? (c) How were bays formed? (d) How do the bays between New York and Florida differ from those of the coast of Maine?

16. (a) How were fiord shorelines formed? (b) Where do they occur?

17. Describe the shoreline of western North America and South America. Why is it different from the eastern shoreline?

18. (a) What are corals? Under what conditions do they grow? (b) How does a coral reef form? How does it grow above sea level? (c) What is a fringing reef? (d) Why does a coral reef grow mainly seaward?

19. (a) What is an atoll? (b) Why is Midway Island used by airplanes as a refueling base?

GENERAL QUESTIONS

1. According to Topic 2, how high is a wave 150 meters long likely to be?

2. What is the velocity of a wave 300 meters long with a period of 25 seconds?

3. According to Topic 3, at what depth will a wave 300 meters long first be felt on the sea floor? A wave 10 meters long?

4. Magnetite grains are frequently found concentrated in parts of a beach. Why?

STUDENT ACTIVITIES

1. Make models representing (a) the features of an irregular shoreline, (b) the features of a coastal plain shoreline, (c) an atoll.

2. Examine beach sands with a magnifying glass. Use a magnet to separate any magnetite grains from the other minerals. List the minerals you identify. Compare beach sands with sands from other sources.

3. If you live near a large lake or the ocean, take a field trip to study features described in this chapter. At the seashore see if you can estimate the length, the height, and the period of the incoming waves and swells.

TOPOGRAPHIC SHEETS

15-minute series
1. *Offshore bar:* Atlantic City, New Jersey; Fire Island, New York; Lake Como, Texas.
2. *Irregular shoreline in hilly region:* Boothbay, Maine; Bar Harbor, Maine.
3. *Irregular shoreline on a coastal plain:* Kilmarnock, Virginia; Barnegat, New Jersey.
4. *Spits and hooks:* Sandy Hook, New Jersey; Brooklyn, New York; Provincetown, Massachusetts.
5. *Sea cliff:* Wellfleet, Massachusetts.
6. *Bay-mouth bars, hooks, cliffed headlands:* Point Reyes, California.

unit three

An island is born! The photograph shows one of the volcanic eruptions that created a new island in the North Atlantic. In the morning of November 14, 1963, a fisherman saw burning in the distance off the coast of Iceland. Several miles away, an observer photographed billowing clouds of steam. Great explosions went on all day. On November 15, scientists discovered a new land mass about 8 meters high. By January 1965, after more than a year of eruptions, the island named Surtsey was nearly 200 meters high with a diameter of more than a kilometer.

Suppose the attack made on the earth's crust from weathering and erosion were to go unchecked. Geologists estimate that only 25 million years would be needed to wear all the continents down to sea level. Why has this not happened in the billions of years since the earth was formed?

The answer is that the earth's crust is being rebuilt at the same time it is attacked. A volcanic eruption may be the most dramatic activity building up the earth's crust. There are others. Continental shelves emerge from the sea to become coastal plains. Plains rise to become plateaus. Parts of the earth's crust are crumpled up into new mountains.

Some of these activities, like the slow rise of a continental shelf, take place quietly and almost unobserved over long periods of time. Others, like volcanic eruptions and the building of a volcanic island like Surtsey, are violent and rapid. Volcanoes, often called "windows to the interior of the earth," give earth scientists great opportunities to study forces that go on beneath the earth's crust.

Forces That Raise the Surface

12

Your teacher can stage a "volcanic eruption" for you. A small shallow heatproof dish is the "crater" of a volcano. Mount it on a tripod or at the top of a plaster model of a volcano. Put two or three heaping teaspoons of granular ammonium bichromate in the dish. Put a ribbon of magnesium metal into the bichromate as a "fuse." Light the fuse with a match or burner flame. The eruption is best seen in a darkened room at a safe distance of 2-3 meters. The bichromate burns to form gases (nitrogen, water vapor) and ashy material (green powdery chromic oxide.)

Volcanism and Plate Tectonics

Volcanic Eruption and Plate Tectonics

1. Lava, Magma, and the Asthenosphere

The molten lavas that erupt from volcanoes are very hot. Their temperatures range between 600° and 1200° C. Recall from Chapter 4, Topic 4, that the lava comes from liquid magmas deep below the surface. But how deep?

In Chapter 1, Topic 12, we introduced the hypothesis of plate tectonics. According to this idea, the plates of the earth's lithosphere are about 70 kilometers thick. At this depth, they rest on a *partly melted* layer of the earth's mantle called the **asthenosphere.** The asthenosphere goes down to about 250 kilometers. Geologists believe that this layer is where the hot liquid magma comes from.

Why do you call liquid rock *magma* inside the crust and *lava* outside? When magma rises through the crust, it changes. Some of its dissolved gases bubble out. It also dissolves new minerals from the rock it goes through. So when it erupts as lava, it *is* different from the magma it was.

Not all magma begins in the asthenosphere. Geologists think that some magma is formed by the melting of the lithosphere as it moves down into the hot asthenosphere. This happens when two plates collide, and one is forced under the other.

The solid plates of the earth are about 70 kilometers thick. Below them, the asthenosphere reaches to a depth of about 250 kilometers. Magma comes from the asthenosphere.

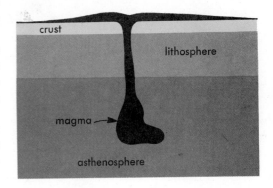

crust
lithosphere
magma →
asthenosphere

2. Why Does Magma Rise?

What makes magma rise 70 kilometers or more through the lithosphere? This happens only in places where there are cracks or other openings in the lithosphere. There is a tremendous pressure from the plates on the partly melted asthenosphere. Where there are cracks, this pressure squeezes out magma. If the magma rises all the way to the surface, volcanic activity—*volcanism*—results.

But where are the main cracks and weaknesses in the lithosphere? At the boundaries between plates! And there is where we find the main zones of volcanic activity.

3. Where Plates Move Apart

One kind of plate boundary forms where two plates are moving away from each other. Many such boundaries can be seen on the ocean floors in the map of the world's lithosphere plates (Chapter 1). For

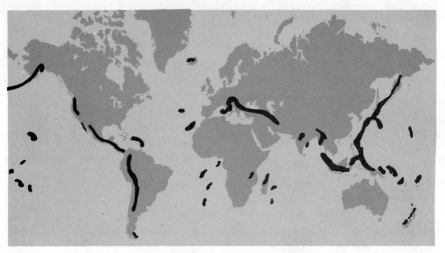

Most active volcanoes are in the areas shown in black.

example, the American and Eurasian plates move away from each other at the middle of the Atlantic Ocean floor. Magma rises to the surface through the whole 16,000 kilometer length of the boundary between these plates.

As the plates spread slowly apart, the magma pours out as lava. The lava spreads to form a new sea floor. It also builds up high at the boundary to form the mountainous Mid-Atlantic Ridge. Here and there on the ridge it builds great volcanoes, such as Mt. Hekla in Iceland.

These two plates are colliding. Note how the ocean floor is lower where the plates meet. As the left-hand plate slides under the one shown on the right, mountains are formed on the upper plate.

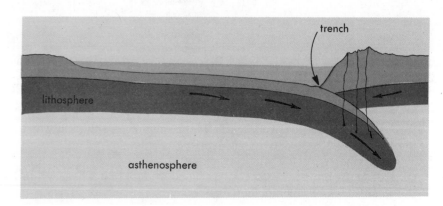

trench

lithosphere

asthenosphere

Where Plates Collide 4.

A second kind of boundary forms where two plates move toward each other. One example occurs at the west coast of South America. Here the eastward-moving Nazca oceanic plate collides with the westward-moving South American Continental plate. The Nazca plate is slowly forced under the thicker continental plate. A long deep ocean *trench*, called the Peru-Chile Trench, forms between the two plates. At the same time, the edge of the South American plate is crumpled up. This forms the Andes mountain range parallel to the trench. Here magma rises to the surface, and many great volcanoes form.

Two ocean plates may also collide to form a volcanic boundary. Again, a deep trench forms between them. But here the rising magma forms a chain of volcanic islands parallel to the trench. These chains are called **island arcs.** Examples are the Kurile Islands north of Japan and the Marianas Islands south of Japan.

5. Volcanism within Plates

Most volcanoes seem to be located on plate boundaries. But there are a few volcanoes that are within the plates rather than at their edges. Geologists believe that these volcanoes get their magma through great well-like openings in the lithosphere. But they do not know why these openings are there.

The best known examples of volcanoes located within a plate are the Hawaiian Island volcanoes.

Materials Erupted From Volcanoes

6. Gases from Magmas

Magma is a liquid. But when it reaches the earth's surface, it may erupt in the form of liquids, solids, and gases. The liquid is lava. The solid material is lava blown so high into the air that it turns solid

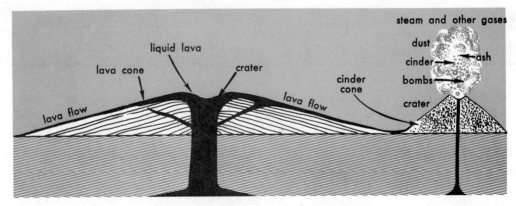

The eruption on the left is quiet. The cone is formed by flowing lava. The eruption on the right is explosive. Its cone is fallen cinders.

before reaching the ground. The gases are mainly steam (hot water vapor) and carbon dioxide. They escape from the magma because there is less pressure once the magma surfaces. Other gases in magmas are sulfur dioxide, sulfur vapor, hydrogen chloride, and hydrogen.

When Lava Flows 7.

Flowing lava is typical of the eruptions of volcanoes in Hawaii and Iceland. In Hawaii the lava may overflow from a circular opening called a *crater* at the top of a mountain. It may also pour out of small fissures on the mountainside. In Iceland the lava may erupt from fissures many kilometers long.

The liquid lava flows downhill until it solidifies into lava rock. Most lava flows are made of basalt or andesite. In some flows the hardened lava has a very rough jagged surface almost impossible to walk on. The Hawaiians call this **aa** (AH AH). In other flows the surface is smooth but twisted into rope-like forms. This is called **pahoehoe** (pah HOE ay HOE ay).

Lava tunnels form when lava continues to flow under a roof formed by the hardened outer crust. When lava flows into seas or lakes, it may solidify in rounded forms called **pillow lava..**

The rough rock here is aa lava as seen in the foreground. (Mexico)

This rope-like rock is pahoehoe lava. (Hawaii)

Fragments of Lava 8.

The eruptions of Hawaiian volcanoes are "quiet" compared with the violent eruptions typical of many volcanoes in the Mediterranean region. In Mediterranean volcanoes lava and gases may explode out of a crater to a height of many kilometers. The lava cools and forms solid pieces while still in the air.

Tiny droplets of lava form fine particles of **volcanic dust.** These are light enough to be carried thousands of kilometers in the upper atmosphere. Larger droplets of lava form fragments about the size of silts, sands, and pebbles. Because of their size, they are called **volcanic ash,** or *volcanic cinders*. (They are not burned-out materials.) These are heavy enough to fall near the volcano from which they erupt.

Large blobs of lava may also turn solid before falling to earth. When they do, they form round or spindle-shaped masses called **volcanic bombs.** Large angular lumps of solid lava are called *blocks*. (Blocks are common in aa lava.) When volcanic ash gets cemented together, it forms a rock called **tuff.**

Gigantic dark clouds, many kilometers high, are likely to form over explosive volcanoes during eruptions. The cloud is made up of water mixed with volcanic dust and ash. The water comes from the huge amount of steam erupted by the volcano.

Large blobs of lava can harden in the air before they fall. Some of them look like bombs lying on the ground.

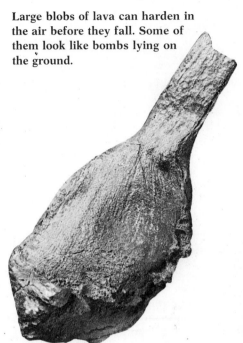

In 1902, hot gases mixed with volcanic dust and ash from Mt. Pelée poured down on St. Pierre. (Martinique, West Indies)

Birth of a Volcano 9.

How is a new volcano born? Early in February, 1943, a series of slight earthquake shocks was felt in Parícutin, a farm village about 300 kilometers from Mexico City. On February 20 cracks appeared in a level corn field about two kilometers from the village. Blasts of hot gases soon followed and shattered the earth. Lava and cinders erupted.

The eruptions continued, and the volcano became so violent by May that the village was evacuated. By September, the volcano had built a cone-shaped mountain nearly two kilometers in diameter and about 450 meters high. Parícutin is no longer erupting. But the mountain it built is still about 400 meters high.

Parícutin grew up from the land. But in 1963, a new volcano arose from the ocean floor off the southwestern coast of Iceland. It began with eruptions of hot gases and ash. These were followed by occasional lava flows that continued for more than a year. The volcano, which had been named Surtsey, became inactive late in 1965. By then it had built an island that stood about 170 meters above sea level. Its area was more than two square kilometers.

Within roughly a two-year period, the volcano, Surtsey, built an island that jutted 170 meters up out of the sea.

10. Is the Volcano Still Alive?

Volcanoes are said to be **active** when they have erupted occasionally in historical times. An example is Mount Etna in Sicily. They are said to be **dormant** when they seem to "rest" for several years after eruptions. Surtsey, for example, is dormant now. A volcano that has shown no signs of activity in recent times is said to be **extinct.** But a volcano may change at any time. Mount Lassen in California was an "extinct" volcano until it erupted in 1914. Mount Baker in Washington, long thought to be extinct, has recently begun to show signs of activity.

Classes of Volcanoes: Famous Eruptions

11. Shield Volcanoes

Volcanoes are classified mainly by the materials of which they are made. **Shield volcanoes** are made mostly of lava. When they erupt, their lavas flow like thick syrup and spread out to great distances. While they spread, the lavas form broad shield-shaped lava domes with very gentle slopes.

The giant crater at the top of Mauna Loa is five kilometers wide. Note the gentle slope of the cone; this is because the cone is made of hardened lava.

Typical shield volcanoes are found in Hawaii and Iceland. The great Hawaiian volcano Mauna Loa has slopes of only 6°. Its base on the floor of the Pacific Ocean is more than 9000 meters below sea level. At that depth it has a diameter of about 100 kilometers. The volcano rises through the ocean and extends more than 4000 meters above sea level. Its **caldera**—the name given to a very large crater—is about five kilometers in diameter.

How long did it take for Mauna Loa's great dome of lava to be born? Geologists think these eruptions took place over a period of more than a million years.

Cinder Cones

Unlike a shield volcano, a **cinder cone** has little or no lava in it. It is made up mostly of volcanic cinders and other pieces. These pile up close to the volcano opening. They form a cone-shaped hill or mountain with steep sides and a narrow base. Because of their loose materials and steep slopes, cinder cones are eroded rapidly. As a result, they never grow as large as shield volcanoes.

Examples of cinder cones include Parícutin in Mexico and Sunset Crater in Arizona.

Composite Volcanoes

Composite volcanoes are made up of layers of lava and cinders. The cinders usually erupt from the crater. The lava is more likely to pour out of fissures in the volcano's sides. Composite cones are much steeper than shield volcanoes but gentler than cinder cones. Their average slope is between 20° and 30°. The more lava in the cone, the gentler its slopes and the broader its base.

A lava cone would be wider and gentler than this composite cone. A cinder cone would be narrower and steeper.

Except for the volcanoes of Iceland and Hawaii, most of the world's great volcanoes are composites. These include Fujiyama in Japan, Vesuvius and Etna in Italy, Popocatepetl in Mexico, and Rainier in the United States.

14. Eruptions from Fissures

More than 400,000 square kilometers of the northwestern United States are covered by basalt lava. The basalts are in layers that total more than 3000 meters in thickness. The region is known as the Columbia lava plateau.

There are almost no volcanoes in the plateau. This leads geologists to believe that the layers of basalt were formed by vast *lava floods*. These poured out of long fissures in the earth's crust many times over millions of years. The basalts formed by the lava floods are called *flood basalts,* or *plateau basalts.* Only basalt magma flows easily enough to spread so widely before turning solid.

Layers of lava are exposed where the Columbia River cuts through the Columbia Plateau.

Only one great fissure eruption has taken place above sea level in recent historic times. This was a great eruption of flood basalt in 1783. It flowed from a fissure in Iceland 30 kilometers long.

Although fissure eruption on land is uncommon, geologists now believe that fissure eruption is always happening on the ocean floor wherever plates are moving apart. The total length of such fissures on the ocean floor is about 50,000 kilometers. Magma has been oozing from these fissures for perhaps 200 million years. From this magma, the basalt rock that covers the ocean floor has been formed. The total volume of this rock is far greater than that of all the volcanic rock formed on the continents.

Mount Pelée. Three miles from the crater of "dormant" Mount Pelée on the West Indian island of Martinique, stood the capital city, St. Pierre. The volcano had been inactive since 1851. When the volcano showed signs of activity in April of 1902, few of the nearly 30,000 inhabitants paid any attention. On May 8 a terrific explosion tore open the crater. A great fiery cloud (in French, *nuée ardente*) of hot poisonous gases and volcanic fragments swept down upon the city. It scorched or smothered the whole population. The only survivor was a prisoner in the city jail. He apparently owed his life to the poor ventilation of his deep dungeon.

Krakatoa. Krakatoa is a volcanic island in the East Indies between Java and Sumatra. On August 27, 1883, an explosive eruption took place that is usually described as "the most violent eruption of historic times." More than half of the island was destroyed and blown away in the explosion. The cloud over the volcano reached nearly 30 kilometers into the air.

The air wave caused by the eruption broke windows 150 kilometers away, and the sound was heard 3000 kilometers away in Australia. Great sea waves flooded nearby coasts, where 36,000 people were drowned. The waves even reached the shore of South Africa, over 8000 kilometers away. The fine volcanic dust from the eruption was carried completely around the world by upper air winds. It caused strangely beautiful sunrise and sunset skies for two years after the eruption.

Mauna Loa. Mauna Loa has been active in recent times. Eruptions occur about every eight years. Between eruptions the great oval caldera is covered with a crust of basalt rock. Underneath the crust lies hot molten lava.

This night picture shows molten lava racing down the side of Mauna Loa.

The coming of an eruption is usually foretold by the rise of lava in the crater. Breaking the crust at various points, the white-hot lava spurts up in "fountains" hundreds of meters high. Before the lava can rise high enough to overflow the crater, it usually breaks through fissures on the volcano's sides. When the lava overflows, it forms streams up to two kilometers in width and 65 kilometers in length. These sometimes flow as far as the ocean.

16. # Crater Lakes and Calderas

Rain and melting snows may partly fill the crater of an extinct volcano to make a **crater lake.** Crater Lake in Oregon occupies a caldera—a giant crater—that is nearly 10 kilometers wide. The caldera's clifflike walls rise in places more than 600 meters above the lake. The lake is nearly 600 meters deep. It is the second deepest lake in North America.

Wizard Island in the middle of Crater Lake is the top of a cone. It has its own crater, which is 100 meters wide.

The cross-section shows how the caldera was formed. This diagram is based upon Crater Lake.

part of cone destroyed

Calderas are believed to form in two different ways. The calderas of Hawaiian volcanoes probably formed when their crater floors collapsed. But the caldera on Mount Katmai, Alaska, was formed in 1912 when a violent eruption blew off the whole top of the volcano.

Igneous Intrusions

Volcanoes and lava flows are the outside activities of volcanism. But much more magma is active below the earth's surface. Magma forces its way into fractures in the bedrock. It squeezes in between rock layers. It pushes up overlying rocks to form domes. Great masses of magma solidify far below the surface to form the cores of mountains.

The rock masses formed when magma cools inside other rocks are called *igneous intrusions*.

Magma forces its way into rock beneath the surface as well as forming volcanoes. Note the different masses formed.

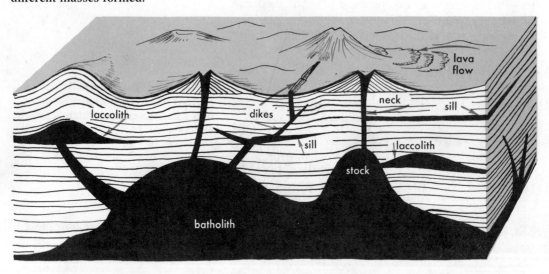

Dikes, Sills, Laccoliths, Necks 18.

Dikes are flat sheets of igneous rock that cut across the rock layers they intrude. They were formed when magma was forced into vertical cracks in the rocks. They come in all lengths and thicknesses. They are common in old volcanic regions. Their rock is usually basalt or diabase.

Dikes cut across rock layers. In contrast to them are **sills.** Sills are sheets of igneous rock that are parallel to the layers they intrude. They were formed when magma was forced along bedding planes between rock layers. They, too, are usually basalt or diabase. They can be hundreds of meters thick and many kilometers long. The

This vertical dike of hardened magma once cut through sedimentary rock. The sedimentary rock has eroded. (Colorado)

Erosion has also exposed this horizontal sill of hardened magma. (Banks Island, Canada)

Palisades of the Hudson River are the face of a great diabase sill that has been exposed by erosion. It is about 50 kilometers long.

In some places, the magmas that intruded between rock layers were very stiff and unable to flow easily. Instead of spreading to form sills, these magmas bulged upward to form domelike masses called **laccoliths.** The rock layers above the laccoliths were also domed up into mountains. Laccoliths can be found in the Henry Mountains of Utah and the Black Hills of South Dakota.

Bear Butte is a laccolith exposed by erosion. (South Dakota)

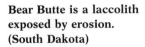

When an extinct volcano is almost completely eroded, a **volcanic neck** may be left. This is the plug of tough rock left in the vent from which magma flowed. One example of a neck is the famous Shiprock in New Mexico. It is 400 meters high. Volcanic necks form the diamond-bearing rock of the great Kimberley mines of South Africa.

The lava and cinder of an old volcano have disappeared. Only the magma that hardened in the core is left.

Note the locations of these batholiths. They form the cores of some of our largest mountain ranges.

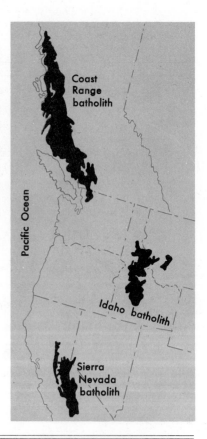

Coast Range batholith

Pacific Ocean

Idaho batholith

Sierra Nevada batholith

Batholiths and Stocks 19.

Batholiths are the largest of all igneous intrusions. They form the cores of many of the world's great mountain ranges. When erosion removes the overlying rock layers, the batholith rocks are exposed. They are usually either granite or granodiorite. The largest batholith in North America forms the core of the Coast Range of British Columbia. It is more than 1600 kilometers long and up to 250 kilometers wide.

If the exposed area of a batholith is less than 100 square kilometers, it is called a **stock**.

Each topic question refers to the topic of the same number within this chapter.

1. (a) What is the asthenosphere? (b) Why do we think that magma comes from the asthenosphere? (c) In what ways is lava different from magma?

2. (a) What makes magma rise to the earth's surface? (b) Where?

3. Describe the volcanic activity that takes place on the ocean floor between plates moving apart.

4. (a) Describe the volcanic activity that occurs when the Nazca and South American plates collide. (b) How does an island arc form? Give examples of island arcs.

5. How can volcanism take place within a plate?

6. What gases occur in magmas?

7. (a) Describe the composition and appearance of the lava flows of Hawaii. What is aa? Pahoehoe? (b) How does a lava tunnel form? Pillow lava?

8. Explain the origin of (a) volcanic dust, (b) volcanic ash, (c) volcanic bombs, (d) tuff, (e) the dark cloud over an erupting volcano.

9. Give a brief description of the "birth" of a volcano.

10. Explain the meanings of *active, dormant,* and *extinct* as they refer to volcanoes.

11. Describe the beginning, composition, shape, and steepness of a shield volcano. What is a caldera?

12. Describe a cinder cone.

13. (a) Compare composite cones with cinder cones and shield volcanoes. (b) Name two composite volcanoes.

14. (a) Describe the beginning of the Columbia lava plateau. (b) Where do fissure eruptions occur on the ocean floor? What do these eruptions form?

15. Describe briefly one of the eruptions listed here.

16. (a) How does a crater lake form? (b) How may a caldera form?

17. Name three or four places where magma intrudes into rock below the surface.

18. Briefly describe and give the origin of (a) a dike, (b) a sill, (c) a laccolith, (d) a volcanic neck.

19. (a) What is a batholith? Give an example. What rock is it usually made of? (b) What is a stock?

1. In the Hawaiian volcanoes lava breaks through fissures far more often than it overflows its craters. How does this affect the shape of the volcanoes? Explain.

2. How is it possible for glaciers to exist on the slopes of an active volcano?

3. What evidence tells us that dikes and sills were not formed at the same time as the rocks in which they occur?

4. In what ways would the eruption of a volcano under water differ from an eruption on land?

5. Using the map of the earth's lithosphere plates, find and name four pairs of plates that are moving apart.

6. Using the same map, find and name four pairs of plates where ocean trenches have formed.

STUDENT ACTIVITIES

1. Make modeling clay or plaster of Paris models of (**a**) a shield volcano, (**b**) a cinder cone, (**c**) a composite cone, (**d**) a volcanic neck, (**e**) a crater lake, (**f**) dikes, sills, laccoliths, and other igneous intrusions.

2. If you live near enough to any features resulting from volcanism, take a field trip to study these features.

3. Visit a museum or college geology department to study specimens of rocks such as volcanic dust, cinder, tuff, and bombs. Also look for specimens of aa, pahoehoe, and pillow lavas.

TOPOGRAPHIC SHEETS

(15-minute series, except as noted)

1. *Volcano:* Lassen Volcanic National Park, California

2. *Eroded volcano:* Shasta, California

3. *Eroded volcano:* Dunsmuir, California (30-minute series)

4. *Volcanic neck and dikes:* Shiprock, New Mexico

5. *Laccolith:* Fort Meade, South Dakota (Bear Butte; 7½-minute series)

13

The damage done in an earthquake comes from the shaking of the earth's crust (Topic 3). You can make a model of this. Take a long thin stick. (A piece of wood about the size of a meterstick or yardstick will work.) Hold one end down firmly at the side of your desk. Allow most of the stick to project beyond the desk. With your free hand, push down gently on the free end of the stick. Why does the stick bend rather than break? Remove your free hand suddenly. What happens to the stick?

Why would a similar motion in the earth's crust be damaging? How is pressure on the crust "suddenly let go"? Show this with your stick model.

Earthquakes and Plate Tectonics

How Earthquakes Originate

What Is an Earthquake? 1.

Earthquakes are the most destructive of all natural occurrences. The most disastrous earthquake on record happened in Shen-shu, China, in 1556. More than 830,000 lives were lost. In 1755 the famous Lisbon, Portugal, earthquake took 60,000 lives. In 1908 an earthquake killed 160,000 people in Messina, Italy. In 1923, the great Tokyo, Japan, earthquake and fire took 99,000 lives and destroyed the city.

But earthquake disasters are not events of the past alone. Almost every year a destructive earthquake strikes some part of the world. In February, 1976, a fearful earthquake in Guatemala left 15,000 people dead, 40,000 injured, and 500,000 homeless.

An **earthquake,** or quake, is defined as any shaking or trembling of the earth's solid crust. Many frightening things may happen in a severe earthquake. Sounds range from low rumbles to thunderous roars. The ground rises and falls. Deep fissures form. Landslides sweep down steep hillsides. Some buildings collapse. Stronger buildings sway, and their walls may crack. Fires may break out as stoves topple, or electrical short circuits develop. This happened in San Francisco in 1906 and in Tokyo in 1923.

Coastal cities face still another danger in earthquakes. Great sea waves raised by the earthquakes may swamp the cities. Much of the loss of life in Lisbon and Messina was the result of such waves.

The earth opened up here in the 1964 Alaskan earthquake. Some buildings and parts of the sidewalk have fallen into the opening. Other buildings are cracked or leaning.

Geologists explain earthquakes—the shaking of the bedrock—by the **elastic rebound theory.** Most earthquakes seem to happen where the earth's crust is split by long, deep cracks. If the blocks of crust on opposite sides of the crack have shifted, the crack is called a **fault.**

A fault may be hundreds of kilometers long and many kilometers deep. Movement of the rocks along the fault is called **faulting.** The movement may be up or down or sideways.

The elastic rebound theory is one explanation for earthquakes. Blocks of crust that meet at a great fault may be squeezed in opposite directions by the movement along the fault. The pressures are either sideways or up and down. For many years, the rocks bend too slowly to be noticed. Then one day the strain becomes too great. Suddenly the two blocks overcome the friction that holds them. They rip apart along the fault.

The slanted line shows a crack in the earth. The arrows show the directions of pressure on the land to each side of the crack. When the pressure gets too great, the land suddenly moves.

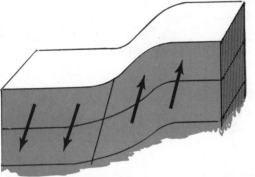
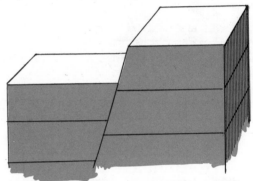

When the two blocks rip apart, violent vibrations follow. These shake the ground even hundreds of kilometers away. The shaking is strongest along the fault. When the vibrations are felt in the bedrock and ground, they are called *shocks.* Strong shocks may last many minutes. In the 1976 earthquake in Guatemala, the first shocks lasted six minutes.

3. Tsunamis

When faulting takes place on the floor of the ocean, it produces the great sea waves called **tsunamis.** Tsunamis are barely noticed in mid-ocean. But they travel thousands of kilometers across the ocean at speeds up to 725 kilometers an hour. When tsunamis break over low coastal areas, they have been known to pile up to heights of more than 50 meters. If they strike populated areas, their effects are disastrous. The force of the "wall of water" causes great destruction, which is followed by flooding.

In 1964, tsunamis from the great Anchorage, Alaska earthquake rolled to almost every part of the North Pacific Ocean. Damage was done as far south as Crescent City, California.

How Deep Do Earthquakes Originate? 4.

Earthquakes happen along faults hundreds of kilometers long. But each quake begins in a part of the fault only a few kilometers long. This is called its **focus** (plural, *foci*). It is always below the surface. The point on the surface directly above the focus is called the **epicenter** (*epi* means above).

Earthquake foci may be as deep as 700 kilometers. Most foci, however, are well above 100 kilometers.

Earthquake Waves 5.

When rocks move at the focus, tremendous energy ripples out in waves.

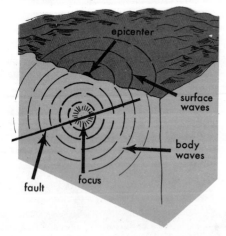

Geologists who specialize in the study of earthquakes are called seismologists (size MOL uh jists). They estimate that a great earthquake may release more energy than a million atomic bombs! How does this energy travel?

When the rocks at the focus of the quake shake, two kinds of waves spread out in all directions. The *primary*, or **P waves,** travel through the earth like sound waves. Their speed is over 5 kilometers a second near the surface. They can pass through any part of the earth—solid or liquid.

Secondary, or **S waves,** travel through the earth like waves in a rope. Their speed is about 3 kilometers a second near the surface. Both **P** and **S** waves travel faster as they go deeper. But unlike **P** waves, **S** waves cannot pass through liquids.

Both **P** and **S** waves are called *body waves* because they travel through the body of the earth. When P and S waves reach the surface, they set up new waves called **L waves.** These travel like ripples on a pond at about 3 kilometers a second.

Locating and Measuring Earthquakes

How can seismologists know within minutes that an earthquake is taking place a thousand kilometers away? How can they locate the epicenter and focus of an earthquake? The answers lie in the **seismograph** (SIZE mo graf). This is an instrument that records earthquake waves.

The seismograph works simply. A heavy weight is attached to a base anchored in bedrock. The weight always stays almost perfectly still. This is true even when the bedrock and base are shaking during an earthquake.

A record sheet—called a *seismogram*—is put on a drum attached to the base. The drum is turned slowly by clockwork. A pen attached to the heavy weight rests its point on the drum. As long as the bedrock is quiet, the pen makes a straight line on the turning drum. But when the bedrock shakes, the drum also shakes slightly. The pen does not shake because it is attached to the heavy weight. The result is a zigzag trace that shows an earthquake is taking place.

Different forms of seismographs are used to record vertical shaking and horizontal shaking. Seismograms show three groups of "zigzags" for a single quake. Each group represents a type of wave. Since the **P** waves travel fastest, they arrive first. **S** waves arrive second, and **L** waves arrive last.

The spring of this seismograph absorbs the earthquake waves. So the weight hangs still. The drum is solidly connected to shaking bedrock. It moves.

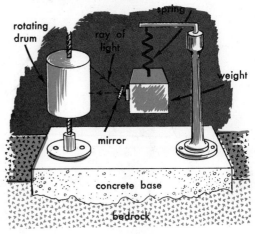

The three different types of earthquake waves are shown in this seismogram. The difference in arrival time is used to find out how far away the earthquake is.

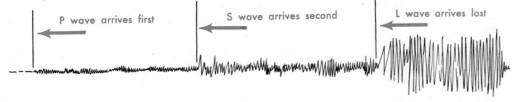

P wave arrives first

S wave arrives second

L wave arrives last

7. How Far Away? What Time?

S waves are slower than **P** waves. The farther away an earthquake is, the longer it will take the **S** waves to arrive. The time it takes for **S** waves to arrive after **P** waves is called *lag*. Seismologists use this lag to tell how far away the epicenter of an earthquake is. They can also use a graph like the one shown here.

There are three different kinds of earthquake waves. This graph shows the speed at which each one travels.

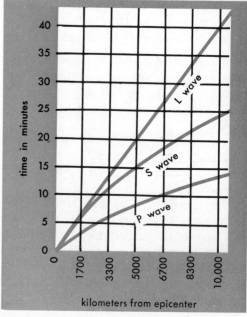

Since seismologists know how far away the epicenter is, they can use this information to tell how long it took the waves to arrive. As a result, they will know how many minutes earlier the quake actually happened.

Where Did It Happen?

To find the location of the epicenter, seismologists use the distances from three different places. Suppose a seismologist in St. Louis finds a quake to be 1800 kilometers away. Another seismologist in Berkeley, California, finds it to be 1300 kilometers away. Someone in Seattle, Washington, finds it to be 900 kilometers away. A circle is drawn on a globe with St. Louis as the center. This circle will be 1800 kilometers away from St. Louis all around. Then, the epicenter must be somewhere on this circle. Another circle is drawn with Berkeley as its center. This circle will be 1300 kilometers away from Berkeley all around. It will cut the first circle in two points. One of these points must be the epicenter. When a 900 kilometer circle is drawn around Seattle, it meets the other two in a single point. This must be the epicenter.

The depth of the focus can be found from the lag of the **L** waves. The deeper the focus, the longer it will take for the **L** waves to start out.

Every year seismographs find more than 800,000 earthquake tremors. Most of these are so faint that people do not feel them. A few hundred are strong enough to do minor damage. A few are really destructive.

Even a small earthquake may be destructive in an area close to its epicenter. To compare the energy of earthquakes, seismologists use the **Richter scale** of *magnitude*. The scale has steps from 1 to 10. Each step means 60 times the energy of the step before it.

Earthquakes with magnitudes from 3 to 5 will be felt, but will do no damage. Above 5, damage may be great. In 1971 an earthquake of magnitude 6.6 struck the San Fernando Valley in California. It caused property damage of over a billion dollars. The strongest earthquakes recorded in modern times had magnitudes ranging from 8.0 to 8.6. Among them were the San Francisco quake of 1906 and the Alaska quake of 1964. The Guatemala quake of 1976 had a magnitude of about 7.5.

The magnitude of an earthquake is found from the height of the trace it makes on the seismograph. This must, of course, be compared with the distance from the quake to give it its proper value.

Plates and the Earth's Interior

Where are most epicenters found? To answer this question, scientists take all of the epicenter locations reported over a period of years. They plot these on a map of the world. As with volcanoes, they find that most earthquakes take place in narrow belts. These belts fall into three classes:

1. Belts running along the crest of mid-ocean ridges. This is where lithosphere plates are moving apart. Volcanoes are also found here.
2. Belts that follow deep sea trenches and the coastal mountain ranges or island arcs that parallel them. These are places where plates are moving together and colliding.
3. Belts that lie along great faults in the earth's crust. These are places where plates are sliding past each other.

Summing up, all of the earthquake belts are located on boundaries between plates. The movements of the plates against each other lead to faulting and earthquakes.

Earthquakes and Plate Tectonics

You can find the epicenter by drawing 3 circles with a compass.

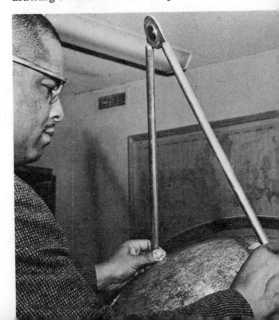

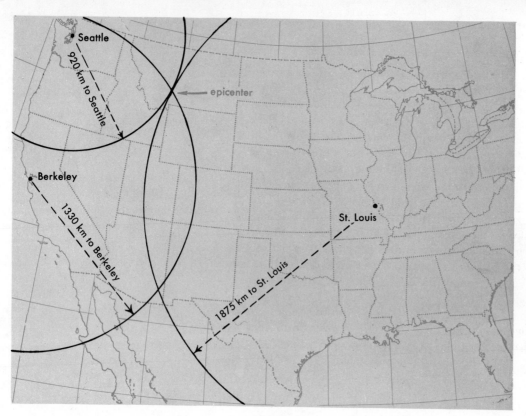

Seattle

920 km to Seattle

← epicenter

Berkeley

1330 km to Berkeley

St. Louis

1875 km to St. Louis

Trace these circular lines. They all go through the epicenter.

Most deep focus earthquakes happen where plates are colliding. One plate forces the other to plunge into the mantle. The bottom plate is pushed deep into the mantle, causing earthquakes.

Where Are the Earthquake Belts? 11.

What geographic areas are in the earthquake belts? One area is called the "ring of fire." It runs around the Pacific Ocean. This area includes the Andes Mountains of South America; the mountains along the Pacific coast in Central America, the United States, and Canada; the Aleutian Islands; Kamchatka; the Kurile Islands; the islands of Japan and the Philippines; New Zealand; and islands in the South Pacific.

Another group of belts also forms a ring that runs around the earth. It passes through the Mediterranean area. This ring includes Italy, Greece, Turkey, North Africa, Indonesia, Burma, China, India and Iran.

The mid-ocean ridges are other areas of frequent earthquakes. These include the Mid-Indian Ocean Ridge; the east Pacific Ocean

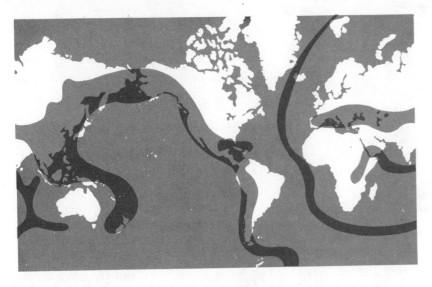

The map shows the main earthquake belts around the world. How are they related to the motion of the tectonic plates?

ridge; the ridges of the Antarctic Ocean; and the Mid-Atlantic Ridge, including Iceland.

A few strong earthquakes happen within plates, not at their boundaries. We shall mention some in Topic 12.

12. Earthquakes in the United States

The main earthquake areas of the United States are the coasts of California and southern Alaska. Both of these areas are near the boundary between the Pacific plate and the North American plate. The Anchorage, Alaska earthquake in March, 1964, had a magnitude of about 8.5. It was the most powerful earthquake ever recorded in North America.

Most earthquakes in California take place along the **San Andreas fault.** The San Andreas fault starts from Point Arena on the coast and runs southeast for over 1000 kilometers. It goes through San Francisco. It passes east of Los Angeles. Then it runs almost to Yuma, Arizona. Movement along this fault caused the great San Francisco earthquake of 1906. It also caused the San Fernando Valley earthquake of 1971.

Strong earthquakes have happened in parts of the United States far from plate boundaries. In 1811 a great quake shook the lower Mississippi Valley. In 1886 a quake rocked a large area around Charleston, South Carolina.

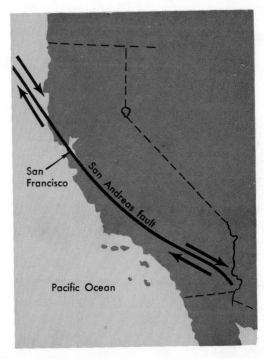

The arrows show how California moves along this fault, causing earthquakes.

Earthquakes and Plate Tectonics

Can Earthquakes Be Predicted? 13.

Seismologists in the United States, in China, in Japan, and in the Soviet Union—and others, too—are working on predicting earthquakes. So far they have some promising leads, but no answers.

Some earthquake damage can be prevented, however. Buildings can be made more or less earthquake proof. Foundations in bedrock are far safer than those in soil. Landslide areas can be avoided. And, of course, nothing should be built on or very close to active faults.

Earthquake Waves and the Moho 14.

Both **P** and **S** waves speed up below depths of about 10 to 65 kilometers. This was discovered in 1909 from a study of seismograms by the Yugoslav seismologist Mohorovicic. Mohorovicic explained that the change in speed was caused by a change in rock type. The upper rock was the earth's crust. The rock beneath it was the mantle. And so a way to measure the thickness of the earth's crust was discovered.

To honor Mohorovicic, the boundary between the crust and the mantle was named the *Mohorovicic discontinuity*. It is called the **Moho** for short.

Note that S waves cannot pass through the core of the earth.

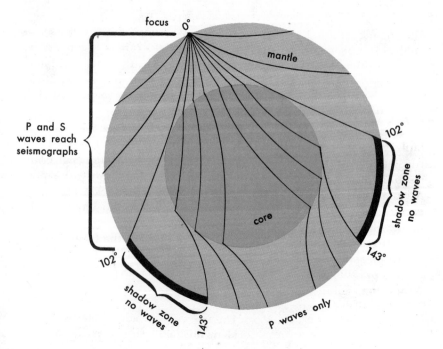

As **P** waves go deeper into the earth, two things happen to them. They slow down suddenly. They also bend sharply. Apparently they are reaching a new kind of rock at this depth. And so the outer core can be located. It is about 2900 kilometers from the surface.

As the **P** waves continue through the core, they speed up again. They are entering the *solid inner core*. It is about 5100 kilometers from the surface. Its thickness is about 2800 kilometers.

What about the **S** waves? Those that reach the outer core do not come through to the opposite side of the earth. Apparently they can not go through the material of the outer core. This tells scientists that the *outer core is liquid!* (See Topic 5.)

Each topic question refers to the topic of the same number within this chapter.

TOPIC QUESTIONS

1. (a) What is an earthquake? (b) Name a few of the things that happen in an earthquake. (c) How do fires break out?

2. (a) What is a fault? (b) What is faulting? (c) Give the "elastic rebound" explanation of how faulting takes place.

3. What is a tsunami? (a) How does one originate? (b) Why is it destructive?

4. (a) What is the difference between the focus of an earthquake and its epicenter? (b) How deep are foci?

5. (a) Compare **P** waves and **S** waves. (b) What are **L** waves?

6. (a) What is a seismograph? (b) How does it work?

7. (a) How does the seismologist tell how far away an epicenter is? (b) How does he know the time of the earthquake?

8. Explain how the location of an epicenter is found.

9. (a) What is the Richter scale? (b) How strong is an earthquake that measures 3 to 5 on the Richter scale? Above 5? Above 8?

10. (a) Describe the three classes of belts where most earthquakes occur. Explain their relation to the plates of the lithosphere. (b) Where do most deep focus quakes occur?

11. In which countries or areas are the earthquake belts located?

12. (a) Which is the main earthquake area of the United States? (b) What is the San Andreas fault? (c) Which great earthquakes occurred within plates in the United States?

13. How can earthquake damage be prevented?

14. (a) What is the Moho? (b) How was it discovered?

15. (a) How was the depth of the outer core found? (b) How was the depth of the inner core found? (c) How did we learn that the outer core was liquid?

1. Earthquakes may also be caused by violent volcanic explosions. Compare the location of the zone of greatest damage in such a quake with that caused by faulting?

2. How can seismographs be used: **(a)** in prospecting for oil, **(b)** in monitoring atom bomb explosions by other countries?

3. Minor earthquakes in the eastern United States are said to be caused by the melting away of the Ice Age glaciers. Can you explain why?

**STUDENT
ACTIVITIES**

1. Use the "time-distance of epicenter" graph to find the distance of an earthquake when the **S** wave's lag is **(a)** 3 minutes, **(b)** 5 minutes **(c)** 10 minutes.

2. Visit a seismic station, or museum, or college where you can see a seismograph in operation.

**TOPOGRAPHIC
SHEETS**

(15-minute series)

Cliff on fault line: Redlands, California; Glacier National Park, Montana; Meriden, Connecticut.

14

Rock layers of mountainous areas may be squeezed and crumpled into great wavelike folds (Topics 4, 5). A simple model shows how this is possible. Use several different colors of modeling clay to make a "plateau" of four layers of "sedimentary rock." Each layer should be about 1 centimeter thick, 15 centimeters long, and 8 centimeters wide. Gently squeeze the two ends of the plateau toward each other so that the clay forms an upfold of the layers. Such folded rock layers are called an anticline.

Level out the plasticene layers again. This time squeeze the ends of the plateau to form a downfold of the layers. Such rock layers are called a syncline. *Now see if you can produce both syncline and anticline together, as in the photograph on page 213. Some cracks may form at the crest of the anticline. Some may form in the trough of the syncline. The cracks are* joints, *like those described in Topic 6.*

The Origin of Mountains

The Rocks Move

The surface of the earth is far from smooth. Large parts of the continents are raised high above their surroundings. The raised parts are called mountains and plateaus. The more level lower areas of the continents are called plains. How were the mountains and plateaus formed?

Part of the answer to this question was given in Chapters 12 and 13. There we saw that volcanic mountains rise along plate boundaries. Lava plateaus come from flows of lava. Mountain ranges are formed along coasts where oceanic and continental plates collide. Island arcs are born. Islands are, of course, mountains and plateaus that rise above the sea.

It is easy to understand how volcanoes become mountains. But most of the world's great mountain ranges are not built by volcanism alone. Their rocks may be sedimentary or metamorphic as well as igneous. They may be faulted or crumpled into great folds. Geologists say that the rocks are *deformed*. How did this happen? How is it related to mountain making?

Mountains Were Raised

Geologists have proof that mountains were raised from lower levels to their present heights. In many mountains there are sedimentary beds that formed below sea level. The fossils in these beds are mainly ocean shellfish and corals. Yet such marine beds are found many kilometers above sea level in the Himalaya and other mountains. They have been uplifted by natural forces.

In many coastal regions we see other evidences of uplift. Sea caves and sea cliffs are found hundreds of meters above sea level. Barnacle shells are still attached to the rocks. Raised beaches can be identified by their sands and their sea shells.

The sea cave in the middle was once at sea level. The rock has since risen.

The two arrows show that the land in front moved down and to the right. Note the two parts of the road.

3. Recent Crustal Movements

Are there any places where uplift has taken place in our own times? Yes. Many sudden uplifts of the rocks have happened in earthquakes. An earthquake in Alaska in 1899 raised parts of the coast about 15 meters. The great Alaskan earthquake of 1964 raised many kilometers of the coastline as much as 13 meters.

Sidewise movements of the rocks have also been seen in recent earthquakes. In the San Francisco earthquake of 1906, roads crossing the San Andreas fault were moved as much as 6 meters. An earthquake in Japan in 1891 moved rock layers more than 3 meters both laterally and vertically. There are many more examples of such movements.

Very slow movements of the crust also are being observed and measured. And they are important. Even a centimeter of uplift a year will amount to a whole kilometer in 100,000 years. And 100,000 years is a "short" geological period. A slow uplift of this amount is now happening on the coast of Sweden. Similar uplifts have been observed in the western United States.

In many places, the rocks themselves show signs of movements of the crust. What are these signs?

In 1669 Nicolaus Steno, a Danish scientist, stated his *Law of Original Horizontality*. This says that sediments deposited in water form layers that are horizontal. Therefore sedimentary rock beds should be found in horizontal positions.

Throughout the world, however, we find many sedimentary beds that are not horizontal. In the Great Plains of the United States, for example, the sedimentary rocks slope from west to east. Some natural force has tilted the whole area while raising it. Even more striking signs are seen in mountains such as the Appalachians. The once-horizontal rocks are crumpled into wavy folds.

Movements of the earth's crust raised and tilted these once-horizontal rocks.

Faulting deforms rocks in a different way. In faulting, horizontal rock layers are cracked and then pushed apart. Faulting can be seen in the offset layers on opposite sides of the fault. It is common in areas of plateaus and mountains.

Folds in the Rocks 5.

How can rocks be folded? Rocks are often under pressure from other rocks. Experiments show that when rocks are under pressure, they can become soft and plastic. Then sidewise pressures can squeeze

The layers of this rock look like swirls of fingerpaint. As pressure made the rock soft, it was pushed into this form.

them into folds. The folds range in size from centimeters to kilometers. Very large folds may form mountains with valleys between them.

There are usually several folds together. The upfolded part is called an **anticline**. The downfolded part is a **syncline**. These names describe the rock structure, not the surface. When first formed, large anticlines form ridges. Synclines form valleys. As time passes, erosion changes the surface. The surface may even be leveled completely. But underneath, the rock layers will still be folded. These folds tell the geologist their earlier history.

When geologists study rock folds in the field, they measure the **dip.** This is the angle a rock layer makes with the horizontal.

Look at what happens to the flat rock when it is pushed in from the sides. It folds into a pattern of curves.

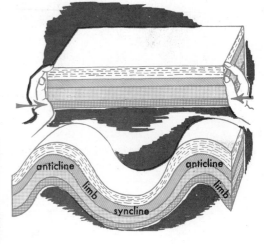

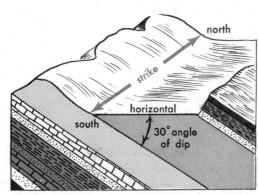

The dip is the 30° angle between the horizontal and the sloping rock layers. The strike is the direction along the blue line.

The Origin of Mountains **213**

The vertical lines show joints in this rock. The horizontal lines show bedding planes.

Fractures in Bedrock: Joints 6.

Look closely at an outcrop of bedrock. Almost all outcrops show cracks or fractures. Some are only centimeters long. Others may run for kilometers. They may be horizontal or vertical. Geologists call these either joints or faults. A **joint** is a fracture along which the rocks have not moved. A **fault** is a fracture along which the rocks have moved.

Joints always come in parallel sets. Vertical joints form in lava rock because hot lava contracts during cooling. Horizontal joints may form when pressure from overlying rocks is removed. Horizontal joints may also result from lateral pressure on rock layers.

Jointed rocks weather more easily, because ground water gets into the joints. In many rocks, joints have been filled by hot lava, forming dikes.

Faulting, Plateaus, and Mountains

Kinds of Faults 7.

When the rocks on both sides of a fracture are moved out of place, there is a fault. Geologists classify faults by the way in which the rocks are displaced. Most faults are not perfectly vertical, so one block of rock overhangs the other. Geologists call it the **hanging wall.**

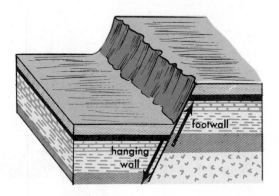

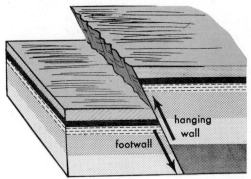

At the left, the wall hanging over the fault has slid down. This is a normal fault.

Below, the wall hanging over the fault has been pushed up. This is a reverse fault.

Normally, gravity makes the overhanging block slide down on the other. Faults in which this seems to have happened are called **normal faults.** In other faults, the overhanging block seems to have been pushed up. These are called **reverse faults.**

Some faults are more nearly horizontal than vertical. In these, reverse faulting almost puts one block on top of the other. These reverse faults are called *thrust faults.*

The compass direction of a fault is called its *strike.* In horizontal faulting, the blocks of rock slip sideways along the strike. So these faults are called **strike-slip faults.** The San Andreas fault is an example.

Normal fault

Reverse fault

Faulting and Landforms 8.

When vertical faulting occurs in a major earthquake, new landforms are seen at once. New cliffs are formed. Rivers flowing over the cliffs form new waterfalls. Landslides may take place, too. Where the crust is suddenly lowered, new lakes may be formed. Lakes can also form where landslides dam up rivers.

Lateral faulting leaves somewhat different effects. Again, the shaking of the crust may cause landslides. One part of a river may no longer meet the other part if the fault runs across the river. Along the fault line the rock is shattered. As a result, the rock is eroded rapidly, and many depressions may be formed.

Faulting and Plateaus 9.

A **plateau** is an area of horizontal rock layers that has high relief. *Relief* is simply the difference between the highest and lowest points of a region. There is no fixed amount of relief for a plateau. As a rule, however, a plateau's relief is 1000 meters or more. Its high points may be well over 1000 meters above sea level. Its low points are the bottoms of its canyons and steep river valleys.

Some plateaus seem to have been raised high above sea level by repeating vertical faulting. The faulting took place over long periods of time—perhaps a million years. Such plateaus are called fault plateaus. The Colorado Plateau in the southwestern United States was raised—at least partly—in this way.

Plateaus can also be formed by the slow rising of the land without faulting. The Appalachian Plateau in the eastern United States was formed in that way.

Note what makes this a plateau:
(1) horizontal layers of rock
(2) a long distance from the low point in the river bed to the high point at the top.

Large blocks of the crust that are raised by faulting may be tilted at the same time. When this happens, the great blocks are called **fault-block mountains,** or block mountains.

Fault-block mountains are rectangular in shape. They have long straight base lines running along the fault. The fault side of the mountain is much steeper than its back slope.

There are many small block mountains in Nevada, Utah, and Oregon. The largest block mountains in the United States are the Sierra Nevadas in California. They are about 650 kilometers long.

At the left is a newly formed fault-block mountain. *At the right* is the same mountain after years of erosion.

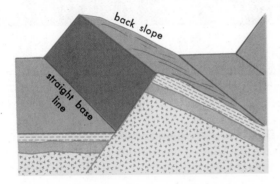
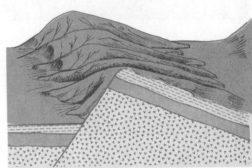

Mountains and Plate Tectonics

In Chapter 12 you learned about *domed mountains* and *volcanic mountains*. In Topic 10 you encountered *fault-block mountains*. But these do not include the earth's greatest mountain ranges. Among the great ranges are the Himalayas in Asia, the Alps and Urals in Europe, and Andes of South America, and the Rockies, the Coast, and the Cascade Ranges of North America.

These great ranges are all alike in certain ways:

1. They are made mainly of folded beds of sedimentary rocks.
2. The rocks are mostly the kinds that form in shallow ocean waters. These include sandstones, shales, and some limestones. They form on continental shelves and in inland seas.

The Origin of Mountains   **217**

Compare this steep side of a fault-block mountain with that shown in the diagram on page 217. The side you can't see falls off gently. (Sierra Nevadas, California)

3. The sedimentary rocks are very thick. Geologists estimate they were at least 10,000 meters thick before being squeezed into folds.
4. They appear to have gigantic cores of granite under the sedimentary rocks.
5. Their rocks are deformed in many ways. They are folded and faulted. Magma has intruded into joints and between beds to form dikes and sills.

Let us see how we can explain these features of these great mountain ranges.

How Can So Much Sediment Accumulate?

Sandstones, shales, and shallow-water limestones are formed in water no more than 300 meters deep. Then how did layers 10,000 meters thick form?

More than 100 years ago the American geologist James Hall gave this answer. Sediments are deposited in great shallow ocean basins bordering the continents, or in shallow inland seas. These basins are never more than 300 meters deep. But they do not fill up because they always stay 300 meters deep. How? *The floor of the basin sinks* at about the same rate as sediments accumulate! The basin is called a **geosyncline** (jee oh SIN kline). It may be over 1500 kilometers long and hundreds of kilometers wide.

Why does the geosyncline's floor sink? One reason is that it sinks because of the added weight of the sediments. A second reason is now supplied by plate tectonics theory. This says that when Pangaea split, the new continents drifted slowly apart. As each continental plate moved, its "broken" edge sank slowly into the mantle.

Is this the correct explanation? We do not know, but scientists are working to prove or disprove it.

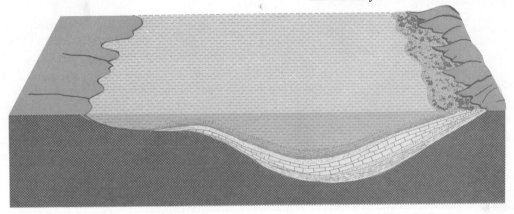

This great shallow inland sea is a geosyncline. Sediments from the land are constantly being deposited in it by rivers and waves. But the basin does not fill up, because its floor sinks slowly and steadily.

13. Colliding Plates Make Mountains

How were the thick sediments of the geosynclines deformed into mountain ranges? Again, plate tectonics offers us an answer. It says that geosynclines are deformed when plates collide. An example can be seen on the west coast of the South American plate. One result is the formation of the great Andes mountain range.

Here are some details of such a collision. The sedimentary rocks of the geosyncline are squeezed together, shortened, and raised. Folding forms great anticlines and synclines. Faulting occurs. This

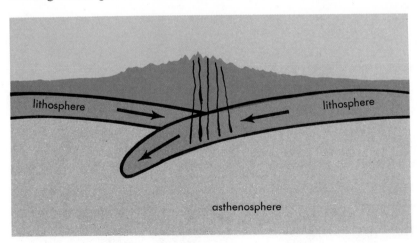

Colliding plates crumple the crust to form mountains. At the same time, hot liquid rock rises from the asthenosphere, helping to build the mountains.

happens especially at the edges of the geosyncline. Here great mountain blocks are forced upward in giant thrust faults. In the middle of the geosyncline, fault plateaus or block mountains may form.

Below the geosyncline, hot magma rises from the mantle. Some of it intrudes into the rock layers. Some may erupt in volcanoes and lava flows. Large masses may solidify to form the cores of the great mountains.

The Himalaya Mountains are in the interior of Asia. They are believed to be formed by collision between two continental plates. One is the Indian plate. The other is the Eurasian plate.

Both high temperatures and high pressures are involved in mountain making. The high temperatures come from magmas and the friction between colliding plates. The pressures come largely from plate movements. Together, heat and pressure combine to change sedimentary rocks into metamorphic rocks.

TOPIC QUESTIONS

Each topic question refers to the topic of the same number within this chapter.

1. What are some of the ways in which great mountain ranges differ from volcanic mountains?

2. (a) How do the rocks of mountains show that they have been raised? (b) What evidences of uplift can be seen on sea coasts?

3. (a) What evidences do we have of recent uplift of the earth's crust? Of lateral movements? (b) Where are very slow movements of the crust occurring? How much?

4. (a) What is Steno's Law? (b) How does the bedrock show the effects of earth movement?

5. (a) How can solid rock be folded? (b) What is an anticline? A syncline? (c) What is dip?

6. (a) What is a joint? (b) What is a fault? (c) How are joints formed?

7. (a) What is a normal fault? (b) What is a reverse fault? (c) What is a strike-slip fault?

8. (a) What landforms result from vertical faulting? (b) What are the effects on the land of lateral faulting?

9. (a) What is a plateau? (b) How was the Colorado Plateau formed? (c) How was the Appalachian Plateau formed?

10. (a) How are fault-block mountains formed? (b) Give examples.

11. (a) Name some of the earth's great mountain ranges. (b) Describe at least three ways in which they are alike.

12. **(a)** Explain what a geosyncline is. **(b)** How can so much sediment accumulate in a geosyncline? **(c)** What makes geosynclines sink?

13. **(a)** Explain how the sedimentary rocks of a geosyncline become mountains. **(b)** What part does faulting play? **(c)** What part does volcanism play? **(d)** How were the Himalayas formed? **(e)** How do metamorphic rocks form in mountain making?

GENERAL QUESTIONS

1. Examine the photographs of chapters 1–14 to see which show: **(a)** joints, **(b)** "original horizontality," **(c)** tilted rock layers, **(d)** folded rocks, **(e)** faults. List the photos that belong under each heading, giving page location and placement on page.

2. Why are alluvial fans likely to form on the steep side of a block mountain?

STUDENT ACTIVITIES

(15-minute series, except as noted)

1. Make modeling clay, plaster of Paris, or other models of **(a)** a normal fault, **(b)** a reverse fault, **(c)** a strike-slip fault, **(d)** anticlines and synclines.

2. Make models of **(a)** a geosyncline, **(b)** fault-block mountains.

TOPOGRAPHIC SHEETS

(15-minute series, except as noted)

1. *Block Mountain:* Furnace Creek, California.

2. *Folded Mountain:* Harrisburg, Pennsylvania.

3. *Domed Mountain:* Hot Springs, South Dakota (7½-minute series)

unit four

The beautiful forms
in the photograph look like strange
rock formations. In fact, they are animals—
corals that live in warm shallow seas. Each form
is a colony of thousands of small animals that live
together in the rocklike homes they have built themselves.
In the middle of the Pacific Ocean there are many large rings
formed of the bodies of dead corals. Coral only grows in the top
50 meters of the ocean, yet these coral rings reach down more than
1000 meters to the floor of the sea. How have these coral islands
formed? What causes them to occur in rings as large as ten kilometers
across? This mystery has been solved by studying the earth's oceans.

The study of the oceans is called oceanography. Oceanography uses many
basic sciences. It uses chemistry to analyze the waters of the sea and the
minerals of the sea floor; it uses physics to measure the depths of the
oceans and the temperatures of their waters; it uses geology to study the
shapes and sediments of the ocean floor; it uses biology to study the plant
and animal life of the ocean waters. Tides are studied with the aid of
astronomy; waves and currents are studied with the aid of meteorology.

Oceanographers may go to sea in specially equipped ships on long
expeditions that may last for years. They may make a base on an
ice floe or an ice island. They may descend into the depths of
the sea in a submersible that can cruise along the bottom
of deep canyons. They may live and work for weeks in
sea labs several dozen meters below the water's
surface. The oceans cover more than 70%
of the earth, so their study is an
important part of earth
science.

The Oceans

15

Oceanographers use chemical tests to find out which minerals are dissolved in sea water. One of these tests is the test for the chloride ion. In this test, silver nitrate is added to a liquid. If chlorides are present, the liquid turns milky white.

Try this test yourself. Most chloride ions in the ocean come from common salt. Dissolve a few grams of salt (sodium chloride) in about 25 milliliters of water. Using a medicine dropper, add a few drops of silver nitrate solution. (Get this chemical from your teacher. Be careful not to get silver nitrate on your skin or clothes. It may stain them.)

What happens to your chloride solution? Would this happen with another chloride, such as potassium chloride? with tap water? Try it.

The Composition and Temperature of Ocean Waters

Early Research: Minerals in Sea Water

1. The World Ocean

The world ocean covers 71 per cent of the earth's surface. Its average depth is about four kilometers. Its deepest trench reaches nearly eleven kilometers below sea level. It is much deeper than the continents are high. The average height of the continents is less than one kilometer. The world's highest peak, Mount Everest, is less than nine kilometers high.

The top of Mount Everest is the highest point on the earth's surface. The bottom of the Marianas Trench is the lowest.

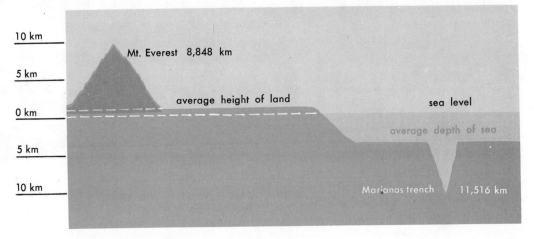

The world ocean is one body of water. But ships traveling through the ocean must "detour" around continents. So geographers recognize five different parts of the world ocean. Each part has been given its own name. The Pacific Ocean stretches from America's west coast to Asia and Australia. The Atlantic Ocean reaches eastward from the Americas to Europe and Africa. The Indian Ocean lies south of Asia. The Arctic Ocean covers the north polar region. The Antarctic Ocean connects the Atlantic, Pacific, and Indian Oceans in the south polar regions.

2. The Beginnings of Oceanography

Oceanography is the scientific study of the oceans. It began in about 1855. In that year Matthew F. Maury published his *Physical Geography of the Sea*. This book was based on Maury's studies of winds, storm tracks, and surface ocean currents while he was a U.S. Navy officer.

The Challenger was the first ship redesigned especially for oceanographic research. It studied the world ocean from the polar waters to the equator.

Matthew F. Maury

In 1872 the British government sponsored the first great study of the oceans. The ship Challenger was fitted up as an oceanographic laboratory. It was staffed with scientists and stocked for a long voyage. The Challenger stayed at sea for 3.5 years.

Challenger scientists studied the ocean at 362 ocean "stations" across the world. They measured depths. They took samples of sea water and of bottom sediments. They recorded temperatures from the surface to the bottom. They collected sea animals and plants. They studied ocean currents. The Challenger returned to England in 1876. It had gathered enough material to form a 50-volume report. Its voyage made oceanography a true science.

Oceanographic Research Today

Many countries are involved in oceanographic research today. In the United States, both Government and private agencies conduct research. Government agencies include the Naval Oceanographic Office, the Coast and Geodetic Survey, and the National Oceanic and Atmospheric Administration.

Private agencies include the Scripps Institution of Oceanography, the Lamont-Doherty Geological Observatory, Wood's Hole Oceanographic Institution, the Institute of Marine Science in Miami, and many others.

The oceanographer uses many special instruments and methods in his work. In this chapter and the two that follow, we shall describe some of them.

A modern research vessel sets out to study the oceans.

4. The Minerals in Sea Water: Salinity

Sea water is salty because it contains dissolved salt. But besides common salt, it contains other dissolved minerals. When 1,000 grams of sea water are evaporated to dryness, about 35 grams of minerals remain. The oceanographer calls the ratio by weight of minerals to sea water its **salinity**. In this case, it is 35 parts per 1000. This is written $35\,^{0}/_{00}$.

We could also say 3.5 parts per 100, or 3.5%. By using "parts per thousand" we avoid one decimal place.

The seven most abundant minerals in sea water, given in parts per thousand, are:

If you boil away 1000 grams of sea water, 35 grams of minerals (salts) are left. So, 965 grams of fresh water have evaporated.

sodium chloride	$27.2\,^{0}/_{00}$
magnesium chloride	$3.8\,^{0}/_{00}$
magnesium sulfate	$1.7\,^{0}/_{00}$
calcium sulfate	$1.3\,^{0}/_{00}$
potassium sulfate	$0.9\,^{0}/_{00}$
calcium carbonate	$0.1\,^{0}/_{00}$
magnesium bromide	$0.1\,^{0}/_{00}$

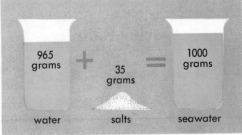

The Composition and Temperature of Ocean Waters **227**

Getting Water Samples 5.

Oceanographers place Nansen bottles and the larger 30-liter capacity Niskin bottles overboard to collect ocean water samples. Some samples are stored for further study.

Samples of sea water at the surface are simply scooped up in a bucket. Samples of deeper water are obtained in *Nansen bottles*.

Nansen bottles are special metal cylinders. As many as ten or twenty of these may be used at once. Each bottle is fastened at a measured point on a strong wire. The wire is then lowered into the sea to the desired depth.

To trap sea water in the bottles, a "messenger weight" is dropped down the wire. When it strikes the first bottle, it releases a catch. The bottle turns upside down, its valves close, and the water inside is trapped. At the same time, the bottle releases another messenger weight. This trips the second bottle down. The "chain reaction" continues until every bottle on the line is tripped. Then the line is hauled up with water samples from many depths.

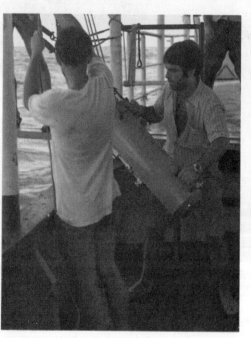

Measuring Salinity 6.

One way to measure the salinity of a sample of sea water is by evaporating it to dryness. But this method is slow, and accuracy is not easy. Nowadays, oceanographers use an instrument called the **salinometer** to measure salinity. It is easy to use, gives instant readings, and is highly accurate.

How does the salinometer work? The minerals dissolved in sea water make it a conductor of electricity. The more mineral matter in the water, the better it conducts. So instead of weighing minerals, oceanographers measure the sea water's *conductivity* in the salinometer. They then compare this result to a table of standard measurements to get the sample's salinity.

7. Salinity Varies

The salinity of ocean waters averages just under 35 $^0/_{00}$. In the deeper waters of the ocean, it hardly varies from that figure. In upper waters, however, there may be much variation. This is why the oceanographer measures salinity.

Salinity is *below average* where large amounts of fresh water enter the ocean. This happens in areas of heavy rainfall, as at the Equator. It also happens where glaciers enter the ocean. Again, it happens at the mouth of a large river. The Baltic Sea has a salinity of only 30 $^0/_{00}$. This is because so many rivers and glaciers drain into it.

Salinity is *above average* in areas of hot dry climate. Here the oceans lose water rapidly by evaporation. These areas lie roughly in latitudes 20° to 30° both north and south of the Equator. (On land, they are the areas of the great tropical deserts.) The Mediterranean Sea and the Red Sea are in this dry belt. Their salinity is about 40 $^0/_{00}$.

Salinity may also be above average in polar waters. When sea water freezes, only fresh-water ice forms at first. This leaves the remaining water saltier than before.

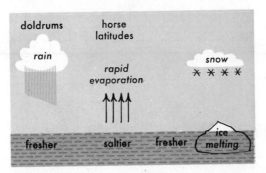

The doldrums are a region near the equator with heavy rainfall. Extra rainwater falls in the sea. In the horse latitudes, it is hot and dry. More fresh water evaporates out of the sea. So the "saltiness" of sea water depends somewhat on latitude.

8. Mineral Composition Does Not Vary

Sea water is amazingly uniform in its mineral makeup. The *relative* amounts of the dissolved minerals are always the same! This holds true no matter what part of the world ocean the sample comes from. It also holds true no matter what the salinity is.

How can we explain this? Apparently, winds and waves and currents do a great job of mixing the ocean's minerals.

The Composition and Temperature of Ocean Waters   **229**

This machinery is used for "harvesting" salt from sea water in shallow ponds. It's not exactly "back to the old salt mines!"

At least 55 elements are found in sea water. They include such important metals as gold, silver, copper, magnesium, and uranium. But almost all of these are present in tiny percentages. The percentage of gold, for example, is 4 parts per 1,000 billion parts of sea water. So "mining" the metals in the sea is still too expensive to be worth doing.

There is one exception. Magnesium is present in fairly large percentages (see Topic 4). Furthermore, it can be taken out from sea water more easily than from its ores.

Common salt can also be mined cheaply from sea water. This is because the only energy needed to evaporate the sea water is sunlight. Salt is taken from the sea in areas of warm sunny climate. One cubic kilometer of sea water contains about 27 million metric tons of salt.

Heat, Gases, and Life in the Sea

10. Sunlight and Marine Life

Plankton is the oceanographer's name for the plants and animals of the sea that are carried about by the winds, waves, and currents. Most such plants and animals are very small. Billions upon billions of these live in the upper waters of the ocean. Here they are a food supply for marine animals ranging in size from tiny shrimp to great whales.

Sea plants, like land plants, need *sunlight* to grow. Sunlight is found in the ocean's upper waters only. Sunlight fades out at about 100 meters. So plant growth ends at this depth. And the fish that feed on these plants are found mainly above this depth.

These single cells are a common form of plankton in the sea. They are seen here under a microscope.

11. Oxygen and Marine Life

All living things need *oxygen* to convert their food into energy. Oxygen gets into the upper ocean waters from the air. These waters also get oxygen given off by plants. So there is plenty of oxygen for both plants and fish. As depth becomes greater, however, the oxygen supply becomes lower, and fewer fish are found.

But even at the bottom of the ocean's deepest trenches, some deep-sea life is found. Here oxygen is provided by cold dense deep-sea currents. These currents start out as surface currents in polar regions. As they move towards the Equator, however, they sink below the warmer and lighter waters. Then they "creep" slowly along the ocean floor into all parts of the ocean.

Deep sea animals "inhale" oxygen and "exhale" carbon dioxide. But in the deep sea there are no plants to use carbon dioxide. So the carbon dioxide remains in the water and accumulates. As a result, deep ocean waters become rich in carbon dioxide.

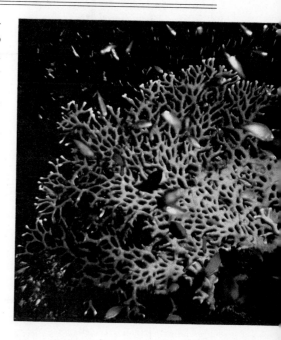

Coral can only live in shallow seas where there is sufficient light and oxygen.

The teakettle on a stove is heated from below. The ocean, on the other hand, is heated mostly from above—by the sun. As we saw in Topic 10, sunlight does not penetrate very far. In fact, most of its heat rays are absorbed in the top few meters of water.

Water is a poor conductor of heat. If the ocean waters were still, only the top few meters would warm up. But winds and waves mix this thin layer with the water under it. This makes what oceanographers call the **mixed layer.** At the Equator it is about 100 meters deep. In other latitudes it may go as deep as 300 meters. Its temperature is nearly the same from top to bottom.

How "warm" is the mixed layer? That depends on the latitude and the season. Near the Equator it may be 30° C. Near the poles it may never go above -2° C. Fresh water freezes at 0° C. Sea water freezes at a lower temperature than fresh water. The more minerals, the lower the freezing point.

Temp.		Depth
27°C	mixed layer	0 m
26°C		90 m
21°C		180 m
16°C	"thermocline"	360 m
	zone of rapid	
10°C	temperature	550 m
	change	
		730 m
5°C		910 m
		1100 m
4.4°C	deep water	1280 m
	uniformly	
	cold	1460 m
		1650 m
3.9°C		1830 m

The labels on the right show the depths of water near the equator. The labels on the left show the temperature at each depth.

Temperature Changes in the Mixed Layer 13.

The mixed layer changes in temperature through the year. The change is greatest in middle latitudes, where seasons change most. At 40° north latitude, the waters are about 10° C colder in winter than in summer. Near the Equator, the change may be as little as 1° C. In polar regions there may be no change at all.

The figures given above are for the open ocean. In shallow-water areas, such as bathing beaches, temperature changes are much larger.

A thermometer sinking through the mixed layer reads almost the same all the way down. But when it passes the bottom of the mixed layer, temperatures begin to drop. The temperature drops rapidly for as far as 1000 meters down. The water layer in which the temperature drops fast is called the **thermocline.**

At the bottom of the thermocline the water is very cold. Even in tropical regions, the temperature is about 5° C or less. From here to the ocean floor, the temperature drops very slowly. The water is all very cold throughout this layer. At the bottom of the deepest trenches in all the oceans the temperature is about 2° C.

In polar waters the ocean is cold from top to bottom. Deep currents from the polar seas creep along the bottom in all latitudes. But some inland seas in warm climates are protected from *polar creep* by shallow straits. The Mediterranean Sea is protected by the Straits of Gibraltar. As a result, the temperature of its bottom water is as high as 12° C.

The temperature of surface water can be measured with a thermometer. For deep water temperatures, special *reversing thermometers* are used. One of these is attached to each Nansen bottle. When the wire holding the Nansen bottles is pulled up, each thermometer automatically records the water temperature at the depth of its Nansen bottle.

The **bathythermograph** automatically makes a *continuous* record of the water temperatures it goes through. However, it is only accurate down to about 300 meters.

A geophysical technician is preparing a device for measuring temperature changes in ocean sediments.

233

Each topic question refers to the topic of the same number within this chapter.

1. **(a)** Compare the depths of the oceans with the heights of the continents. **(b)** Locate the five oceans.

2. **(a)** What was Maury's contribution to the study of oceanography? **(b)** Name 4 kinds of observations made by the Challenger.

3. Who carries on research in oceanography nowadays?

4. **(a)** The average salinity of sea water is about 35 parts per 1000. What does this mean? **(b)** Name the four most abundant minerals in sea water.

5. How are samples of sea water from different depths obtained?

6. **(a)** What is the salinometer used for? **(b)** How does it work?

7. **(a)** Where is the ocean's salinity below average? **(b)** Where is it above average?

8. **(a)** Explain what is meant by saying that "sea water's mineral composition is uniform." **(b)** Why is it so uniform?

9. **(a)** Why aren't gold and silver "mined" from sea water? **(b)** Why is magnesium extracted from sea water? **(c)** How is sea salt extracted from sea water?

10. **(a)** What is plankton? Where is plankton found? **(b)** Why is plant life found only in the upper 100 meters of ocean waters?

11. **(a)** Why do all living things require oxygen? **(b)** Why are the upper waters of the ocean rich in oxygen? **(c)** How does oxygen reach the deep waters of the ocean? **(d)** Why are the deep waters rich in carbon dioxide?

12. **(a)** How is heating of ocean waters different from the heating of water in a kettle? **(b)** What is the ocean's mixed layer? **(c)** How deep is the mixed layer? **(d)** How warm is it?

13. What seasonal changes take place in mixed layers?

14. **(a)** What is the thermocline? **(b)** How cold is the bottom of the thermocline? **(c)** How does the water temperature change from the bottom of the thermocline to the ocean floor? **(d)** Why is the bottom of the Mediterranean Sea so warm?

15. **(a)** How are deep water temperatures measured? **(b)** What does a bathythermograph do?

1. **(a)** Why should salinity be above average in the Persian Gulf? **(b)** Why would it be below average on the east coast of South America near the Equator?

2. Why are the bottom waters of the Mediterranean Sea likely to be poor in oxygen?

3. Why are seasonal changes greater in shallow ocean beach areas than in the open sea? (Topic 13)

If a sample of sea water can be obtained, measure its salinity as follows:

    (a) Weigh out 100 grams of sea water.
    (b) Evaporate it to dryness.
    (c) Weigh the mineral matter that is left. The weight in grams gives you the percentage of salinity.

16

1. The picture on the next page shows a part of the floor of the North Atlantic Ocean. For a rough idea of the area it covers, look at the upper left corner of the picture. It shows parts of Canada and the United States. Compare this part of the ocean with the whole Atlantic Ocean.

Find one canyon that can be traced to a river on land. Find one in the picture that is not connected to a river on land. Locate a mid-ocean canyon. Find two great undersea plains. Locate a mountain range. Find a deep "trench."

2. Microscopic shells form a large part of the oozes (fine muds) that cover the deep ocean floor. Many shells are the remains of tiny marine plants called diatoms (DIE uh toms). Diatomite, or diatomaceous earth, is a soft white rock made of diatom shells.

If your teacher has some diatomite, examine it as follows: Pick up a bit with the end of a toothpick. Spread it out in a drop of water on a microscope slide. Place a cover glass over it. Look at it under a microscope. Make sketches of the diatom shells.

The Ocean Floor and Its Sediments

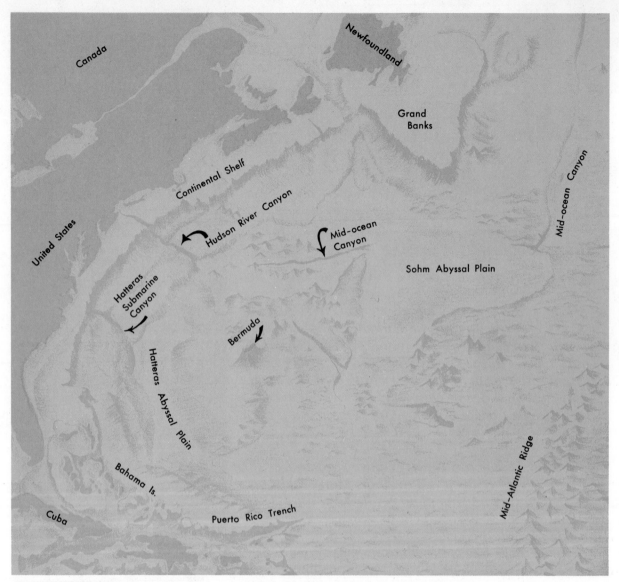

Canada

Newfoundland

Grand
Banks

Continental Shelf

United States

Hudson River Canyon

Mid-ocean
Canyon

Mid-ocean Canyon

Hatteras
Submarine
Canyon

Sohm Abyssal Plain

Hatteras Abyssal Plain

Bermuda

Bahama Is.

Mid-Atlantic Ridge

Cuba

Puerto Rico Trench

**This is a map of the ocean floor
off the east coast of the U. S.**

Features of the Ocean Floor

Shape of
the Ocean Basin 1.

The oceans lie in a huge basin covering 71 percent of the earth's
surface. The rims of the basin are gently sloping *continental shelves*
that reach out from the continents. The shelves end in much steeper

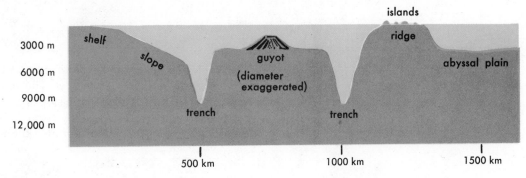

This side view shows features of the ocean floor. Note that the horizontal and vertical scales are different.

continental slopes. These lead steeply downward to the main floor of the ocean basin.

The floor of the ocean basin is marked by many features. Leaving the steep continental slope, it continues gently downward as the fairly level *continental rise.* The rise gradually runs into large level areas called *abyssal plains* and gently rolling areas of *abyssal hills.*

But much of the sea floor is far from level. Mountainous *mid-ocean ridges* cover one-third of its total area. Great hollows called *trenches* plunge to depths of over 10 kilometers. Thousands of tall single peaks called *seamounts* dot the sea floor.

Let us take a closer look at these features.

2. Continental Shelves: Rims of the Basin

The Atlantic Coastal Plain stretches from New York to Florida. The Gulf Coastal Plain stretches from Florida to Texas. These plains do not end at the coastline. Instead, they extend below sea level far out to sea. It is these extensions of coastal plains that we call **continental shelves.**

The continental shelf ends where the continental slope begins. The depth of water here is variable, but it averages about 120 meters. On the average the continental shelves drop less than two meters per kilometer. They are very gentle indeed. But they are not perfectly smooth. Their generally level surfaces have low hills, shallow depressions, and occasional valleys.

Continental shelves differ greatly in width. Off the coasts of Siberia and Brazil there are shelves hundreds of kilometers wide. On the other hand, much of the west coast of South America has no continental shelves at all. Most shelves, however, are about 60 kilometers wide on the average.

The Ocean Floor and Its Sediments **237**

Continental Slopes: Submarine Canyons 3.

The **continental slopes** begin at the outer edges of the continental shelves. Here the sea floor becomes steeper. The gentlest slopes drop at a rate of one meter in every forty. Some slopes drop as much as one meter in every six. Their width is usually from 15 to 30 kilometers. They go down to an average depth of about 3 kilometers.

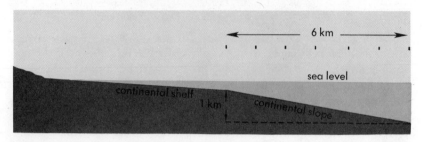

This diagram shows the maximum steepness of a continental slope. It is drawn to true scale.

The continental slopes are cut by many gullies and small valleys. These valleys are probably the results of mud slides. But the slopes are also cut in places by gigantic canyons. Some canyons rival the Grand Canyon of the Colorado River in size. These **submarine canyons** usually begin on the continental shelf and continue to the end of the slope. Some are extensions of river valleys on the coastal plain. Others are not.

There are many submarine canyons on the sea floor off the eastern United States. The best known of these is the Hudson River Canyon. It extends about 300 kilometers out to sea from the mouth of the Hudson River. At the end of the continental slope the canyon is three kilometers deep. Another great submarine canyon is the Monterey Canyon off the California coast.

Origin of Submarine Canyons 4.

How did submarine canyons begin? Some, like the Hudson River Canyon, extend out from coastal plain rivers. The upper part of the canyon is on the continental shelf. The lower part cuts deep into the continental slope.

Geologists think the upper parts of submarine canyons were formed during the Ice Age. At that time sea level was perhaps 100 meters lower than now. The continental shelves were parts of the continents. Rivers such as the Hudson River cut valleys to the ends of the shelves. Then the glaciers melted, sea level rose, and the valleys were drowned.

But what about the lower canyons? These hollows extend thousands of meters into the continental slopes. They cannot be explained by a 100-meter fall in sea level. Furthermore, most canyons show no connection with rivers on the continents.

Geologists believe that canyons on the continental slopes have a different origin. They believe that these canyons were caused by powerful currents that ran like flash floods down the steep continental slopes. Such currents form when great landslides of mud and sand come down the slopes. The landslides may be started by earthquakes or simply by gravity.

The landslide sweeps water ahead of it at high speed. Its muds and sands mix with the water. Together they make a current called a **turbidity current.** (*Turbid* means muddy.) With its high speed (sometimes 50 kilometers an hour) and its cutting tools, the current is a powerful agent of erosion. Turbidity currents caused by undersea earthquakes have snapped telegraph cables on the ocean floor. They have also built up great fan-shaped deposits at the mouths of many submarine canyons. Some have been traced a distance of more than 500 kilometers along the sea floor.

The upper part of this submarine canyon was formed by the river. The deeper part was formed by undersea currents.

5. Continental Rise; Abyssal Plain, Hills.

Where the steep continental slopes end, the **continental rises** begin. Here the slope becomes very gentle again. It averages about one meter in a hundred. The rises are covered with muds and sands probably deposited by turbidity currents. They reach seaward from the continental slopes for hundreds of kilometers.

Most of the ocean basin floor lies at a depth of 4000 meters or more. In general, this floor has a rolling surface of low *abyssal hills.* But huge areas have been buried in sediments to form **abyssal plains.** These are far flatter than any plains on the continents. They are the most nearly level areas of the earth's surface.

Abyssal plains are much fewer in the Pacific Ocean than in the Atlantic. Why? Perhaps the sediments carried by turbidity currents are "trapped" in the deep trenches around the Pacific coasts. The Atlantic Ocean has no such coastal trenches. (See Topic 7.)

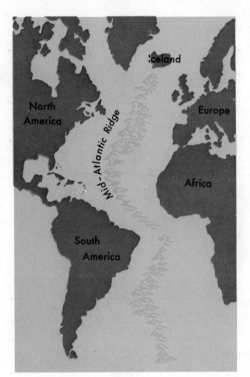

The **mid-ocean ridges** are great undersea mountain ranges. They form a nearly continuous chain 65,000 kilometers long. Their total area is equal to that of all the continents. They rise steeply to heights of two kilometers or more. In places, their highest peaks reach above sea level as islands. Ridges split every ocean basin into two or more smaller basins.

The **Mid-Atlantic Ridge** zigzags from Iceland almost to Antarctica. It runs roughly parallel to the shorelines of the continents that border the Atlantic Ocean. Some of its volcanic peaks have grown above sea level. These include the Azores Islands in the North Atlantic; Ascension Island, St. Helena, and Tristan da Cunha in the South Atlantic.

A striking feature of the ridge is its great **rift valley.** This hollow runs the full length of the ridge near its center. It is up to three kilometers deep and 50 kilometers wide.

The Mid-Atlantic Ridge separates the American tectonic plates from the Eurasian and African plates.

Trenches and Island Arcs 7.

The ocean's greatest depths are found in its great **trenches.** These long narrow hollows may exceed 1500 kilometers in length. They may be 150 kilometers wide. They may reach six kilometers below the usual level of the ocean floor.

In the Pacific Ocean most trenches are found beside island arcs. These arcs include the Aleutian, Kuril, and Philippine islands, and the islands of Japan and Indonesia. In the Atlantic Ocean the West Indies form an island arc.

Another great Pacific trench, the Peru-Chile Trench, lies close to the west coast of South America. It is nearly 3000 kilometers long.

The greatest ocean depth yet discovered is about 10,900 meters. This was found in the Pacific Ocean's Marianas Trench in 1960 by a U.S. Navy bathyscaphe (a deep-sea exploration ship). The record depth for the Atlantic Ocean is about 9200 meters. It is in the Puerto Rico Trench.

Seamounts are single mountain peaks that rise high above the ocean floor. There are many in the Pacific Ocean. Most seamounts are cone-shaped. They seem to be extinct volcanoes.

Some seamounts look as though they have had their tops sliced off. These flat-topped peaks are called **guyots** (GHEE ohs). They, too, are found mostly in the Pacific Ocean. Their tops are usually at least 1000 meters below sea level.

This cone once stood high above sea level. Waves sliced off its top. Later the sea floor sank.

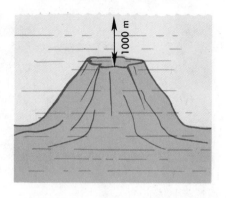

9. Measuring Depth of Water

The depth of any part of the ocean is found by **sounding.** In the days of the Challenger, the depth of the sea was measured with a line. A lead weight was lowered on a rope—later a wire—until it touched bottom. In very deep water one measurement took hours.

About 1920 the echo sounder came into use. It sends a sound wave through the sea from the ship's hull. When the sound wave hits

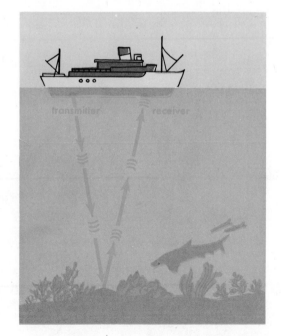

The arrows show how a sound wave from a ship bounces off the ocean floor and back to the ship. The time this takes is used to compute the depth of the ocean floor.

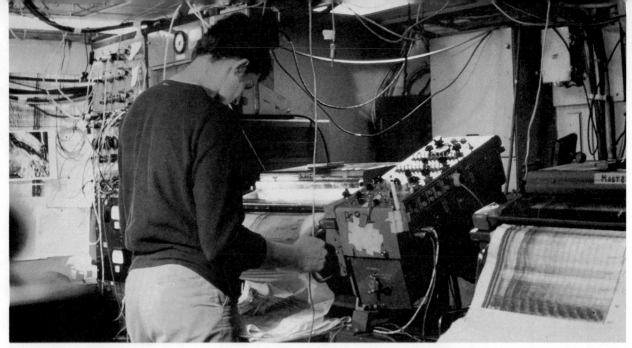

The echo sounder can tell the depth of the ocean floor. This Precision Graphic Recorder can also pick up layering of oozes and schools of fish.

bottom, it is echoed back through the water. The echo is picked up by a receiver on the ship's hull. Sound waves travel about 1500 meters per second in sea water. By measuring the time it takes to receive the echo, the depth can be found. In water 1500 meters deep, the echo will return in two seconds.

Echo sounders of today work as a ship sails along. The soundings are recorded automatically. The result is a profile of the sea floor over which the ship sailed.

As the ship moves, a pen on an echo machine draws this side view of the ocean floor. The longer it takes an echo to bounce back, the further down the pen line is.

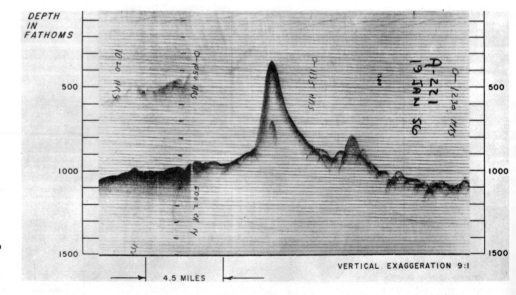

DEPTH IN FATHOMS

VERTICAL EXAGGERATION 9:1

4.5 MILES

Sediments of the Ocean Floor

10. Measuring Thickness of Sediments

The sound waves of the echo sounder are too weak to go beyond the ocean floor. So to measure the thickness of the **sediments,** stronger sounds are used. These are made by small underwater explosions. The sound waves pass through the sediments, but are echoed back from the underlying bedrock. Then the depth of water is subtracted from the depth of the bedrock. This shows the thickness of the sediments.

11. Samples of Sea-Floor Sediments

In oceanography's early days, tiny samples of bottom sediments were all that could be taken. Tallow, a substance like wax, was placed in a hole on the bottom of the line weight. When the tallow touched bottom, sediment would stick to it.

Nowadays larger samples can be taken with **grab samplers.** They resemble small steam shovels. Metal *dredges* are also used to scrape up loose rock samples.

The coring tube, or **corer,** is the most important sediment sampler used by oceanographers. It brings up a thin shaft of "undisturbed" sediments in their natural layers. The simplest type of corer is

A piston corer hangs alongside the research ship Vema. It will be lowered to the floor of the ocean where it can recover cores up to 30 meters long.

Another type of corer is the box corer, which samples a greater area of the ocean floor than the piston corer does, but it does not go so deep. In the first picture you see a box corer being lowered into the sea. When the core is retrieved, scientists examine it carefully. They then store it away for future study at the end of the voyage.

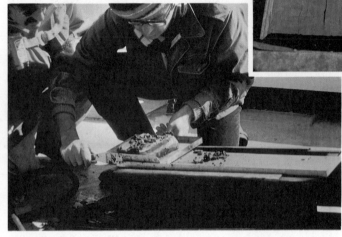

just a steel tube. It usually has a heavy weight at the top. This drives the tube into the sediments. A sample or core may be only one or two meters long.

The *piston corer* can bring up cores more than 20 meters long.

Deep Sea Drilling Project 12.

The National Science Foundation has been sponsoring a **Deep Sea Drilling Project** for some years. The Project uses the ship Glomar Challenger. The ship has drilled into thousands of places in the ocean floor. As a result, many thousands of sediment and rock cores have been brought up.

The drilling has cut through more than 600 meters of sediments. It has cut into the underlying bedrock. The cores brought up are studied for many things:

the kind and age of their sediments;
their relation to ocean currents;

the changes of climate they show;
the origin of the ocean basins.

Ocean cores have provided a very accurate time-scale for part of the last Ice Age. This scale has helped scientists to explain Ice Age climates.

13. Sediments from the Land

Much of the sediment on the sea floor comes from the land. Rivers, glaciers, waves, and winds bring gravel, sand, silt, and clay. Most of these materials settle on the continental shelves. Some reach the continental slope. Turbidity currents may carry them farther out to the continental rises and abyssal plains. Deposits by turbidity currents are also found on the floors of submarine canyons.

Some sediments from the land are found even farther out at sea. Boulders from Greenland and Antarctica are carried hundreds of kilometers out to sea by icebergs. Layers of ash and pumice are deposited in mid-ocean by island volcanoes. Dust, from the lands and from volcanic eruptions, is carried to all parts of the ocean by the wind.

14. Sediments from Sea Waters

Much of the sea floor beyond the continental slopes is covered by fine-grained sediments. These include two main kinds of materials. One kind is organic. It is made up of the tiny shells or skeletons of plankton. The other kind of material is inorganic. It is made up mainly of tiny bits of clay, quartz, mica and other rock minerals.

The sediments are soft and slimy. They are called **oozes** if they contain more than 30 percent shell material. If they contain less, they are called **red clays.**

15. Oozes on the Sea Floor

Plankton shells are made of either lime (calcium carbonate) or silica (silicon dioxide). Most plankton organisms are lime forming. Oozes made of mainly lime shells are called **calcareous oozes.** They cover about half of the entire ocean floor. Most shells in these oozes come from tiny marine animals called **Globigerina** (glo bij uh RYE nuh). Their shells are the size of sand grains.

Microscopic plants and animals once lived in all these shells. The lime shells on the left form calcareous ooze. The silica shells on the right form siliceous ooze.

Oozes made of mainly silica shells are called **siliceous oozes.** They are mostly the remains of **Radiolaria** and **diatoms.** Radiolaria are microscopic one-celled animals. Diatoms are even smaller one-celled plants.

Oozes build up on the sea floor very slowly. It may take more than a thousand years to form a layer of ooze one centimeter thick.

Red Clays in the Deeps 16.

The deep waters of the ocean trenches are rich in carbon dioxide. Such waters easily dissolve both lime and silica. As a result, very few plankton shells reach the floors of the trenches. With so little organic material, oozes do not form. Instead red clays are formed on the floors and walls of the trenches.

The minerals in red clay are thought to come from the continents. But, owing to the tiny size of the particles in the red clays, ocean currents carry the red clays everywhere. Some of them are so fine that they take hundreds of years to sink to the bottom. Red clays pile up as slowly as one centimeter in 20,000 years.

"Red clays" are not always red. They may also be brown, yellowish, or gray. The red or brown is due to rusted iron. Red clay may also contain bits of meteorites and sharks' teeth.

Thickness of Deep Sea Deposits 17.

The thickness of oozes and red clays is measured as described in Topic 10. These measurements show an average thickness of about 600 meters in the Atlantic Ocean. In the Pacific Ocean, the average thickness is only half as large. Why? Perhaps it is because fewer large rivers carry sediments into the Pacific Ocean. Also, the Pacific's ring of trenches may trap much of the sediment.

Sediments in general are thickest in hollows, such as trenches and canyons. They are thinnest on heights, especially on the mid-ocean ridges.

18. Reading a Sediment Core

Suppose an oceanographer brings up a core of ooze five meters long. An all-ooze core could have taken half a million years to build up. But suppose part of the core is a half-meter layer of volcanic ash. This could have been deposited in just a few days. So, this would sharply lower the age of the bottom of the core. It would also mean that a volcanic eruption had taken place fairly close by. The time the eruption took place could be estimated from the position of the ash in the core.

Suppose layers of sand or silt are in the core. They would show that turbidity currents had probably reached here. Again, the time when this happened could be estimated.

Cores might also show changes of climate. Suppose one layer of ooze contains only shells of cold-water plankton. Above it is a layer of warm-water shells. The oceanographer can tell when, and for how long, each climate existed.

Many kinds of sediment have been brought up in this sediment core, which is shown here in sections.

Cores from the North Atlantic Ocean have told us when the last Ice Age ended. A thin layer of "warm" sediments forms the top of each core. Radiocarbon measurements (see Chapter 33) show that these layers started to form about 11,000 years ago.

The age and thickness of a layer tell us its rate of build-up. If we use the same rate for the sediments underneath, we can date them, too.

Managanese Nodules

In 1875 the Challenger expedition discovered metallic lumps, or "nodules", on the deep-sea floor. They were widespread in the Pacific Ocean. The nodules ranged in diameter from about one to twenty-five centimeters. They were shaped like potatoes, and were made mainly of oxides of manganese and iron. Large ones weighed 100 kilograms and more.

Oceanographers think these **manganese nodules** were made by deposition from the sea water. They seem to be formed around bits of bone, shark teeth, and volcanic glass. The rate of build-up is now estimated at about one centimeter in 2 million years.

These nodules are now known to be plentiful in parts of the Indian and Atlantic oceans too. Since manganese is important in making steel, the nodules can be of great importance. But so far, no cheap method of mining them has been found.

Underwater Photography

Photographs of the sea floor are taken by special cameras. These are equipped with electronic flash units and automatic film advance. The camera is lowered to the bottom by cable. When the camera touches the sea floor, it operates automatically. The shutter is released, the light flashes, and the picture is taken. Each time the camera touches a new spot, another picture is taken.

Special television cameras are used to look at things underseas. They can be used to guide the operators of offshore oil drills. They are also used to guide operators of underwater mechanical arms. Marine biologists use deep-water television to watch marine life. Videotapes can be made at the same time.

Each topic question refers to the topic of the same number within this chapter.

1. (a) Name the two features that enclose the main ocean floor. (b) Name the features found on the main ocean floor.

2. (a) How are continental shelves related to coastal plains? (b) What are the width and depth of an average continental shelf? (c) How level are continental shelves?

3. (a) Give the average dimensions of the continental slope. (b) Describe the Hudson River submarine canyon.

4. (a) How may the continental shelf part of a submarine canyon have formed? (b) How may the continental slope part of a submarine canyon have formed? (c) How are turbidity currents formed?

5. (a) Describe the continental rise. (b) What is an abyssal plain? (c) Why are there fewer abyssal plains in the Pacific Ocean than in the Atlantic?

6. (a) Describe the mid-ocean ridges. (b) Where is the Mid-Atlantic Ridge? (c) What is the ridge's rift valley?

7. (a) How large and how deep can an ocean trench be? (b) Where are most of the Pacific's trenches? (c) Where are the deepest points in the Pacific and Atlantic oceans?

8. (a) What is a seamount? (b) What is a guyot?

9. (a) What is sounding? (b) How does the echo sounder measure depth?

10. How is the thickness of sea floor sediments measured?

11. (a) How are samples of sea floor sediments gotten now? (b) How does a corer work? (c) Why is a corer's sample more valuable to the oceanographer than a grab sampler's?

12. What is the Deep Sea Drilling Project?

13. (a) How do sediments from the land reach the continental shelf? (b) How do they reach deeper parts of the sea? (c) How do boulders from the land reach the ocean deeps?

14. (a) What does the organic sediment of the sea floor contain? (b) What materials does the inorganic sediment contain? (c) What is the difference between ooze and red clay?

15. (a) What is a calcareous ooze? (b) What are Globigerina? How large are their shells? (c) What is a siliceous ooze? (d) What are Radiolaria? (e) What are diatoms? (f) How fast do oozes build up?

16. (a) Why do red clays form on the floors of the ocean trenches? (b) What gives red clay its reddish or brownish color?

17. (a) Compare the average thickness of oozes and red clays in the Pacific and Atlantic oceans. (b) How is the difference explained?

18. What would each of the following mean in a deep-sea sediment core: (a) a layer of ash, (b) a layer of sand, (c) cold-water shells on top of a layer of warm-water shells, (d) a thin layer of warm-water ooze at the very top of a thick cold-water layer?

19. **(a)** What are manganese nodules? **(b)** Where are they found? **(c)** Why may they be important?

20. **(a)** How are deep-sea photos taken? **(b)** What uses of television cameras are made underseas?

GENERAL QUESTIONS

1. Make a sketch to illustrate the continental shelves and slopes as described in Topics 2 and 3.

2. Using the figures given in Topics 15 and 16, calculate the number of years it takes to form a 5-meter-thick layer of **(a)** ooze, **(b)** red clay.

3. How may a guyot have been formed from a seamount?

STUDENT ACTIVITIES

1. Topic 17 says that "fewer large rivers carry sediments into the Pacific Ocean." Study a physical map of North America and South America to see why this is so. Give your reason or reasons. Name the "large rivers" that empty into each ocean.

2. Make a modeling-clay or plaster-of-Paris model of part of the sea floor that shows at least 5 different features.

17

1. A density current is formed when dense water sinks below lighter water next to it. Set up a density current. Fill an old-fashioned soup plate—one with a flat rim—with water. Imagine the plate to be a model of the ocean: the rim is the continental shelf, the wall of the bowl is the continental slope, the bottom of the bowl is the ocean basin. Squirt a few drops of ink into the water at the very edge of the plate. Watch how the denser ink forms a "current" that slowly moves down the "continental shelf," then streams swiftly down the "slope" until it reaches the "basin."

2. A "drift bottle" floats just below the surface of the water. There it is moved by currents but not by winds.

To make a drift bottle, fill a small bottle (or test tube) with water. Cover or stopper it tightly. Also fill a large aquarium, wide-mouthed jar, or beaker with water. Place the bottle in the water. What happens to the bottle? Why? Remove the bottle. Now pour off water from the bottle a little at a time. Restopper it and test the bottle each time until it just floats fully submerged. A medicine dropper to take out or add water will help you get it right.

What information must be enclosed in a drift bottle if it is to be of any use?

Ocean Currents

Currents Under the Surface

Ocean Currents 1.

The waters of the sea move in many different ways. The surface of the sea rises and falls in rhythm. These movements are **waves.** Waves include the tides, the tsunamis, and the swells of ocean beaches. Waters also flow like rivers in the sea. These movements are called **currents**. They include the Gulf Stream in the Atlantic Ocean and the longshore currents of coastal waters.

Ocean currents may move at the surface or far below the surface. The Gulf Stream and the California Current are *surface currents*. Turbidity currents and polar creep are *subsurface currents*.

How do these currents form? Where do they go? What do they do? Let us begin with subsurface currents.

Subsurface Currents 2.

The black ink dropped into this wash basin is heavier than the blue water. When it slides down the slope, it creates a density current.

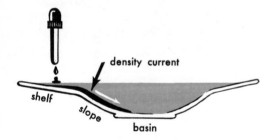

When heavier water meets lighter water, it sinks underneath it. If the supply of the heavier water is large enough, it continues under the lighter water as a subsurface current. Since the heavier water is *denser*, all such currents are called *density currents*. The turbidity currents we studied in Chapter 16 are density currents. Because their waters are mixed with mud, turbidity currents are denser than the waters which surround them.

There are two other ways by which one part of the ocean becomes much denser than another part. One is by the rapid evaporation that occurs in a warm dry climate. The water left behind is saltier. The more salt in the water, the denser it is. The second is by the excessive cooling that occurs in polar regions. When water cools, it contracts and gets denser until just before it freezes.

Let us look at examples of density currents formed in these two ways.

Density Current by Evaporation 3.

A density current formed by evaporation is found in the Mediterranean Sea. Here the hot dry climate evaporates far more water than the Mediterranean gets from rain and rivers. This makes the water saltier than ocean water. The loss of water should also make the Mediterranean shrink.

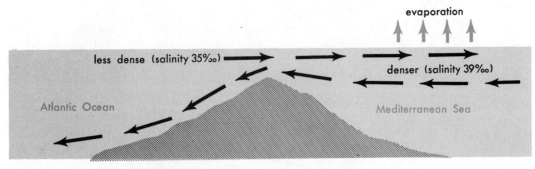

Heavier water flows out of the Mediterranean down the slope of the Atlantic. Lighter water flows in to take its place.

But the Mediterranean is connected with the Atlantic Ocean by the Strait of Gibraltar. On the Atlantic side the water's salinity is about $35^0/_{00}$. On the Mediterranean side its salinity is much higher—about $40^0/_{00}$. So a two-way flow results. Light Atlantic water pours into the Mediterranean at the surface. This replaces water lost by evaporation. At the same time, denser Mediterranean water runs out to the Atlantic beneath the inflowing current.

Outside the strait, the dense Mediterranean water sinks in the Atlantic to a depth of 1000 meters. (The floor of the strait is about 275 meters below sea level. The water on both sides of the strait is much deeper.) Dense Mediterranean water forms a stream many times as large as the Mississippi. Its branches have been traced to Greenland and Bermuda.

 Density Currents from Polar Waters

Oceanographers have traced three great density currents of cold water at different depths in the Atlantic Ocean. Two of these currents come from the Antarctic Ocean. The third comes from the Arctic Ocean near Greenland.

All three currents begin as surface currents in different parts of the polar oceans. As they move away from the poles, they meet warmer waters and sink beneath them.

Their density is very high for two reasons. First, their temperature is close to freezing. Second, when sea water freezes, only its water freezes. Its salt is left behind, which increases the salinity of the surrounding unfrozen water.

Why are these currents at different depths? Every density current stops sinking when it reaches water of equal density. (Remember, ocean water gets colder with depth, so it also gets denser as depth increases.) The three currents do not start out equally cold and dense. The Antarctic Bottom Water (see diagram) is densest. The North Atlantic Deep Water is next. The Antarctic Intermediate Water is lightest.

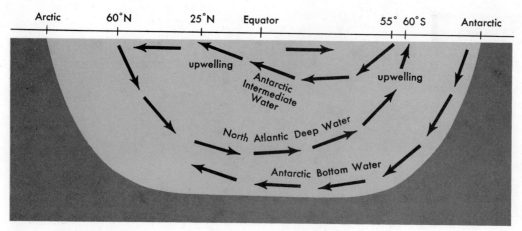

The arrows show the cold subsurface currents from the polar regions in the Atlantic.

Polar Creep; Upwelling 5.

Cold deep currents such as those described in Topic 4 are found in all parts of the ocean. This phenomenon is called **polar creep.** On the average the cold deep currents move very slowly. It takes the water dozens of years to travel from the polar areas to the Equator.

Without polar creep, there might be no animal life in the deep sea. The deep waters are poor in oxygen, which is needed by the animals. Polar creep brings them oxygen from the surface waters of polar regions.

The deep cold waters are perhaps even more important when they rise to the surface. This rising to the surface is called **upwelling.** Wherever upwelling occurs, the surface waters are filled with plankton and fish. Why? Because plankton need nitrate and phosphate minerals to grow. The deep waters of the ocean are rich in such "fertilizer" minerals. This is because they are the receivers of dead organisms that "rain" down from above. Plankton and fish from the surface sink to the bottom when they die. When the dead bodies decompose, their minerals are returned to the water.

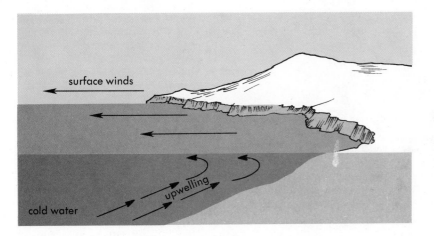

surface winds

upwelling

cold water

The remains of fish and plants sink to the bottom and produce fertilizer minerals. Upwelling brings these minerals to an area near the surface. Plankton, which need these minerals, abound here. So, the area has many fish and whales, which feed on plankton.

6. Examples of Upwelling

Upwelling takes place in the Antarctic Ocean at about 60 degrees south latitude. Here the North Atlantic Deep Water wells up. The result is an area teeming with fish and whales. A similar area is found at the Grand Banks of Newfoundland in the North Atlantic Ocean.

Upwelling also occurs along the west coasts of Peru, California, and north and south Africa. Here, steady winds blow warm surface waters away from the coast. Then cold water upwells to replace the surface water. Again, plankton live and there is much other marine life. The waters off Peru, in particular, are famous fishing grounds.

Surface Currents

7. Origin of Surface Currents

The Equator divides the Atlantic and Pacific oceans into northern and southern halves. Each of these "half oceans" has a complete circle of surface currents. In the North Atlantic and North Pacific, these circles move clockwise. In the South Atlantic and South Pacific, they move counterclockwise.

The driving force for these surface currents is the wind. How do we know? The answer comes from the northern Indian Ocean. Here the winds (called *monsoons*) travel in opposite directions in summer

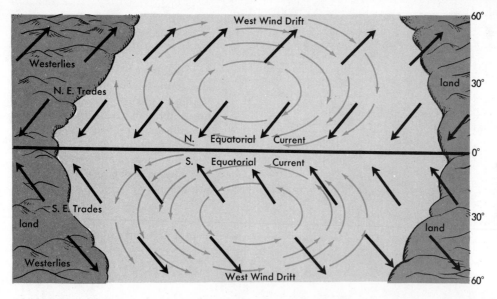

The black arrows show winds. The blue arrows show surface currents in an ocean.

Trace the arrows. They show the major currents and countercurrents of the world's oceans.

and winter. And when the winds reverse, so do the surface ocean currents. This example shows that the winds cause the currents. In the other oceans, the prevailing winds form circular patterns that do not reverse each season.

Where in the circle do the currents begin? In the North Atlantic a current moves from east to west along the Equator. The same thing

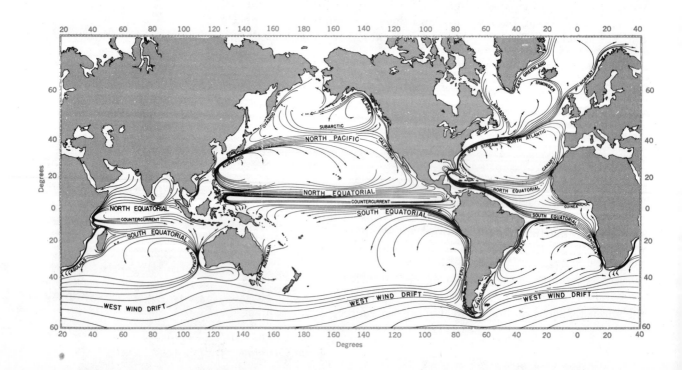

happens in the South Atlantic, the North Pacific, and the South Pacific. These **equatorial currents** are created by the driving force of the *trade winds*. They are world-wide winds that blow steadily from east to west throughout the tropics.

In each ocean, the current north of the Equator is called the *North Equatorial Current*. The one south of the Equator is the *South Equatorial Current*. As each current moves westward, it reaches a continent or a group of large islands. When it does, it swings away from the Equator. (This is north in the northern oceans, south in the southern oceans.) Why? First, because the continental outlines push them in those directions. Second, because the earth's rotation turns all moving streams—winds, rivers, and currents. It turns them to their right in the Northern Hemisphere. It turns them to their left in the Southern Hemisphere.

8. Moving out of the Tropics

After turning away from the Equator, the currents continue until they reach nearly halfway to the Poles. Here they turn eastward. Again, there are two reasons. One is the continuing effect of the earth's rotation. The other is the driving force of a second set of world-wide winds. These are the *prevailing westerlies*. They blow from west to east.

By this time, the currents have become much wider and slower than when they started out. They are now usually called **west wind drifts.** But they are still mighty "ocean rivers." They may be several hundred kilometers wide and hundreds of meters deep. They may move at speeds of about 1 or 2 kilometers a day.

When the drifts reach the eastern ends of the oceans, they turn toward the Equator. Continuing, they complete the circles described in Topic 7.

Now take a closer look at some specific currents.

9. The Gulf Stream: the Sargasso Sea

The Gulf Stream is the most famous of all ocean currents. How does it start? Where does it flow?

The North Equatorial Current in the Atlantic Ocean flows westward until it strikes the West Indies. Most of the current enters the Gulf of Mexico and circles it. Then it comes out between Florida and Cuba as the Gulf Stream. It is a very warm "river," at least a thousand times as large as the Mississippi.

The Gulf Stream follows the coast of the United States northward to Cape Hatteras, North Carolina. Then it swings northeastward to Newfoundland. Off the Grand Banks it heads eastward toward Europe. (From here on, it is often called the North Atlantic Drift.) By this time it has cooled off a good deal. But it is still much warmer than the cold ocean waters of the North Atlantic. So when the Gulf Stream passes lands in these latitudes, it takes much of the chill out of their climate. It does this by sending branches to Iceland, Scandinavia, and the British Isles.

The Gulf Stream closes its circle by turning south at the Canary Islands Current.

Inside the circle of North Atlantic Ocean currents, the water is quiet. The winds are light, and great masses of seaweed float on the surface. This region is known as the **Sargasso Sea.** Very little upwelling occurs in the Sargasso Sea, so it holds little marine life.

Other "sargasso seas" are found in similar areas in the other oceans.

These currents form a complete "circle" around the quiet waters of the Sargasso Sea.

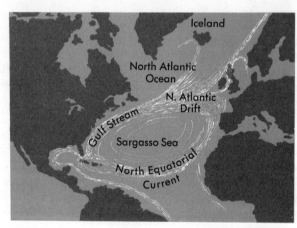

The Labrador Current; Cold Currents

The **Labrador Current** is a cold current. It flows out of the Arctic Ocean from Baffin Island to Labrador. With it come icebergs and sea ice. At the Grand Banks of Newfoundland it meets the Gulf Stream. Some of their waters mix, but most of the Labrador Current continues southward. It follows the Atlantic Coast past New England as far south as New York. Some of it joins the North Atlantic Drift heading toward Europe. When warm moist air from the Gulf Stream blows over the cold Labrador Current, the famous fogs of Newfoundland form.

Two other important cold currents flow out of the Arctic Ocean. The *East Greenland Current* flows into the North Atlantic through the Strait of Denmark. The **Kamchatka Current** (or Oyashio) flows into the North Pacific between Siberia and Alaska.

11. The North Pacific Circulation

In the North Pacific Ocean the North Equatorial Current flows westward until it meets the islands and mainland of southeast Asia. Here it turns north and is known as the **Japan Current,** or *Kuroshio.* The Kuroshio passes the islands of Japan and turns eastward. Then it crosses the ocean as a West Wind Drift.

The west wind drift splits into two main branches. One flows north as the Alaska Current. It warms the southern coast of Alaska. The other flows south along the coasts of Washington, Oregon, and northern California. This branch is called the **California Current.** Because of upwelling along the California coast, the California Current is much cooler than the land in summer.

12. The Equatorial Countercurrents

The details of the South Atlantic and South Pacific circulations are easily seen on the world map of ocean currents. A study of this map shows narrow **countercurrents** slightly north of the Equator in both oceans. These are surface currents. They flow fast between the north and south equatorial currents, in the *opposite direction*, eastward.

The countercurrents lie in a belt of calm air. This belt separates the trade winds of the northern and southern hemispheres. The countercurrents are probably formed by water returning from the westward-flowing equatorial currents.

13. Measuring Currents

Surface currents can be studied by the use of **drift bottles.** These are weighted so that they float just below the surface. In this position they are not affected by winds. Each bottle carries a dated card and instructions for reporting the discovery of the bottle. The finder gives the date and location of his find. From this, the direction and speed of the current can be found.

Currents below the surface are studied with *current meters* of various types. Another device for measuring the flow of deep currents is the **Swallow float.** This electronic device is floated below the surface at some chosen depth. Its transmitter sends out "pings." These sounds are picked up by a research ship's receiver, which uses them to trace the float's movements.

Current meters can also be used to study surface currents.

Ocean Currents

Scientists now use current meters that can be placed on the ocean's floor.

Countercurrents
beneath the Surface 14.

The surface equatorial countercurrents are not the only known kind. Countercurrents have been found under surface currents as well as alongside them. Two of these are well known. The **Cromwell Current** was discovered in 1952. It flows *eastward* under the *westward*-flowing South Equatorial Current in the Pacific Ocean. It seems to be about 200 meters deep and 400 kilometers wide. It has been traced through the Pacific over a distance of 5000 kilometers.

The **Gulf Stream Countercurrent** is much deeper. It was discovered in 1957 with the help of the Swallow float. It flows *southward* under the northward-flowing Gulf Stream. It lies nearly three kilometers below the Gulf Stream. Of course its waters are cold.

As oceanographic exploration continues, more deep countercurrents will probably be found.

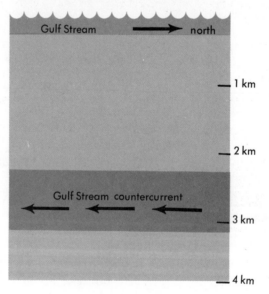

The labels show the depth of the Gulf Stream and of its countercurrent underneath.

TOPIC QUESTIONS

Each topic question refers to the topic of the same number within this chapter.

1. (a) What is the difference between ocean waves and currents. (b) What are the two kinds of currents? Give examples.

2. (a) How does a subsurface current get started? (b) Give three ways by which sea water increases in density.

3. (a) Why is Mediterranean Sea water saltier than the ocean waters? (b) Describe the two-way water movements through the Strait of Gibraltar.

4. (a) Give two reasons why polar waters are denser than average sea water. (b) Why do not all density currents reach the same depth?

5. (a) What is polar creep? (b) What is upwelling? (c) How does upwelling enrich the surface waters?

6. (a) Give examples of upwelling in the Antarctic and North Atlantic Oceans. (b) Why does upwelling happen along the west coasts of Peru and California? (c) What does this do to their waters?

7. (a) What arrangement of surface currents is found in the Atlantic and Pacific oceans? (b) What evidence is there that winds make the surface currents? (c) What is an equatorial current? How does it start? (d) Why do the equatorial currents turn away from the Equator?

8. (a) Why do the currents in all oceans turn eastward? (b) Why are they called "west wind drifts"? (c) When do the drifts return to the Equator?

9. (a) How does the Gulf Stream begin? (b) Briefly trace its course. (c) What are its climatic effects? (d) What is the Sargasso Sea?

10. (a) Where does the Labrador current begin? (b) Where does it flow? (c) Locate the Kamchatka Current.

11. How does each of the following begin: (a) the Japan Current; (b) the California Current; (c) the Alaska Current.

12. (a) What are the equatorial countercurrents? (b) How do they form?

13. (a) What is a drift bottle? How is it used in the study of surface currents? (b) Describe the Swallow float. How is it used?

14. (a) What is the Cromwell Current? (b) Where is the Gulf Stream Countercurrent?

1. In what way do both freezing and evaporation act alike in making sea water denser?

2. From what sources can deep sea fish get their food?

3. Why is deep sea life so sparse compared with the life in surface waters?

4. What effects does upwelling along the California coast have on San Francisco's climate?

5. The West Wind Drift in the Southern Hemisphere goes completely around the world from west to east. In the Northern Hemisphere it does not. Why?

6. Topic 3 describes the two-way flow of water through the Strait of Gibraltar. Is the volume of inflowing Atlantic Ocean water equal to the volume of outflowing Mediterranean water? Explain your answer.

STUDENT ACTIVITIES

1. To demonstrate a density current due to "saltier water," do the following: (a) Make a strong solution of salt water. Add a few drops of dye or ink to color it. (b) Slowly pour this denser salt water into the side of an aquarium or large jar of ordinary tap water and observe its flow.

2. (a) Make a map or model of the surface currents of the North Atlantic Ocean. (b) Do the same for the North Pacific Ocean.

Ocean Currents **261**

unit five

Have you ever seen
the star patterns called constellations? In the winter you can see the constellation *Orion* in the nighttime sky. Orion was a
legendary hunter. The three bright stars that make up
his belt will help you find this constellation. The photograph of *Orion* on the opposite page was taken with a large
telescope. It shows many more stars than you can see with
unaided eyes or even with binoculars or a small telescope.

Astronomy is the study of objects in the universe. Until Galileo invented
the telescope, the only ones that could be studied were those visible to
the unaided eye—the sun; the moon; the planets Mercury, Venus, earth,
Mars, Jupiter, and Saturn; meteors and occasional comets; and about
5,000 stars.

Galileo's simple telescopes revealed thousands of stars invisible to the
unaided eye in the region early astronomers named the Milky Way. Now
our largest telescopes show that the Milky Way is made up of billions of
stars, and that there are billions of other galaxies, each one with millions
or even billions of stars.

Our sun is one of billions of stars in the universe. With so many
other stars, there must be other solar systems! In 1963, astronomers observed a strange motion of Barnard's star, a near
neighbor of our sun. Astronomers concluded that this
motion was caused by a planet-sized object—invisible
to the telescopes—that must be revolving around
Barnard's star. This discovery represents the
first indirect evidence that other
planets may exist outside our
own solar system.

The Earth and the Universe

18

Fewer than 3000 stars can be seen without a telescope in the Northern Hemisphere sky. See for yourself.

Start with a clear moonless night. Find as dark an area as possible, away from street lights and house lights. Choose any part of the sky. Count the number of stars you can see in that part. Then decide how large your part of the sky is when compared to the whole sky. Multiply your count by the proper number. If your part was one-fiftieth of the sky, multiply by 50, and so on. Compare your answer with the number given above. What things will affect the "accuracy" of your count? How can you make it more accurate?

Studying the Heavens

How Telescopes Work

Stars are seen best on dark nights when there is no moon. Nowadays it is not easy to find a really dark place from which to see the stars. When "seeing" conditions are good, the sky seems to have an infinite number of stars. Actually, when the whole sky in both hemispheres is considered, only about 5000 stars can be seen with the unaided eye. When powerful telescopes are used, however, millions of stars can be seen.

The *optical telescope* is a tool that helps the eye to see distant things. The eye has a tiny lens, but the optical telescope uses a much larger lens or mirror. This lens or mirror gathers many rays of light from a star and focuses them in one spot. If the eye is near that spot, it can see thousands of times more of the star's light than with its own lens.

In this way, millions of stars invisible to the human eye can be seen with the optical telescope. In addition, millions of even fainter stars can be photographed with sensitive film. The photos can be studied by the astronomer even during the daytime.

The light-gathering power of a telescope depends on the *area* of its lens or mirror. The area of a circle varies with the *square* of its radius ($A = \pi r^2$). If the radius of a circular lens or mirror is doubled, its light-gathering power becomes four times as great.

The round roofs of the two large buildings below open at the seams. Large telescopes look out through the openings. (Mount Wilson Observatory, California)

The Refracting Telescope 2.

A telescope that uses a lens to gather starlight is called a *refracting telescope,* or **refractor.** The lens *refracts* (bends) the rays of light together to form the star's image. The lens is like a magnifying glass that is used to focus the sun's rays on a piece of paper. The bright spot of sunlight on the paper is really an image of the sun.

The refractor's lens is called the *objective.* It is at the top of the telescope tube. A smaller lens, called the *eyepiece,* is put at the bottom end of the tube. The eyepiece magnifies the small bright image made by the objective.

The world's largest refractor is located at the Yerkes Observatory in Williams Bay, Wisconsin. Its objective lens is more than a meter in diameter. The Lick Observatory's refractor is nearly as large. It is located on Mount Hamilton in southern California.

Telescope observatories are usually built on distant mountain tops in dry regions. "Seeing" is better in such places for two reasons.

The straight lines show how light rays travel through a refracting telescope.

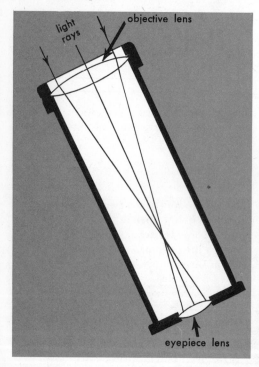

light rays

objective lens

eyepiece lens

This is the refracting telescope at the Lick Observatory in California. Its objective lens is nearly a meter in diameter.

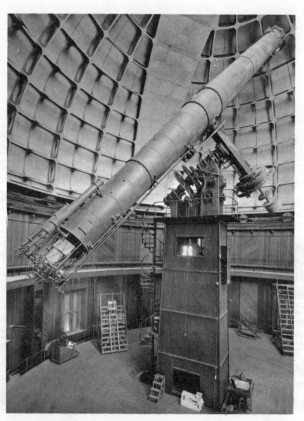

The air is usually clear and steady. And the disturbing lights of cities are far away and seem very faint.

In recent years, small telescopes have been sent into orbit on space satellites. These telescopes have the great advantage of being far above the earth's atmosphere, so they "see" better than telescopes on the ground.

3. The Reflecting Telescope

The *reflecting telescope*, or **reflector**, uses a curved mirror to gather and to focus starlight. The mirror is known as the *objective*. It is glass coated with a thin film of aluminum.

The objective mirror is set at the *bottom* of the telescope tube. When it is pointed at a star, it forms a small bright image of the star near the *top* of the tube. This image is usually reflected to the observer by a small mirror. As in the refractor, the observer views the image through an eyepiece.

The world's largest reflectors are the six-meter telescope in the Soviet Union, the 200-inch (about 5 meters) telescope on Mount Palomar in California, the 158-inch (about 4 meters) telescope on Kitt Peak in Arizona, and its twin at Cerro Tololo in Chile. These are so large that the observer can sit in a special cage *inside the tube* to view the image.

Note how the light rays (arrows) are reflected by the mirror in this reflecting telescope.

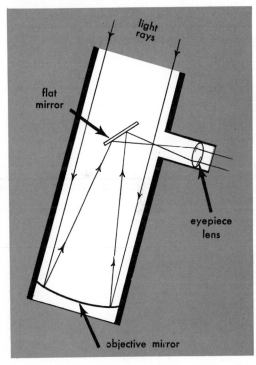

The Hale telescope at Mt. Palomar, California is the largest reflecting telescope in the United States. Its mirror has a diameter of 200 inches (5.08 meters).

Advantages of the Reflector

Why are the largest reflector mirrors so much bigger than the largest refractor lens? There are several good reasons:

1. Light rays do not go *through* a mirror. Therefore its glass need not be as perfect as the glass used for a refractor lens.
2. Only one face of a mirror must be ground to the perfect curved surface needed. On a lens, two faces must be ground.
3. The whole back of a mirror can be supported. A lens can be supported only at its edges. (The Yerkes refractor lens weighs about 350 kilograms, which is a heavy weight to support at the edges.)
4. A refractor needs a longer tube than a reflector (See diagram).

The Telescope as a Camera

How does the astronomer use the telescope as a sky camera? He removes the eyepiece and puts photographic film in its place. However, the field of view for such a "camera" is very small.

The **Schmidt telescope** is a special form of reflector used for photographing the sky. Like a wide-angle camera, it has a large field of view.

The Electromagnetic Spectrum 6.

The heat and light we get from the sun are forms of energy. They travel through space by means of **electromagnetic waves**, or **radiations.** But **heat** and **light** are not the only forms of electromagnetic radiations. When metals are bombarded by high-speed electrons, the metals give off radiations called **X-rays.** When uranium decomposes, it gives off **gamma rays.** When electrons move back and forth rapidly, they give off **radio waves.**

All of these radiations travel at the speed of light—about 300,000 kilometers a second. But the radiations differ very much in their wavelengths. Gamma rays are only millionths of a centimeter in wavelength. Radio waves may be hundreds of meters long. Short or long, all radiations together form the *electromagnetic spectrum.* The light rays that we can see are only a small part of this spectrum. All the other radiations are invisible to our eyes.

This diagram shows different kinds of electromagnetic energy. As you go from left to right, the lengths of the energy waves get shorter.

radio waves	heat or infrared rays	visible light	ultraviolet rays	x-rays	gamma rays	cosmic rays

yellow, orange, red — green, blue, violet

longest   shortest

How are the invisible radiations found? Gamma rays can be detected by an instrument called a Geiger counter. X-rays, ultraviolet rays, and infrared heat waves can be picked up by special camera films. Radio waves can be found by radio receivers. All of these forms of radiation come to the earth from objects in the heavens. Along with visible light, they have something to tell the astronomer about the heavenly bodies that radiated them.

Radio Waves; the Spectroscope

7. Radio Astronomy

In 1931 scientists discovered that radio waves were coming to the earth from outer space. Their origin was a mystery. But they soon learned that the waves came from many directions. These included the sun, some of the planets, and the Milky Way, as well as many dark areas of the heavens that appear to be empty to telescopes that use light. By the early 1940's the science of *radio astronomy* was born.

Radio astronomy is the study of radio waves from outer space. Its purpose is to find out what kinds of heavenly bodies the radio waves come from. Unlike light rays, radio waves can pass through the great clouds of fine dust that lie between stars. So radio waves can bring us information about parts of the heavens from which we receive no light. Radio waves from space can also pass through our own clouds. They can be received during the day as well as at night.

One of the great discoveries of radio astronomy is that dark areas of the sky are not empty. Many of them contain vast clouds of hydrogen atoms. Astronomers can now draw maps of the heavens that show the strength and sources of radio waves from space.

The Radio Telescope 8.

Radio telescopes collect and concentrate radio waves from outer space. Instead of glass lenses or mirrors, radio telescopes use giant antennas. They "collect" the radio waves and feed them into special receivers. The receivers record the direction, strength, and wavelength of the signals received.

A metal "saucer" or "dish" nearly 80 meters in diameter is the antenna of a radio telescope at **Jodrell Bank**, England. This "dish" can be turned to face different directions. So, it is said to be *steerable*. The great nonsteerable radio telescope at **Arecibo**, Puerto Rico, is much larger. Its antenna is over 300 meters in diameter.

The antenna of this great radio telescope is 300 meters in diameter. It is not a "dish." Instead, it consists of many connected TV-type antennas. (Arecibo, Puerto Rico)

The Spectroscope 9.

The optical telescope lets astronomers see the heavenly bodies. But the **spectroscope** tells them their composition, their temperature, and their speed of movement. Let us see how.

Everyone has seen the visible spectrum. This is the rainbow of colors that forms when sunlight passes through a triangular glass prism. Sunlight is a mixture of many colors. Each color has a different wavelength, with red longest and violet shortest. When light waves pass from air into the glass prism and out again, they are bent, or *refracted*. But long waves are bent less than short waves. As a result, the different colors are split apart, and a band of colors is formed.

The spectroscope is basically a combination of a prism and a tiny viewing telescope. The prism splits the light it receives into a spectrum of different wavelengths. This is viewed through the telescope. If the spectrum is to be photographed, a photographic plate replaces the telescope's eyepiece. The instrument is then called a *spectrograph*.

To study the light of a star, the spectrograph is used with an astronomical telescope. The telescope's eyepiece is removed, and the spectrograph is put in its place.

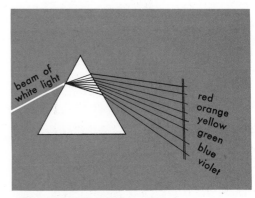

White light (all colors) comes in from the left. Colors with longer waves bend less and come out on top.

$\mathbb{10}.$ Reading the Spectrum

Three different types of spectra may be seen in a spectroscope. Each one tells a story about the source of its light.

A **continuous spectrum** is an unbroken band of colors. The unbroken band of colors shows that its source is sending out light of all visible wavelengths. Such a spectrum can come from three kinds of materials:

1. A glowing solid, such as the hot filament of an electric light;
2. a glowing liquid, such as molten iron;
3. the hot, squeezed gases deep inside a star.

A **bright-line spectrum** is an unevenly spaced series of *lines* of different colors and brightness. This shows that its source is sending out light in certain wavelengths only. Bright-line spectra come from chemical elements. The elements are in the form of a glowing thin gas

The horizontal band shows part of the continuous spectrum of the sun. The vertical lines show the bright line spectrum of iron vapor. The iron vapor's lines can be matched with dark lines that form part of the sun's band. So, the sun's atmosphere contains iron vapor.

or vapor. One example is the neon gas in a glowing neon lamp. Another example is the sodium vapor in a glowing sodium lamp. Each element has its own bright-line spectrum. No two are alike. The different wavelengths (which we see as colors) appear as bright lines at different places on the spectrum for each element.

A **dark-line spectrum** is a continuous spectrum with dark lines. The dark lines are in exactly the same places as the bright lines of glowing gases in a bright-line spectrum. The dark lines form when the light from a continuous spectrum passes through cooler gas. The gas then absorbs the same wavelengths as it would give off if heated. This leaves the places for these wavelengths in the spectrum dark. The dark lines identify the cooler gas just as well as its bright lines would.

Dark-line Spectra and the Sun

Because its dark lines are caused by absorption, a dark-line spectrum is also called an **absorption spectrum.** The sun's spectrum is an absorption spectrum. The hot squeezed gases of its interior radiate a continuous spectrum. When these radiations pass through the sun's own cooler atmosphere, absorption happens. As a result, the sun's spectrum has thousands of dark lines. When these are matched with bright-line spectra, they tell us what elements are in the sun's atmosphere. Sixty-seven elements have been identified in the sun.

Absorption spectra can also tell us about the atmospheres of the planets. The planets shine by reflected sunlight. Suppose the spectrum of a planet shows dark lines that are not found in the sun's spectrum. They must be caused by substances in the planet's atmosphere.

Like the sun, almost all stars form absorption spectra.

Doppler Effect in the Spectrum

When the spectrum of a star is compared with the bright-line spectrum of an element, examined in the laboratory, a strange thing is noted. The black lines in the star's spectrum are shifted. They are found somewhat to the left or right of the bright lines formed by the element in the laboratory. If the shift is toward the red end of the spectrum, it means that longer wavelengths are coming from the star. If the shift is toward the violet end, it means that shorter wavelengths are coming from the star. Why?

Astronomers explain that these shifts happen because the star is moving away from or toward the earth. If the star is moving *away*

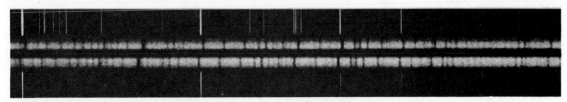

The two broken horizontal white bands are the dark-line spectra of a star that revolves around another star in space. The right end of the spectrum is its long-wave red end. The left end is the shorter-wave violet end. Bright-line spectra of earth elements are shown above and below the star's spectra. When astronomers match the upper bright-line spectrum with the upper dark-line spectrum, they see that the star's dark lines are shifted to the right (red) end of the spectrum. This tells them that the star is moving away from the earth. In the lower star spectrum, taken at a different time, the dark lines are shifted to the left (violet) end. Why? Because the star is now moving toward the earth.

from the earth, the wavelengths it radiates seem to become longer. This causes all of its spectral lines to shift toward the red end of the spectrum. The faster the star *recedes* (moves away) from the earth, the greater the **red-shift** of its spectrum. Putting this in reverse, we can tell by the red-shift how fast a star is moving away from the earth.

If a star's spectrum is shifted toward the shorter wavelengths (violet), it means the star is moving *towards* the earth. But if a star is moving at right angles to "the line of sight," the spectral lines do not shift.

The principle of the red-shift was explained by the physicist Doppler in 1842. It works the same way with sound waves. You may have noticed how the sound of a moving train siren or auto horn changes. As it approaches, its pitch rises. As it recedes, its pitch becomes lower.

Each topic question refers to the topic of the same number within this chapter.

TOPIC QUESTIONS

1. (a) Compare the number of stars visible without and with the telescope. (b) How does the telescope make faint stars visible? (c) Why does a 2-inch lens have four times the light-gathering power of a 1-inch lens?

2. What is a refractor? What does the name mean? (b) How is a refractor constructed? What advantages does an orbiting space telescope have?

3. (a) What is a reflector? (b) How is a reflector constructed? (c) Describe and locate the world's largest reflectors.

4. Why can large reflectors be built more easily than large refractors?

5. (a) How is the telescope used as a camera? (b) What is a Schmidt telescope?

Studying the Heavens **273**

6. (a) Name the different forms of electromagnetic radiation. (b) How are these different radiations detected? (c) Which radiations does the astronomer make use of?

7. (a) What are the sources of radio waves that come from outer space? (b) Why can these waves bring us information unobtainable from light waves?

8. (a) What is a radio telescope? How does it work? (b) Name and locate two famous radio telescopes.

9. (a) What use is made of the spectroscope by astronomers? (b) What is the visible spectrum? How is it formed? (c) What does the spectroscope consist of? (d) How is a spectroscope used to take a photograph? (e) How is the spectroscope used to study the spectrum of a star?

10. (a) Describe the appearance and source of: 1. a continuous spectrum, 2. a bright-line spectrum, 3. a dark-line spectrum. (b) How are elements identified from: 1. bright-line spectra, 2. dark-line spectra?

11. (a) What is an absorption spectrum? (b) Why does the sun have an absorption spectrum? (c) How can a planet's spectrum give information about its atmosphere?

12. (a) What is a red-shift? What does it mean? (b) How is this effect noticed in connection with sound?

1. Why is it possible to photograph stars that are invisible to the eye?

2. A few stars have bright lines in their spectra. How can you explain this?

3. Explain why there is no shift in spectral lines of a star moving at right angles to the "line of sight."

4. Compare the light-gathering power of a 3-meter reflector with that of each of the four reflectors described in Topic 3.

1. Make a simple spectroscope as follows: (a) Get a cardboard tube about 8 inches long and 1½ inches in diameter. (b) Glue a replica diffraction grating* across one end of the tube. (c) Glue or fasten a sheet of heavy aluminum foil across the other end. Cut a straight narrow slit in the foil. (Other materials may be used for the slit end.)

   Observe the spectra of daylight, an incandescent light, glowing gas tubes, etc.

2. Make a simple astronomical telescope with two convex lenses as follows: (a) Determine the focal length of each lens by forming an image of any distant object on a wall or screen. The image distance is its focal length. If the lenses have different focal lengths, use the longer focal length lens as your telescope objective lens and the shorter one as your eyepiece. (b) Hold the eyepiece lens close to your eye. Now place the objective lens in front of your eye, at a distance slightly less than the sum of the two focal lengths, and aim at any distant object. *(But not at the sun, or you will injure your eye.)* "Focus" by moving the objective back and forth slightly until a clear image is seen. The image is inverted. Why? (See telescope diagram.)

   To make a permanent telescope, mount the objective lens in one tube, and the eyepiece lens in a smaller tube which slides inside the first tube.

* Obtainable from Edmund Scientific Co., Barrington, N.J.

19

HOW DO YOU KNOW THAT...?

Stars differ in brightness. Long before the telescope was invented, astronomers had grouped the stars into six "magnitudes", or levels, of brightness. First magnitude stars were the brightest stars in the sky. Sixth magnitude stars were those barely seen by the unaided eye.

Look at the sky on a clear moonless night. Count the number of stars that you would call "first magnitude."

Polaris, the North Star, is a second magnitude star. Polaris is the last star in the handle of the Little Dipper. You can find it by following the "pointer stars" in the bowl of the Big Dipper. Other stars in the Little Dipper are second, third, and fourth magnitude stars. See if you agree. Use them to measure the brightness of other stars.

Stars differ in color, too. The color is related to the star's temperature. Most stars will look blue or blue white. But see if you can find some that look red, orange, or yellow.

Stars and Galaxies

What Stars Are Like

How Astronomers Find Out 1.

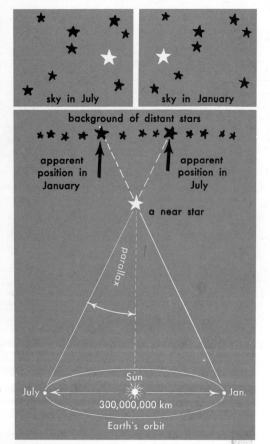

sky in July

sky in January

background of distant stars

apparent position in January

apparent position in July

a near star

parallax

July

Sun

300,000,000 km

Jan.

Earth's orbit

In the following Topics you will find out some of the things astronomers have learned about the stars. But first, think about a few methods astronomers use.

The **distance** between the earth and about 6000 "near" stars can be measured by using triangles. Astronomers choose a star and look at this same star at two dates six months apart. These viewings are therefore from opposite ends of the earth's orbit. At each viewing they sight a line to the star and measure the angle of the line. Thus, a diameter of the earth's orbit becomes the base of a triangle. The two sight lines form its other two sides. Since the length of the baseline is known, the star's distance can be found. For more distant stars, other methods are used. One of these is discussed in Topic 21.

The **surface temperature** of a star can be found from its spectrum. In general, the bluer the light, the higher the temperature.

The **size** of a star can be found if its distance and temperature are known. The astronomers measure the star's **brightness.** They then find how large its surface must be to appear so bright from so far away.

The *mass* of a star can be found in a number of ways by mathematics that is too complicated to explain here. When a star's mass and size are known, its **density** can be found from the formula:

$$\text{Density} = \text{Mass} \div \text{Volume}$$

The **chemical elements** in a star are found from its spectrum.

Imagine that the distant stars are on the ceiling of a room. If you stand at July and look up at the near star, the ceiling will look like the small picture at the left.

Size, Mass, and Density of Stars 2.

Our sun is an "average star" in many ways. Its diameter is about 1,380,000 kilometers. Its average density is about 1.4 times that of water. Its mass is about 300,000 times that of the earth. The sun is *our* star. How do the other stars in the universe compare with it?

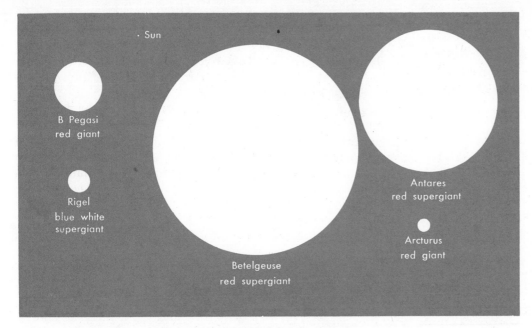

Our sun is shown by the dot near the top of this scale drawing. Note how tiny it is compared to the giants and supergiants.

Stars cover a great range in size. The smallest stars may be smaller than the earth. The largest star known is more than 2000 times the diameter of the sun.

Stars differ even more in density. The star Betelgeuse (BET el jooz) is only one ten-millionth as dense as the sun. But our brightest star, Sirius, has a neighbor so dense that one teaspoonful of it would weigh a ton on earth!

Stars differ less in mass. The largest mass is only about ten times that of the sun. The smallest is about one-fifth that of the sun. Most stars are fairly close to the sun in mass.

 **How Far to a Star?**

The average distance between the earth and the sun is about 150 million kilometers. Astronomers call this the astronomical unit, abbreviated A. U.

How far away is the next nearest star? Imagine that the earth is a dot one centimeter from the sun. The next nearest star, Alpha Centauri, would be more than 2.5 kilometers away! It is nearly 300,000 times as far from the earth as the sun—about 40 trillion kilometers off.

Because star distances are so large, they are expressed in special units. The **light-year** is such a unit of distance—not time. It is the distance a ray of light travels in one year. The speed of light is about 300,000 kilometers a second. In one year light travels about 9.5 trillion kilometers. Alpha Centauri's distance from the earth, expressed this way, is about 4.3 light-years.

Alpha Centauri is the second brightest star in the Southern Hemisphere sky. Other "near" stars are Sirius, 9 light-years distant; Vega, our brightest summer star, about 27 light-years away; and Polaris, the North Star, about 680 light-years off. By contrast, sunlight reaches us in about 8 minutes; that is, the sun is 8 light-minutes from earth.

Star Colors and Temperatures 4.

Stars differ in color. Betelgeuse is red, our sun is yellow, Sirius is blue. The hotter the star, the bluer the color. The cooler the star, the redder the color. All stars radiate all colors, but hotter stars emit more blue and less red.

We see the same thing when an iron bar is heated. As it gets hotter, its color goes from red to orange to yellow to white to blue-white. In stars, "red hot" may mean only 3000° C at the surface. "Blue hot" may be over 30,000° C. Our sun has a surface temperature of about 5500° C.

The Elements in Stars 5.

Spectrum analysis tells us what stars are made of. Most stars are made up of mainly hydrogen and helium. One to two per cent of the star's mass may be of heavier elements. These include iron, titanium, calcium, sodium, and others. Our sun appears to be about 70 per cent hydrogen, 28 per cent helium, and 2 per cent heavier elements.

The spectrum radiated by a star depends on both its composition and its temperature. Since no two stars have exactly the same composition and temperature, each star has its own individual spectrum.

Stars and Their Brightness

Sirius appears to be the brightest star in the sky of both hemispheres. It shines about ten times as brightly as the star Antares. Yet Antares is actually about 250 times as bright as Sirius. Antares, however, is much farther off in space. The brightness we see is called **apparent magnitude.** The real brightness of a star is called its *luminosity*.

The luminosity of a star depends only on its size and its hotness. The apparent magnitude depends on its distance from the earth. A 100-watt lamp has greater luminosity than a small flashlight. But a flashlight up close looks brighter than the lamp a kilometer away.

Long before the telescope was invented, early astronomers spoke of six classes of star magnitude. First magnitude stars were the "brightest" stars, such as Sirius and Vega. Sixth magnitude stars were those barely seen. But today the telescope and the photographic plate enable us to "see" stars more than a billion times fainter than Vega. These are called 24th magnitude stars.

Modern astronomers find it useful to give each magnitude a numerical value. They use a ratio system. The ratio of brightness from one magnitude to the next one is 2.5. This means that a first magnitude star is 2.5 times as bright as a second magnitude star. A fifth magnitude star is 2.5 times as bright as a sixth. First magnitude stars are about 100 times as bright as sixth magnitude stars (2.5 × 2.5 × 2.5 × 2.5 × 2.5). Using this idea stars can be given more accurate magnitudes. For example, Spica is 1.0, and Altair is 0.80.

Some stars are brighter than first magnitude. Their magnitudes must be less than 1.0. For example, Vega has a magnitude of 0.04, which means it is 2.5 times as bright as Spica. Sirius is so bright that its magnitude has to be given as a minus number, −1.43. It is nearly 1½ magnitudes brighter than Vega.

Apparent magnitudes are also used with the planets, moon, and sun. At their brightest, the planets Venus, Mars, and Jupiter are brighter than any stars. Their apparent magnitudes are then −4.4, −2.5, and −2.8 respectively. The full moon's magnitude is −12.6. The sun's is −26.8. Remember, the lower the magnitude number, the brighter the star or planet.

7. Absolute Magnitude

How do astronomers measure a star's true brightness or luminosity? If all stars were "placed" at the same distance from the earth, their true brightness could be measured. Astronomers use a special measure to compare the luminosity of stars from the same distance. This measure is called **absolute magnitude.** Absolute magnitude is the apparent magnitude a star would have if placed at a distance of 32.6 light-years from the sun.

As we have already seen, our sun is an average star. Its absolute magnitude is 4.8. By contrast the bright star Rigel's absolute magnitude is −6.4. But most stars are not even so luminous as our sun.

Giants, Supergiants, Dwarfs

The bluer the star, the hotter it is. Usually, the most luminous stars are blue. The least luminous are red. But there are many exceptions. Let us see why.

Sirius and Vega are hot blue-white stars. They are highly luminous. But the cooler red stars Capella and Arcturus are even more luminous. Why? Because their size is so great. They radiate more light than hotter but smaller stars. Astronomers call Capella and Arcturus **red giants.**

Some stars are hundreds of times as luminous as the red giants. These stars are called **supergiants.** They include blue-white Rigel,

Choose a red supergiant. Now find a blue star that is the same distance up. These two stars have the same true brightness. The blue star is hotter but smaller than the red star.

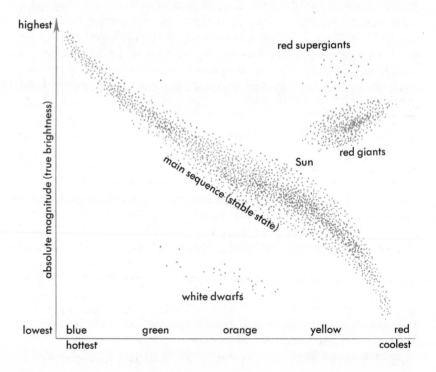

white-yellow Canopus, and the red supergiants Antares and Betelgeuse. Again, the red supergiants must be much larger than the blue or white ones to be equally luminous. They are the largest of all stars.

The less luminous stars are called dwarfs. These stars have an absolute magnitude of + 1 or less (more numerically). (Remember that in the astronomer's absolute magnitude scale, higher numbers mean less luminosity.) Most dwarfs (our sun is one) are red, orange, or yellow. But again there are exceptions. These exceptional dwarfs are white. Yet they are very faint because they are *really* very small. These **white dwarfs** are very dense because the nuclei of their atoms are packed closely together.

9. Cepheids and Eclipsing Binaries

Most stars shine with a steady brightness. But some change in brightness. They change at regular periods or cycles that take from days to years. These are called **variable stars.** There are different kinds of variable stars.

Pulsating stars change in brightness as they expand and contract. Contraction makes them hotter and brighter. Expansion makes them cooler and dimmer. Examples of pulsating stars are the **cepheid** (SEE fee id) variables first discovered in the constellation Cepheus (SEE fee us). They are yellow supergiants whose bright-dim-bright periods range from about one day to 50 days. Most are about five days.

Cepheids have given the astronomer a way of finding the distance of many galaxies. Astronomers have found that the true brightness of a cepheid is related to the time of its bright-dim-bright period. The longer and slower the bright-dim-bright period, the greater the absolute magnitude. Astronomers have worked out tables that show the absolute magnitude a cepheid will have for any time period. Then, if they compare a cepheid's apparent and absolute magnitudes, they can find its distance. In this way astronomers can get the distance of any galaxy in which there is a cepheid.

A star may change in brightness because it is not one but really two stars. They are of unequal brightness. The two stars revolve around each other. As they do, the dim one eclipses the bright one at regular intervals as seen from earth. Two stars like this are called an **eclipsing binary.** The best known eclipsing binary is the second magnitude star Algol and its dim companion in the constellation Perseus. Algol is eclipsed to about one-third its normal brightness every 69 hours.

In Topic 11 another kind of variable star is discussed—the *pulsar.*

Novas and Supernovas 10.

A supernova flared up in 1054. This huge cloud of gas in Taurus is all that is left. (Crab Nebula)

Faint stars sometimes flare up suddenly into intense brightness. Such a star is called a **nova** which means new one. Astronomers believe that a nova is formed by an explosion inside the star. The explosion blows away the outer atmosphere of the faint star. Energy is radiated so rapidly from inside the star that the nova glows like a supergiant for months or even years. Then it fades to its former luminosity.

A few rare times a star has flared into such brightness that astronomers have called it a **supernova.** Supernova explosions probably blow away a large part of the parent star.

Chinese astronomers recorded the flaring of a supernova in the year 1054 A.D. The brilliant star faded after a year. But it left behind a great expanding cloud of gas. Today that cloud is known as the **Crab Nebula.** It is in the constellation of Taurus, the Bull.

Nova Hercules flared into intense brightness and then in about two months time faded back to a faint star.

1935 Mar. 10

1935 May 6

Quasars and Pulsars 11.

In 1961 astronomers discovered strange new types of heavenly objects. These objects looked like stars, and they emitted radio waves. So they were named **quasars** for "quasi-stellar radio sources" (radio sources like stars). But quasars are very different from stars.

Quasars are faint objects in the telescope because they are so far distant. But calculations show them to be the most luminous objects in the universe. They are far larger and more massive than any star. They radiate light and radio waves at a rate too high for scientists to explain.

Let us describe a quasar that astronomers call **3C-273.** In a powerful telescope it looks like a faint star of about 13th magnitude. But its red-shift shows it to be about two billion light-years away. At this distance, no star we know can be seen even in the great telescopes. Even galaxies of billions of stars are barely visible. How then is 3C-273 visible? It must be billions of times as bright as our sun! And it must have the mass of hundreds of millions of suns.

In 1967 astronomers discovered still another kind of strange heavenly object. At first these seemed to be invisible. But all of them gave off powerful bursts of radio waves every second or less. One source of these radio waves seemed to be in the Crab Nebula. After much study, it was found that a star in the Crab Nebula was flickering in time with the radio pulses. Apparently it was the source of both the light and the radio waves. Astronomers named it a **pulsar.** They think it is the remains of the star that exploded into a supernova before becoming the Crab Nebula. Several dozen pulsars are now known. All are believed to be the remains of supernovas.

Life History of Stars

12. Clouds of Gas and Dust

Huge clouds of gas and dust occur in parts of space between stars. Their density is very low. Nevertheless, because the clouds are so large, they contain at least as much material as stars do.

These clouds are usually about 99 per cent gas. Most of this is hydrogen. The remaining one per cent or so of the cloud is a strange kind of dust. The grains of this dust are very tiny, with diameters of about one ten-thousandth of a centimeter or less. Astronomers think that the dust grains may consist of hydrogen, carbon, nitrogen, oxygen, and possible other elements. These are probably in the form of tiny ice-like crystals formed in the intense cold of outer space.

Where does this gas and dust come from? One possible source is the explosion of stars that have formed novas.

13. Origin of a Star

According to modern theory, stars are forming continually wherever clouds of gas and dust exist. An average cloud is about 25 light-years in diameter. Each cloud may contain enough material to make many suns. Gravitation causes the atoms of gas and the grains of dust in the cloud to attract each other. Throughout the cloud huge areas become denser. They contract and get hotter. In time they get so hot that they glow. The glowing clouds are large, gaseous stars.

As contraction continues, the stars become hotter and brighter. The more massive stars are so hot that they glow blue or white. The less massive stars are cooler and glow yellow or orange. Eventually the star's center gets so hot that a fusion reaction begins. This means that light hydrogen atoms unite to form heavier helium atoms. Huge amounts of energy are radiated in the process. When this happens the star stops contracting. It is now in a stable state. The outward pressure of the hot gaseous center just balances the weight of the gases above. The massive blue stars may reach this stage in a few hundred thousand years. The less massive yellow and orange stars contract more slowly. They may take millions of years to reach this stable state.

From Stable State to Giant 14.

In the stable state, the star's diameter and radiation remain the same for millions or even billions of years. Eventually, however, so much of the core's light atoms are used up that the star loses its stability. The core contracts again. It gets so hot that its gas pressure makes the star's outer layers expand. This enlarges the star's surface area. So, it radiates more light and appears brighter. In the meantime a fusion reaction begins again, this time in the outer layers. The star expands further, and it becomes a red giant or supergiant.

If the star's core gets hot enough, helium atoms "burn" in a reaction that forms still heavier atoms. Then when the temperature rises still higher, iron and other heavy elements are formed.

This picture shows how a stable star shrinks, then expands to a giant star.

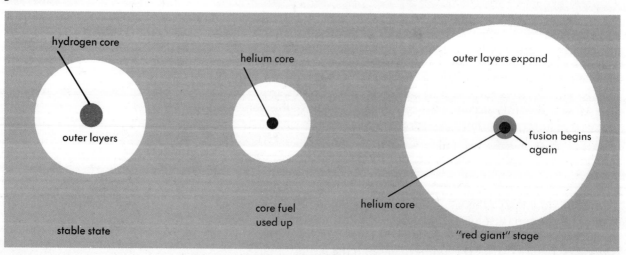

hydrogen core

outer layers

stable state

helium core

core fuel used up

outer layers expand

fusion begins again

helium core

"red giant" stage

Finally, the time comes when most of the star's fuel is used up. Its core can no longer support the weight of its outer layers.

The giant collapses. The nuclei of its atoms are squeezed tightly together. The star becomes a white dwarf. It is no larger, perhaps, than the earth.

Since its fuel is gone, the star can produce no more heat. But it is still hot enough to glow faintly for perhaps a billion years. Then it will become cold and dark.

Our sun is thought to be at least five billion years old now. It is still in its stable stage. Astronomers expect it to remain stable for another five billion years before it swells to a red giant. When it does, the earth will certainly be too hot for life.

Galaxies and the Universe

16. Galaxies: Island Universes

Without the telescope we can see several thousand stars. We can also see a few hazy patches of light in the night sky. Small telescopes show thousands more of these "patches." Early observers named them nebulae (clouds).

Today the nebulae are studied with our powerful modern telescopes. They show that many nebulae are systems containing millions or even billions of stars. We call these systems **galaxies.** Telescopes show us that space contains at least a billion galaxies. But space is so vast that most galaxies are millions of light-years apart.

The galaxy to which we belong is the **Milky Way** galaxy. In it our sun is one star among 100 billion. Every star that we see with the unaided eye belongs to our galaxy.

Our galaxy is shaped like a large thin convex lens with a large central bulge. Its size is huge. Its diameter is about 80,000 light years. Its greatest thickness is about 10,000 light-years. The sun is about two-thirds of the way out from the galaxy's center.

You're looking at a side-view of our Milky Way from far out in the universe. Note where our solar system is.

When we look through the galaxy in its long direction, we see so many stars that the sky looks "milky." Men called this part of the sky the Milky Way long before they knew what it was. When we look through the short direction of the galaxy, we see fewer stars.

The Local Group 17.

This map of part of the Local Cluster shows our galaxy and some "neighbor" galaxies.

Our galaxy belongs to a "small cluster" of 17 galaxies. Astronomers call this cluster the **Local Group.** Our nearest neighbors in the Local Group, the two Magellanic Clouds, are in the Southern Hemisphere

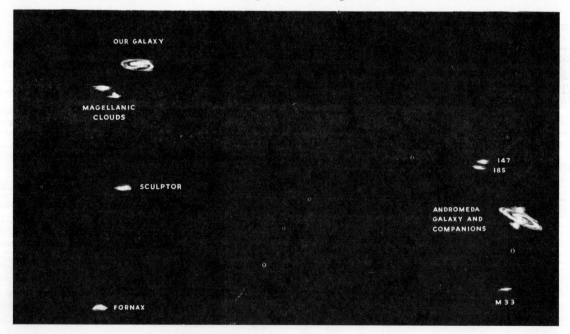

OUR GALAXY

MAGELLANIC CLOUDS

SCULPTOR

147
185

ANDROMEDA GALAXY AND COMPANIONS

FORNAX

M 33

Light travels from our sun to the earth in 8 minutes. This huge spiral galaxy in Andromeda is much further away. The light from Andromeda that created this picture took 2,000,000 years to reach the camera on the earth!

sky. They can be seen without a telescope. Another "neighbor", the great **Andromeda Galaxy,** is faintly visible to the unaided eye in our sky. It is believed to be even larger than our galaxy. Its distance from us is thought to be about two million light-years.

18. Types of Galaxies

Galaxies are of three main types. **Spiral galaxies** have a central lens-shaped bright nucleus made up of millions of stars. Around the nucleus may be a fainter flat disk of stars. Spiral arms, usually two, come out from opposite sides of the nucleus. The arms trail behind the galaxy as it rotates. There are millions of stars in the arms. The stars also contain great clouds of dust and gas. Between the arms there are few stars and almost no dust or gas.

From the earth we see the flatter side of the spiral galaxy M51—like looking at a plaque on a wall. Note the two spiral arms above and below. The irregular galaxy at the right orbits around M51. (in the Constellation Canes Venatici, The Hunting Dogs)

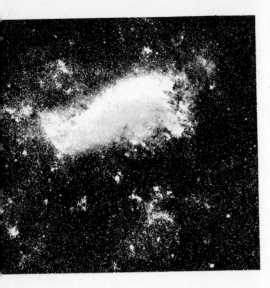

About three-fourths of all galaxies are probably spirals. Our own galaxy and the Andromeda galaxy are spirals.

Elliptical galaxies range from nearly ball-shaped to lens-shaped. Their brightness patterns shows that most of their stars are close to the center. They have no arms, and almost no gas and dust clouds.

Irregular galaxies are smaller, fainter, and less common than the others. Their stars are spread unevenly. The two Magellanic Clouds are of this type.

The Large Magellanic Cloud is an irregular galaxy. It has an uneven shape. This galaxy orbits around our Milky Way.

Origin of the Universe 19.

How do scientists explain the universe of galaxies? Most astronomers believe in the *expanding universe* hypothesis. This is also called the **big-bang hypothesis.** It begins with the whole universe packed into one dense globe of hydrogen. The entire globe is thought to have been not much larger than our sun is today.

 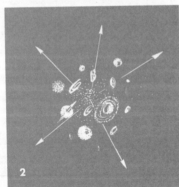 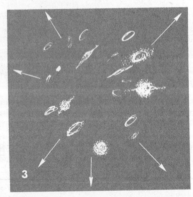

How did the universe begin? The big-bang hypothesis is one theory:
1. **A dense hydrogen ball explodes.**
2. **A huge hydrogen cloud moves out. The cloud parts condense into galaxies.**
3. **The galaxies keep moving out.**

About ten billions years ago this mass of hydrogen exploded. It formed a gigantic expanding cloud. Some parts of the cloud moved faster than others. But all of them moved outward, away from the center. As they moved, they condensed into galaxies. Billions of galaxies were formed. All of the galaxies continued moving outward, away from the center and from each other. Those with the highest speeds are now farthest out in space.

What is the evidence for this hypothesis? In 1929 astronomer Edwin Hubble found red-shifts in the spectra of the galaxies he studied. This showed that all of the galaxies were receding from the earth. (See Chapter 18, Topic 12, Doppler effect.) Furthermore, he found that the more distant the galaxy, the faster it receded. Surely the universe is expanding!

The most distant galaxies seem to be receding at nearly half the speed of light. (The speed of light is 300,000 kilometers a second.) This speed of the galaxies is so great that some astronomers question it. These astronomers think that the observed red-shifts may not be Doppler effects. But no other explanation has yet been given.

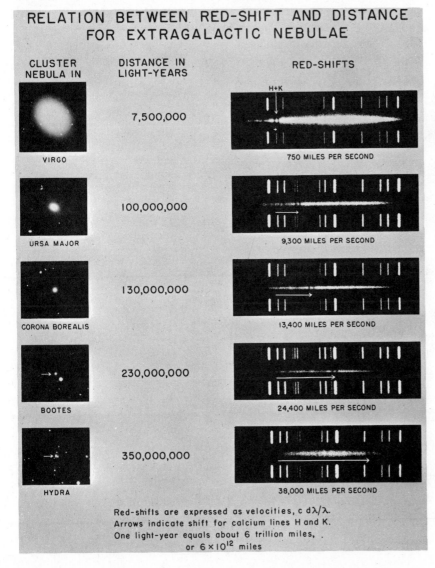

RELATION BETWEEN RED-SHIFT AND DISTANCE FOR EXTRAGALACTIC NEBULAE

CLUSTER NEBULA IN	DISTANCE IN LIGHT-YEARS	RED-SHIFTS
VIRGO	7,500,000	H+K 750 MILES PER SECOND
URSA MAJOR	100,000,000	9,300 MILES PER SECOND
CORONA BOREALIS	130,000,000	13,400 MILES PER SECOND
BOOTES	230,000,000	24,400 MILES PER SECOND
HYDRA	350,000,000	38,000 MILES PER SECOND

Red-shifts are expressed as velocities, c dλ/λ.
Arrows indicate shift for calcium lines H and K.
One light-year equals about 6 trillion miles,
or 6×10^{12} miles

The vertical arrow above the top spectrum shows where the galaxy's spectrum matches two lines in the spectrum of the element calcium. The horizontal arrows show how much these lines have shifted toward the red in each galaxy's spectrum. The larger the red shift, the faster the galaxy is moving away from the earth. Which galaxies move faster, the nearer ones or the more distant ones?

How the Stars Look From Earth

Constellations: Star Patterns in Our Galaxy 20.

Leo the Lion; Ursa Major, the Great Bear; Orion, the Mighty Hunter. These are names given by ancient sky watchers to what appear to be groups of stars *(constellations)* in the skies. In most cases the names come from stories in their mythologies. The stars in these groups are all in our galaxy. Otherwise, however, they are not really "related" to one another.

The best known constellation is probably *Ursa Major*. In it, the "Big Dipper" forms the tail and part of the back of the bear. A line through the "pointer" stars in the Big Dipper points to Polaris, the

Next summer, look up at the stars. If you live in the Northern Hemisphere, you'll see these constellations.

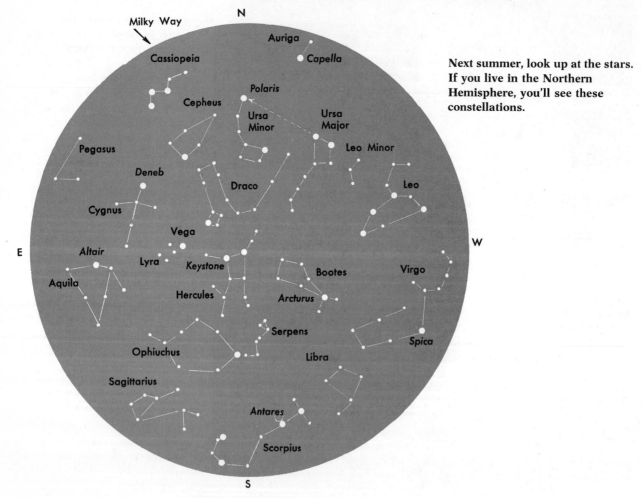

North Star. Polaris itself is the end star in the handle of the *Little Dipper*. Opposite the Big Dipper can be seen *Queen Cassiopeia's Chair*. These three constellations can be seen all year.

Constellations seen in summer include Lyra, the Lyre, with the brilliant star Vega; Cygnus, the Swan, in which the Northern Cross lies; Scorpius, the Scorpion, with the red supergiant star Antares. In winter we see Orion, the Mighty Hunter, with its two bright stars: red supergiant Betelgeuse, and blue supergiant Rigel. We also see Canis Major, the hunter's Big Dog, with Sirius, brightest of all our stars. Nearby we see Taurus the Bull and the Pleiades, or Seven Sisters.

Of course, the stars in most constellations only appear to be together because we see them in the same direction in space. Actually each star is moving toward or away from the other stars at high speed. But because stars are so far away, it takes thousands of years before constellations look very different from earth. In 50,000 years, for example, the Big Dipper will almost reverse its appearance.

These are the constellations you see in winter from the Northern Hemisphere. Would you see the same constellations from Brazil?

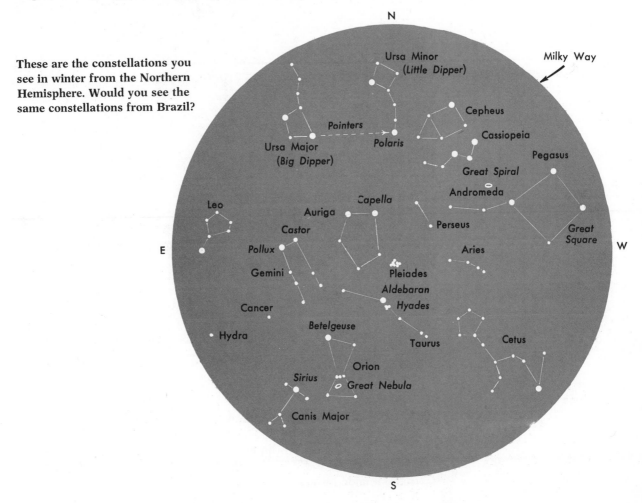

Turning of the Heavens 21.

The earth rotates on its axis from west to east. As a result, the whole sky appears to turn from east to west. That is why the sun, the moon, and the stars "rise in the east and set in the west." The part of the sky directly above the earth's axis, however, does not rise or set. Why?

The earth's axis is pointed almost exactly at the North Star. When the earth turns on its axis; the North Star seems almost stationary in the sky. The stars near it seem to go around in circles from east to west. These *circumpolar stars* therefore can be seen all night in our sky. Their **"tracks"** can be photographed with ordinary cameras by time exposure.

This photo was made with a camera lens open all night. It looks up from the North Pole. The circles show the stars changing position in the sky as the earth turns. The bright trail near the center is the North Star.

Nebulae 22.

In Topic 16 we learned that many "nebulae" in the sky are not clouds at all—instead, they are distant galaxies. But some nebulae actually are dense clouds of gas and dust. These are called **diffuse nebulae.** The brightest of these is the Great Nebula in Orion. It is barely visible to the unaided eye, close to the middle star in Orion's sword.

The cloud of gas and dust on the left is bright because nearby stars shine on it. (Great Nebula in Orion)

There are no bright stars near the cloud of gas and dust below. So, it appears dark. (Horsehead Nebula in Orion)

A diffuse nebula has no light of its own. It shines only when a bright star is near enough to light it up. If no bright star is near it, the nebula shows up as a dark part of the sky. It is then called a **dark nebula.** The Horsehead Nebula in Orion is a famous dark nebula.

Each topic question refers to the topic of the same number within this chapter.

TOPIC QUESTIONS

1. In simple terms explain how an astronomer determines a star's (a) distance, (b) surface temperature, (c) size, (d) density, (e) chemical composition.

2. (a) What are the sun's dimensions? (b) Describe how stars range in size, density, and mass.

3. (a) What is an Astronomical Unit? (b) Name the star nearest to the sun. How far off is it? (c) What is a light-year? How many miles is it? Express the distance of a few stars in terms of light-years.

4. (a) How is the color of a star related to its temperature? (b) Give examples.

Stars and Galaxies **293**

5. (a) Of what elements are stars made? (b) Why do star spectra differ?

6. (a) What is the apparent magnitude of a star? (b) In the early days of astronomy how were star magnitudes defined? (c) How is magnitude compared today? Give some examples. (d) How is magnitude stated for stars brighter than first magnitude? Give examples. (e) How bright are the planets? the full moon? the sun?

7. (a) What is absolute magnitude? (b) Compare the absolute magnitude of Rigel, the sun, and most stars.

8. (a) What is a red giant? Give examples. (b) Why must a red supergiant be larger than a blue-white supergiant? (c) How is a dwarf star defined? Give examples. (d) What is a white dwarf? Why are they so dense?

9. (a) What are variable stars? What is a pulsating star? (b) What is a cepheid? (c) What is the great importance of cepheids? (d) What is an eclipsing binary? Describe a famous example.

10. (a) Describe the formation and decline of a nova. (b) What is a supernova? How does it form? What is the Crab Nebula?

11. (a) What is a quasar? How does it differ from a star? (b) Describe quasar 3C-273. (c) What is a pulsar? How were pulsars discovered.

12. (a) Describe an interstellar dust and gas cloud. What is it made of? (b) How may it have originated?

13. (a) How are stars born? (b) How are blue or white stars formed? yellow or orange stars? (c) Explain how fusion begins and contraction stops. How long does it take?

14. (a) What is the "stable state"? Why does it end? (b) Explain how the star becomes a red giant.

15. (a) How does a star become a "white dwarf"? (b) Summarize our sun's past and future.

16. (a) What are galaxies? (b) What is the Milky Way? Describe its shape and size.

17. (a) What is the Local Group? (b) What are the Magellanic Clouds? (c) What is the Andromeda Galaxy?

18. Name and describe the three main types of galaxies.

19. Describe the big-bang hypothesis and the evidence for it.

20. Name some of the familiar constellations of summer, winter, and all year.

21. What are star tracks? What do they show?

22. (a) What are diffuse nebulae? Name one. Where do they get their light? (b) What is a dark nebula? Name one.

GENERAL QUESTIONS

1. Why should the interior of a star be hotter than its surface?

2. How can planets be brighter than stars?

3. Where would one have to go in order to photograph star trails that were complete circles? Why?

4. Approximately how many times as bright as Mars is the full moon? (Use figures given in Topic 6.)

5. The moon's average distance from the earth is about 380,000 kilometers. How long does it take moonlight to reach us?

6. If the diameter of Betelgeuse is 400 times as great as the sun's diameter, how does the volume of Betelgeuse compare with the volume of the sun? (Volume of a sphere $= \frac{4}{3}\pi r^3$.)

7. Compare the masses of Betelgeuse and the sun. (See Topics 1 and 2, and General Question 6.)

1. Learn to identify the major constellations of summer and winter skies. Locate the first magnitude stars listed in this chapter, and see if their colors and relative brightnesses appear to you as they are described in the text.

2. Visit a planetarium or observatory.

3. Photograph the tracks of circumpolar stars by exposing your film for at least 3 hours with an open shutter and your camera, mounted on a stand or tripod, pointed at the North Star. Your location must be shielded from all other lights. Choose a night with no moon.

20

The sun must never be viewed directly with the unaided eye or through a lens. Its strong rays will injure the eye, especially when the rays are focused by a lens or telescope. Here is a way to make an image of the sun that you can look at.

Get as large a magnifying glass as possible. Choose a day when the sun is not behind clouds. Set up a white paper or cardboard screen at right angles to the direction from sun to screen.

Now, hold the magnifying glass parallel to the screen. Move it to the place near the screen where it forms the smallest and sharpest bright spot possible. This is an "image" of the sun. The magnifying glass has taken all the sunlight that strikes its large area and focused it into a much smaller area. This is why the "image" is so much brighter and hotter than direct sunlight.

Can you see any sunspots in your "image"? Use lenses of different diameters and different curvatures to find out the answers to this question. How does the size of a lens affect the size of the image of the sun it forms?

The Sun and the Solar System

The Sun

1. Observing the Sun

Astronomers use special instruments to study the sun. Long focus **tower telescopes** can form images of the sun nearly a meter in diameter. Special **space telescopes** are carried by unpiloted balloons. These photograph the sun from above the dust and clouds of the lower atmosphere. **Coronagraphs** find out things about the sun that previously could only be seen when it was eclipsed. However, coronagraphs make artificial eclipses every day. There is also a special instrument that measures the rate at which we receive solar energy.

This is the world's largest solar telescope. The sun's image has a diameter of 86 centimeters. It is formed by reflecting the sun's rays into the slanting shaft. The shaft goes underground for a total length of 131 meters. The vertical tower is only 33 meters high. (Kitt Peak National Observatory, Arizona)

2. How Big? How Hot?

The sun is an average-sized star. Compared with the earth, however, it is gigantic. Its diameter of 1,380,000 kilometers is about 110 times the earth's. Its volume can hold more than a million earth's. Even though it is made entirely of light gases, its mass is 300,000 times that of the earth. In fact, its mass is 700 times as large as that of all the planets together.

The surface temperature of the sun is about 5500° C. Its interior temperature is more than 1,000,000° C.

The Sun's Surface 3.

Note the mottled look of the sun's photosphere. This photo was taken from an unmanned balloon about 25 kilometers above the earth.

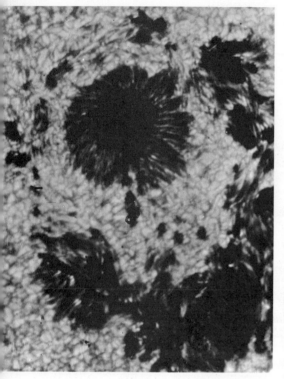

The bright yellow surface of the sun is called the sun's **photosphere.** Through the telescope, the photosphere appears as a mottled surface of bright spots crowded together on a darker background. The bright spots are thought to be great "bubbles" of hot gases. They boil up from the sun's interior and disappear within minutes.

Above the photosphere lies the sun's atmosphere. Without special instruments, the atmosphere can be seen only during an eclipse. At the bottom of the atmosphere is the **chromosphere,** colored red by glowing hydrogen. It extends about 8000 kilometers above the photosphere. The lower part of the chromosphere creates the dark lines in the solar spectrum. It does this by absorbing radiation passing through it from the hotter photosphere.

Above the chromosphere is the corona. The **corona,** the sun's outer atmosphere, surrounds the sun to a height of over a million kilometers. During an eclipse, it is seen glowing with a faint pearly light.

Solar prominences are great flamelike clouds of gas. They may extend a million kilometers above the sun's surface into the corona. They glow bright red against the sky during an eclipse.

This solar prominence flared out above the surface of the sun more than 68 times the distance from San Francisco to New York.

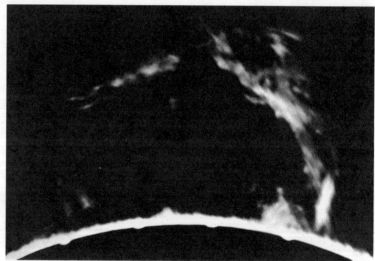

Sunspots 4.

Sunspots are seen as dark spots on the photosphere. Some are barely visible in large telescopes. Others reach more than one tenth of the way across the sun. The spots are cooler parts of the photosphere.

They appear dark by contrast with the hotter and brighter background.

Sunspots are believed to be storms in the lower atmosphere of the sun. Like storms on the earth, they are temporary features. They form in a clear solar "sky" and then either disappear soon or grow larger. Those that grow larger usually form in groups that last weeks or even months. They always appear to move across the sun from its eastern edge to its western edge.

The movement of sunspots shows the rotation of the sun. The sun rotates faster near its equator than near its poles. (Remember that the sun is not solid; it is made of gases!) At its equator its rotation period is about 25 days.

Most sunspots are found within about 30° of the sun's equator. They never occur near the poles. The number of spots is always changing. It is greatest about every 11 years. The cause of this regular change in number is unknown.

Sunspots have strong magnetic fields.

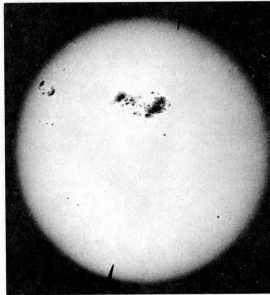

In the photo above, note the large sunspot group above the sun's center. This group is shown in detail at the left. The distance from right to left across the cluster of sunspots is about 70 times the distance from New York to San Francisco.

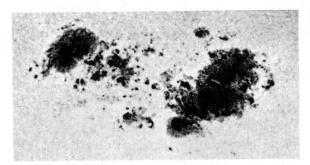

5. Flares, Magnetic Storms, Solar Wind

On rare occasions, large sunspot groups are accompanied by **solar flares.** These seem to be great masses of glowing gas erupting into the photosphere. Large flares may last more than an hour.

A solar flare causes strange effects on the earth. Its intense light and ultraviolet rays reach the earth's atmosphere in about eight minutes. The ultraviolet rays disrupt radio communications. The flare also creates radio waves. These cause static in radio sets for many minutes.

High speed atomic particles are also shot into space by a flare. Some of these reach the earth after one to two days. They cause **magnetic storms** and **auroras.** Magnetic storms disturb the earth's magnetic field. Compasses give strange readings, and telephone and telegraph communications are upset. Auroras, the "northern lights," form in the area around the south pole as well as in the far north.

Observations by spacecraft show that the sun's corona always gives off a thin stream of protons. The protons are hydrogen nuclei. They move into space in all directions. As they pass the earth, their speed is more than a million kilometers an hour. Scientists call this stream of protons the **solar wind.**

Source of the Sun's Energy 6.

The life story of a star was described in chapter 19. Remember that the fusion of light elements into heavier ones was given as the source of a star's energy. How does this fusion reaction take place? Why does it provide energy?

Albert Einstein provided the key to the answer in 1905 with his famous $E = mc^2$ equation. This stated that *matter can be converted into energy,* and vice versa.

The sun is mostly hydrogen. Four hydrogen nuclei weigh about 4.030 units of atomic weight. In fusion, four hydrogen nuclei are joined to form a helium nucleus. One helium nucleus weighs about 4.003 units. Thus when a helium nucleus is formed from four hydrogen nuclei, there is some weight left over. This weight is changed into energy. How much energy?

Calculations show that the total conversion of a kilogram of matter would release enough energy to raise a billion metric tons 10 kilometers above the earth's surface. Astronomers believe that about 4 million tons of matter are being converted into energy in the sun every second. This happens as 564 million tons of hydrogen in the sun become 560 million tons of helium. How long can the sun keep this up? The mass of the sun is so great that it can continue to provide energy at this rate for another 5 billion years!

The Planets and Kepler's Laws

The Solar System 7.

The sun's family is known as the **solar system.** It includes objects ranging in size from tiny sandlike grains to gigantic spheres many thousands of kilometers in diameter. In the sun's family there are

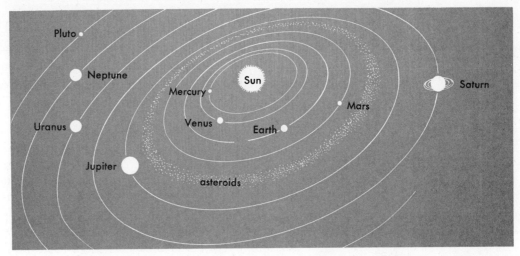

Note the members of the solar system.

nine planets, 33 satellites, thousands of asteroids, millions of meteors, and numerous comets. These bodies travel around the sun at high speeds. They travel in paths called **orbits.** The distances of the orbits from the sun range from millions to billions of kilometers.

 Recognizing a Planet

Have you seen the members of the solar family? The sun is familiar. So is the earth's moon. Meteors are often seen as "shooting stars." Comets are seen rather rarely, but most of us have seen pictures that would help us identify a comet. Five planets can easily be seen in the sky with the naked eye. The asteroids and three distant planets can be seen only through telescopes.

To the unaided eye planets look very much like stars. But several visible differences let us tell them apart.

First, planets are very much closer to the earth than stars are. Therefore their motion around the sun is plainly seen as a shifting of their positions in the sky. As ancient astronomers observed, the planets "wander" among the constellations. True stars appear to keep the same formations for thousands of years.

The second difference is that stars always twinkle. Planets shine steadily except when they are close to the horizon.

Because stars are so very far away, the telescope can only make them look brighter, but not larger. Most planets, on the other hand, are magnified by the telescope. They appear as bright circles rather than just bright pinpoints of light. The astronomer calls these circles *visible disks.* On them, details of the surface of the planets may be seen.

Classifying the Planets 9.

In order of increasing distance from the sun, the planets are Mercury, Venus, earth, Mars, Jupiter, Saturn, Uranus, Neptune, and Pluto. Between Mars and Jupiter are the *asteroids,* or *minor planets.*

Scientists classify the planets in a number of different ways. **Inferior planets** are those nearer to the sun than the earth. **Superior planets** are those farther from the sun than the earth. If the asteroids are used as a "dividing line," then Mercury, Venus, earth, and Mars are the **inner** planets, and the other five are the **outer** planets. If size is used as a basis for grouping, then Mercury, Venus, earth, Mars, and Pluto are called **terrestrial planets,** whereas Jupiter, Saturn, Uranus, and Neptune are **major planets.**

Terrestrial means "earthly." Mercury, Venus, earth, and Mars are all made of solid, earthlike materials that are much denser than water. In contrast, the major planets are largely gaseous, and much less dense.

What Is an Ellipse? 10.

A circle is a curve on which every point is at the same distance from a point called its center. An **ellipse** is one kind of curve that has two points called its *foci* (singular: focus) instead of a single center. For any point on the ellipse, the sum of its distances from the two foci is the same. The ellipse resembles a flattened circle.

Suppose you want to construct an ellipse. Tie together two ends of a string to make a loop about 20 centimeters long. Mark the two foci by placing thumb tacks about 5 centimeters apart on a piece of cardboard. Loop the string around the tacks. Then pull the string tight with a pencil held vertically inside the loop. Hold the string *tight* with the pencil point against the paper. Move the pencil completely around the two foci until a closed curve is completed.

If the foci are placed farther apart, a "flatter" or more **eccentric** (off center) ellipse will be formed. If the foci are closer together, the ellipse will be more nearly circular. In fact, when the two foci meet, the "ellipse" is a circle.

Move the pencil along the string keeping the string tight. You'll get the blue ellipse.

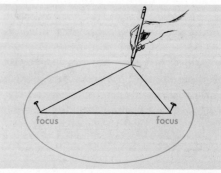

focus   focus

Ancient peoples believed that the stars and planets moved around the earth. Copernicus published a different theory of the motions of the planets in 1543. He believed that the planets revolved around the sun. This motion was in circular orbits or in combinations of circles. In the later 1500's the Danish astronomer Tycho Brahe made many observations of the planets. These did not quite fit Copernicus' theory. In 1609, Johannes Kepler published his first and second **laws of planetary motion.** They were based on Brahe's observations. These laws correctly described the movements of the planets as follows: (1) *The orbit of each planet is an ellipse in which the sun is at one of the two foci.* (2) *Each planet revolves so that a line from the planet to the sun (called the "radius vector") sweeps over equal areas in equal times.* The second law is known as the Law of Equal Areas.

By Kepler's first law the distance between a planet and the sun is always changing. It increases half the time and decreases in the other half.

By Kepler's second law each planet's speed of revolution around the sun is also always changing. In order for the *radius vector* to cover equal areas in equal time, the planet must move faster when it is nearer the sun. And it must move more slowly when it is farther away.

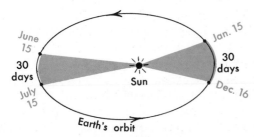

Imagine a string from the sun to the earth. It sweeps out these two wedges, which have the same area. The string is shorter in the winter, so the curved edge must be longer. This means the earth goes faster in winter because the time for each wedge is the same.

Kepler published his first two laws of planetary motion. But he wondered whether the planets' periods of revolution were related. In 1618 he published the answer to this problem in his *third* law of planetary motion. This law is also known as the Harmonic Law. It states that *the ratio of the squares of the periods of revolution of any two planets is equal to the ratio of the cubes of their average distances from the sun.* To illustrate this law, let us find the period of the planet Jupiter, if we know its distance from the sun.

The earth's period of revolution is 1 year, and the earth's distance from the sun is, by definition, 1 astronomical unit (1 A.U.). Jupiter's distance from the sun is about 5.2 A.U. By Kepler's third law,

$$\frac{\text{(Jupiter's period)}^2}{\text{(earth's period)}^2} = \frac{\text{(Jupiter's distance)}^3}{\text{(earth's distance)}^3}$$

$$\frac{\text{(Jupiter's period)}^2}{1} = \frac{(5.2)^3}{1}.$$

This means that the square of Jupiter's period is 140. (It is easy to calculate this if you have a hand-held calculator.) Taking the square root, you find that Jupiter's period is about 12 earth years.

Using Kepler's third law, we find that the farther a planet is from the sun, the longer is its period of revolution. This is partly because its orbit is larger. Also, it moves more slowly than do nearer planets. The average speed of the earth in its orbit is about 30 kilometers a second. Mercury, nearest to the sun, has an average speed of about 48 kilometers a second. Pluto, farthest from the sun, moves at only 5 kilometers a second.

Orbits of the Planets 12.

The orbit of each planet is an ellipse in which the sun is at one focus. At one end of each orbit, then, there is a point at which the planet is nearest to the sun. This point is called its **perihelion** (*per* = near, *helion* = sun.) At the opposite end of the orbit, the planet is farthest from the sun. This point is called its **aphelion.**

Although the orbits of the planets are ellipses, all but those of Mercury and Pluto are nearly circular. Pluto's orbit is so eccentric that at aphelion it is almost twice as far away as at perihelion.

All the planets revolve in their orbits *from west to east.* Except for Mercury and Pluto, the planets' orbits lie in the **plane of the ecliptic** (the plane in which the earth's orbit lies). Mercury's orbit is inclined about 7° to this plane. Pluto's orbit is inclined 17°.

The time a planet takes to travel once around its orbit is its *period of revolution.* Pluto's period is 248 of our years. Mercury's period is only 88 of our days.

This scale drawing shows the relative distances of the planets from the sun.

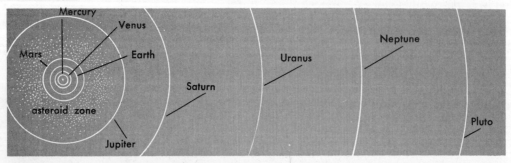

Describing the Planets

All of the planets are roughly spherical in shape. All but Venus and Uranus rotate on their axes from west to east. Rotation tends to make a planet bulge at its equator and flatten at its poles. This forms a shape called an **oblate spheroid.**

The planets have a great range in density. Mercury, Venus, earth, Mars, and probably Pluto, consist largely of rock, and have high densities. Jupiter, Saturn, Uranus, and Neptune are gaseous, and their densities are much lower. Mercury and earth are about 5.5 times as heavy as water.

The approximate densities of the others are Venus, 5; Mars, 4; Neptune, 2.3; Uranus, 1.6; Jupiter, 1.3; Saturn, 0.7; Pluto, unknown.

Now to return to the shapes of the planets. The amount of bulging at the equator depends on three things: the planet's speed of rotation, its size, and its density. Jupiter and Saturn are the two largest planets. They also rotate most rapidly and are the least dense. As a result, they bulge a lot at the equator and are very flattened at the poles.

Note in the table that Mars and earth have nearly the same rotation period; that all four major planets rotate more rapidly than the other planets; and that Mercury and Venus rotate very slowly. Mercury rotates only once in 59 days. Venus takes 243 days for one rotation. (What do you think the minus signs in the table's "Period of Rotation" column mean? See the first paragraph in this Topic.)

Statistics of the Planets

Name	Average Distance in Kilometers from Sun	Equatorial Diameter in Kilometers	Period of Revolution	Period of Rotation	Number of Natural Satellites
Mercury	58 million	4,880	88 days	59 days	0
Venus	108 million	12,100	225 days	−243 days	0
Earth	150 million	12,756	365¼ days	23h. 56m.	1
Mars	228 million	6,787	687 days	24h. 37m.	2
Jupiter	778 million	142,800	12 years	9h. 50m.	13
Saturn	1427 million	120,000	29½ years	10h. 14m.	10
Uranus	2870 million	51,800	84 years	−11h.	5
Neptune	4497 million	49,500	165 years	16h.	2
Pluto	5900 million	6,000	248 years	6.4 days	?

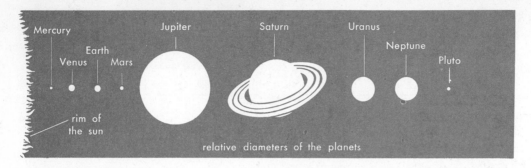

relative diameters of the planets

This scale drawing shows the relative sizes of the planets.

The sizes of the planets are given in the table on page 305. Their relative sizes are shown in the diagram above.

Studying Distant Planets 14.

Life on earth needs an atmosphere containing water vapor, oxygen, and carbon dioxide. It also needs favorable temperatures. Can life exist on other planets? The answer probably depends to a large extent on their atmospheres and weather.

How does the scientist study the atmosphere and weather of a distant planet? Optical telescopes can show clouds and signs of winds and storms. Spectroscopes give clues as to the composition and pressure of the atmosphere. Other instruments help to measure surface temperatures.

Observations with telescopes can tell us a planet's period of rotation. From this we get the length of its day and night. From its period of revolution we find the length of its seasons. Its distance from the sun tells us how much solar energy it gets.

Now planets are being explored more directly by spacecraft. Some of these are "flyby" craft. Others go into orbit around a planet. Still others land on the planet. All of these send photos and other observations back to earth by radio.

The Planet Mercury 15.

Mercury is the planet nearest to the sun. It is also the smallest planet, with a diameter about one-third that of earth. Its density is about the same as earth's. Its gravity is much weaker than earth's. One hundred kilograms would weigh about 37 kilograms on Mercury. (The kilogram is a measure of mass, not weight. In ordinary use, however, we speak of weight in kilograms because the mass of an object on earth can be determined from its weight.)

Because Mercury is so near the sun, it receives intense sunlight. Mercury rotates on its axis very slowly, taking 59 earth days to complete its own day. Its daytime and nighttime each last nearly one of our months. Because of the strong sunlight and the long day, Mercury's surface temperature goes above 400° C. During the long night, however, the temperature drops to nearly 200° C. below zero.

Mercury has no atmosphere. Its low gravity and its high daytime temperature make it impossible for it to hold gases. Its lack of atmosphere also helps explain why it cools down so much at night.

Until Mercury was explored by unpiloted spacecraft, we knew little about its surface. In 1974 and 1975, Mariner 10 did three flyby observations of Mercury. The nearest of these was only 300 kilometers above the planet! Mariner 10 is now in orbit around the sun. Its period is exactly twice that of Mercury's 88 days, so every 176 days it revisits Mercury.

Mariner 10's photos of Mercury show a surface similar to the moon's. The rocky landscape is marked by basins, craters, plains, and low cliffs. Because Mercury is much denser than the moon, scientists think it has an iron core. Mercury has a magnetic field, perhaps caused in some way by the iron core.

Mariner 10 took these photos of Mercury. Note how similar the surface of Mercury is to that of the moon.

The Planet Venus 16.

Venus has been called earth's twin. Second in distance from the sun it comes nearer to earth than any other planet. Its diameter, density, mass, and gravity are all close to earth's. Its year is about three fifths as long as earth's. Its rotation, however, is quite different. It takes 243 of our days—more than its year—to turn once on its axis. Furthermore, it turns from east to west, instead of west to east, as most planets do (hence the minus sign in the table on page 305.)

Venus is covered by clouds so dense that telescopes show nothing of its surface. Since 1962, however, several American and Soviet unpiloted spacecraft have explored Venus. On its way to Mercury in 1974, Mariner 10 photographed Venus. In 1975, the Soviet Veneras 9 and 10 landed on Venus and sent back photos of its surface by radio.

Mariner 10 also took this photo of Venus. The clouds covering the planet show as alternating light and dark bands.

Before spacecraft exploration, radar waves had been used to study the surface of Venus. They indicated that much of it was pitted with huge shallow craters. The Venera photos covered much smaller areas close up. They showed a rocky, bouldery surface. The rocks were generally sharp-edged, with few signs of erosion. Scientists think that Venus may resemble earth in structure. This means it may have a rocky crust, a mantle layer, and a partly liquid core.

Venus' atmosphere seems to be made of mostly carbon dioxide, with traces of carbon monoxide, water vapor, and oxygen. Its thick clouds have a strange yellow color. They may be composed of droplets of sulfuric acid. The atmosphere is so dense that its surface pressure is 90 times that of the earth's. The dense atmosphere has a very strong "greenhouse" effect. It lets some sunshine reach Venus' surface, but then keeps heat from escaping. As a result, Venus' daytime surface temperature is a very hot 480° C.

Venus has no magnetic field.

17. The Planet Mars

Unlike Venus, Mars has no cloud cover to hide it. It is easily seen in our great telescopes. Since 1965 it has been photographed by both Soviet and American spacecraft. Some of these were flybys. Others went into orbit around Mars.

In 1976 two American spacecraft landed on Mars. They sent back photographs and the results of tests on the soil and atmosphere. From them we have learned much about "the red planet."

The surface of Mars seems to have an "older" part and a younger part. The older part strongly resembles the back of our moon. Vast plains are pitted with many meteorite craters apparently formed several billion years ago. In these areas there are no signs of recent geological activity. But other parts of Mars show more recent geological features. There are areas of rolling hills without craters. There is a region of gigantic volcanoes far larger than any on the earth. Most surprising of all, there is a series of great canyons long enough to reach almost across the United States.

Another spacecraft, Mariner 9, photographed Mars here. The photo shows mountain ranges, craters, and plains. The apparent square patterns are not really on Mars, however. They are a result of the method used in making the photograph.

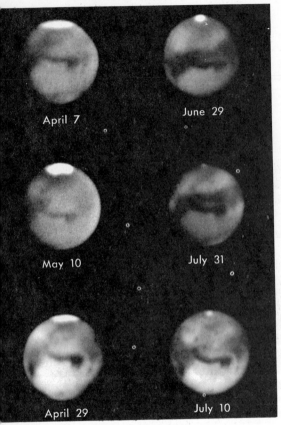

Each row shows Mars photographed in a different year. The season changes from spring on the left to summer on the right. Note the changes in the dark areas and the polar ice cap. (The dates given are for the Martian "year," which is about twice as long as earth's year.)

April 7

June 29

May 10

July 31

April 29

July 10

The largest of the volcanoes is called Olympus Mons. It is 600 kilometers in diameter and 25 kilometers high. At its summit is a caldera 65 kilometers in diameter. The largest of the canyons is called Titonius Chasm. It is far larger than our Grand Canyon. Its width is more than 100 kilometers. Its depth is about 6 kilometers. It appears to have many tributaries, and its walls show signs of erosion by water. It is this that has surprised scientists, because Mars' atmosphere contains almost no water. There are, however, other signs that water once did flow on Mars. These are long meandering channels that look like dry river beds.

Great basins on Mars are filled with thick layers of rock dust. The dust was probably formed during billions of years of bombardment by meteorites. Strong winds up to 300 kilometers an hour cause frequent local dust storms. And once in every Martian year, a great dust storm covers nearly the entire planet.

Mars' year is almost twice as long as an earth year. Mars' day is nearly the same in length as our day. Furthermore, Mars' axis tilts almost the same amount as the earth's. For these reasons, Mars has four seasons similar to those on earth, but twice as long. Afternoon temperatures on Mars range from 0° C to 27° C. At night the temperature drops sharply to a low near −125° C.

The rapid night cooling of Mars is due to its thin atmosphere. At the surface of Mars atmospheric pressure is only about one two hundredth of that at the earth's surface. About 95 percent of the atmosphere at the surface of Mars is carbon dioxide gas. The rest is mostly nitrogen (nearly three percent) and argon (nearly two percent).

Long before spacecraft visited Mars, the planet was seen to have polar "ice" caps. They were at its north pole or its south pole as seasons changed. We now believe that the ice caps consist mainly of frozen carbon dioxide dry ice. This forms in Mars' cold winter but evaporates in summer. Frozen water also forms a small part of the polar caps.

Looking through telescopes, astronomers had long noticed seasonal changes in the appearance of Mars. Some thought these might be due to seasonal growth of vegetation. It is now believed that these changes in appearance are caused largely by the shifting of great dust dunes during dust storms.

The interior structure of Mars is believed to resemble the earth's—rock crust, mantle, iron core. Is there life on Mars? With so little oxygen and water vapor, scientists did not expect to find earth-like "men" on Mars. But they did think that simple forms of life might have developed there. In 1976 two specially equipped spacecraft, Viking 1 and Viking 2, landed on Mars to explore this question. Their experiments showed strange chemical processes taking place at the surface of Mars. None, however, was a sure sign of any kind of life. So we still do not have the answer to the question—is there life on Mars?

Until 1973, Jupiter was known to us only by telescope. But in 1973 and 1974, Pioneer spacecraft did flyby missions to Jupiter. The journeys from earth to Jupiter took about 1.5 years. The nearest approach to Jupiter was made by Pioneer 11 on December 3, 1974, when it was "only" 75,000 kilometers from the planet.

Jupiter is the largest planet. Its density is only about 1.3, but even so it has more than twice the total mass of the other eight planets.

What is Jupiter made of? Like Venus, Jupiter's surface is hidden from us by thick cloud layers. But from the data obtained both before and after the Pioneers, scientists have formed a picture of Jupiter's likely structure. They believe that Jupiter is composed mainly of hydrogen, except for a central core of iron and silicate rocks. The hydrogen is in two layers. The inner layer is liquid atomic hydrogen. In this form it acts like a metal and conducts electricity. The outer layer is liquid too, but the hydrogen atoms are joined as molecules and cannot conduct electricity.

Above the outer layer of hydrogen is Jupiter's atmosphere, perhaps 1000 kilometers thick. Water droplets and ice crystals are present in the warmer lower atmosphere. At higher and colder levels, ammonia crystals and hydrogen gas occur. Methane gas and helium are also found in the atmosphere.

Seen through the telescope, Jupiter's central region is covered by a series of alternate light and dark bands. These run parallel to its equator. Scientists now think that the light-colored bands are zones of rising gases in Jupiter's atmosphere. The dark-colored bands are belts of descending gases.

The most striking feature of Jupiter's visible disk is its **Great Red Spot.** This oval-shaped area is about 14,000 kilometers wide and from 30,000 to 40,000 kilometers long. It has been seen for more than 300 years. Scientists believe it is a vast storm area similar to hurricanes on the earth.

Pioneer 10 took this photo of Jupiter. Note its oval Great Red Spot (at the center of its left edge) and its light and dark bands. The black spot (center) is the shadow of one of its moons!

Jupiter has a strong magnetic field. Jupiter is also surrounded by an intense radiation field. It is a strong source of radio waves. And unlike the earth, Jupiter radiates more heat back to space than it gets from the sun. Most scientists think it is still radiating heat it had when it first formed.

Saturn, Uranus, Neptune, and Pluto 19.

No space probe has yet visited any of these outer planets, so they are known to us only from telescopic observations. Saturn greatly resembles Jupiter. Like Jupiter, it has a banded cloudy surface. It is believed to have a small rocky core surrounded by ice and liquid hydrogen. Saturn's atmosphere is thought to be mainly hydrogen and helium. Its clouds are probably made of ammonia crystals.

Uranus and Neptune are also thought to have rocky cores surrounded by thick layers of ice and liquid hydrogen. Their spectra show atmospheres made of hydrogen and methane gas. Helium is also believed to be present.

Pluto is so far off and so small that almost nothing is known about its structure and its atmosphere.

Neptune and its satellite Triton show against a background of stars. Triton may be the largest natural satellite in the solar system.

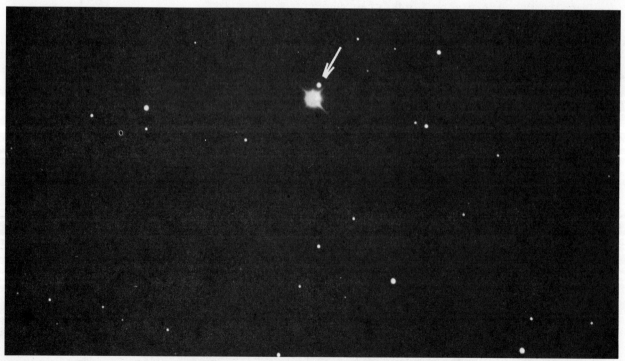

Other Parts of the Solar System

20. The Asteroids

For a long time early astronomers had felt that a planet "belonged" in the great space between Mars and Jupiter. In 1801 the Italian astronomer Piazzi discovered the "planet" Ceres. This soon turned out to be merely the largest of many "minor planets." These were named **asteroids** (starlike) because in telescopes they looked like faint stars. Since Piazzi's discovery, many thousands of asteroids have been found.

Asteroids appear to be solid rocklike masses. Only the two largest, Ceres and Pallas, are spherical. Ceres has a diameter of about 950 kilometers. All other asteroids are believed to be irregular in shape. This is shown by the way they change in brightness as they rotate. Most asteroids are only a kilometer long or less.

All of the asteroids revolve around the sun counterclockwise, as the planets do. Most of their orbits are nearly circular and lie between Mars and Jupiter. A few, however, have highly eccentric orbits that reach close to Mercury or as far out as Saturn.

Was there ever a planet between Mars and Jupiter? Some scientists think that the asteroids are original planetesimals still left from the solar system's planet-forming time. Collisions between large asteroids may have formed many of the smaller ones.

21. Satellites of the Planets

Bodies that revolve around planets are called **satellites.** Our moon is a satellite of the earth. There are 33 satellites in our solar system. Except for Mercury, Venus, and probably Pluto, each planet has at least one satellite. Our moon is 3476 kilometers in diameter. It is about 386,000 kilometers from the earth. It takes $27\frac{1}{3}$ days to circle the earth. How do other satellites compare with our moon?

Mars has two tiny satellites. Both are much smaller than the larger asteroids, and very irregular in shape. Phobos, the larger and nearer one, is only about 28 kilometers long. It is about 6500 kilometers from the surface of Mars. It revolves around Mars in only eight hours—three times a day! When the spacecraft Mariner 9 orbited Mars in 1971, it took good photos of Phobos and its sister moon, Deimos.

Jupiter has 13 moons. Its most distant one was discovered in 1974. Its four inner moons are all about as large or larger than our moon. Two of them are larger than the planet Mercury. These four moons were discovered by Galileo through the telescope in 1610.

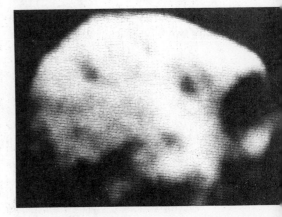

Phobos, the larger of Mars' two moons, is only 28 kilometers long. It looks like a lumpy, cratered potato.

Saturn has 10 satellites, one of which was discovered in 1967. Its largest satellite, Titan, is even larger than any of Jupiter's moons. Recent evidence shows it to have an atmosphere of methane and hydrogen. Two of Jupiter's moons also seem to have very thin atmospheres.

Uranus has five satellites, all smaller than our moon. Neptune has only two satellites. One of them, Triton, may be the largest satellite in the solar system. But it is so far off that accurate measurements are not yet possible.

Most of the satellites revolve from west to east, as the planets do. Exceptions include Jupiter's four outermost moons, Saturn's outermost moon, and Neptune's Triton.

Planetary Rings 22.

Saturn's rings make it a beautiful sight in the telescope. There are four rings, all in the plane of its equator. The outermost ring reaches about 75,000 kilometers beyond the surface of Saturn. It is a fairly bright ring about 16,000 kilometers wide. Then comes a 5,000 kilometer dark gap called Cassini's division. This is followed by the *bright ring*, about 25,000 kilometers wide. From the bright ring to Jupiter, everything looks dark. But powerful telescopes show two more faint rings separated by another dark gap. The outer of these two is called the *crape ring*. The thickness of the rings is believed to be only a few kilometers.

Though the rings look "solid," they actually consist of billions of particles. Most are probably no more than a few centimeters in diameter. Recent radar studies, however, suggest that some may be as

Inside Saturn's two bright rings are two faint, dark rings.

much as a meter in diameter. Scientists think the particles are snow or bits of rock covered by snow. They shine by reflecting sunlight.

Where did these particles come from? One hypothesis is that they are "uncollected" material left over when Saturn was formed. Another hypothesis is that they were formed by the collision of large planetesimals. A third suggestion is that they are the fragments of a satellite that was torn apart when it came too close to Saturn.

In March, 1977, scientists discovered five Saturn-like rings around the planet Uranus. They were observed through a 36-inch telescope carried in an airplane high above the earth's surface.

23. Comets

Every year now several new comets are likely to be discovered. Most, however, can be seen only through telescopes. Comets visible to the naked eye are not too common. Spectacular comets are rare.

The photograph of a comet shows a glowing **head** and a long bright **tail**. The head has a small bright *nucleus* surrounded by a hazy *coma*. The nucleus of a comet seems to be only a few kilometers in diameter. The tail may be millions of kilometers long.

What is a comet made of? Astronomer F. L. Whipple described the nucleus of a comet as a "dirty iceberg". It is thought to consist of tiny particles of rock frozen into a loose spongy mass of ice. The "ice" is mostly frozen water, ammonia, carbon dioxide, and methane.

Far out in space, a comet has no tail. Its head shines by reflected sunlight. But when it comes near the sun, some of its ice evaporates. A cloud of gases then forms around the nucleus to become the coma. Beyond the coma a long tail of gases and rock dust gradually stretches off into space. The tail always points away from the sun. This is because the pressure of the solar wind repels the comet's gases. The gases glow with energy from the sun's radiation.

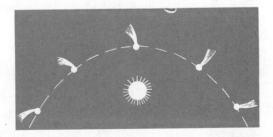

The tail of a comet always points away from the sun.

Most comets have very eccentric orbits. That is, a comet comes very close to the sun at perihelion and then goes very far away at aphelion. A comet may not return to the neighborhood of the sun for

The Sun and the Solar System **315**

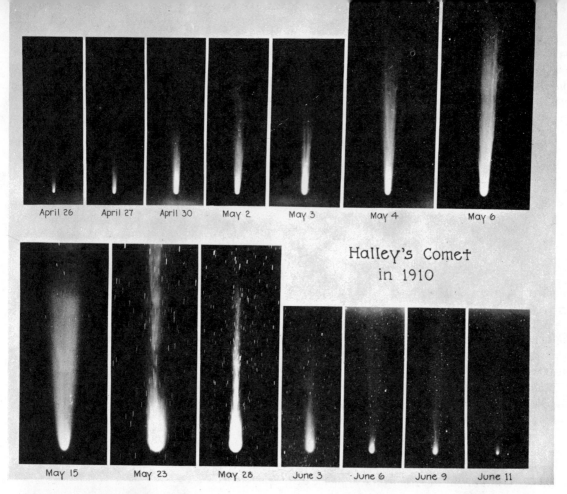

Halley's Comet
in 1910

April 26　April 27　April 30　May 2　May 3　May 4　May 6

May 15　May 23　May 28　June 3　June 6　June 9　June 11

These photos show Halley's comet as it passed by the sun in 1910. Note how the tail got longer as the comet approached the sun and shorter as it went away.

thousands of years. A few comets have smaller orbits that bring them back sooner. The nearest, Encke's comet, returns to our sky every 3.3 years. It can usually be seen only with the telescope.

Our most famous comet is **Halley's comet.** Edmund Halley was an 18th century English astronomer. In studying records of comets, Halley observed that bright naked-eye comets had appeared in 1531, 1607, and 1682. Halley became certain that these were all one comet

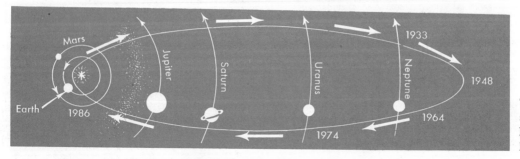

Mars

Jupiter

Saturn

Uranus

Neptune

1933

1948

Earth　1986

1974

1964

The arrows show the path of Halley's comet. Note the dates.

whose orbital period was about 76 years. He then predicted its return in 1758–1759. The comet appeared early in 1759, and again in 1835 and 1910. It is one of our brightest comets, easily seen by the unaided eye. It is expected to reappear in 1986.

24. Meteors and Meteoroids

Space scientists call rock fragments traveling in space **meteoroids.** When a meteoroid streaks through our atmosphere, the light it makes is called a **meteor.** Meteoroids may be as large as boulders or as small as sand grains. Some travel alone. Others revolve around the sun in great *meteoroid swarms* consisting of billions of tiny particles.

Meteoroids travel at a speed of 20 kilometers a second or more. When a meteoroid hits our atmosphere it is intensely heated by friction. About 100 kilometers above the surface of the earth it reaches white heat. Then for about a second it blazes as a meteor before it burns up or becomes vapor. An unusually large bright meteor is called a *fireball.*

It is estimated that nearly 100 million meteoroids strike us daily. Most are tiny and burn up in the atmosphere. The dust and gas from them adds a few tons a day to the earth.

25. Meteorites, Meteorite Craters

A large meteoroid may not be completely destroyed in our atmosphere. The part that reaches the earth's surface is called a **meteorite.**

Meteorites are of two main types. Stony meteorites, or **stones,** strongly resemble our dark igneous rocks. They cannot be easily identified except by experts. The largest known stone weighs about a ton. It landed in Furnas County, Nebraska, in 1948. Iron meteorites, or **irons,** are usually black outside and silvery inside. They consist largely of iron and nickel, and so are much heavier than stones. One of the world's largest irons was found in Greenland by Admiral Peary in 1895. It weighs about 34 tons, and is now at the Hayden Planetarium in New York City.

At a number of places on the earth great **meteorite craters** are found. These were blasted out when giant meteorites crashed into the surface and exploded. The Barringer Meteorite Crater (Meteor Crater) in Arizona is about 1300 meters in diameter and nearly 200 meters deep. Scientists think the meteorite that made it was perhaps 20 meters in diameter. Fragments of the meteorite were scattered a mile or more from the crater.

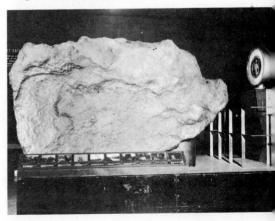

The meteorite that Admiral Peary brought to New York City from Greenland now rests on a scale at the Hayden Planetarium. It weighs about 34 tons.

Craters even larger than Meteor Crater have been found in Canada, Australia, and Africa. Chubb Crater in Northern Quebec is about 3000 meters in diameter and more than 300 meters deep.

Have large meteorites struck the earth in recent times? In 1908 a great meteorite crashed in the Tunguska River region of Central Siberia. Its explosion destroyed forests and formed craters up to 50 meters across. In 1947 another great meteorite fall occurred in southeastern Siberia. Many small craters were formed, and many irons were found in the area.

Origin of Meteoroids: "Showers" 26.

Where do meteoroids come from? Many single meteoroids, especially the very large ones, are thought to form from collisions of asteroids. Meteoroid swarms, however, seem to be streams of tiny rock particles that come from the comets in whose orbits they move.

Meteor showers occur when the earth crosses the orbit of a meteoroid swarm. Large numbers of meteors are seen at these times. The "showers" are named for the constellation from whose direction the meteors come. Among the best-known meteor showers are the Perseids about August 12; the Orionids about October 20; the Taurids about November 10; and the Geminids about December 10.

Are meteoroids a danger to spacecraft? Apparently not. Spacecraft have been struck by many tiny meteoroids without damage. Large meteoroids would do serious damage, but they are so rare that the probability of a collision is very small.

Evening and Morning Stars 27.

Venus is nearer the sun than the earth is. Therefore it can appear in our sky only when we face in the general direction of the sun. During most of the daytime the sun is too bright to allow us to see Venus, especially if it is nearly in line with the sun. When Venus is east of the sun, however, the sun sets before it. Then Venus can be seen clearly in the evening twilight of the western sky. There it is called the "evening star." Venus can be seen for as long as three hours after sunset, before it sets in the west.

When Venus is west of the sun, it rises before the sun does. It is then seen in the eastern sky as a "morning star." Venus can never be on the nighttime side of the earth. That is why we can never see it in the hours close to midnight.

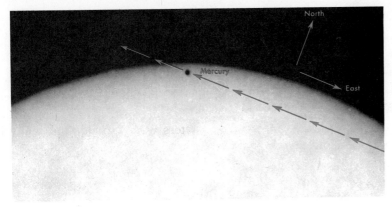

The small black dot is Mercury passing between the sun and the earth. The arrows show its path.

Mercury lies even closer to the sun than Venus. It too is seen only as a morning or evening star. Mercury is smaller than Venus and not so bright. It moves much more rapidly in its smaller orbit. It is much nearer the sun. For all these reasons Mercury is very difficult to see. Venus, on the other hand, is visible most of the year as either a morning or an evening star.

On rare occasions either Mercury or Venus may pass directly between the earth and the face of the sun. In this position it looks like a dark spot on the solar disk. These crossings are called *transits*.

When Mars, Jupiter, and Saturn are close to the sun in the sky, they too are seen as morning or evening stars. But these planets have orbits beyond the earth's, therefore they also appear in our nighttime sky much of the year.

TOPIC QUESTIONS

Each topic question refers to the topic of the same number within this chapter.

1. What does each of the following instruments do? **(a)** tower telescope, **(b)** space telescope, **(c)** coronagraph.

2. **(a)** Compare the sun's dimensions with those of the earth. **(b)** How hot is the sun?

3. Explain what each of the following is: photosphere, chromosphere, prominence, corona.

4. **(a)** Describe the appearance, size, and temperature of sunspots. **(b)** What do sunspots tell us about the sun's rotation? **(c)** Where are most sunspots located?

5. **(a)** What is a solar flare? **(b)** How do solar flares disturb radio communications and cause static? **(c)** How do solar flares cause magnetic storms and auroras? **(d)** What is a magnetic storm? **(e)** What is the solar wind?

6. **(a)** How does Einstein's equation explain the sun's energy? **(b)** Explain simply why the fusion of hydrogen into helium provides energy.

7. What does the solar system include?

8. How can planets be distinguished from stars?

9. Explain how the planets are classified as (a) inferior and superior, (b) inner and outer, (c) terrestrial and major. (d) What is the period of revolution?

10. What is an ellipse? What determines how eccentric it is?

11. (a) What part was played by Copernicus, Brahe, and Kepler in explaining planetary motion? (b) State and explain Kepler's laws.

12. (a) How eccentric is Pluto's orbit? Explain. Define perihelion and aphelion. (b) In what direction do the planets revolve? In what plane?

13. (a) Which way do the planets rotate? (b) What is an oblate spheroid? (c) How do the planets differ in density? (d) Why do Jupiter and Saturn bulge the most of all planets at the equator?

14. Describe some of the ways in which scientists study the atmosphere and weather of a distant planet.

15. (a) Describe the surface of Mercury. (b) Why is Mercury so hot by day and so cold at night? (c) Why do scientists think it has an iron core?

16. (a) Describe the surface of Venus. (b) Describe the probable composition, temperature, and pressure of Venus' atmosphere.

17. (a) Describe the surface of Mars. (b) Describe the dust storms of Mars. (c) Why are Mars' seasons similar to ours? (d) Describe Mars' atmosphere. (e) Describe the composition and seasonal changes of Mars' polar caps. (f) How do we now explain the other seasonal changes in Mars' appearance?

18. (a) Describe the scientist's present "picture" of Jupiter's structure from its core to the top of its atmosphere. (b) How do scientists explain Jupiter's colored bands? Its Great Red Spot?

19. Describe the structure and atmosphere of (a) Saturn, (b) Uranus and Neptune.

20. (a) Describe the size, shape, and orbits of the asteroids. (b) How may the asteroids have originated?

21. (a) What is a satellite? (b) Which planets have no satellites? (c) Describe some of the interesting satellites of Mars, Jupiter, Saturn, and Neptune.

22. Describe Saturn's rings. How did they originate?

23. (a) Describe the appearance of a comet. (b) What is the head made of? (c) How is the tail formed? Why does it glow? (d) What kind of orbits do comets have? Explain. (e) Describe Halley's comet.

24. (a) Distinguish between a meteoroid and a meteor. (b) How does a meteoroid become a meteor?

25. (a) What is a meteorite? (b) Explain the difference between stones and irons. (c) How is a meteorite crater formed? (d) Give examples of meteorite craters.

26. (a) Where do meteoroids originate? (b) Why do meteor showers occur? (c) Name and give the dates of a few meteor showers.

27. (a) Why are Venus and Mercury only seen as evening or morning stars? (b) Why can other planets be seen all night?

1. Even planets twinkle when they are close to the horizon. Why?

2. Why are seasons on Mars almost twice as long as those on the earth?

3. Phobos revolves from west to east around Mars faster than Mars rotates on its axis from west to east. In what direction does Phobos rise and set?

4. As an evening star, Venus can be seen only in the west; as a morning star, it can be seen only in the east. Why?

5. Which is better for "focusing the sun's rays to a point," a long focus lens or a short focus lens? Explain your answer.

6. Vesta is the only asteroid ever visible with the unaided eye, yet Ceres is larger than Vesta. How is this explained?

7. Calculate the period of a planet that is four times as far from the sun as the earth is.

1. To illustrate Kepler's second law that a planet moves faster when it is nearer the sun: **(a)** Tie a small weight to a string. Swing it in a circle around your head with just enough velocity to keep it moving "in orbit" by itself for several circuits. **(b)** Shorten the string and repeat the experiment.

2. Vary the above experiment as follows: **(a)** Tie the string to a stick. Again, swing it around your head until the weight "orbits" by itself. **(b)** Now let the string wind up on the stick. Notice how the "orbiting" speed of the weight increases as its string shortens.

3. With the aid of weekly or monthly sky maps in such publications as *Science News Letter, Sky and Telescope*, or local newspapers, locate the currently visible planets. Observe their changes of position on successive nights. Notice their differences in appearance to the unaided eye and, if possible, observe them through a small telescope or good binoculars.

4. Measure the distance from the sun to you in the following way: **(a)** Form a sharp image of the sun with a magnifying glass on a sheet of paper or screen. **(b)** Measure the diameter of the image as accurately as possible. **(c)** Measure the distance from lens to screen. (Be careful not to look *at* the sun.) Now from geometry we know that

$$\frac{\textbf{Diameter of the sun}}{\textbf{Diameter of image}} = \frac{\textbf{Distance of sun}}{\textbf{Distance of image}}$$

Assume the sun's diameter to be 1.5 million kilometers for very approximate calculations. Use the above equation to calculate the sun's distance.

21

Until the 1960's, when American and Russian camera-carrying space ships circled the moon, we had never "seen" the "back" of the moon. To understand how the moon can revolve around the earth without showing us its far side, do the following activity.

Pin a sign to your back. Now walk slowly around the entire classroom in such a way that no one in the class can see the sign. What did you have to do to hide the sign? How much did you (the moon) rotate as you revolved around the class (the earth)? Now walk slowly around the classroom without rotating at all, always facing the front of the room. Do your classmates see the sign?

Our Moon

Studying the Moon

Until the year 1611, people could see the moon only with their un-aided eyes. Then Galileo invented the optical telescope. For more than 350 years the telescope was the chief instrument for moon study. Telescopes grew larger and more powerful. Photos of the moon showed more and more detail. But the moon is far from the earth, and many things about it remained unknown.

Then in 1964 we entered a new phase of moon exploration. Spacecraft of many kinds flew to the moon for close-up study. The spacecraft included crash-landing American "Rangers," soft-landing American "Surveyors" and Soviet "Lunas," and fly-around American "Lunar Orbiters" and Soviet "Luniks." These took many thousands of closeup photographs. They telecast them back to the earth. They "analyzed" the moon's soil and made other observations.

The height of lunar exploration came when human beings landed on the moon. Between July 20, 1969 and December 14, 1972, six Apollo missions visited the moon. In each mission, two astronauts explored the moon for several days. A third astronaut stayed with the orbiting spacecraft. Photographs were taken, rock samples were collected, and experiments carried out. Automatic instruments were left on the moon to study its heat flow, its magnetism, its "moonquakes," and other activity.

At last people were studying the moon at first hand.

ALSEP, this automatic observatory, was put on the moon by Apollo astronauts.

323

When Neil Armstrong stepped down from this landing vehicle in 1969, "earthlings" had finally reached the moon.

The Moon and the Earth 2.

Our moon is far from being the largest satellite in the solar system. It is, however, closer in size to its planet (earth) than any other satellite. Its diameter is 3476 kilometers. This is more than one-fourth of the earth's diameter. Roughly the moon and earth compare in size about as a baseball and a basketball do.

The moon's density is about 3.3. The earth's is 5.5. The moon's mass is about one-eightieth that of the earth. Its surface gravity is only about one-sixth that of the earth. To escape from the moon's gravity, a spacecraft needs a speed of about 2.5 kilometers a second. (This is called the *velocity of escape.*) Velocity of escape from the earth is about 11 kilometers a second.

The Lunar Landscape's History 3.

The "man in the moon" is only a pattern of light and dark areas. With a good telescope we begin to see its details. The **light areas** are highlands made up of mountains and craters. The **dark areas** are smooth basins or level plains. Galileo thought the basins were water-filled seas. He named them maria (MAR ee uh), the Latin word for seas.

Apollo astronauts collected hundreds of rock samples from both the highlands and the maria. Spacecraft cameras took thousands of detailed photographs. Special scientific instruments made many observations. From all of this information, scientists have worked out a history of the moon.

Scientists believe that the moon formed at the same time as the earth, about 4.6 billion years ago. Shortly after its formation, the moon's surface was fiercely hot and liquid. In time, the hot magma cooled to form a rocky crust many kilometers thick. The crust covered the entire surface of the moon.

As soon as the crust turned solid, another stage of lunar history began. Great showers of rock planetesimals pelted the moon's surface. When the largest of these struck the crust, they exploded with a force equal to millions of tons of dynamite. Great basins were blasted out to become the maria. Smaller explosions formed craters of all sizes. Tiny planetesimals ground and pitted the surface. Rock debris spread over the landscape.

The bombardment lasted for hundreds of millions of years. As it slowed down, a new stage of moon history began. Hot lava poured out of fissures in the rock crust of the maria. The lava hardened into thick layers of dark basalt-like rocks. The eruptions continued for nearly a billion years. The maria floors became dark and smooth. Finally volcanic activity ended. The moon became geologically dead about three billion years ago.

For three billion years now, the moon's interior has been quiet. No volcanoes have erupted. No moonquakes have shaken its surface. No crustal plates have formed and moved. But meteorites from space have continued to bombard the moon's surface.

There have been no giant meteorites large enough to make new maria. But smaller meteorites have formed many craters on the floors of the maria. These are younger than most of the highland craters. A large part of the bombardment has been done by meteorites no larger than sand grains. These are called *micrometeorites*.

4. Erosion on the Moon

Because of its weak gravity, the moon has no atmosphere. Gas molecules often move faster than 2.5 kilometers per second. Thus, they escape into space from the moon. Neither is there any water on the moon's surface. Without atmosphere and water, no weathering takes place. There is no erosion by winds, waves, streams, or glaciers. The maria, the highlands, and the craters remain almost unchanged since their formation three billion years ago.

There is, however, one kind of erosion on the moon. Because the moon has no atmosphere, it has no defense against the constant rain of meteoroids that pours onto it from outer space. Since its formation, billions of micrometeorites have struck its surface at speeds up to 40 kilometers a second. Their effect is like that of a continuous sand blast. The sharp edges of mountain peaks and craters are rounded off. The surfaces of rocks and boulders are marked by microscopic pits. The floors of craters are slowly covered by a fine powdery "soil" in which nothing grows.

Large meteoroids were relatively rare in lunar history. When they struck, they exploded to form maria and craters. But their explosions also scattered the rock debris from the craters far and wide. Some of this debris filled in or covered up older craters.

The Moon's Surface Features

The Lunar Maria 5.

Despite their name, the lunar maria contain no water. There are no signs that they ever did hold water. They look dark because their smooth floors reflect less sunlight than the rugged highlands. But closeup photos of the maria floors show thousands of smaller craters. These were formed by meteorites after the lava floors had hardened.

The word *mare* is the singular form of maria. *Mare* means "sea" and is pronounced MAH ray. Long ago astronomers gave 14 lunar "seas" Latin names. Among these are Mare Imbrium (Sea of Rains), Mare Crisium (Sea of Tears), Mare Serenitatis (Sea of Serenity). The largest "sea" is Oceanus Procellarum (Ocean of Storms) where Apollo 12 landed. The maria are roughly circular. They are hundreds of kilometers in diameter.

The Lunar Mountains 6.

The **lunar highlands** are seen by us as the bright areas of the full moon. They are brighter than the maria because their rough surfaces reflect more sunlight. They include a few mountain ranges and many craters.

Most of the mountain ranges are at the edges of the maria. One great range forms the western border of Mare Imbrium. It includes the lunar Alps, Apennines, and Caucasus mountains. They reach a height of about five kilometers above the mare floor. The highest lunar mountains are the **Doerfels.** They are located near the moon's south pole.

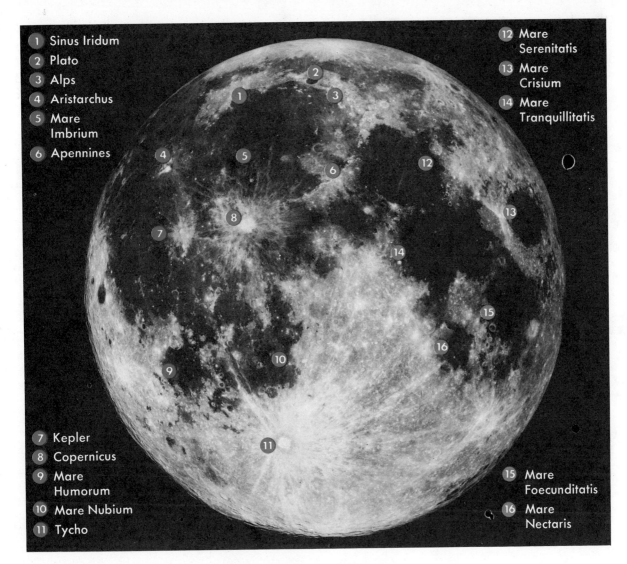

1 Sinus Iridum
2 Plato
3 Alps
4 Aristarchus
5 Mare Imbrium
6 Apennines

12 Mare Serenitatis
13 Mare Crisium
14 Mare Tranquillitatis

7 Kepler
8 Copernicus
9 Mare Humorum
10 Mare Nubium
11 Tycho

15 Mare Foecunditatis
16 Mare Nectaris

The bright (white) areas of the moon are mountains and highlands.
The dark areas are the more level maria or "seas." Note the "rays"
that surround such craters as Copernicus and Tycho.

Moon scientists think that the lunar Apennines were "splashed
up" by the great meteorite explosion that formed Mare Imbrium.
Perhaps all lunar mountains that border maria were formed this way.
How can such great rock masses be thrown so high? One reason is
that with no atmosphere, there is no air resistance. For these reasons,
pieces of rock may be found hundreds of kilometers away from the
craters out of which they were blasted.

In a few places on the moon, small extinct volcanoes are found.

The Apennine Mountains run from lower left to upper right. Below them, note the sun's shadow in the two craters. Where is the sun?

Many craters show in this part of the moon. Find Clavius, the moon's largest crater, near the top. It measures 240 kilometers across. The darker area at the lower right is part of Mare Nubium.

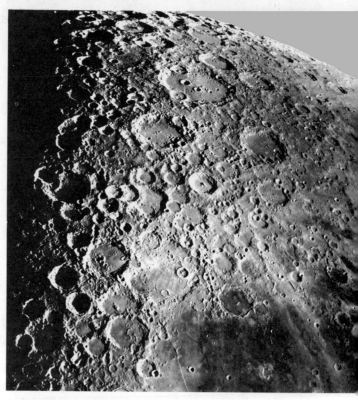

Lunar Craters 7.

Lunar craters come in all sizes. The smallest is no more than a tiny pit in a boulder. The largest, the great crater Clavius, is about 240 kilometers across. Almost all lunar craters were formed by meteorites crashing into the moon.

The craters are roughly circular in shape. Their rims are rugged cliffs. In large craters, the rims may be thousands of meters above the plains. The crater floors, on the other hand, may be a thousand meters lower than the surrounding plains. In a few craters, however, the floors are actually higher than the outside plains.

Start at the crater Copernicus on the right, and look carefully across the page. There are light lines shooting out from this crater. These rays are rocks and dust shot out when a meteorite hit the moon and carved the crater.

Most crater floors are dotted with many small peaks and craters. Like the lunar highlands, they reflect much sunlight and appear bright.

Lunar craters are named after great scholars and scientists. Examples are the craters Plato, Aristotle, Archimedes, Kepler, and Copernicus.

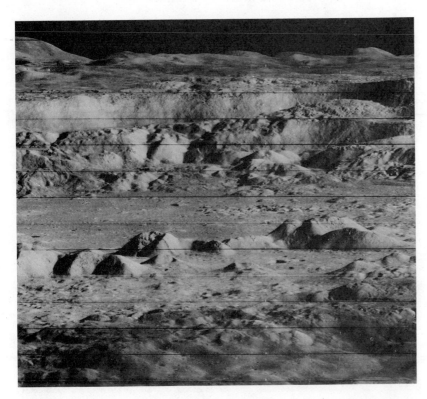

Lunar Orbiter II photographed part of the crater Copernicus from less than 50 kilometers above the moon. The cliffs near the top of the picture are about 300 meters high.

Rays and Rilles

Telescope photos of the moon show bright streaks radiating from some craters. These include the craters Tycho, Copernicus, Kepler, and about ten others. The streaks are called **rays**. The rays of Tycho and other large craters are thousands of kilometers long. They cross mountains, plains, and even other craters.

For a long time the rays were a mystery. We now know that they consist of shattered rock and rock dust from the craters. These were "splashed" out in all directions by the violent meteorite explosions that formed the craters.

Why don't all craters have rays? Scientists think that most craters probably did have rays. The rays of the older craters have been "erased". How? On the moon this could only be done by lava flows or by other meteorite explosions. In general, however, craters with rays are likely to be younger than rayless craters.

Rilles are long clefts or cracks running through the maria bedrock. The best known of these is **Hadley Rille.** It is located in Mare Imbrium close to the Apennine Mountains. Hadley Rille was studied by the Apollo 15 astronauts. Its origin is still unknown. One idea is that it was left when the roof of a lava tunnel caved in.

A close-up of one of the rays of Copernicus shows it as a bright streak. Going still closer would reveal that it is composed of shattered rock and rock dust.

Astronauts from Apollo 15 drove this Lunar Rover to Hadley Rille.

Many samples of moon rocks were returned to earth by Apollo astronauts. Almost all of them fall into one of three types. One type includes rocks from the lunar maria. The other two types come from the lunar highlands.

The maria rocks strongly resemble the basalts found in lava flows on the earth. Scientists call them **mare basalts.** Like our basalts, they are fine-grained crystalline rocks. Their colors are dark gray or black. Their main minerals are plagioclase feldspar and pyroxene.

The main rock of the lunar highlands is an igneous rock called *anorthosite.* It is a coarse crystalline rock made almost entirely of plagioclase feldspar. Its color is lighter than that of the mare basalts. Lunar scientists think that the entire lunar crust, 50 to 100 kilometers deep, is anorthosite. Anorthosite is rather rare on the earth. Some occurs in the Adirondacks, the Laramie Range, and Scandinavia.

The less common rock of the highlands is the *lunar breccia.* Breccias are rocks made of rock fragments mixed with fine material. On the earth, such rocks are formed in volcanic eruptions. On the moon, they seem to have formed through meteorite impact. Fragments of lunar rock and soil were melted together by the heat of the impact. Lunar breccias are mostly gray to dark gray in color.

All lunar rocks differ from earth rocks in several ways. They contain no water at all. They are much richer in hard-to-melt elements such as titanium and zirconium. They are poorer in gases or easy-to-melt elements such as nitrogen, chlorine, sulfur, and lead.

How old are the lunar rocks? The highland rocks are believed to be as old as the moon itself—about 4.6 billion years. But the oldest rocks yet measured are about 4 billion years old. The mare basalts were formed later. Samples of these rocks range in age from 3.7 to 3.1 billion years. Apparently no new lunar rocks have formed in over 3 billion years.

Apollo astronauts brought this rock back from the moon.

10. Lunar Soil

Lunar "soil" is not really soil. Scientists call it *regolith.* It is a grayish-brown mixture of small rock pieces and finer rock particles. These range in size from sand grains to the finest of rock dust. The regolith was formed by the smashing blows of meteorites of all sizes.

The regolith ranges in thickness from perhaps one meter to twenty. It is likely to consist of chips from many different kinds of rocks and minerals. It also includes tiny beads of glassy material. These formed from rock melted by high speed meteorite impacts.

The "soil" of the moon is a mixture of small rocks and rock dust called regolith.

Droplets of the melted rock turned solid forming glassy beads. Some of the melted rock also solidified as a glaze on other rocks.

The fine dust of the regolith was a nuisance to the Apollo astronauts. It clung to their space suits and was easily stirred up into "dust clouds."

Man on the Moon

The space suits worn by the Apollo astronauts had to meet harsh conditions. Many of these conditions were due to the moon's lack of atmosphere. On the moon there was no protection from cosmic rays, ultraviolet rays, meteorites, and the blinding light of the sun. Temperatures at the moon's surface reached 100° C in the daytime. At night they dropped to −150° C.

On the other hand, the moon's weak gravity was helpful to the astronauts. (A 72-kilogram person weighs only about 12 kilograms on the moon.) Less power was needed to slow down the landing vehicle. Less power was needed to launch it for the return trip. The astronauts themselves found little trouble in moving about and lifting.

Apollo 11 astronaut Edwin Aldrin is taking a soil sample from the moon.

The Earth and the Universe

12. How Was the Moon Formed?

Scientists do not know how the moon was formed. They now agree that the moon was formed at the same time as the earth. This was about 4.6 billion years ago. They also agree that the moon was formed in the same part of the solar system as the earth. But how? Three main hypotheses have been suggested.

One hypothesis says the moon was split off from the earth. A second hypothesis says that the moon formed by itself, but fairly close to the earth. The earth then "captured" it. The third hypothesis says that the moon formed from billions of particles already spinning around the earth. The particles clumped together by collision and by gravity to form one large moon. This moon simply continued to revolve around the earth.

The Moon's Motions

13. The Moon's Orbit

The moon revolves around the earth from west to east. This is the same direction as that of the earth's rotation and revolution. The moon's period of revolution is $27\frac{1}{3}$ days. Its average distance from the earth is about 386,000 kilometers. Light from the moon reaches the earth in only $1\frac{1}{4}$ seconds.

The moon revolves around the earth. While it does this, however, the earth is revolving around the sun. This means that the moon, too, is revolving around the sun. The actual path of the moon is shown in the diagram.

Note how the moon goes around the earth as the earth is orbiting around the sun. The earth pulls the moon around the sun also.

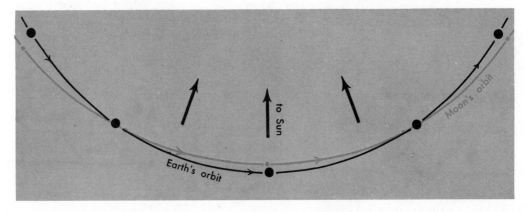

Earth's orbit

to Sun

Moon's orbit

The moon's orbit is not in the same plane as the earth's orbit. It is at an angle of about 5° to the earth's orbit. (See diagram) This fact determines how often eclipses occur. It is discussed in Topics 21 and 24.

The sun's diameter is about 400 times as large as the moon's. Yet both seem about the same size in our sky. Why? The answer is that the sun is just about 400 times as far away from us as the moon. It is just a coincidence.

The earth moves in the blue plane. The moon moves in the gray plane. So, the moon goes higher and lower than the earth.

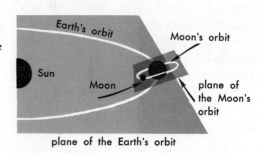

Moonrise and Moonset 14.

The moon rises in the east and sets in the west every day. Like the sun's rising and setting, this motion is an apparent one. It is caused by the earth's turning on its axis from west to east.

If the moon did not revolve around the earth, we would see it in the same place in the sky at the same time each day. Each day, however, the moon revolves about $\frac{1}{27}$ of the way around the earth. Twenty-four hours later, then, the moon is no longer in the same place in the sky. To "catch up," the earth must turn more on its axis. This takes about 50 minutes. As a result, the moon rises about 50 minutes later each day. Since it rises later, it also sets later.

Since the moon rises later each day, it can be in the sky during the day as well as at night. When the moon is opposite the sun, we see it mostly at night. When the moon is between us and the sun, it is mostly in the daytime sky. Of course it is less noticed then.

The Moon's Rotation 15.

The moon's period of rotation is just the same—$27\frac{1}{3}$ days—as its period of revolution. In other words, it turns just once on its axis while it goes around the earth. The effect is to have the "man-in-the-moon" side always facing the earth. This leaves the other side of the moon invisible to us. Since 1959, however, orbiting spacecraft have photographed the back of the moon.

If the moon produced light by itself, as the sun does, we would see a full moon every day. But the moon shines by reflected sunlight. Only one half of it can be lit up at any time.

The sun lights up the half of the moon that faces it. But, except for a short time each month, this is not the half that faces us. The half we see changes in its lighting each day. In about two weeks it goes from all dark to all light. Then in the next two weeks it goes gradually back to all dark. These daily changes in its appearance are called *phases*.

The diagram shows the moon at eight points in its orbit. Each point is about half a week from the next. The half of the moon facing the sun is always fully lit. From the earth, however, we see a different amount of the lighted half at each "phase". The column at the left shows *what we see* at each phase.

From new moon to full moon, the moon is said to be *waxing*. From full moon to new moon, it is *waning*. All the phase names in the diagram explain themselves, except *gibbous*. This might be called "lopsided."

At new moon, the moon's dark half faces us. We see "no moon." At crescent phases, only one edge of the light half faces us. We see that edge as a bright crescent. At quarter phases, the half facing us is half light, half dark. At gibbous phases, almost all of the bright half faces us. At the full moon phase, all of the bright half faces us.

The arrows from the left show light coming from the sun. The moon is shown in eight of its positions around the earth. Imagine that you're looking up at the moon in position 8. You'll see the part of the moon between the dotted lines. This is phase 8, shown at the far left.

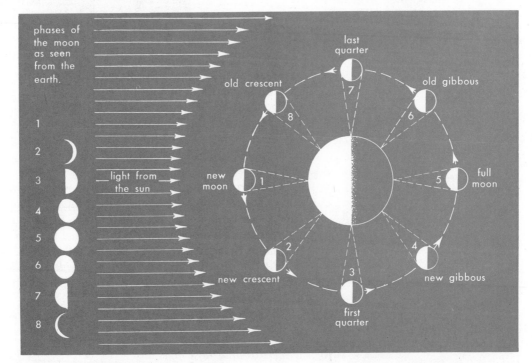

At the moon's crescent phases, we see a bright "crescent moon." But often we also see the rest of the moon dimly lit up. Why? The bright crescent is shining in direct sunlight. The rest of the moon, however, is being lit up by indirect sunlight. This sunlight is reflected from the daylight side of the earth to the dark side of the moon. It is called **earthshine.**

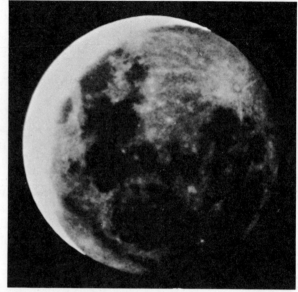

The bright crescent is lit by direct sunshine. The darker area is lit by earthshine, or sunlight bouncing off the earth to the moon.

Phases and Time of Day 18.

The diagram of the moon's phases shows us at what hours the moon is in our sky. If the moon is on the same side of the earth as the sun, it will be mostly a "daytime moon." This happens at the new and crescent phases. At the quarter phases it is in the sky about as many daylight hours as night hours. At the full and gibbous phases the moon is on the nighttime side of the earth. It is then seen mostly in the night sky.

The arrangements of moon, earth, and sun that make the phases can easily be seen. For example, the phases diagram shows the earth between the moon and sun at full moon. Stand outdoors at sunset on a day when the moon is full. You will see the sun setting in the west, the moon rising in the east, and yourself right between them.

At first quarter phase you will see the sun setting in the west when the moon is in the south. You will form the corner of a right angle.

Notice that the bright side of the moon always faces the sun.

19. Months

The early Roman calendar was based on the motions of the moon. The word *month* comes from moon. In our calendar, a month may be 28, 29, 30, or 31 days. The astronomer's month is much more definite.

The lunar month is the time from new moon to new moon. It is about $29\frac{1}{2}$ days. Why is it longer than the moon's revolution period of $27\frac{1}{3}$ days? This is because the earth moves around the sun about one degree a day. The moon has to revolve more than two extra days around the earth to "catch up" again to a new moon position.

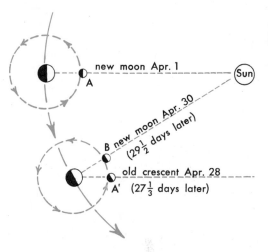

The moon at A is a new moon. After one complete orbit to A', it is a crescent. It must get to B before it is a new moon again.

The Moon and Eclipses

20. Earth's Shadow on the Moon

As the earth revolves around the sun, it casts a shadow. This shadow has two parts. One part is the *umbra*, or total shadow. The other part is the *penumbra*, or partial shadow. The umbra is a long narrow cone. Its tip reaches nearly 1,400,000 kilometers behind the earth. The penumbra is also a cone, but it widens and gets lighter as it stretches off into space.

When the earth's umbra falls on the moon, an eclipse of the moon takes places. If the moon is fully in the umbra, the eclipse is *total*. If the moon is only partly in the umbra, the eclipse is *partial*.

Trace the white lines of sunlight in this diagram at a lunar eclipse. Note how the earth blocks all sunlight in the dark umbra. Part of the sunlight is blocked in the shadowy penumbra. The moon moves into the umbra during a lunar eclipse. What phase is the moon in then?

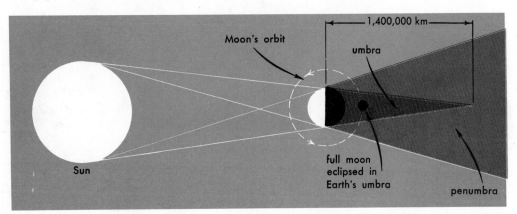

Time of Lunar Eclipse 21.

Every month the moon passes behind the earth at *full moon phase.* Why isn't there an eclipse of the moon every month? There would be, if the moon's orbit and the earth's orbit were in the same plane. But the moon's orbit is at an angle of about five degrees to the earth's orbit. For this reason, the full moon is usually above or below the earth's shadow, and there is no eclipse. At least twice a year, however, the moon does enter the earth's shadow, and an eclipse occurs.

At the moon's distance from the earth, the earth's umbra is nearly three times as wide as the moon. If the moon goes through the center of the umbra, the eclipse is total for nearly two hours.

Seeing a Lunar Eclipse 22.

On the average, at least one total eclipse of the moon occurs every year. If the weather is clear, the entire nighttime half of the earth can see it.

The earth's umbra is not completely dark. This is because the earth's atmosphere acts like a lens. It bends some sunlight into the umbra. As a result, the moon is not completely blacked out. Instead, it has a dusky red or coppery color.

Moon's Shadow on the Earth 23.

Like the earth, the moon casts a cone-shaped shadow into space. The moon's umbra is long enough to reach the earth at perigee (moon nearest earth). At apogee (moon farthest away) the umbra does not quite reach.

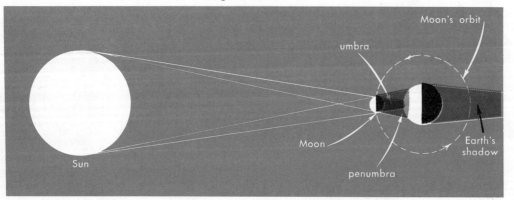

Sun | Moon | umbra | penumbra | Earth's shadow | Moon's orbit

Again trace the white lines of sunlight during a solar eclipse. The umbra of the moon darkens a spot on the earth. What phase is the moon in then?

Only the tip of the moon's umbra reaches the earth. Its maximum width where it touches the earth is about 269 kilometers. The penumbra is much wider, of course. It gets larger and lighter as it stretches away from the moon.

When the moon's shadow falls on the earth, an eclipse of the sun occurs. (The moon blocks out our view of the sun.) In the umbra, the eclipse is *total*. In the penumbra, the eclipse is partial.

24. Time of Solar Eclipse

Every month the moon passes between the earth and the sun at *new moon phase*. Why doesn't a solar eclipse occur every month? The answer is the same as for lunar eclipses. The moon's orbit is at an angle to the plane of the earth's orbit.

Solar eclipses can occur from two to five times a year. Only three of these eclipses in a year can be total.

As already mentioned, the umbra shadow on the earth is never wider than 269 kilometers. It may be much less. This means that only a small part of the world can see any solar eclipse as a total eclipse. The penumbra falls on a much larger area. There the eclipse is seen as a partial eclipse.

A total solar eclipse does not last very long. The moon's revolution makes the narrow shadow race across the earth at over 1600 kilometers an hour. The shadow's track on the earth is called the **eclipse path.** It may be thousands of kilometers long. At any one point, a total solar eclipse can last only $7\frac{1}{2}$ minutes. Usually it lasts only a few minutes.

25. Seeing a Solar Eclipse

Solar eclipses happen at least as often as lunar eclipses. However, the area covered by the umbra is relatively tiny. For this reason, any one spot on the earth averages only one total eclipse in 300 years! The most recent total solar eclipse seen in any part of the United States occurred on March 7, 1970. It crossed Florida and then followed the Atlantic Coast northward.

In a total solar eclipse, the moon covers the entire photosphere of the sun. The sky is dark. Bright stars and planets can be seen with the unaided eye. The sun's chromosphere and corona glow above the blacked-out disk of the sun.

A solar eclipse is caused by the moon's shadow.

Sun, Moon, and Tides

The daily rise and fall of the ocean waters is called the tides. Like the moon, the tides rise 50 minutes later each day on the average. Tides are unusually large at new moon and full moon. They are unusually small at times of quarter moon. All of these facts show that the moon and the tides are related.

Sir Isaac Newton first explained how the moon causes the tides. According to Newton, the moon's gravity pulls the earth and its oceans unequally. The ocean waters on the side of the earth facing the moon are nearest the moon. The ocean waters on the far side of the earth are farthest away. In between is the solid earth. It is attracted at its center of gravity. This is midway between the two halves of the ocean.

The moon, said Newton, pulls the ocean waters on the near side more strongly than it pulls the solid earth. This causes the waters to bulge toward the moon in a *direct high tide*. On the far side of the earth the ocean waters are pulled less strongly than the solid earth. The result is a bulge away from the earth's surface. This is called the *indirect high tide*. Halfway between the two high tides, low tides are formed. This happens because ocean water flows to the high tide locations.

The moon is shown here at **M**. There is a direct high tide at **H$_D$**, an indirect high tide at **H$_I$**, and low tides at **L** and **L'**. Pick a point now at high tide. Where will it be in 6 hours and 12.5 minutes—at high tide or low tide?

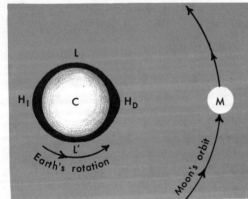

If the earth and moon stood still, the tides would always be in the same places. But the earth turns on its axis, and the moon moves around the earth. As the earth rotates, all parts of the ocean pass under the moon in 24 hours and 50 minutes. In one-fourth of this time—about 6 hours and 12.5 minutes—the tides change. Each high tide area moves to low tide. Each low tide area moves to high tide. Then 6 hours and 12.5 minutes later the tides change again. The original high tides are high again. The low tides are low again. In the next 12 hours and 25 minutes this sequence is repeated.

As the earth and moon move, the tides continue their regular rise and fall. Each day the cycle starts over again, about 50 minutes later than the day before. The "model" timetable that follows gives *average* times for a day of high and low tides. They are often much more irregular. The shape of the oceans and ocean bottoms influences the tides. Some areas have only one high tide and one low tide a day. Examples are the Gulf of Mexico and many Pacific islands.

Tide	Date	Time	Interval Since First High Tide
High	July 4	1:00 AM	
Low	July 4	7:13 AM	6 hrs. 13 min.
High	July 4	1:25 PM	12 hrs. 25 min.
Low	July 4	7:38 PM	18 hrs. 38 min.
High	July 5	1:50 AM	24 hrs. 50 min.

28. Spring and Neap Tides

The sun has the same kind of effect on the earth's waters as the moon has. But the sun is much farther away than the moon. Therefore its tide-making effect is only about half that of the moon. The moon is the chief maker of tides. The sun, however, can strengthen or weaken the moon's effects.

The sun is helping the moon's pull at the left. It is weakening the moon's pull at the right. Compare the high tides and the low tides.

Tides are always high in line with the moon. They are always low midway between the moon's high tide points. When the sun is *in line* with the moon, its effect is added to the moon's tides. When the sun is 90 degrees away from the moon, its effect weakens the moon's tides.

At new moon and full moon, the sun and moon are working together. This makes very high high-tides and very low low-tides. The **tidal range** (difference in level between high and low tide) is large. These tides are called **spring tides.** They come twice a month.

At quarter phases, the sun is opposing the moon. This makes high tides that are not very high, and low tides that are not very low. The tidal range is small. These tides are called **neap tides.**

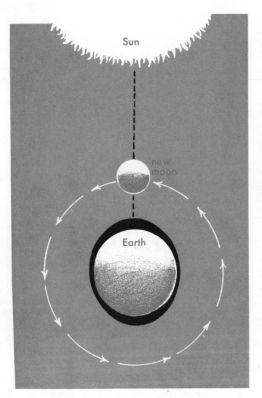 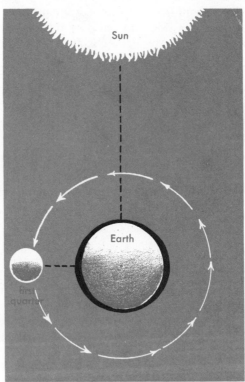

At the left, the sun, moon, and earth lie in a straight line. So, the sun helps the moon's pull. At the right, the moon pulls to the left while the sun pulls up. So, the sun weakens the moon's pull.

Ocean Basins, Shorelines, Tidal Range 29.

Tidal ranges differ greatly for many reasons. Small lakes show no tides at all. Even great Lake Superior has a tidal range of only a few centimeters. In the open ocean the tidal range averages less than a meter.

Tidal ranges differ greatly on ocean shores, too. In the Gulf of Mexico the tidal range may be only half a meter. In the Bay of Fundy (on the coast of Nova Scotia), it may reach 20 meters!

How do we explain these differences? The Bay of Fundy is a long V-shaped bay. Water from the ocean tide is funneled into the wide end of the V. Then it piles up high at the narrow end. The Gulf of Mexico does just the opposite. It has a shoreline much broader than its mouth. As the ocean tide enters the Gulf, its waters spread out over the long shoreline.

Each topic question refers to the topic of the same number within this chapter.

1. Describe the great advances made recently in our ability to study the moon.

2. (a) Compare the size of the earth and the moon. (b) Compare the moon's surface gravity and velocity of escape with the earth's.

3. (a) What are the light areas of the moon? The dark areas? (b) Briefly outline or describe four stages in the moon's history.

4. (a) Why is there no "earth-style" weathering or erosion on the moon? (b) Describe the kind of erosion that does take place on the moon.

5. (a) Describe the shape, size, and appearance of the lunar maria. (b) Give the Latin and English names of two lunar maria.

6. (a) Where are lunar mountains usually located? Name and locate some. (b) Where are the Doerfels? (c) Describe the probable origin of the lunar mountains.

7. (a) Describe the lunar craters. (b) Explain their origin.

8. (a) What are lunar "rays"? (b) How were they formed? (c) Why don't all craters have rays? (d) What is a rille? (e) How may Hadley Rille have formed?

9. (a) Describe the mare basalts. (b) Describe the two highland rocks. (c) How do moon rocks differ from earth rocks? (d) How old are the different lunar rocks?

10. Describe the lunar "soil."

11. (a) What "harsh" conditions" did astronauts find on the moon? (b) How was the moon's weak gravity helpful to the astronauts?

12. State three hypotheses of the origin of the moon.

13. (a) Describe the moon's orbit as to direction, period, plane, and size. (b) Why do the sun and moon look equally large in our sky?

14. (a) Why does the moon rise in the east and set in the west? (b) Why does it rise about 50 minutes later each day?

15. Explain why one side of the moon always faces the earth.

16. Why isn't the moon full all the time? Explain its phases, using a diagram.

17. Explain what earthshine is and when it is seen best.

18. What phases of the moon are seen chiefly at night? in the daytime? half and half?

19. (a) How long is a lunar month? (b) Explain why it is longer than the moon's period of revolution.

20. Describe the earth's shadow. How is it related to eclipses of the moon?

21. (a) At what phase does a lunar eclipse occur? Why does it not occur every month? (b) How long may a total lunar eclipse last? (c) Make a diagram showing how a lunar eclipse occurs.

22. (a) How much of the world can see each lunar eclipse? Why? (b) Why is the moon not completely darkened in a total lunar eclipse?

23. Describe the moon's shadow and its relation to eclipses of the sun.

24. (a) At what phase does a solar eclipse occur? Why does it not occur every month? (b) How long can a total solar eclipse last? Why? (c) What is the eclipse path? (d) Make a diagram of a solar eclipse.

25. (a) Why are total solar eclipses such rare sights even though they happen almost every year? (b) Describe a total solar eclipse.

26. (a) What facts indicate a connection between the moon and the tides? (b) Explain how the moon causes the tides. (c) Make a diagram showing where high and low tides are in relation to the moon's position.

27. (a) Explain why tides rise or fall every 6 hours and 13 minutes. (b) Explain why the tides come 50 minutes later each day.

28. (a) How does the sun affect tides? Explain. (b) Define tidal range. (c) What are spring tides? How and when do they occur? (d) What are neap tides? How and when do they occur?

29. (a) What is the tidal range of lakes? of the open ocean? (b) Explain the large tidal range of the Bay of Fundy. (c) Explain the small tidal range of the Gulf of Mexico.

GENERAL QUESTIONS

1. Make a diagram to show that very little earthshine can strike the moon at a gibbous phase.

2. It was once thought that there was a planet closer to the sun than Mercury. Why were observations of solar eclipses necessary to disprove this?

3. Direct and indirect high tides are about the same height when the moon is in the plane of the earth's Equator, but may be very unequal when the moon is above or below the Equator. Show this in a diagram.

4. (a) What combination of factors (moon's distance from earth, earth's distance from sun) would produce the largest spring tides? (b) What combination would produce the smallest neap tides?

5. Work out approximate times of moonrise and moonset for the eight phases shown in the moon's phases diagram.

1. Observe the moon with telescopes, binoculars, and the unaided eye.

2. Observe and record the time of moonrise and moonset at various phases of the moon.

3. Collect photographs of the moon.

4. Build a model to show the inclination of the moon's orbit to the plane of the earth's orbit.

5. Observe and record the relative positions of sun, earth, and moon at various phases.

6. Demonstrate an "eclipse" of sun or moon with globes and electric lights.

7. Record and plot the time of the tides.

8. Observe the relation of tidal range to the moon's phases from actual observation or tide tables in the newspapers, almanacs, or other sources.

22

One effect of the earth's rotation on its axis is the apparent daily movement of the sun through the sky. To see this without watching the sun itself, stand a tall slender rod in a vertical position in a sunny window. Trace its shadow every 10 minutes for at least half an hour. Why does the shadow change in length as well as in direction?

The change in the sun's height in the sky from day to day is caused by the earth's revolution around the sun. Keep a record of the length of the shadow cast by the rod at the same time each day. Between which dates does the shadow get longer? Between which dates does it get shorter?

The Earth's Motions

Revolution and Rotation

The motion of the earth in its orbit is called *revolution*. The earth's orbit, like those of the other planets, is an ellipse with the sun at one focus. The orbit lies in a level surface called the **plane of the earth's orbit.** The earth revolves around the sun from west to east at 30 kilometers a second. Its *period of revolution* is one year, or 365.25 days.

An amount of turning is often measured in degrees. One complete turn is 360°, or three hundred sixty degrees. Since the earth revolves 360° in 365.25 days, its *rate of revolution* is about 1° a day.

Because the earth's orbit is an ellipse, the distance between the earth and the sun changes every day. The average distance is about 150,000,000 kilometers. The sun is about 2,400,000 kilometers from the orbit's center. At perihelion, the earth is about 2,400,000 kilometers nearer the sun than the average distance. At aphelion the earth is that much farther away. Perihelion comes about January 1. Aphelion comes about July 1.

What proof of the earth's revolution do we have? Astronomers compare the nighttime sky on two dates six months apart. They notice that the nearer stars show a definite change in position against the background of the more distant stars.

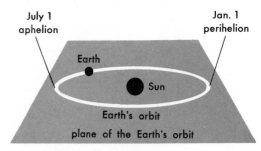

Draw an ellipse on a piece of paper. The ellipse is like the earth's orbit. The paper is like the plane of the earth's orbit. Look carefully at the drawing above. The sun is a little closer to the perihelion than it is to the aphelion.

At the same time as the earth revolves around the sun, it spins around like a top. We call this spinning motion **rotation.** The earth rotates around an imaginary line through its center. This line is called its *axis*. The ends of the axis are the North Pole and the South Pole. Every day the earth makes one complete rotation on its axis. This may sound like "slow motion" until we remember that the circumference of the earth at the Equator is about 40,000 kilometers. At the Equator, then, the earth's surface is spinning at the rate of nearly 1700 kilometers an hour. Of course, the kilometers-per-hour rate of rotation gets less and less as the Poles are approached. This is because the distance around the earth decreases. At New York City's latitude, the rate of rotation is only about 1300 kilometers an hour. At the Poles it is zero.

The rate of the earth's rotation may also be expressed in degrees. All points on the earth rotate one full turn, or 360°, in nearly 24 hours. This means a **rate of rotation** of about 15° an hour, or 1° in 4 minutes.

How do we know that the earth rotates? Many *effects* of rotation are known. One is the daily change from day to night. But the first *proof* of rotation was not provided until 1851. In that year, the French physicist Foucault did his famous "pendulum" experiment at the Pantheon in Paris.

Foucault hung a heavy iron ball from the dome by a 60-meter wire. Then he set the ball swinging along a meridian (north-south line). Once started, such a long heavy pendulum has enough energy to keep swinging for many hours.

Scientists have shown that a freely swinging pendulum never changes its direction of swing. Yet Foucault's pendulum steadily seemed to change direction. Each hour it moved about 11 degrees in a clockwise direction. After eight hours it was swinging *from east to west.*

What was the explanation? If the pendulum had not changed its position, the earth must have moved under the pendulum? At the North Pole the earth will turn 15 degrees an hour under a Foucault pendulum, or completely around in one day.

Foucault pendulums can be seen nowadays in many science museums and college science buildings.

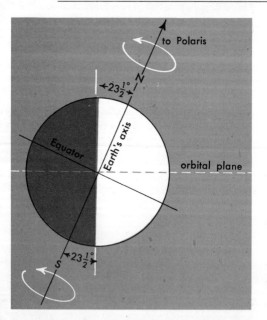

The earth rotates on its axis in a west-to-east direction. Viewed from above the North Pole, the earth appears to rotate *counterclockwise.* From beneath the South Pole the direction of rotation is clockwise. (Try it with a globe.)

The earth's axis is not perpendicular to the plane of the earth's orbit. Instead, it makes an angle of 23.5° with the perpendicular.

When the axis is "extended" into the heavens, the north end comes very close to the North Star, which is also known as Polaris. Polaris is thus valuable to navigators as an indicator of *north.*

You're looking at the earth's orbit from the side. (Look back at July 1 on the diagram on page 347.) The plane of the earth's orbit looks like a line. (It is dotted here.) Where is the sun? The earth rotates about the line through the North and South Poles. Which hemisphere gets more light now—the Northern or Southern?

The Earth and the Universe

Daylight, Night, and the Seasons

5. Why Daylight and Night Are Unequal

Let us call the part of the day when it is not night "daylight." That way we won't confuse this part of the day with the whole day. Daylight and night exist on the earth because the earth is a solid sphere. Only half of the sphere can be lit up by the sun at any time. If the earth stood still in space, one half would always have daylight. The other half would always have night. But this does not happen. *The earth's rotation causes daylight and night to alternate* every 24 hours for most parts of the earth. (In the "land of the midnight sun" near the North Pole and the South Pole, daylight lasts several months in summer, and nighttime lasts several months in winter.)

What if the earth's axis were perpendicular to the plane of its orbit? All parts of the earth would have equal daylight and night—about 12 hours each—on every day of the year. But the axis is tilted. So on all but two days of the year one hemisphere leans toward the sun more than the other. This results in unequal sunlight on the earth. The hemisphere that leans toward the sun has *longer* daylight periods than nights. The hemisphere that leans away from the sun has *shorter* daylight periods than nights.

6. Why Daylight and Night Change in Length

The tilt of the earth's axis makes daylight and night usually unequal in length. The lengths change from day to day and season to season, however. If the earth did not revolve around the sun, the length of daylight and night would remain fixed for each part of the world. *Daylight and night change in length because the earth revolves around the sun.* This causes a small daily change in the amount that each hemisphere leans toward or away from the sun. The result is a gradual change in the lengths of daylight and night.

To illustrate the "change of leaning," do this simple experiment. Hold your left fist in front of you to represent the sun. Grasp a pencil in your right hand. Your right hand will represent the earth; the pencil will be its axis. place this "earth" to the left of the "sun," with its "North Pole" pointing about 23.5° to the right, toward the "sun." Now *keeping the axis parallel to its first position,* revolve the "earth" around the "sun." Notice how the *North Pole leans away from the sun at the opposite* (right) *end of the orbit.* Notice also that neither Pole

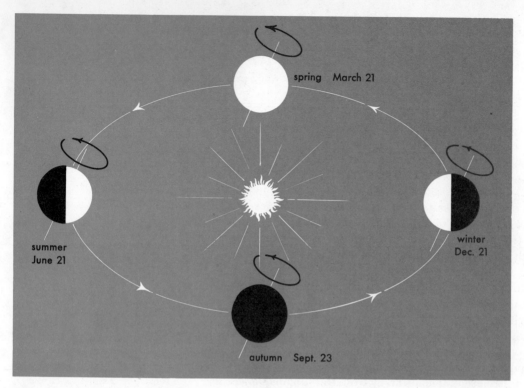

spring   March 21

summer
June 21

winter
Dec. 21

autumn   Sept. 23

The white lines coming out of the earth show its axis. Note when the poles are light and when they are dark.

leans toward the "sun" at the two points midway between the two extreme positions. Through the entire revolution the axis *remains parallel to itself*. It points to the same direction in space, the direction of the North Star. This behavior of the earth's axis is called its **parallelism**.

Daylight at the Solstices 7.

The day of the year on which the North Pole leans the full 23.5° into the sun is *June 21 or 22*. This day is known as the **summer solstice**. It has the longest daylight of the year for the Northern Hemisphere. It has the shortest daylight for the Southern Hemisphere.

The day when the North Pole leans 23.5° away from the sun is *December 21 or 22*. This is known as the **winter solstice**. It has the shortest daylight for the Northern Hemisphere. It has the longest daylight for the Southern Hemisphere.

The diagram shows the earth at the summer solstice. Only the Equator has equal daylight and night. In the Northern Hemisphere the amount of daylight increases from 12 hours at the Equator to 24 hours at the Arctic Circle (the parallel of latitude that is 23.5° from the North Pole). From the Arctic Circle to the North Pole is the "land of the midnight sun." Here daylight remains for periods longer than 24 hours. These periods range from days to weeks or even months. At the North Pole the daylight is six months long. In the Southern Hemisphere conditions are reversed. The South Pole is then in the middle of a six-month long night. June 21 is called the "summer solstice" even though on that date the weather in the Southern Hemisphere is not like the weather in the United States. In fact, it is winter in Argentina during the summer solstice.

The same diagram shows the earth at the winter solstice. Now the Northern Hemisphere has its shortest daylight, while the Southern Hemisphere has its long daylight. Again, daylight and night are equal in length only at the Equator.

The name solstice (sol = sun; stice = stop) is given to June 21 because on that date the sun stops its apparent movement northward in our sky. Similarly, December 21 is a solstice, because on that day the sun stops its apparent movement southward in our sky. From June 21 to December 21, daylight decreases in the Northern Hemisphere and increases in the Southern Hemisphere. From December 21 to June 21 the reverse takes place.

The boundary between the daylight and nighttime halves of the earth is called the *twilight circle*. In our diagrams this circle is seen "edge on" (that is, our eye is in the plane of the circle). The circle is shown therefore as a straight vertical line.

Pick a point on the Tropic of Capricorn. When does this point get more light—during the summer solstice at the left or the winter solstice at the right?

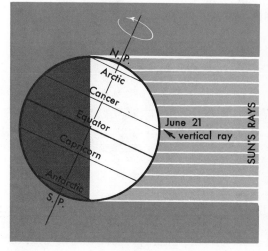

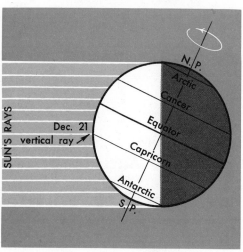

This area north of the Arctic Circle has many weeks of continuous daylight in summer. Here its "midnight sun" was photographed every 15 minutes from 10:45 P.M. to 1:15 A.M. on July 25. (Baffin Bay, Canada)

Daylight at the Equinoxes 8.

There are two days a year when neither pole leans toward the sun. They are *March 21 or 22* and *September 22 or 23*. On these dates, daylight and night are equal in length over all the world. Each date is therefore known as an equinox (equi = equal; nox = night). On the spring equinox, March 21 or 22, the North Pole begins its six-month daylight. On the fall equinox, September 22 or 23, the South Pole begins its six-month daylight.

Neither pole points to the sun here. Note how every point on the earth has equal day and night.

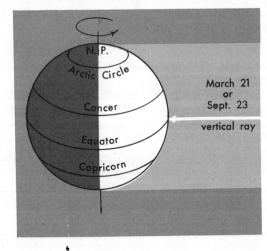

N. P.

Arctic Circle

Cancer

Equator

Capricorn

March 21 or Sept. 23

vertical ray

Angle of the Sun's Rays 9.

The diagram shows why all the rays of the sun that reach the earth are practically parallel to each other. However, the surface of the earth is curved. As a result, the rays make angles with the surface that range

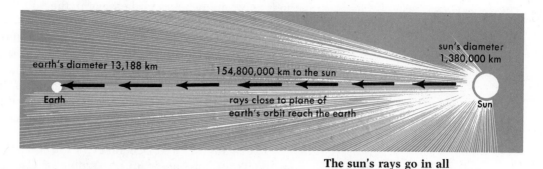

earth's diameter 13,188 km

154,800,000 km to the sun

rays close to plane of
earth's orbit reach the earth

Earth

Sun

sun's diameter
1,380,000 km

from 0° to 90° at any moment. (See the June 21 diagram.) When the sun is directly overhead (angle 90°), it is said to be in the **zenith.** The zenith is the point in the sky directly above the observer. When the sun is in the zenith, its rays are vertical.

When the sun is just rising or setting (angle 0°), it is on the **horizon.** The angle of the sun above the horizon is its **altitude.** Its angle below the zenith is its **zenith distance.**

The closer the sun's rays are to the vertical, the stronger and hotter they are. On any day of the year the sun's rays are strongest at noon, when the sun is highest in the sky. In the continental United States (except Hawaii) the strongest sun comes on June 21. The sun is then at its highest position in our sky for the year.

The sun's rays go in all directions. But this diagram shows why the rays that reach the earth must all be "parallel rays."

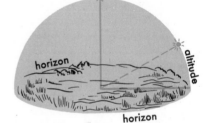

When the sun reaches the zenith, its altitude will be 90°.

⟲⚬ **The Solstices and the Seasons**

The June 21 and December 21 diagram shows why summer and winter occur when they do. Notice that on June 21 the Northern Hemisphere (from the Equator to the North Pole) receives far more than half of the sun's rays. A large part of its rays are close to the vertical on the earth. The parallel where the sun's vertical ray hits is called the Tropic of Cancer. It is 23.5° north of the equator, because that is how far the Northern Hemisphere is tilted into the sun. The Southern Hemisphere receives a much smaller share of sunlight at this time. Most of it is at a low angle.

Why is this time of the year summer time for the Northern Hemisphere? It is summer mainly for two reasons. First, the Northern Hemisphere receives strong sunshine. Second, its long daylight periods allow many hours for heating. In the Southern Hemisphere it is winter for just the opposite reasons. The sun's rays are slanting and weak, and short periods of daylight permit little time for heating.

On December 21 conditions are reversed. The sun's vertical ray is 23.5° south of the Equator at the Tropic of Capricorn. Now the Southern Hemisphere receives the lion's share of the sunshine. The rays are strong, and its daylight periods are longer than its nights. It is summer in the Southern Hemisphere and winter in the Northern Hemisphere.

Between June 21 and December 21 the sun's vertical ray travels from the Tropic of Cancer to the Tropic of Capricorn. Then from December 21 to June 21 it returns over the same area. This 47° wide belt is called the Torrid Zone.

The Torrid Zone has no true winter or summer. Its daylight periods are never far from 12 hours in length. The sun's rays are never far from vertical. As a result, temperatures remain high throughout the year. At the Equator, center of the Torrid Zone, the sun's rays are vertical on the equinoxes. At these times sunlight is distributed evenly over the earth. This gives us our moderate spring and fall seasons. (See Topic 8.)

The Sun at Noon 11.

In all parts of the world the sun reaches its highest position in the sky each day at noon. It is then midway between its rising and setting positions. However, it comes to the zenith only in the Torrid Zone (from Cancer to Capricorn). Even there it is in the zenith at any particular place only twice a year. In the United States the sun reaches the zenith only in the Hawaiian Islands. Why?

In all other parts of the United States the sun is highest on June 21 and lowest on December 21. At noon the sun is always directly south of the zenith in this country, except in the Hawaiian Islands.

Summary: What Causes Seasons; Effect of Distance 12.

You can summarize the causes of seasons as: (1) tilt of the earth's axis, (2) parallelism of the axis, (3) rotation of the earth on its axis, and (4) revolution of the earth around the sun.

People sometimes say wrongly that "the earth is nearest the sun in winter and farthest away in summer." Only the Northern Hemisphere has winter when the earth is nearest the sun. At the same time the Southern Hemisphere has its summer.

Six months later, the Northern Hemisphere has its summer. It is then farthest from the sun. At the same time it is winter in the Southern Hemisphere. Obviously, changing distance from the sun is not the cause of the seasons. If it were, the whole earth would have the same season at the same time.

Why is our changing distance from the sun so unimportant? The answer is simple. The difference between perihelion distance and aphelion distance is about 4,800,000 kilometers. This seems like a great distance, but in relation to the total distance it is small. It is only about $\frac{1}{31}$ of the total distance between earth and sun.

Imagine yourself 31 meters from a campfire. If you felt cold, you could certainly get warmer by moving closer to the fire. But moving one meter closer would make very little difference. So it is with the earth.

The earth as a whole does receive a little more heat from the sun in January than in July. However, if its orbit were as eccentric as Pluto's the change in distance would affect the seasons strongly.

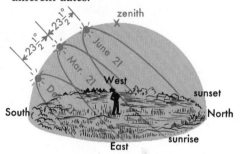

Imagine that you live at 41° latitude, the same latitude as New York City. The blue circles show how the sun travels in the sky at different dates.

Each topic question refers to the topic of the same number within this chapter.

1. (a) Describe the earth's orbit and the speed and direction of the earth in the orbit. (b) Give the date and distance of the earth at perihelion and aphelion. (c) How do we know that the earth revolves around the sun?

2. What is the earth's rotation? What is its rate?

3. Describe the experiment by which Foucault proved that the earth rotates.

4. (a) In what direction does the earth rotate? As seen from the North Pole? South Pole? (b) Describe the position of the axis.

5. (a) Why do daylight and night alternate? (b) Why are they unequal?

6. (a) Why do daylight and night change in length? (b) What is axis parallelism?

7. Describe the distribution of daylight and night over the earth on (a) the summer solstice and (b) the winter solstice. Give their dates.

8. (a) Why are daylight and night equal everywhere on the equinoxes? (b) Give the names and dates of the equinoxes.

9. (a) Explain the meaning of zenith, horizon, altitude, and zenith distance. Use a diagram. (b) How is the angle of the sun's rays related to their strength?

10. (a) What is the Tropic of Cancer? (b) Explain why June 21 is a time of warm weather in the Northern Hemisphere and cold weather in the Southern Hemisphere. (c) Why are weather conditions reversed on December 21? (d) What is the Torrid Zone? Why is it warm all year? (e) Explain why spring and fall are our "moderate" seasons.

11. Why is the sun always below the zenith in the continental United States at noontime? In which direction is it always seen at noon?

12. (a) State the causes of the regular change of seasons. (b) What evidence is there that our seasons are not caused by changing distance from the sun? (c) Why is a change in distance of 4,800,000 kilometers so unimportant?

GENERAL QUESTIONS

1. How do the earth's rotation and revolution affect conditions for life on earth?

2. Compare the length of daylight and night in your city or town with that in Mexico City, Montreal, and Buenos Aires on June 21 and December 21.

3. Where would the noon sun be in the sky at the Equator on the two equinoxes and the two solstices?

4. How would increased inclination of the earth's axis change (a) the length of daylight and night? (b) the seasons?

5. Suppose the earth rotated from east to west at twice its present rate. What changes would be made in our day?

STUDENT ACTIVITIES

1. The last diagram in this chapter shows that the sun rises to the north of east and sets to the north of west on all dates from March 21 to September 23. Similarly, the sun rises south of east and sets south of west in fall and winter. This is true for all places on earth.

Check this by actual observation of the sun in your locality for a period of several weeks in both spring and fall terms.

2. Topic 11 tells us that the noon sun, in all of the United States except Hawaii, is south of the zenith regardless of the dates. Check this by actual observation for a period of several weeks in both winter and summer.

Measure the approximate noon zenith distance of the sun at weekly intervals for a few weeks before and after the winter solstice, when the sun's zenith distance is greatest. Do the same at the time of the summer solstice, when the zenith distance is least.

A crude measurement of the sun's zenith distance may be made with a blackboard compass, pointing one arm of the compass at the zenith and the other at the sun. Accurate measurements can be made with a sextant. (See next chapter.) Do not look directly at the sun!

3. Make a model of the earth at the solstices and equinoxes in its orbit.

4. Make a model to illustrate the Foucault pendulum.

23

In the United States (except Hawaii during part of the summer) the sun is always directly to the south when it is highest in the sky. At that time, the shadow of a vertical post will point north—to the earth's North Pole. This happens every day. At about 11 A.M. standard time set up a long slender vertical post, outdoors or indoors, in sunlight. Stand the post on a surface on which you can mark the line of its shadow. Mark this line every five minutes. Why does it change direction? Why does it get shorter? Now watch carefully for the moment when the shadow first gets longer. The shadow just before this may be taken as the shortest shadow—the true north-south line. Make a permanent record of this direction for future reference.

Location, Navigation, and Time

Latitude and Longitude

How does the captain of a ship in mid-ocean know where he is? How does a pilot flying over the Atlantic locate his plane's position? How are the boundaries between the states defined?

In most towns, you can find your location by noting which streets meet near you. But there are no streets in the countryside or on the oceans.

Geographers long ago set up a location scheme for the earth. Two sets of imaginary "streets" were created. One set ran north and south through the North Pole and the South Pole. These "streets" were called **meridians** of longitude. The other set ran east and west around the earth. These "streets" were called **parallels** of latitude. All of these "streets" are circles (or half circles) because they run on the surface of a globe.

Why do we call meridians and parallels "imaginary?" They are real enough to be drawn on maps and charts. In a city, every street that runs north and south is part of a meridian. Every street that runs east and west is part of a parallel. On the ocean, however, they have to be "imagined."

Meridians run north and south. They all have the same length. Parallels run east and west. Their circumferences increase from the poles to the Equator.

Our system of latitude and longitude starts with the earth's North Pole and South Pole. A circle is drawn around the earth exactly halfway between the Poles. This circle is called the **Equator.** It divides the earth into a Northern Hemisphere and a Southern Hemisphere.

Now we can define latitude. **Latitude** is the distance north or south of the Equator. To measure latitude, distances from the Equator are marked off by circles called parallels. They are called *parallels* because they are parallel to the Equator. The closer a parallel is to a Pole, the smaller a circle it is.

Latitude is measured in degrees. You know that a full turn or complete circle is three hundred sixty degrees. So, the distance around a circle around the earth is also 360°. Since the Equator is the starting point for measuring latitude, its number is 0° (zero degrees). Places north of the Equator have north latitude. Places south of the Equator have south latitude. The two Poles are the points farthest

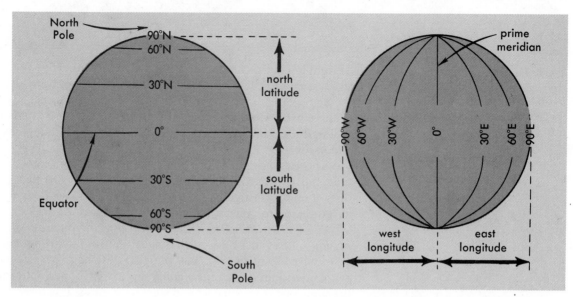

Latitude is measured in degrees north or south of the Equator. Longitude is measured in degrees east or west of the prime meridian through Greenwich, England.

from the Equator. The North Pole's latitude is 90° N. The South Pole's latitude is 90° S. (From the Equator to either Pole is one fourth of the way around the earth. One fourth of 360° is 90°.)

There are four parallels that have names besides numbers. They are the Tropic of Cancer, 23.5° N; the Tropic of Capricorn, 23.5° S; the Arctic Circle, 66.5° N; the Antarctic Circle, 66.5° S.

3. Latitude and Distance

It is easy to find the number of kilometers in a degree of latitude. The distance around the earth through the Poles is about 40,000 kilometers. Divided by 360, this gives an average of about 111 kilometers to a **degree** of latitude. But the earth is not perfectly round. The length of a degree of latitude changes slightly from the Equator to the Poles. At the Poles, where the earth is flattest, a degree of latitude is about one kilometer longer than at the Equator.

Degrees alone are too large for precise locations on the earth. Therefore they are divided into *minutes* and *seconds*. A degree includes 60 minutes (written as 60′); each minute includes 60 seconds (written as 60″). To find the length of one minute (1′), we divide 111 kilometers (in 1° of latitude) by 60. A minute of latitude therefore equals nearly 2 kilometers.

A minute of latitude also equals one *nautical mile*.

Longitude in Degrees 4.

You're looking down at the earth from above the North Pole. Note the 180th meridian. It is just as far from 0° going around west as it is going around east.

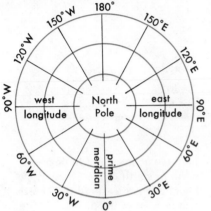

At right angles to the parallels are the *meridians*. They are the north-south streets of the earth. All meridians extend from the North Pole to the South Pole. Each meridian is therefore a semicircle covering half of the earth's circumference. Distance between meridians is known as **longitude.** Like latitude, longitude is measured in degrees, minutes and seconds.

There is no natural midpoint like the Equator from which longitude can be measured. The meridian that runs through Greenwich (near London), England, is used for this purpose. This meridian is called the **prime meridian** and is numbered 0°.

Longitude is the distance in degrees east or west of the prime meridian. The half of the earth that lies east of the prime meridian has *east longitude* up to 180° (half of 360°). The half that lies west of the prime meridian has *west longitude* up to 180°. The 180th meridian is the same one for both east and west longitudes. It is directly opposite the prime meridian on the earth's surface.

The North Pole and South Pole have no longitude. All the meridians meet there.

Longitude and Distance 5.

The distance between any two parallels is the same around the earth. But meridians are not parallel to each other. All the meridians come together as they get near the Poles. Because of this, there is no fixed distance for a degree of longitude.

At the Equator a degree of longitude is about as long as a degree of latitude—about 111 kilometers. In higher latitudes (nearer the Poles) the length of a degree of longitude steadily decreases. At the Poles it is zero. At 40° latitude a degree of longitude equals about 85 kilometers.

Location by Latitude and Longitude 6.

Geometry tells us that two straight lines meet in only one point. The same is true for a particular parallel and meridian. The latitude and longitude of City Hall in New York City are 40°42′44″ N and 74°00′24″ W. That means that City Hall lies at the intersection of those two lines on the earth's surface. Similarly, we may locate Chicago at about 42° N and 88° W; St. Louis at 39° N and 90° W; Boston at 42° N and 71° W; London at 51° N and 0°; and Melbourne, Australia at 38° S and 145° E.

Navigation

Without landmarks, the navigator of a ship or plane has two main problems. To go in the right direction he needs to know the "points of the compass." To plot his course correctly he has to locate his ship's position (latitude and longitude) from time to time. A ship's position can be found by observations of the sun, moon, planets, or stars. Doing this is **celestial navigation.**

8. **Finding North**

As a rule, directions are determined by first finding north. If one faces north, south is to the rear, east is to the right and west is to the left. Several different methods may be used to find north.

1. At night, north is given almost exactly by the position of Polaris, the North Star. This is easily found by following the pointer stars of the Big Dipper.

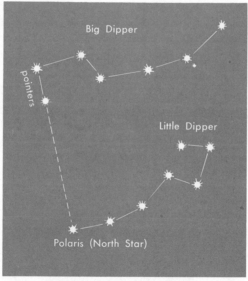

Trace the stars in the Big Dipper starting at the end of the handle. The last two stars in the bowl point to the North Star.

2. In the daytime, north may be found with the help of the sun at local (not clock) noon. At local noon, the shadow of a vertical post will run along a true north-and-south line. You can tell local noon by the fact that shadows are shortest at that time. This is because the sun is at its highest point in the sky. (See "How Do You Know That . . . ?")

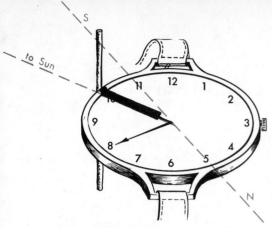

When the shadow of the vertical stick falls right on the hour hand, the hour hand points right at the sun. Then south is half-way between the hour hand and 12 o'clock.

Approximate north may be found whenever the sun is shining. Point the hour hand of a watch directly at the sun. The point halfway between the hour hand and 12 o'clock is south. Directly opposite is north.

3. The magnetic compass gives *magnetic north*. From this, true north can be obtained by making the proper corrections for *magnetic variation. Magnetic variation is the angle by which the compass needle varies from true north.* The north magnetic pole of the earth, toward which the compass points, is not at the earth's North Pole. The navigator carries charts that tell him the magnetic variation for all parts of the earth.

4. Like Foucault's pendulum, a spinning gyroscope does not change its direction of vibration after it has been set in motion. This principle is used in the **gyrocompass,** which is a nonmagnetic compass. The gyroscope in this compass is pointed north, with its spin axis parallel to the earth's axis. It is then kept spinning by a small motor. Gyroscopes are used in space vehicles because they keep a constant direction.

5. The **radio compass** finds north from the direction of the radio signals it receives from stations whose locations are known.

Finding Latitude 9.

At different latitudes the stars and the sun appear at different altitudes in the sky. For any point in the Northern Hemisphere, *the altitude of the North Star is equal to the latitude of the observer.* For example, at the North Pole, latitude 90° N, the North Star is in the zenith. Its altitude is 90° N. At New York City, latitude 41° N, the North Star's altitude is 41°. If the captain of a ship observes the North Star at an altitude of 46°, he knows that he is in latitude 46° N. The instruments used to measure the altitude of stars, planets, and the sun are the **sextant** or **octant.**

At the North Pole, the North Star is always overhead.

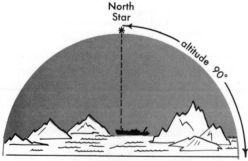

at North Pole, 90°N latitude

at New York City, 41°N latitude

The North Star is 41° above the horizon in New York City. So, New York is at 41° N latitude.

Latitude is found in the daytime from the sun's noon position in the sky. The sextant (or octant) is used to "shoot the sun"; that is, to measure its altitude. The *Nautical Almanac* or *Air Almanac* is then consulted. It tells in which latitude the sun has the observed noon altitude on the day of observation.

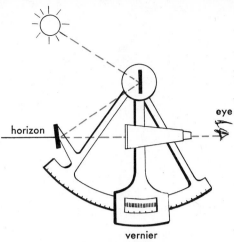

The upper heavy vertical line is a mirror. The lower heavy vertical line is half mirror, half clear glass. Through the clear glass the observer sights the horizon. Then he moves the vertical sliding arm until it reflects the sun into the lower mirror, "sitting on the horizon." At this point he can read the sun's altitude from the sextant's scale.

This observer's left hand moves the sliding arm of the sextant.

10. Determining Longitude

Differences in time exist between the prime meridian and places east or west of it. These differences are equal to one hour for every 15 degrees of longitude. Since the sun rises in the east, places east of the prime meridian have later time. Places west of the prime meridian have earlier time.

If the ship's observer can find the difference in time between his location and Greenwich, he can calculate his longitude. For example, suppose that sun time at his location (called local time) is two hours earlier than Greenwich time. His ship is then at 30° W longitude.

Greenwich time is obtained simply. The ship carries a very accurate clock called a **chronometer.** This is set at Greenwich time and kept running that way. Greenwich time signals are also transmitted over government radio stations at regular intervals. Local time is obtained most accurately at noon, when the sun is highest in the sky, as explained in Topic 8.

The practice is to read the chronometer at local noon and then calculate the longitude. For example, suppose the ship's chronometer says 8 A.M. at local noon. It means that the ship's time (12 noon) is four hours later than Greenwich time (8 A.M.). The ship is therefore at 60° E longitude.

The chronometer is a 24-hour clock. A 12-hour clock would not show whether the time was A.M. or P.M. at Greenwich.

Dead Reckoning

Usually a navigator knows the approximate direction and speed at which he has been traveling. He can then determine his position on his charts (maps). Finding the position of a ship in this way is known as **dead reckoning.** The reckoning can be brought up to date as often as desired. Positions determined by dead reckoning are not entirely accurate. They are valuable in cloudy weather and between observations of the sun and stars.

The speed of a ship is measured in knots. **A knot** is one nautical mile per hour.

Great-Circle Routes

The great-circle route from A to B is much shorter than the route along the parallel.

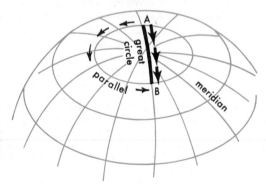

Circles drawn on the surface of a sphere may be either *great circles* or *small circles*. A **great circle** is a circle whose plane passes through the center of the sphere. Perhaps it is simpler to say that any circle that divides the sphere in half is a great circle. All other circles drawn on the sphere are called *small circles*.

On the earth the Equator is a great circle. All other parallels are small circles. Each meridian is half of a great circle. The meridian opposite it in the other hemisphere is the other half. Great circles may also be drawn in slanting positions between the Equator and the Poles. Think of an orange that may be cut in half in any direction.

Great circles are important in navigation. This is because a *great-circle route is the shortest distance between two points on a sphere.* On a sphere a small circle is an indirect route.

The diagram shows a great-circle route between two points, *A* and *B*, that are on the same small-circle parallel. Great-circle routes are the shortest routes. They are always the most desirable for airplanes. But they are not always the best for ships. Winds, ocean currents, icebergs, and other factors must also be considered. Great-circle routes between cities in high latitudes pass over or near the Poles. To find a great-circle route between any two points on a globe, simply stretch a string between the two points.

Time and Date

Places that are on the same meridian have the same local (sun) time. On the other hand, places that are even a short distance east or west of each other have different local time. This is because the rotation of the earth brings the sun across each meridian at a different instant. The differences in local time amount to one hour for every 15° of longitude, or 4 minutes for each 1° of longitude. For example, New York City's longitude is about 74° W; Philadelphia's is about 75° W. Because of this difference of about 1°, the sun is highest in the sky at New York City about 4 minutes before it reaches its high point at Philadelphia.

Until 1883 most cities and other localities in the United States kept their own local time. Fifty-three different kinds of time were used by the country's railroads. Cities through which several railroads ran had as many as five different time systems. On November 18, 1883, American railroads adopted *standard time*. It is in worldwide use today.

14. **Standard Time**

In standard time, meridians are marked off at intervals of 15° east and west of the prime meridian at Greenwich, England. These 24 meridians—15° E, 15° W, 30° E, 30° W, and so on, up to 180°—are called *time meridians*. Each time meridian is the center of a **standard-time zone** that is 15° wide, 7½° on each side. The entire zone has the same time. All clocks show the *local time of the time meridian in that zone.* In the zone to the east the time is exactly one hour later. In the zone to the west it is exactly one hour earlier. Changes of time are made only when crossing from one zone into the next.

How do we calculate the standard time in any part of the world? We merely add one hour for each 15-degree zone to the east. We subtract one hour for each 15-degree zone to the west. For example, when it is 10 A.M. at London, 0° longitude, it is 11 A.M. in Rome, in the 15° E zone; 5 A.M. in Philadelphia, 75° W; 3 A.M. in Denver, 105° W; and so on. A rhyme that may help you to remember this rule is

As you go to the east
The time doth increase.
As you go to the west
The time will grow less.

You're looking down at the earth from above the North Pole. The sun is off to the right.

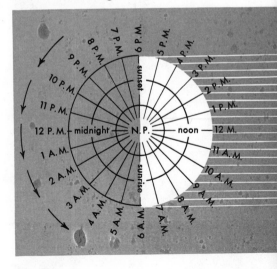

Each standard time zone should be exactly 15° wide. On land, however, such exactness is not desirable and not necessary. It is not desirable because an exact boundary might cut right through a city. It might separate cities that wish to keep the same time. It is not necessary as long as the irregular zones (called belts) *average 15°* in width.

Four time meridians pass through the United States (except Alaska and Hawaii). The United States therefore has four standard time belts, all with highly irregular boundaries, The belts and their time meridians are Eastern, 75° W; Central, 90° W; Mountain, 105° W; Pacific, 120° W.

It is 10:00 in Phoenix and in the rest of that blue area. The clocks at the top show the time in the other areas. The dotted lines are the time meridians.

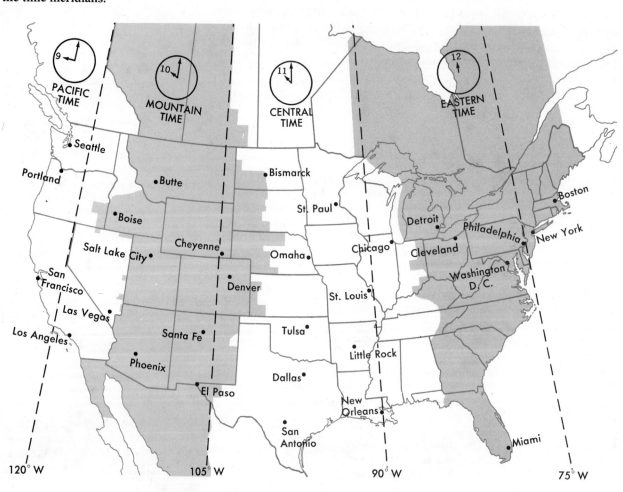

The Pacific Belt is 45° (or three belts) to the west of the Eastern Belt. It is therefore 3 hours earlier. When it is 5 P.M. in New York, it is 2 P.M. in Los Angeles. (Alaska stretches through three time belts whose meridians are 135° W, 150° W and 165° W. Hawaii is in the last of these.)

Most of the United States uses **daylight time** from late April to late October. Clocks are set one hour ahead of standard time. Daylight then ends one hour later in the evening. A sunset that would occur at 7 P.M. standard time takes place at 8:00 P.M. daylight time. Daylight time reduces the use of electricity for lighting.

When in spring we set our clocks ahead for daylight time, we "lose" an hour. When we set our clocks back again to standard time, we "gain" an hour.

16. The International Date Line

A traveler going eastward from one time belt to another also "loses" an hour. A westward traveler "gains" an hour with each time belt. Suppose one of these travelers completes a trip around the world. He will have "lost" or "gained" 24 hours. In his reckoning he will be either a day ahead or a day behind the place from which he started.

To prevent "date" confusion, the **international date line** was established. As a traveler on ship or plane crosses this line, he changes the date. This makes up for the "losses" or "gains" of time. The *westward traveler* (who has been turning his watch back) *moves his calendar forward*, as from Sunday to Monday. The *eastward* traveler (who has been turning his watch forward) *moves his calendar back*, as from Saturday to Friday.

The international date line is located entirely in the ocean. In this way, all changes of date are made on ship or plane. No body of land is divided by the date line. For the most part it follows the 180th meridian.

The international date line is inside a time belt. Therefore no change in clock time is made when it is crossed. The change is in the date alone. The western half of this time belt is always one day ahead of the eastern half. It is the part of the world in which each new date begins. With each passing hour, the new date moves westward, one belt at a time, around the earth. Except for the instant when the midnight line crosses the international date line, there are always two dates on the earth at any moment. For a good part of our day, we are behind the date in eastern Asia and the far Pacific islands.

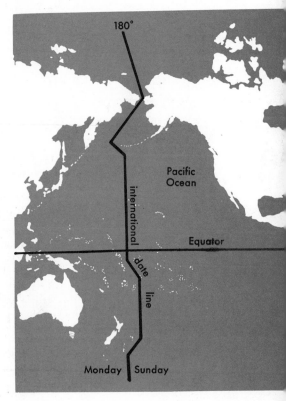

> Suppose you're in a ship just east of the international date line. It is 1 A.M. *Monday*. As you sail over the date line, it will become 1 A.M. *Tuesday*.

Each topic question refers to the topic of the same number within this chapter.

1. Describe the location system set up for the earth by geographers.

2. (a) Explain how the latitude system of the earth is set up. (b) Define latitude, Equator, parallels. (c) Explain and give examples of the manner in which latitude is expressed.

3. (a) How long is each of the following: (1) a degree of latitude, (2) a minute of latitude. (b) Explain why and and how much a degree of latitude changes in length over the earth.

4. (a) Explain how the longitude system of the earth is set up. (b) Define longitude. (c) Explain the relation between meridians and the prime meridian. (d) Explain the division of the world into longitude degrees.

5. Explain why no single value can be given for the number of miles in a degree of longitude.

6. (a) How do the latitude and longitude of a place indicate its exact location? (b) Give the latitude and longitude (degrees only) of three big cities.

7. (a) What are the main problems of the navigator working without landmarks? (b) What is celestial navigation?

8. (a) Explain how to find north using (1) Polaris, (2) the sun, (3) the magnetic compass. (b) What is a gyrocompass? a radio compass?

9. (a) Explain how the North Star is used to determine latitude. (b) How is the sun used in determining latitude? (c) What are the sextant and octant?

10. (a) How is longitude determined? Give examples. (b) What is a chronometer? (c) Why is longitude on a ship usually determined at local noon?

11. (a) Describe dead reckoning and explain its uses. (b) What is a knot?

12. (a) What are great circles? Give some examples. (b) Why are great circles important in navigation? (c) How are they found on a globe?

13. (a) Explain, with examples, why places that are even short distances east and west of each other have different local time. (b) Why was a standard time system adopted in 1883?

14. Explain the standard time system for the world.

15. (a) Why do standard time zones have irregular boundaries on land? (b) Name the standard time belts of the United States (except Alaska and Hawaii) with their time meridians. (c) Explain what daylight time is and why it is used.

16. (a) Explain why we have an international date line. (b) Where is the date line? (c) How does a traveler change his calendar when crossing the date line? (d) Describe the start and progress of a new date.

1. Approximately how many kilometers is it to the Equator and to the North Pole from each of the following cities: New York, London, Buenos Aires, Hong Kong?

2. Explain why the rule for finding north by the use of a watch should be true.

3. At local noon on board a ship on June 21 the sun is in the zenith and the chronometer time is 3 P.M. What are the ship's latitude and longitude?

4. What is the altitude of the North Star at each of the cities listed in Topic 6?

5. In Topic 12 it is stated that airplanes are more likely than ships to be able to make use of great-circle routes. Why?

6. In Topic 11 it is stated that positions obtained by dead reckoning are not entirely accurate. Why?

7. What is the greatest possible difference between the standard time of a zone and the local time of any place in it? (Assume that the time meridian is exactly in the middle of the zone.) Explain.

8. Name four important cities in each United States standard time belt.

9. What time is it in each United States standard time belt when the new date is just beginning at the international date line?

10. What are the time and day in Manila, Tokyo, Honolulu, Melbourne, Buenos Aires, London, Moscow, and Calcutta when it is 10 P.M. Monday in Washington, D.C.?

11. What objection would there be to having the whole earth keep the same hour and date?

1. Find north by the first three methods described in Topic 8. For the magnetic compass method you will need to know the magnetic variation of your locality. This may be found from any local U.S.G.S. quadrangle map.

2. Using the method described in Topic 12, determine the great-circle route between two selected middle-latitude cities of approximately equal latitude but differing greatly in longitude; e.g., New York City and Tokyo, Seattle and Moscow, London and Shanghai, or any other widely separated locations. Then (a) Plot the great-circle route on a Mercator outline map of the world. (This is done most easily by plotting the points where your great-circle route crosses meridians on the globe.) (b) Compare the great-circle route, with respect to both distance and direction, with the one-directional route obtained by joining the two cities with a straight line on the Mercator map.

3. Find your latitude at night from the altitude of the North Star.

4. Build a sundial. Instructions may be found in a U.S. Government Printing Office leaflet on sundials, in Mayall's book on sundials, etc.

Do you recognize the
kind of storm illustrated on the
opposite page? From its shape, how do you
think it moves? Spinning like a top and roaring
like a hundred airplanes, this smallest but most dangerous of all storms is a tornado. A tornado's whirling
winds are terrifying and destructive. As it twists over the
land, buildings can be blown to pieces. Walls collapse or topple
outward. Objects can be lifted up and hurled great distances. Yet the
tornado is just an intensive form of one kind of weather pattern that
occurs almost daily. It can be understood according to the same
principles as our ordinary weather.

Tornadoes occur in many parts of the world. The most favorable place for
their formation is the central part of the United States. Meteorologists,
people who study the weather, analyze and interpret many weather charts
to identify the conditions and areas where a tornado may develop. In this
unit you will explore some of these weather conditions—air temperature,
air pressure, moisture in the air, the movement of air as wind.

Meteorology is the study of the atmosphere and its effects on the
earth's surface, its oceans, and life in general. Its goals are explanation, prediction, and control over certain atmospheric events.
Climatology is a part of atmospheric science. Climatology
focuses on the collective, long-term weather conditions in
a specific area known as climate. In recent years our
concept of the atmosphere has been extended by
modern research tools such as weather
balloons, earth satellites, and
space probes.

Atmospheric Science

24

Half fill a large wide-mouthed jar or aquarium tank with water. Float a piece of cork on the water to show the water level plainly. Mark the water level. Now turn an empty drinking glass over the cork and push the glass straight down into the water. Hold it there. Look at the position of the cork. Was the glass empty? What evidence do you have that it is really filled with something (that we call air)? What evidence do you have that the air in the glass is compressible? Why is the air at sea level denser than the air at higher elevations?

The Heating of the Atmosphere

Composition and Structure

1.

The earth's lower atmosphere is a mixture of many gases. The mixture is called air. The two main gases in air are nitrogen and oxygen. Together they form about 99 per cent of the air by volume. Most of the remaining 1 percent is argon and carbon dioxide. The atmosphere also contains tiny amounts of helium, hydrogen, neon, ozone, and other gases. Roughly the percentages by volume are: nitrogen, 78; oxygen, 21; argon, almost 1; carbon dioxide, 0.03; all others, 0.01.

The air thins out fast with height above the earth's surface. Its composition by percent remains the same, however, to a height of about 80 kilometers. Above this level the air is so thin it would be considered a good vacuum at sea level. Here scientists have found that the atmosphere changes to layers of one gas only. A layer of oxygen reaches to about 1000 kilometers. Then comes a layer of helium to about 2400 kilometers. Above this, a layer of hydrogen reaches off into space.

The molecules of gases at the bottom of the atmosphere are squeezed together by the gases above them. As a result, 99 percent of the atmosphere's weight is found within about 32 kilometers of the earth's surface.

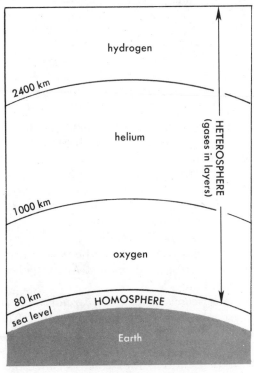

Below 80 kilometers, gases are mixed throughout the atmosphere. Above that, the gases are in separate layers.

Water Vapor, Ozone, and Dust

Air almost always contains **water vapor,** too. Unlike the other gases, however, water vapor varies greatly in percentage. Dry air in desert regions may have almost no water vapor. Humid air may have as much as five percent water vapor. Water vapor enters the air by evaporation from the ocean and from water on land. The percentage in the air depends mainly on the place, the season, and the time of day.

Ozone is a very active form of oxygen gas. Its percentage in air is very small. It is, nevertheless, very important, because it absorbs the sun's ultraviolet rays. If the air had no ozone, we would be badly burned by the sun's rays. Ozone is concentrated at heights of about 15 to 50 kilometers. This part of the air is called the **ozonosphere.**

Ozone is destroyed by a number of gases made by man. Among them are the gases from spray cans and supersonic aircraft. When these pollute the air, they can weaken our protection from ultraviolet rays.

Dust is an important part of air. Dust includes tiny grains of rocks and minerals, pollen grains from plants, crystals of salt from sea spray, chemicals from fires and industrial plants, and bacteria. Microscopic dust grains in the air cause hazy skies. Grains of salt and chemicals help to form fog and rain. They do this because water vapor condenses into droplets of water around them.

The Atmosphere's Temperature Layers 3.

Scientists divide the atmosphere into four layers, based on temperature changes. You can "see" these layers in the drawing and graph.

The lowest layer is called the *troposphere*. It starts at the earth's surface. Its height depends on the latitude. At the Equator it is about 18 kilometers. At the Poles it is only about 8 kilometers. The troposphere is the part of the atmosphere we live in. It is the layer in which the weather is always changing.

In the troposphere, the higher you go, the colder it gets. The top of the troposphere is called the *tropopause*. When this is reached, the temperature stops dropping. At the Poles the tropopause temperature is about −55° C.

The second layer is the *stratosphere*. It reaches from the tropopause to a height of about 50 kilometers. The stratosphere is clear and dry. It has strong steady winds and few weather changes. The lower part of the stratosphere is as cold as the tropopause. Then it warms up steadily right to its top, which is called the *stratopause*.

The temperature scale is at the bottom. Note how the temperature changes with the altitude.

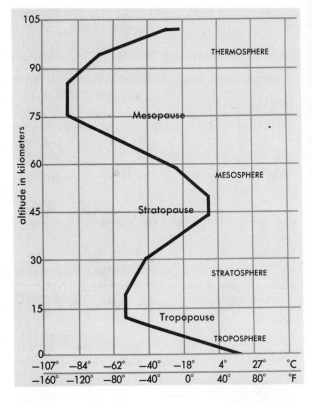

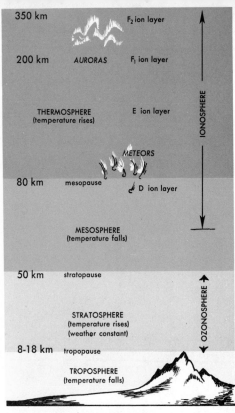

Note the characteristics of each layer of the atmosphere.

The third and fourth layers are the *mesosphere* and the *thermosphere*. Their heights and temperatures are shown in the diagrams.

4. The Ionosphere

At heights between 65 kilometers and 500 kilometers, the air is highly ionized. The ions are formed when ultraviolet rays knock electrons out of oxygen atoms. This part of the atmosphere is called the **ionosphere.**

The ions and electrons are concentrated in layers at four different levels. Each layer has the power to reflect radio waves of different wave lengths. Radio waves from broadcasting stations travel in a straight line. Without the ionosphere, they would reach only a small part of the earth. But the ionosphere bounces them back to earth. This greatly increases the area in which they can be received.

The ionosphere does not reflect the short waves used to transmit television. Those waves, however, are often picked up and rebroadcast by special satellites high above the earth.

Radio waves bounced off the ionosphere can be picked up far away.

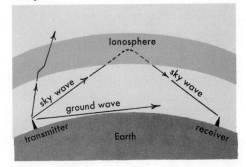

The Heating of the Atmosphere   **375**

Heating of the Atmosphere

Weather and the Sun's Energy 5.

Weather is the state of the atmosphere. It includes changes in temperature, movements of air, evaporation of water, formation of clouds, and the falling of rain and snow. Energy is needed to make all these things happen. That energy comes from the sun.

The sun radiates energy because it is a hot body. Its energy goes into space in all directions. The earth, tiny by comparison and far away, receives only one two-billionth of the sun's rays. What happens when these rays reach earth?

Our atmosphere is always "partly cloudy." The clouds reflect about 34 percent of the sun's rays back to space. About 19 percent of the sun's rays are absorbed by the atmosphere. Most of this happens in its denser lower layers. Here the chief absorbers, carbon dioxide and water vapor, are concentrated. The remainder of the sun's rays, about 47 percent, reach the earth's surface.

Scientists give the name **insolation** to all the sun's rays that strike the earth.

Clouds bounce some of the sun's energy back into space. The air absorbs some more of the energy. The rest reaches the surface.

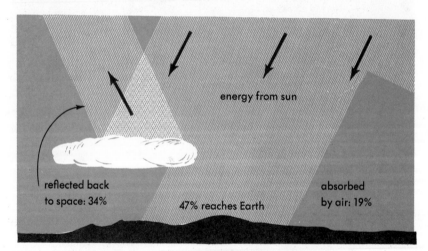

energy from sun

reflected back to space: 34%

47% reaches Earth

absorbed by air: 19%

Absorption; the Greenhouse Effect 6.

What happens to the sun's rays that reach the earth's surface? A hot body, such as the sun, radiates mainly short waves. These include ultraviolet rays, visible light, and short infrared rays. Air does not absorb these short waves well. Rock, soil, and water absorb these waves very well. The rock and water warm up while the sun shines.

Then they too radiate their energy. Being much cooler than the sun, however, they radiate mainly very long infrared waves. These are rays that the air can absorb. The result is that heat from the surface warms the air above it.

The earth's atmosphere is often compared to the glass roof of a greenhouse. The greenhouse roof lets the sun's short waves enter and warm the soil. But the roof does not allow the heat from the soil to escape. The earth's atmosphere acts in much the same way. Scientists therefore call its action "the **greenhouse effect.**"

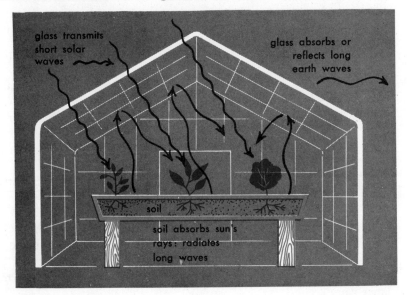

glass transmits
short solar
waves

glass absorbs or
reflects long
earth waves

soil

soil absorbs sun's
rays; radiates
long waves

Note what the glass in this greenhouse does to solar waves. Water and carbon dioxide in the atmosphere do the same thing to solar waves.

7. How Heat Moves

Heat energy gets into the atmosphere, or moves through it, in four different ways.

The first way is **radiation.** Hot bodies such as the sun radiate their energy mainly in the form of short waves. Cooler bodies such as the earth radiate their energy as long waves. Since both long and short waves are electromagnetic waves, they both travel through space at the speed of light.

The second way is **conduction.** Here an object receives heat by actually touching a hotter object. A pan on a hot stove is heated mainly by conduction. The air touching a hot radiator is heated mainly by conduction. So is the air that touches warm ground or the warm ocean.

The third way is **convection.** This can happen only in liquids and gases. The heat is moved by currents in the heated material itself. Take a kettle of water on a hot stove as an example. The bottom of the

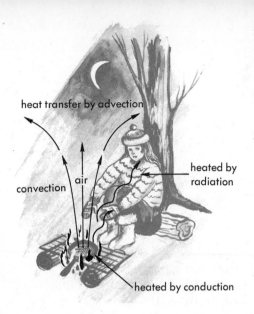

heat transfer by advection

convection

air

heated by radiation

heated by conduction

kettle gets hot by conduction. The bottom water then gets hot by conduction. It expands and becomes less dense. The denser cold water above it sinks, forcing the warm water up. A steady flow called a *convection current* forms. In time the heat at the bottom reaches all the water. If the heat is at the top, convection does not work. Why?

Convection is very important in moving heat through our atmosphere. In doing this, it forms air currents and winds. Winds transfer heat from one place to another. For example, winds from the tropics can bring heat into temperate latitudes. Cool ocean breezes can *remove* heat from hot beaches. This transfer of heat by winds is called **advection.** It is simply the bottom part of a large convection current.

Follow the arrows. They show four ways the fire heats other things.

Temperature Drops with Altitude

Air at the surface is normally warmer than air above. The middle of this diagram shows three reasons. The labels on the left show the temperature at the altitudes on the right.

In summertime, many people go to the "mountains" to escape the heat. The higher you go, the cooler it gets. Scientists have measured the rate of cooling with altitude. It averages about 1° C for every 160 meters. This change in temperature with altitude is called the **normal lapse rate.**

Why is the troposphere warmest at the earth's surface? The entire troposphere is heated in two ways. One is by the rays of the sun.

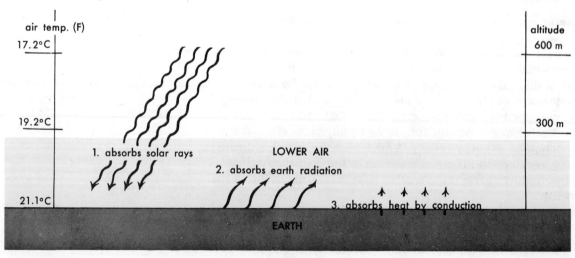

air temp. (F)

17.2°C

19.2°C

21.1°C

altitude

600 m

300 m

1. absorbs solar rays

LOWER AIR

2. absorbs earth radiation

3. absorbs heat by conduction

EARTH

The other is by radiation from the earth. But the bottom air is also heated in a third way. It gets heat by conduction from the land and sea it touches. It also has two other smaller advantages. The bottom air is closer to the source of earth radiations. It is a better absorber than the upper air because it is denser.

9. The Sun's Rays and Seasons

Do all parts of the earth receive equal amounts of solar energy? Not at all. They would if the earth were flat. In that case, the angle of the sun's rays would be the same everywhere. But the earth is round, so the sun's rays strike the surface at angles ranging from 90 degrees to zero.

When the sun is directly overhead, the *angle of insolation* is 90 degrees. The sun's rays are vertical, and the earth's surface gets all the energy possible. As the rays slant, however, their energy is spread out. The more slanted they are, the less they can heat the earth.

How is this connected with temperatures on the earth? Places near the Equator get nearly vertical rays all through the year. This gives them hot climates. Places in middle latitudes (New England, for example) get near-vertical rays in summer. Their summers are hot. They get slanting rays in winter, and their winters are cold. Places in high latitudes (near the Poles, for example) never get a high sun. They may even have no sun at all part of the year. They are cold all year round.

Of course the angle of the sun's rays varies throughout every day. The sun is warmest when it is highest, at local noon. Its rays are least warm when they are lowest—at sunrise and sunset.

The vertical rays concentrate all their energy between A and B. The slanted rays are of the same width. They bring the same energy. But this energy is spread out between A and C.

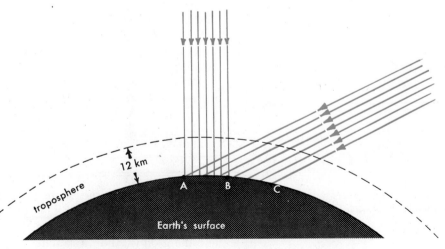

The Heating of the Atmosphere **379**

Heating of Land and Water 10.

All points on a parallel of latitude get equal solar energy. Do they all have the same temperatures? Not at all! Perhaps they would if the earth's surface were all the same material. But water and land warm up and cool off very differently.

Water warms much more slowly than land for many reasons.
1. In water, the sun's rays go to a depth of many meters. On land, the sun's rays heat only the top few centimeters of soil.
2. Water spreads its heat by moving about. Land cannot.
3. Water needs more energy than land to raise its temperature the same amount.
4. Some solar energy is used up in evaporating water. This leaves less solar energy to warm the water than land gets.

Water cools much more slowly than land for these reasons:
1. Its heat is spread through a larger amount of material.
2. Most of the warm water is far from the surface.
3. Water is a poorer conductor of heat than land.

For these reasons, water and land in the same latitude reach very different temperatures. On a sunny day in summer, dry beach sands are much warmer than the nearby water. At night the same sands are usually much colder. On a larger scale, continents are warmer than nearby ocean waters in summer. In winter, the same continents become much colder than the nearby waters.

Land Heats up Unevenly 11.

Unlike the water, the land has many kinds of surface materials. Some of these absorb the sun's rays better than others. Dark soils and rocks are better absorbers than light-colored ones. Dry ground warms up faster than wet ground. Meadows warm up more quickly than forests. Pavements get warm long before grassy lawns.

The surfaces that warm up faster also cool off faster. They are warmer in the sunshine and colder at night.

Warmest and Coldest Hours 12.

Local noon is the time of the strongest sun. Even so, the warmest hour of a sunny day is usually in the afternoon. Why? For several hours after noon, the lower air still receives more heat (from the sun and the ground) than it radiates off. So its temperature keeps rising until well into the afternoon. The warmest hour is usually later in summer than winter. Why?

The coldest hour usually comes just before sunrise. This is because the lower air loses heat all through the night. The coldest hour is usually later in winter than in summer. Why?

The difference between the highest and lowest temperature is the **temperature range.** For any one day, it is the *daily temperature range.* For example, a high of 35° C and a low of 10° C give a range of 25° C.

The daily temperature range is usually large when skies are clear. The clear skies allow strong heating by day. At night they allow rapid loss of heat by radiation.

The daily temperature range is small on cloudy days. The clouds keep out sunshine by day, so the air hardly warms up. At night the clouds keep the air from radiating its heat out to space. This "blanket" effect keeps the air from cooling much at night.

You will often hear about the *average temperature* for a day. This is the sum of the high and low temperatures divided by two. This daily average is then averaged in the normal way to give average, or mean temperatures for months, years, or other periods of time.

13. Warmest and Coldest Months

In the Northern Hemisphere's middle latitudes, July is usually the warmest month. January is usually the coldest month. In the Southern Hemisphere—New Zealand or Argentina, for example—it is just the reverse.

The **annual temperature range** is the difference between the average, or mean, temperatures of a place's warmest and coldest months. Oceans have a small annual temperature range. They are relatively cool in summer and warm in winter. Continents and large land masses have a large annual temperature range. They are relatively hot in summer and cool in winter.

14. Temperature Inversions

Normally the air gets colder as you go up in the troposphere. Sometimes, however, the air gets warmer for a hundred meters or more. This "upside down" condition is called a **temperature inversion.**

Temperature inversions are most likely to happen on clear dry nights. On these nights, the lower air cools rapidly by radiation. But the air close to the ground is also cooling by conduction. Very often

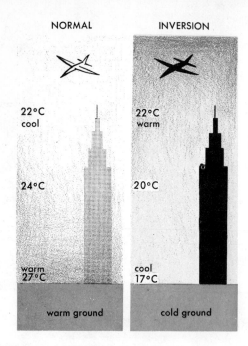

NORMAL   INVERSION

22°C
cool

22°C
warm

24°C

20°C

warm
27°C

cool
17°C

warm ground   cold ground

this makes the bottom layer colder than the air above it. The result is an inversion—cold air below, warmer air above. Usually this kind of inversion reaches no more than 100 meters above the ground.

Another important cause of inversion will be studied in Chapter 28. Inversions often cause fog, smog, sleet, and air pollution, as you will see in Chapters 27 and 28.

Look at the normal condition at the left. Note how the temperature drops as you go up. But, in the inversion at the right, the temperature rises as you go up.

Measuring Air Temperature

Thermometers 15.

Thermometers are instruments that measure temperature. Two different types are usually used to measure air temperature. Both work on the principle that a rise in temperature causes expansion in most materials.

Liquid thermometers use mercury or alcohol as the expanding material. Mercury is naturally silver-colored. Alcohol is colorless but is usually dyed red or blue. The liquid fills the broad *bulb* part of a long narrow glass tube. When the temperature rises, the liquid expands into the tube's narrow stem. (This has had the air driven out of it. It has then been sealed.)

This diagram shows the structure of an ordinary liquid thermometer.

bulb   magnifying glass   stem

mercury or alcohol   vacuum

Mercury thermometers are more accurate than alcohol thermometers. This is because mercury expands more evenly. However, mercury cannot be used at very low temperatures. It freezes at about −40° C. Alcohol freezes at about −129° C.

Metal thermometers have two equally long strips of different metals. Brass and iron are a common pair. The two strips are bonded together, one on top of the other. This forms a bar called a *bimetal*. Because the metals expand at different rates, a rise in temperature makes the bar curl. A drop in temperature curls it the other way. As a rule the bimetal is shaped into a coil and fastened at one end. A pointer is attached to the free end. A scale is mounted behind the pointer. As the temperature changes, the coil winds or unwinds. The pointer moves over the scale.

A **thermograph** is a self-recording metal thermometer. A **maximum thermometer** stays at the highest temperature it has reached. (A doctor's clinical thermometer is one.) The **minimum thermometer** stays at the lowest temperature it has reached.

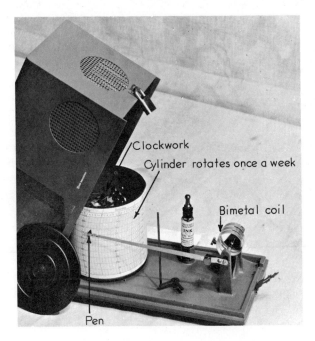

Clockwork

Cylinder rotates once a week

Bimetal coil

Pen

This is a thermograph. Its rotating cylinder is covered with a paper scale. As the temperature rises and falls, the pen rises and falls. The result is a temperature line.

16. Temperature Scales

Temperatures are measured in degrees. Temperature degrees have nothing to do with turning or with angles. A *degree* of temperature is a definite fraction of the difference between two "**fixed points**." Usually these are the temperatures of melting ice and boiling water.

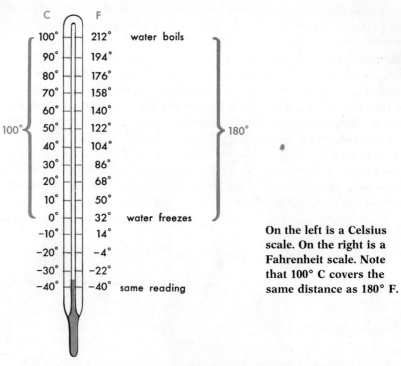

C	F	
100°	212°	water boils
90°	194°	
80°	176°	
70°	158°	
60°	140°	
50°	122°	
40°	104°	
30°	86°	
20°	68°	
10°	50°	
0°	32°	water freezes
−10°	14°	
−20°	−4°	
−30°	−22°	
−40°	−40°	same reading

On the left is a Celsius scale. On the right is a Fahrenheit scale. Note that 100° C covers the same distance as 180° F.

On the Celsius scale (formerly called the centigrade scale) the fixed points are 0° and 100°. One degree Celsius is therefore $\frac{1}{100}$ of their difference. On the Fahrenheit scale, the fixed points are 32° and 212°. One degree Fahrenheit is therefore $\frac{1}{180}$ of their difference. (212 − 32 = 180).

Note that a Celsius degree is almost twice as large as a Fahrenheit degree. To be exact,

$$1°\ C = 1.8°\ F,\ \text{or } 1°\ F = \tfrac{5}{9}°\ C.$$

To change Fahrenheit into Celsius or vice versa, use these formulas:

$$F = \tfrac{9}{5}\,C + 32 \qquad C = \tfrac{5}{9}\,(F - 32)$$

Isotherms 17.

Isotherms are lines drawn on maps to show places with the same temperature at a given time. They are used on weather maps and climate maps. There is usually one isotherm for each 5 or 10 degrees difference in temperature.

The **heat equator** is sometimes shown on isothermal maps of the world. The heat equator joins the hottest places for each meridian at a given time. These places do not have the same temperature. Therefore the heat equator is not an isotherm.

The maps on this page and the next show average world temperatures for July and January. If the earth were all water, isotherms would follow parallels of latitude. But as you saw in Topic 10, land and water heat up and cool off differently. So the isotherms are not straight lines around the earth. They are, however, much more regular in the Southern Hemisphere than the Northern Hemisphere. Why? Because the Southern Hemisphere is mostly water.

Where an isotherm "bends," what does it mean? It means that some part of a parallel of latitude has a different temperature from the rest. Where an isotherm bends toward the Pole, that spot is warmer. Where an isotherm bends toward the Equator, that spot is colder.

The thin black lines are isotherms (temperature lines) for July. The heat equator connects the hottest places for each meridian.

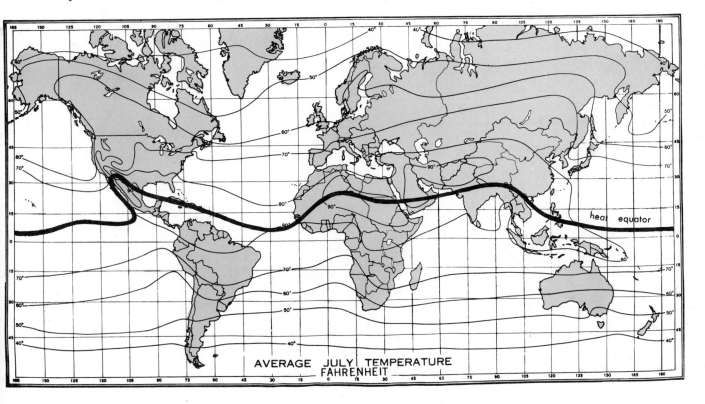

AVERAGE JULY TEMPERATURE FAHRENHEIT

The Heating of the Atmosphere **385**

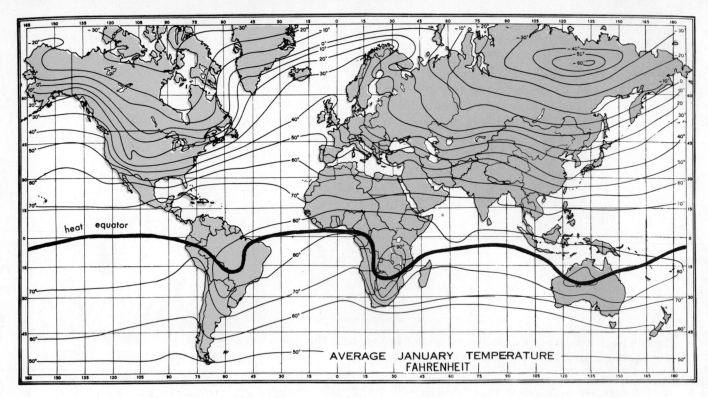

These isotherms show temperature in January. The heat equator is now in the Southern Hemisphere.

July is the warmest month in the Northern Hemisphere. January is its coldest month. So of course the isotherms will shift their positions from July to January. The isotherms "move with the sun." They shift northward in July. They shift southward in January.

What else do the world temperature maps show you? See if you can check these facts:

1. The isotherms shift more over the Northern Hemisphere than over the Southern Hemisphere.
2. The isotherms shift more over continents than over oceans.
3. The hottest and coldest places are on land.
4. The North Pole is not the Northern Hemisphere's coldest spot.
   Can you explain these facts?

How much energy do we get from the sun? Scientists have measured the rate at which solar energy reaches the top of our atmosphere. It is about 2 calories a minute on a square centimeter, when the sun's rays are vertical. (A calorie is the heat needed to raise the temperature of one gram of water 1° C.)

How much energy is this over the whole earth? It is enough—in one minute—to supply the United States with electricity for a whole year!

Scientists believe that the atmosphere as a whole is neither gaining nor losing heat. At present its "heat budget" is in balance. It radiates as much heat back to space as it gets from the sun.

Each topic question refers to the topic of the same number within this chapter.

1. (a) Give the names and percentages of the gases in the lower air. (b) What gases are found above 80 kilometers, and how are they arranged?

2. (a) How much water vapor is in the air? Where does the water vapor come from? (b) Why is ozone important to us? What is the ozonosphere? What destroys ozone? (c) What is dust made of? (d) How do salt and chemical grains help to make fog?

3. (a) On what basis is the atmosphere divided into the four layers described in this Topic? (b) Give a brief description of the four layers.

4. (a) Describe the ionosphere with respect to its location, the origin of its ions, and its layers. (b) How does it help radio transmission?

5. (a) What does "weather" mean? (b) What happens to the sun's rays when they reach the earth's atmosphere? (c) What is insolation?

6. (a) Explain how the rock, soil, and water help to heat the lower atmosphere. (b) Why is this called "the greenhouse effect"?

7. Explain how heat is transferred by radiation, conduction, convection, and advection.

8. (a) What is the normal lapse rate? (b) Explain why the atmosphere is usually warmest at the earth's surface.

9. (a) What is the relation between the angle of the sun's rays and the heating effect? (b) How is this related to the climate of low, middle, and high latitudes?

10. (a) Why does sunlight warm water more slowly than land? (b) Why does water hold its heat longer than land? (c) Compare the temperatures of water and nearby land during daytime and nighttime. (d) Compare them in summer and winter.

11. Why does land warm up unevenly?

12. (a) Explain why the warmest hour of the day is usually in the afternoon. (b) Why is the coldest hour just before sunrise? (c) Define temperature range. Why is it larger on clear days than on cloudy ones?

13. (a) Which are usually the warmest and coldest months in the Northern Hemisphere? Southern Hemisphere? (b) Define annual temperature range.

14. (a) Explain what a temperature inversion is. (b) How do temperature inversions occur?

15. (a) How does a liquid thermometer work? (b) How does a metal thermometer work? (c) What is a thermograph? (d) What is a maximum thermometer? a minimum thermometer?

16. (a) What are the fixed points of any thermometer? (b) What are the fixed-point temperatures on the Fahrenheit and Celsius scales?

17. (a) What is an isotherm? (b) What is the heat equator? Explain how it differs from an isotherm?

18. (a) Why are isotherms so regular in the Southern Hemisphere? (b) Name two causes of irregularity in isotherms. (c) What is the meaning of poleward bending of an isotherm? of equatorward bending?

19. (a) Why do the world's isotherms shift? (b) Where do isotherms show the greatest shifts? (c) Where are the hottest and coldest regions (1) in July? (2) in January?

20. (a) How much energy do we get from the sun? (b) Explain the heat balance of the atmosphere.

GENERAL QUESTIONS

1. Make a diagram showing the convection currents in the air of a room heated by (1) a central stove, (2) a radiator against one wall.

2. Why is a lake not heated by convection? (see Topic 7).

3. How do convection currents help to cool the waters of a lake in autumn?

4. Why does the stratosphere contain very little dust or water vapor?

5. Why is there very little variation in the time of the warmest and coldest hours of the day at the Equator?

6. Even though you hold your face vertically to the rays of the sun in December, you will not sunburn as much in the same time as you would in June. Why?

7. Why are temperature inversions unlikely on cloudy nights?

8. Why is the stratopause colder at the Equator than at the Poles?

STUDENT ACTIVITIES

1. Check the fixed points of a thermometer in boiling water and melting ice.

2. Expose equal areas of water (in a beaker or other suitable container) and sand to the rays of the sun, or to an electric light bulb equidistant from both the water and sand. Note the temperature of the upper layers at regular intervals as the water and sand warm up. Remove the source of heat and again note the temperatures as the materials cool off. Do your observations bear out what was said in Topic 10?

3. Study the records of a thermograph to determine the warmest and coldest hour of each day of the week. See if these agree with the "predictions" of Topic 12. Where there are exceptions, try to explain them.

25

A barometer is an instrument that measures atmospheric pressure. A kind of barometer that is easy to carry is called an aneroid barometer.

Using an aneroid barometer, measure the atmospheric pressure at the street level of your school or another building that has more than one story. Write down your reading. Now carry the barometer to the top floor of the building. Again read the atmospheric pressure and write it down. Compare the readings. Explain the difference.

Atmospheric pressure changes with height above the earth's surface. At what rate did it change in your experiment? To find out, you will have to measure how high you went up from street level. The easiest way is to count the number of steps. Then multiply by the height of the steps. At what rate did the pressure change?

(To increase your air-pressure change in this experiment, start in the basement and go up to the roof, if possible.)

Atmospheric Pressure and Winds

Studying Air Pressure

Air Pressure and Weather 1.

You probably learned in elementary science that the pressure of the air at sea level is about 15 pounds per square inch or about one kilogram per square centimeter. You also learned that the cause of air pressure was simply the weight of the whole atmosphere.

Why do we study air pressure again in earth science? One reason is that differences in air pressure cause the earth's winds. A second reason is that daily changes in air pressure are related to weather changes. For these reasons, the study of the atmosphere's pressure is very important in weather study.

Measuring Air Pressure 2.

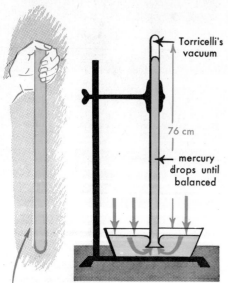

full of mercury:
no air in tube

Air presses down on the mercury in this dish. The mercury goes up into the vacuum in the tube. The greater the air pressure is, the higher the mercury goes.

The instrument used to measure air pressure is the **barometer.** There are two main types of barometers.

The *mercury barometer* was invented in 1643 by the Italian physicist Torricelli. Using the instrument, Torricelli proved that air pressure was due to the weight of the atmosphere. First he read the air pressure at sea level. Then he carried his barometer up a mountain. There it gave a much lower reading. Torricelli explained that this was because less air was pressing on the barometer.

The diagram shows how a mercury barometer works. The air pressure on the surface of the mercury in the dish holds up a column of mercury (a very heavy liquid metal). At sea level, the column is about 76 centimeters (30 inches) high. The space above the mercury is a vacuum. If air pressure increases, the mercury column rises. If air pressure drops, the mercury column falls.

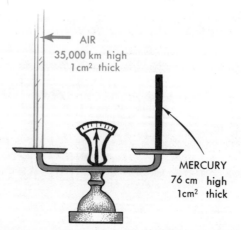

The column of air and the column of mercury weigh the same. They are both one square centimeter thick. But, the mercury column is 76 centimeters high, while the air column is 35,000 kilometers high. Mercury is much heavier than air.

390

The second common type of barometer is the **aneroid barometer.** Its name comes from the Greek meaning "without liquid." It is not so accurate as a mercury barometer. However, it can be carried easily.

The aneroid barometer consists mainly of a thin flexible metal can. By pumping most of the air out of the can, the can is made "sensitive" to air pressure. A pointer is attached to the can. As the can changes shape with changes of air pressure, the pointer moves over a scale. The scale is adjusted to read the same as a mercury barometer would.

Since air pressure changes with height, a barometer can be used to measure altitude. An **altimeter** (height meter) is merely an aneroid barometer with a scale that reads height above sea level.

Roughly, the barometer reading drops about 1 centimeter for every 123 meters (or about one inch for every 1000 feet) above sea level. This rate only applies to the first few kilometers of air near the earth's surface. Above this level, the air thins out rapidly, and pressure changes more slowly. Half the weight of the atmosphere lies within 5.5 kilometers of the earth's surface.

To keep a record of the air pressure, the **barograph** is used. It is simply an aneroid barometer with pen, ink, and scaled paper on clockwork.

The inside of an aneroid barometer is shown here. A is the "vacuum can." The spring at B supports the can and moves when the can moves. Levers, such as the one at D, carry this movement to a pointer (not shown) swinging from C.

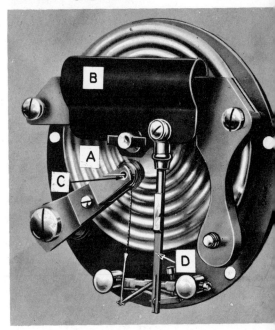

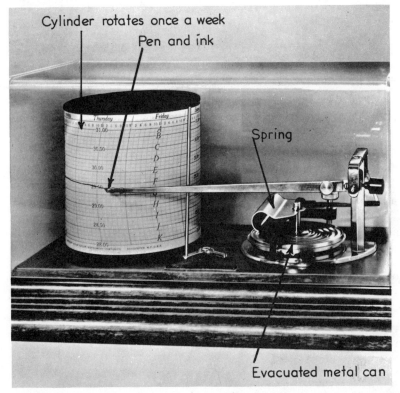

Cylinder rotates once a week

Pen and ink

Spring

Evacuated metal can

Increased air pressure makes the can collapse. The spring falls. The pen rises. This results in a rise in the line drawn on the paper of this barograph.

Air pressure is reported in two different ways. The first way simply gives the height of the mercury column in the barometer. It may be given in inches or in centimeters.

The second way uses a metric unit of pressure called a **millibar** (abbreviated mb.). A millibar equals about one thousandth of "standard" sea level air pressure. The following table shows how inch units and millibars are related. Standard sea level air pressure is 1013.2 millibars, or 29.92 inches of mercury. It is the average air pressure at sea level for the whole world.

The number 1050 millibars in the table is about as high as the barometer usually reads at sea level. Similarly 982.1 is about the lowest ordinary reading. In hurricanes and tornadoes, the readings may go much lower.

Inches of Mercury	Millibars of Pressure
31.00	1050.0
30.00	1015.9
29.92	1013.2
29.53	1000.0
29.00	982.1
1.00*	34.0 (approx.)
0.10	3.4 (approx.)
0.12	4.0** (approx.)
0.03	1.0† (approx.)

* Use this value to convert inches of mercury into millibars.
** Pressure interval used on United States weather maps.
† Use this value to convert millibars into inches of mercury.

Barometer Readings on Weather Maps 5.

The National Weather Service prints a daily weather map. Barometer readings are shown in two different ways on these maps. Both ways use millibars.

The first way shows the actual barometer reading in millibars. This number is placed just to the right of the "station circle" (the symbol on a weather map that shows the city's location).

The second way of showing barometer readings uses **isobars** (EYE so barz). Isobars are lines that join points having the same air pressure at a given time. On the Weather Service daily weather maps, isobars are drawn for every 4 millibars. They are drawn as solid lines and numbered at each end. Isobars make it easy to see how barometer readings compare over large areas.

Weather maps printed in newspapers also use isobars. Usually, however, these are marked in inches of mercury rather than in millibars. As our table shows, 4 millibars equal about 0.12 inch of mercury.

6. Why Air Pressure Changes

Observe a barometer or barograph for several days. You will see that the air pressure at your location is always changing. Why?

The first reason for daily changes in air pressure is *changing temperature*. *Warm air is lighter than cold air.* (Its molecules are farther apart.) So when warm air replaces cold air, the air pressure at the ground falls. If cold air replaces warm air, the air pressure rises.

The second reason for daily changes in air pressure is *changing humidity*. *The more water vapor the air contains, the lighter it is.* This sounds wrong, but is easily explained. When water vapor enters the atmosphere, it *pushes out* an equal volume of dry air. For example, a cubic meter of dry air is about 99 per cent nitrogen and oxygen. A cubic meter of humid air with 4 per cent water vapor is only 95 per cent nitrogen and oxygen. *But water vapor is lighter than the nitrogen and oxygen it pushed out.* Therefore the humid air weighs less than the dry air.

When dry air becomes humid, water vapor replaces some of the nitrogen and oxygen. Water vapor is lighter than nitrogen and oxygen. So, humid air is lighter than dry air.

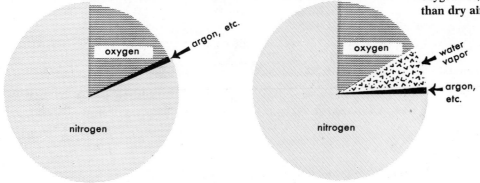

dry air: 7.17 g per m^3 humid air: 7.05 g per m^3

7. The Barometer and the Weather

You have just seen why warm humid air is lighter than cool dry air. Check this by watching the barometer or barograph for several weeks. When the air pressure falls, is the weather warmer and more humid? When the air pressure rises, does the weather get cooler and dryer? Are there exceptions?

In general, weather scientists have found that a "falling barometer" means warmer weather. It also means more humid air. It may mean rain or snow. A "rising barometer" usually means cooler, drier weather. This gives a simple way of forecasting the weather. Modern weather scientists do not, however, rely on the barometer alone for their forecasts.

Reducing Barometer Readings to Sea Level

The normal air pressure for any place depends on its altitude. In New York City or Los Angeles 30 inches is a normal reading as it would be reported in the newspaper. But Denver, Colorado, is more than 1600 meters above sea level. Its normal reading is about 25 inches.

How can we compare such different "normal" readings when their numbers are so different? We "reduce" all readings to sea level. In other words, we give Denver's reading as if Denver were at sea level. We do the same for all cities, regardless of elevation. Then when we put their readings on weather maps, we can really compare them.

Normal air pressure at sea level is 76 centimeters. For every 123 meters above sea level, subtract 1 centimeter from 76 centimeters. This gives the normal air pressure at that altitude.

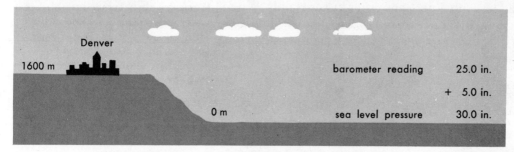

Readings are "reduced to sea level" by adding about one inch (or 34 millibars) for every 1000 feet (or 305 meters) of altitude. The National Weather Service does this with highly accurate tables.

Highs, Lows, Pressure Gradients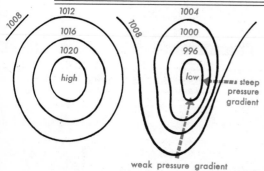

Look at the isobars on a weather map. You will find many of the isobars forming sets of closed curves, one inside the other. Now read the pressure numbers on the isobars. You will see that the sets of isobars are of two kinds.

In one kind, the *inside isobar has the highest pressure reading.* Going out from the center, each isobar has a lower reading. A set of isobars such as these shows a part of the atmosphere where air pressure is higher than its surroundings. This part of the atmosphere is called a **high.** A high is like a hill in the atmosphere. The air in a high is generally cool and dry.

394 *Atmospheric Science*

In the second kind of isobar set, things are just the opposite. The *inside isobar has the lowest pressure reading.* Going out from the center, each isobar has a higher reading. This set of isobars shows a part of the atmosphere where air pressure is lower than its surroundings. Such a part of the atmosphere is called a **low.** A low is like a basin or depression in the atmosphere. The air in a low is generally warmer and more humid.

When isobars are close together, it means that air pressure changes quickly between two places. When isobars are far apart, air pressure changes slowly. Scientists call this rate of change between two isobars the **pressure gradient.** Isobars close together are said to have a steep or strong pressure gradient. Isobars far apart have a gentle, or weak, pressure gradient.

10. Primary Highs and Lows

The accompanying *isobaric map* shows the world's average air pressure for January. Similar maps have been made for every month of the year. Notice the many highs and lows. They are marked with H for high and L for low.

Some of the highs and lows are found in the same areas most of the year. These highs and lows are called **primary highs and lows.**

In the Northern Hemisphere there are four primary highs and two primary lows. Two of the highs are over ocean areas. One is the Pacific High in the Pacific Ocean west of California. The second is the Bermuda High in the Atlantic Ocean east of Florida. The other two highs are over Canada and Siberia. They are especially strong in winter when land is very cold.

The two primary lows are both over ocean areas. One is the Aleutian Low in the Pacific Ocean southwest of Alaska. The other is the Icelandic low in the North Atlantic Ocean near Iceland. Primary highs and lows are very important as sources of cold waves, heat waves, and other kinds of weather.

In this isobaric map of the world for January, the Northern Hemisphere primary highs include the Siberian, Canadian, Pacific and Bermuda Highs.

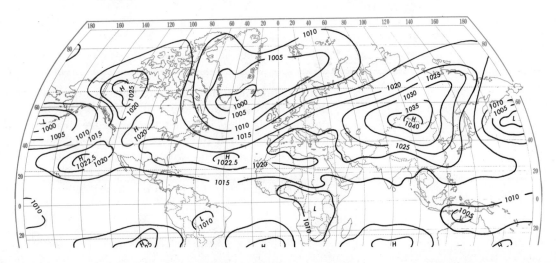

Studying Winds

How Winds Begin 11.

How do winds begin to blow? The diagram shows a simple illustration.

The island in the drawing is located in the temperate zone. In summer, as you learned, the land gets warmer than the sea. The warm air rising over the island forms a low. The cooler air over the sea forms highs. The cool air moves toward the island to replace the rising warm air. This movement of air from sea to land is the beginning of the wind. It is a movement from high pressure to low pressure.

In winter the process is reversed. The land gets colder than the sea. Now the high pressure area is over the island. The lows with their rising air are over the warmer sea. Cold winds blow from the island to the sea. Again, the wind is moving from high pressure to low pressure.

All winds result from unequal heating of the atmosphere. *They always move from highs to lows.* The speed of the wind depends on the pressure gradient. The closer the isobars, the steeper the pressure gradient, and the stronger the wind.

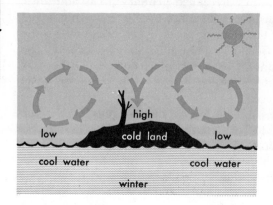

Compare the temperatures of land and water in the summer. Then compare them in the winter. Note how lows form over the warmer surfaces. Winds blow from highs to lows. Trace wind directions in summer, then in winter.

The Coriolis Force 12.

When winds blow from highs to lows, what path do they follow? Do they blow in a perpendicular line from one isobar to the next? This perpendicular line is called the **pressure gradient direction.** They would, if the earth did not rotate. Actually, however, they usually blow at an angle to the isobars. Let us see how.

The earth's rotation causes an effect called the **Coriolis** (kor ee OH lis) **force.** The effect is felt by all objects moving toward or away from the Equator. The Coriolis force makes Northern Hemisphere winds turn to the right of the pressure gradient direction. In the Southern Hemisphere the winds turn to the left. You probably remember the same effect makes ocean currents turn.

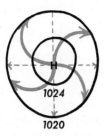

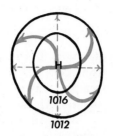

Northern Hemisphere
deflection to right

Southern Hemisphere
deflection to left

The dotted arrows show the pressure gradient direction. The colored arrows show how the Coriolis force pushes the winds.

13. Wind Direction and Speed; Gusts

The Coriolis force makes winds at the surface blow at angles to the isobars. The angle is usually about 10° over water and about 30° over land. The rougher the surface, the larger the angle.

The speed of the wind varies with the pressure gradient. Speed is also affected by friction with the earth's surface. Friction is greatest at the surface and gets less upward. Over smooth land wind speeds usually increase up to about 1000 meters in height. This limit is slightly lower over water. Here the effects of surface friction end. At these levels winds blow *along the isobars,* not across them.

The black arrows show wind directions as seen from above the earth's surface. At 1000 meters, winds blow along the isobars. At the surface, they blow at angles to the isobars.

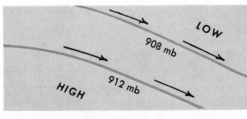

At 1000 m

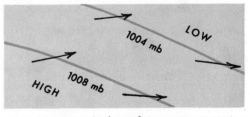

At the surface

Wind speeds are generally greater over water than over land. Why? They are generally greater in winter than in summer. This is because pressure gradients are usually steeper in winter.

Winds are rarely steady. They often blow in spurts called *gusts,* and often change direction briefly. Gusts are due mainly to rough surfaces. Winds are much less gusty over water than over land.

Winds are named for the direction *from* which they come. For example, a sea breeze comes *from* the sea. A south wind comes *from* the south.

Wind and weather are closely related. Winds from a northerly direction (north, northeast, or northwest) come in North America from cooler latitudes. Therefore, they are likely to bring cooler weather. Similarly, winds from a southerly direction bring warmer weather. The opposite is true in the Southern Hemisphere.

Winds from the sea carry much water vapor. They are likely to bring clouds and rain or snow. Winds from the interior are usually drier. They are more likely to bring fair weather.

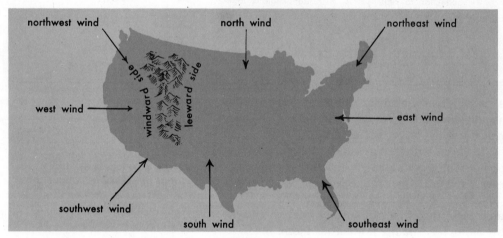

Note where each wind comes from. The wind is named by this direction. Which side of the mountains does the wind hit? This is called the windward side. The mountains protect the leeward side from the wind.

Observing the Wind 15.

The wind vane (commonly called a weather vane) shows the wind from the north. The anemometer whirls to show the wind's speed.

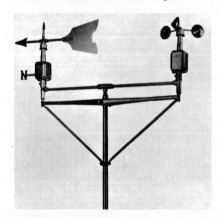

Wind direction is usually found by use of the **wind vane.** The wind vane has a broad "tail". This resists the wind more than the slender arrowhead end. If a south wind is blowing, it will swing the tail to the north. The arrowhead then points south, *into the wind.* A wind vane always points to the direction the wind is coming from. Wind vanes may be connected to electrical indicators.

The *wind sock* is used at airports to show wind direction. It can be made very large so that it will be easily seen by a pilot from the plane.

Wind speed near the surface is measured by the **anemometer.** The cup anemometer is used by many observers. The cups are hollow cones or hemispheres, all facing the same way. They catch the wind on their open sides from any direction. The stronger the wind, the faster the cups turn, and the higher the meter's reading.

Atmospheric Science

How are the speed and direction of upper-air winds found? Special weather balloons are released into the upper air. Then observers track the flight by telescope or radar.

In the telescope method, a helium-filled **pilot balloon** is set free. Its flight is followed by a weather observer with a telescope. The observer knows how fast the balloon rises. If there is no wind, the balloon goes straight up in the air. When there is a wind, the balloon flies at an angle. From the angle of flight, the observer can calculate the speed and direction of the upper winds. At night, a small light is hung on the balloon. However, day or night, fair weather is needed for this method.

In the radar method, the special weather balloon carries a radio transmitter. It is tracked by special receivers on the ground. Balloons can be tracked to heights of 30 kilometers this way. Another advantage is that they can be tracked even in bad weather.

The flight of the released pilot balloon is followed by an observer with a telescope. The observer calculates the speed and direction of upper-air winds by the angle the balloon takes when it is released into the air.

Wind directions are shown on our weather maps by arrows that "fly with the wind." The arrow is attached to the station model. To save space, the point of the arrow is left off.

Wind speed is shown by *feathers* and *flags* on the arrow's left side. On our weather maps wind speeds are given in *knots*. Each full feather means a speed of 10 knots. Each half feather means 5 knots. A flag means a speed of 50 knots. (A knot is one nautical mile per hour. A nautical mile equals $1\frac{1}{6}$ ordinary miles.

Symbol	Miles (Statute) Per Hour	Knots	Symbol	Miles (Statute) Per Hour	Knots
◎	Calm	Calm		44 – 49	38 – 42
	1 – 2	1 – 2		50 – 54	43 – 47
	3 – 8	3 – 7		55 – 60	48 – 52
	9 – 14	8 – 12		61 – 66	53 – 57
	15 – 20	13 – 17		67 – 71	58 – 62
	21 – 25	18 – 22		72 – 77	63 – 67
	26 – 31	23 – 27		78 – 83	68 – 72
	32 – 37	28 – 32		84 – 89	73 – 77
	38 – 43	33 – 37		119 – 123	103 – 107

Each of the U.S. National Weather Service symbols stands for a different wind speed. Knots, or nautical miles per hour, are the units sailors use for speed. Statute miles per hour are used by "landlubbers." The two columns show equal speeds.

TOPIC QUESTIONS

Each topic question refers to the topic of the same number within this chapter.

1 (a) What causes air pressure? How much is it at sea level? **(b)** Why is air pressure important in weather study?

2 (a) What is a barometer? **(b)** How did Torricelli prove that air pressure is due to the weight of the atmosphere?

3 (a) How does an aneroid barometer differ from a mercury barometer? (b) What is an altimeter? a barograph? (c) At what rate does pressure drop with altitude in the lower air?

4 (a) How can the air pressure be "30 inches"? Explain. (b) What is a millibar? (c) What is the importance of the number 1013.2 millibars? (d) How many millibars equal one inch of mercury? (See table)

5 (a) How is a city's air pressure shown on the daily weather map? (b) What is an isobar? Why are isobars used? (c) What isobar "interval" is used on our weather maps?

6. (a) How does the temperature of the atmosphere affect its pressure? (b) Why is humid air lighter than dry air?

7. What is the relation between changing air pressure and weather?

8. Why are barometer readings reduced to sea level? How is it done?

9. (a) Explain what a high is. (b) What is a low? (c) Define *pressure gradient*. (d) How do isobars show pressure gradients?

10. (a) What is meant by "primary" highs and lows? (b) Locate two primary highs in the Northern Hemisphere. (c) Locate one primary low in the Northern Hemisphere. (d) Why are they important in weather study?

11. (a) Explain how winds may start blowing toward an island in summer. (b) How is the wind direction connected with highs and lows? (c) How is wind speed connected with the pressure gradient?

12. (a) What is the "pressure gradient" direction? (b) What is the Coriolis force? (c) How does the Coriolis force change the wind direction? Why?

13. (a) In what direction does the Coriolis force make the wind blow? (b) How does wind speed change with altitude? With the type of surface? With the season? Explain why in each case. (c) In what direction does the wind blow above 1,000 meters? Why? (d) What are gusts? What causes them?

14. (a) Explain, with examples, how winds are named. (b) How is weather related to wind direction?

15. (a) How does a wind vane work? (b) How does an anemometer work?

16. (a) Explain how the speed and direction of upper air winds are found with (1) pilot balloons directly, (2) balloons and radar. (b) What advantages does the radar method have?

17. Explain how wind direction and speed are shown on weather maps.

GENERAL QUESTIONS

1. If the 1020 millibar isobar is marked 30.12 inches, what is the inch reading on the 1016 millibar isobar and the 1024 millibar isobar?

2. How high would the atmosphere be if its density throughout were the same as at sea level? Explain.

3. Why does the low near Iceland persist even in summer when the ocean should be cooler than the adjoining land?

26

HOW DO YOU KNOW THAT... ?

Set up a two-hole convection box with a sliding window on one side. Place glass chimneys over the two openings in the top. Place a short lighted candle directly beneath one hole. Close the window. Hold a piece of burning "smoke paper" or a match flame over each chimney. Observe the movement of air at each chimney. Also note the movement of the air inside the box. Explain the wind pattern you observed. How is this pattern related to winds in the atmosphere? Now cover the hole over the "cold chimney," and open the window a few centimeters. Observe and explain the new air movements.

The "wind pattern" of your classroom may be observed in winter if there are radiators. Clap a chalk-filled eraser just above a hot radiator. Watch the movement of the chalk powder as high and as far as you can follow it. Now clap the eraser near the floor just below the radiator. Describe and explain the "wind pattern."

World Wind Belts

Origin of World Wind Belts

Winds blow out of high pressure areas and into low pressure areas. Knowing this, you might think that the earth should have a simple pattern of winds. Warm air rising at the Equator would make this region a low pressure belt. Cold air sinking at the Poles would make two high pressure belts. Winds would then blow from the Poles to the Equator at the earth's surface. Air would return from the Equator to the Poles in the upper atmosphere.

But a map of the world's winds does not show so simple a pattern. Weather scientists say there are two reasons for this. One is that the earth rotates on its axis. (This causes the Coriolis force.) The other reason is the unequal heating of land and water.

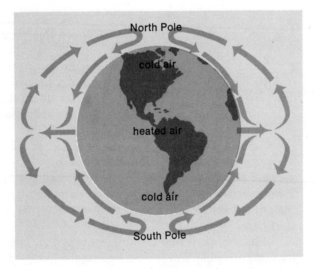

Suppose (1) the oceans covered all the earth's surface, and (2) the earth did not rotate. The blue arrows show how the air in the atmosphere would flow.

2. The 0°-to-30° Cells

Rotation changes the simple wind pattern described in Topic 1.

Warm air rises at the Equator as described in Topic 1. This area becomes a worldwide belt of low air pressure. The rising air flows toward both Poles in the *upper troposphere*. But the Coriolis force of the earth's rotation turns the flowing air strongly. In the Northern Hemisphere the air flow is turned to the right, or eastward. In the Southern Hemisphere it is turned to the left, also eastward.

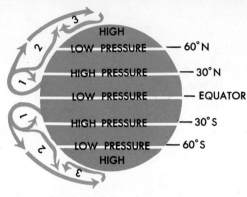

The earth does rotate. This creates three air circulation belts in each hemisphere.

As the latitude increases, the Coriolis force increases. When the upper-air winds reach about 30° N and 30° S latitudes, they are moving almost due east. The air therefore piles up at 30° latitude. This makes a belt of high air pressure in each hemisphere.

Some of the upper air sinks to form a down current here. The rest goes on toward the Poles. What happens when the down current nears the earth's surface? It splits into two parts. One part flows back to the Equator. The other part flows toward the Poles.

Weather scientists call this part of the atmosphere—from the Equator to about 30°—a "cell of circulation." Each hemisphere has one. Each cell includes a complete and simple convection pattern. These twin cells are called the Equator-to-30° cells.

The 60°-to-Pole Cells 3.

A second set of twin cells forms between the 30° and 60° latitudes. A third set forms between the 60° and 90° latitudes. Let us see how.

Some of the overflow from the Equator comes down in polar regions. This helps to create high pressure belts at both Poles. Air then flows from the Poles toward the Equator along the surface. At about 60° latitude it meets the air flowing poleward from the 30° high pressure belt.

Coming together at 60°, both streams of air rise. The result is a low pressure belt—one in each hemisphere. But the two streams are very different. The air from 30° latitude is very warm. The air from the Pole is very cold. Weather scientists name the surface between them the **polar front.** Many storms that travel across the middle latitudes start here.

What happens to the rising column of air at 60°? When it reaches the upper troposphere, it flows poleward along with the flow from the Equator. This completes the circulation in the 60°-to-Pole cells.

The 30°-to-60° Cells 4.

Now picture the middle cells of the three-cell system. At 30° latitude, sinking air from the 0°-to-30° high pressure belt reaches the surface. As we said in Topic 2, some of the air at the surface flows toward the Poles. At 60° latitude, it meets the air from the Poles in the polar front. There it rises and joins the upper troposphere winds flowing to the Poles.

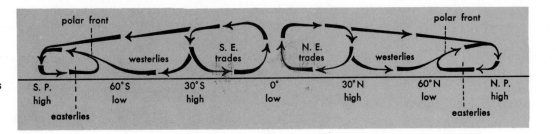

The horizontal line represents the earth's surface from South Pole to North Pole. The arrows show how air moves in the troposphere.

The pressure belts and air streams described in Topics 2–4 have names. The low pressure belt at the Equator is called the **doldrums belt.** The high pressure belts at 30° are called the **horse latitudes,** or *subtropical highs.* The low pressure belts at 60° are called the **subpolar lows.** The high pressure belts at the Poles are called the **polar highs.** Notice how lows and highs alternate. Low at 0°, high at 30°, low at 60°, high at 90°.

Now look at the wind belts between the pressure belts. (See diagram.) All of the winds blow from high pressure to low pressure.

The wavy black lines show the earth's air pressure belts. The blue arrows show the wind belts that form between them.

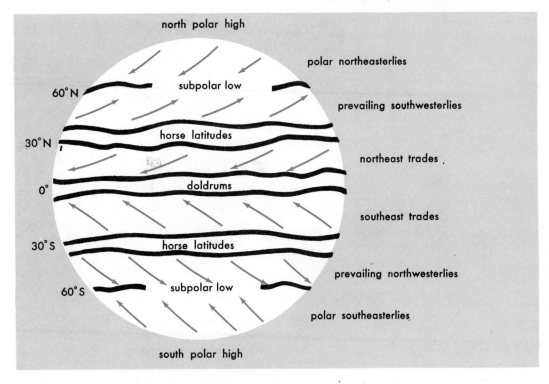

Winds bends to the right in the Northern Hemisphere. They bend to the left in the Southern Hemisphere. In the Northern Hemisphere this gives us these three sets of winds:

1. *Polar northeasterlies,* blowing from the polar high to the subpolar low;
2. *Prevailing southwesterlies,* from the horse latitudes to the subpolar low;
3. *Northeast trade winds,* from the horse latitudes to the doldrums low.

The Southern Hemisphere has a matching set of winds. Their names are polar southeasterlies, prevailing northwesterlies, and southeast trades.

Notice that the trade winds blow into the doldrums from both sides of the Equator. Since the trades converge (come together) here, the doldrums belt is also called the **intertropical convergence zone.**

Other Winds and Wind Shifts

The Upper-Air Winds 6.

Observations show that above 7,500 meters, all upper-air winds are westerlies. That is, they blow from west to east. We know, however, that from 0° to 30°, and from 60° to 90°, the surface winds blow from east to west. At what heights do the wind directions change?

The trade winds blow from east to west in the 0°-30° belts. The trades are the most strongly developed winds of the three sets of winds. They continue as easterlies high above the earth's surface. At a height of about 7,500 meters, however, the winds above the trades become westerly winds.

In the 30°-60° belts, the surface winds are the prevailing westerlies. Since they are westerlies, there is no reversal of direction as they rise into the upper troposphere.

The polar easterlies blow from east to west in the 60°-90° belts. They do not reach as high above the surface as the trades. At about 3,000 meters in these belts, the upper-air westerlies are met.

Wind speeds are very high in the upper troposphere. It is here that the spectacular jet stream is found.

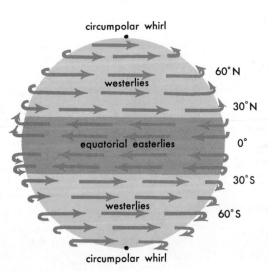

The blue arrows show the main direction of winds at 6000 meters. Above 7500 meters, all winds are westerlies.

The **jet stream** is a fairly narrow stream of air in the upper troposphere. It moves eastward at high speed, usually in middle latitudes. Sometimes it forms a single meandering band around the entire earth. More often it is made of two or more separate streams.

The jet stream shifts position with the seasons. It moves north in summer and south in winter. Its most common location is at about 40° N.

The height of the jet stream ranges from about 6,000 to 12,000 meters. Its strongest winds are about 10,500 meters above the earth. Its separate streams may be from 1600 to 4000 kilometers long, about one-tenth as wide, and about one kilometer thick. Wind speeds are usually about 150 knots. They may go up to 300 knots.

Two or more jet streams may be over a continent at once. In the Northern Hemisphere they may reach as far south as 20° N. Jet streams can help eastward-flying planes to have higher ground speeds. They slow westward planes.

Jet streams seem to have very great effects on the weather. They appear to cause huge "outbreaks" of polar air. These "outbreaks" produce winter cold waves. In summer they may produce outbreaks of tropical air that cause heat waves. There is still much to be learned about them.

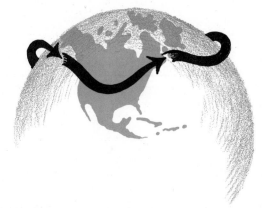

The black band shows one of the typical positions of the Northern Hemisphere jet stream.

The arrows show how wind speed changed with height above the ground on a winter day in central United States. The very long arrow shows the jet stream.

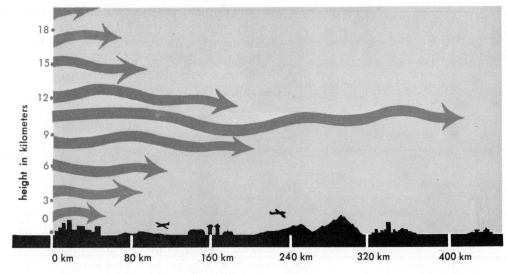

height in kilometers

0 km   80 km   160 km   240 km   320 km   400 km

wind speed in kilometers

More about Wind and Pressure Belts

Here are a few more details about the belts described in Topic 5.

The doldrums. This is a hot humid belt of rising air, light breezes, and frequent calms (times when there is no wind). Sailing vessels, which cannot move without wind, often used to be stuck in the doldrums for days at a time. In those days it was said that "the wind blew *up* the mast."

The horse latitudes. These two belts are warm and dry. Air movements are largely vertical (but downward) so these are calm belts too.

Why are they called "horse latitudes"? Sailing vessels carrying horses from Europe to America were often stuck in a calm here. When that happened—so the story goes—some horses were thrown overboard to save drinking water.

The trade winds. In the Northern Hemisphere, the trades are *northeast trades.* In the Southern Hemisphere, they are *southeast trades.* The trade winds are very steady in both direction and speed (which is about 10 to 15 knots). Because of this, sailing ships carrying goods used these belts wherever possible. Such regular routes are called "trade routes." That is how the trade winds got their name. They are very warm winds.

The prevailing westerlies. These are *southwesterlies* in the Northern Hemisphere. They are *northwesterlies* in the Southern Hemisphere. Unlike the trade winds, they change both direction and speed frequently. The word "prevailing" just means that they blow from the named direction most often.

The speed of the westerlies increases with latitude. They are faster over oceans than over land. The Southern Hemisphere's middle latitudes are almost all ocean. As a result, the westerlies there are very strong. They are called the "roaring forties."

The polar easterlies. Like the trades, these are *northeasterlies* in the Northern Hemisphere. They are *southeasterlies* in the Southern Hemisphere. Their weather is cold and stormy.

The subpolar lows and *the polar highs*, like the polar easterlies, are areas of cold stormy weather.

Pressure and Wind Belts Shift

The location of the doldrums belt changes with the seasons. In late summer it is north of the Equator. In the late winter it is south of the Equator. But its change of position is not the same everywhere. It is much more over the continents than over the oceans. Why? It is also greater over Asia than over the other continents. Why? (See maps on pages 412 and 413.)

When the doldrums belt shifts, all the other belts shift with it. On the average, the yearly shift is about 5° of latitude. It is more over the continents, less over the oceans.

When the wind belts shift, large areas find themselves in two different belts during the year. Each belt may give these areas a very different kind of weather. There are two important cases of this kind. Places near the Equator (such as A in the diagram) may be in both doldrums and trade winds during the year. Places in or near the horse latitudes may also be in the trades, westerlies, or both during the year. (See B, C, and D.)

The September half of the diagram shows **hooked trade winds.** These form when trade winds must cross the Equator to reach the doldrums. In the Southern Hemisphere the Coriolis force turns them to the left. But as they cross the Equator the Coriolis force turns them to the right. Although they start as south*east* winds, they become "hooked" south*west* trades.

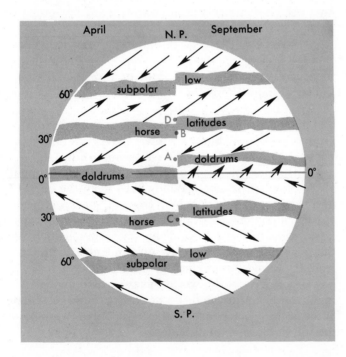

At left are the average positions of the wind and pressure belts in early spring. At right are their positions in early fall. Note how they shift over the summer.

 **Monsoons**

In winter, continents are colder than nearby ocean waters. They become centers of sinking cold air and high pressure. Winds tend to blow outward *from them* to the ocean.

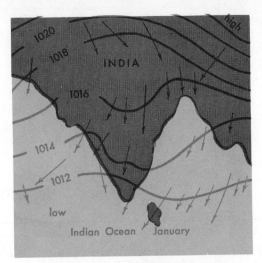

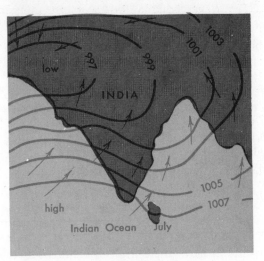

The arrows at the left show how India's dry monsoon blows in the winter. At the right is the wet monsoon in the summer.

In summer, continents are warmer than nearby ocean waters. They become centers of rising warm air and low pressure. Winds tend to blow *into them* from the ocean.

This seasonal change of wind direction is called the **monsoon effect.** Its changing winds are *monsoons.* The best developed monsoon winds in the world form over India, southeast Asia, and the Indian Ocean. There the winds turn around completely between winter and summer.

In winter a great high pressure area forms over cold Central Asia. From there winds blow southward over India and southeast Asia. These *cold dry* winds are the **winter monsoon.**

In summer things are reversed. The hot continent becomes an area of low air pressure. Winds blow from the cooler Indian Ocean into the continent. The winds from the ocean are filled with water vapor. When they rise over the highlands of India and southeast Asia, heavy rains fall. These winds are the **summer monsoon,** also called the *wet monsoon.* (Southeast Asia includes Vietnam, Burma, Thailand, Laos, and Cambodia.)

Other parts of the world have seasonal changes of wind too. In most, however, the winds do not turn around so sharply as in India. Some of these places are northern Australia, South Africa, Spain, and the southeastern United States.

Land and Sea Breezes

These breezes may be called the "daily monsoons." In the daytime, coastal lands warm up more than the nearby waters. The land becomes an area of rising air. The water becomes an area of sinking air.

Then a cool breeze blows from water to land. Along seacoasts this **sea breeze** usually begins gently about 11 A.M. It increases in speed until midafternoon, and dies down toward sunset. It is felt inland for not more than 15 or 20 kilometers. It reaches upward about 300 meters into the atmosphere.

At night, the land usually gets cooler than the nearby waters. The land is then an area of sinking air. The water is an area of rising air. A breeze blows from land to sea. This **land breeze** starts long before midnight and dies down toward sunrise.

Sea breezes are usually better developed than land breezes. They are certainly more noticeable, particularly on hot days.

Similar breezes develop along lake shores, especially on large lakes such as our Great Lakes.

The sea breeze in the day is like a small wet monsoon. The land breeze at night is like a small dry monsoon. Note how the difference in land and sea temperatures causes the breezes.

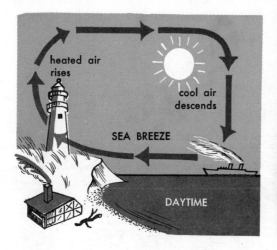

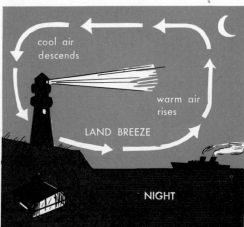

12. Mountain and Valley Breezes

Mountain regions also have their "daily monsoons." At night, cold heavy air sinks from mountain tops into valleys. The narrower the valley, the stronger the breeze. Coming from the mountains, it is called the **mountain breeze.**

During the daytime, warm air rises from the sunny mountain slopes. This forms a **valley breeze** that blows up from the valley. Its speed is generally much less than that of the downhill mountain breeze. People who fly gliders, hang gliders, and balloons "ride" the rising warm air in mountain regions.

Topics 2–6 considered the wind and pressure belts as if they reached evenly across the entire world. The accompanying maps show them as actually observed in January and July.

The *doldrums* are seen as a series of lows rather than as a single low pressure belt. In January these lows are centered over the three continental areas south of the Equator. In July the doldrums are mostly north of the Equator. One great low extends far north into India.

The *trades* are easily identified. In January, northeast trades and southeast trades blow into the doldrums. Near the west coast of Africa and near Australia, the northeast trades cross the Equator to become *hooked northwest trades*. In July the southeast trades hook

The blue arrows show the wind directions in January. The wavy blue lines are isobars. They show the pressure belts.

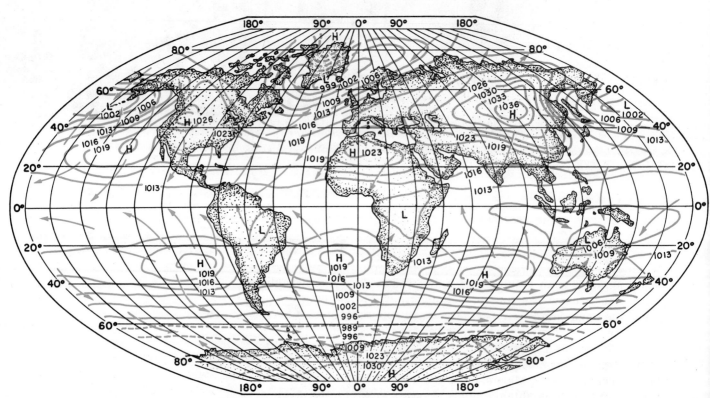

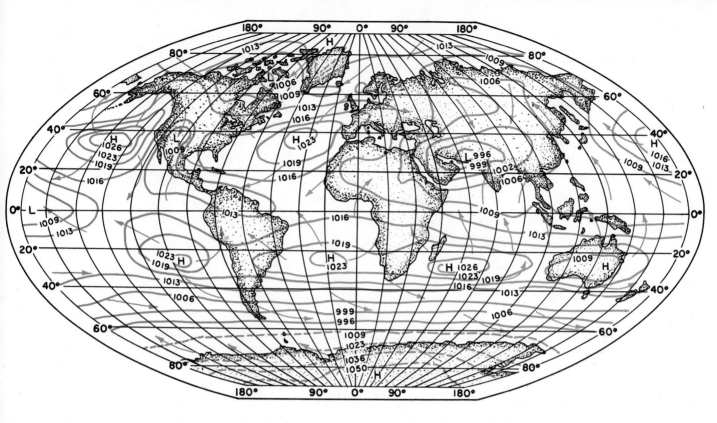

This map of the world shows the wind directions and pressure belts in July.

across the Equator to form the southwest monsoon of India and Africa.

The *horse latitude belts*, 30° to 35° latitude, are seen as a series of highs. These highs are very obvious in the Southern Hemisphere, which is mostly ocean. They are less distinct in the Northern Hemisphere. They do not change much from January to July.

The *prevailing westerlies* reach from the horse latitudes through the middle latitudes. They are plainly seen in the Southern Hemisphere over the great ocean areas. In North America and Eurasia however, there is a strong monsoon effect. As a result, this belt is very different from the simple "model" and is quite different from January to July.

The *subpolar low* forms a single belt in latitude 60° to 65° in the Southern Hemisphere. In the Northern Hemisphere it appears as lows near Iceland and Alaska. The *polar easterlies* blow into these lows. They come from the *polar highs* over Antarctica and Greenland.

Each topic question refers to the topic of the same number within this chapter.

1. What kind of circulation would the atmosphere probably have if the earth did not rotate? Describe it.

2. With the aid of a diagram describe the air circulation in the Equator-to-30° cells.

3. (a) With the aid of a diagram describe the air circulation in the 60°-to-Pole cells. (b) What is the polar front?

4. With the aid of a diagram describe the air circulation in the 30°-to-60° cells.

5. (a) What are the doldrums, the horse latitudes, the subpolar lows, and the polar highs? (b) Name and locate the three sets of winds of the Northern Hemisphere. (c) What is the intertropical convergence zone?

6. Describe the directions of the upper air winds.

7. (a) Describe the jet stream. (b) How are jet streams believed to affect the weather?

8. (a) Work out and draw the simple diagram of the earth's wind and calm belts. (b) Briefly describe each wind and calm belt.

9. (a) Why and how much do the wind belts shift? (b) Where do shifting wind belts cause weather changes? (c) Explain how hooked trade winds develop.

10. (a) What is the monsoon effect? How does it develop? (b) Describe the summer and winter monsoons of India.

11. Describe sea breezes and land breezes.

12. Explain the origin of mountain and valley breezes.

13. Explain the actual pressure and wind belts around the world as shown on the maps at the end of the chapter.

1. Make a diagram (similar to that in Topic 9) showing how hooked northwest trade winds develop when the doldrums are south of the Equator in February.

2. Make a diagram to show the probable summer and winter monsoon winds of Australia. Compare your diagram with actual conditions shown in the maps in Topic 13.

3. What parts of the United States show marked seasonal changes of winds? See the chapter-end maps.

4. On what time schedule might a fishing fleet of sailing vessels make best use of land and sea breezes?

1. Keep daily records of barometer readings, wind direction, cloudiness, and precipitation. Study them for any relation between the rise or fall of the barometer, the wind direction, and the weather.

2. Make a wind vane and an anemometer. (See *Weather for a Hobby* by R. F. Yates.)

27

HOW DO YOU KNOW THAT...?

It takes energy to evaporate a liquid. Heat is the form of energy that usually makes evaporation take place (Topic 3). Put a drop of water and a drop of alcohol on your wrist about 3 centimeters apart. Your body heat will supply energy to evaporate the liquids. Which one evaporates first? Which one makes your wrist feel cooler? Why?

The water that evaporated joins the water vapor already present in the atmosphere. This water vapor can be turned back into a liquid by reversing the process that made it water vapor—by cooling it.

Fill a dry glass or metal cup with a mixture of ice and water. After a minute or two, observe the mist that forms on the outside of the glass. Where does this water come from? What makes it form?

Evaporation and Condensation

Evaporation

The Three States of Water 1.

Water exists in the atmosphere in all of the three states of matter: **solid**, as snow and hail and ice particles; **liquid**, as rain or cloud droplets; and **gas**, as invisible water vapor.

Water may change from any one state into any other. The change from solid ice to liquid water is **melting**; the reverse process is **freezing**. The change from ice or liquid water to water vapor is **evaporation**. The change from water vapor to liquid water or ice is **condensation**. The meteorologist is most interested in changes involving water vapor.

Put yourself at one of the three stages of water—water, ice, or water vapor. Follow the arrows to see how you can change form. Each time you change, you gain or lose heat.

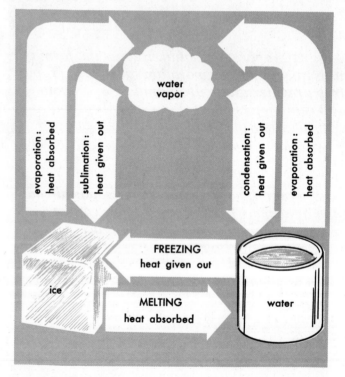

Sources of Water Vapor 2.

Most water vapor in the atmosphere comes from oceans, lakes, marshes, and glaciers. Some also comes from moist ground, from the leaves of plants, and from erupting volcanoes.

Most water vapor is found near the surfaces from which it arises. It is spread throughout the troposphere, however, by rising and falling air and by winds. It may be carried more than a thousand kilometers inland from the oceans. Since rising air currents stop at the tropopause, there is very little water vapor in the stratosphere.

3. Energy for Evaporation

The molecules of liquid water are always in motion. Molecules that reach the water surface and escape into the atmosphere are said to "evaporate." At ordinary temperatures evaporation is slow because the molecules are not moving very fast. As energy in the form of heat enters the water, the molecules speed up their motion and escape more rapidly. *The higher the temperature, the higher the rate of evaporation.* When water evaporates, water vapor enters the atmosphere.

How much energy is needed to evaporate water? About 540 calories of heat will evaporate one gram of water at the normal 100° C boiling point. If the water is colder to begin with, more heat is needed.

Water and other liquids absorb heat from their surroundings when they evaporate. This makes evaporation a cooling process. For example, a fevered patient may have alcohol rubbed on the skin. The patient is cooled when the alcohol evaporates. An electric refrigerator is chilled when special liquids evaporate in its coils.

4. Specific Humidity and Capacity

The **capacity** of air for holding water vapor depends on the temperature of the air. The higher its temperature, the more water vapor air can hold. The amount of water vapor in the air is called the **specific humidity.** It is the *number of grams of water vapor in one kilogram of air.* (A gram is one-thousandth of a kilogram.) Obviously, specific humidity is normally less than or equal to the capacity.

When the specific humidity equals the capacity, the air is **saturated.** The air between the water surface and the glass cover of a fish tank is likely to be saturated. Notice the drops of water hanging from the underside of the cover. Water continues to evaporate from the warm tank. But an equal amount of water must leave the already saturated air, which keeps drops of water on the cover. (Under very special conditions air can become *supersaturated;* that is, specific humidity can exceed capacity.)

The capacity of air for holding water vapor is roughly doubled for every rise in temperature of about 11° C. For example, a kilogram of air at 15.5° C has a capacity of about 11 grams of water vapor. A kilogram at 26.5° C has a capacity of about 22 grams.

Each kilogram of air has as much water vapor as it can hold. Note how the amount of water vapor increases as the temperature rises.

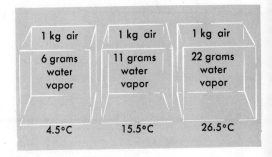

1 kg air	1 kg air	1 kg air
6 grams water vapor	11 grams water vapor	22 grams water vapor
4.5°C	15.5°C	26.5°C

Relative Humidity and Condensation

Relative Humidity 5.

Each kilogram of air is at 26.5° C and *can* hold up to 22 grams. Its relative humidity (R.H.) tells us what *percentage* it actually contains.

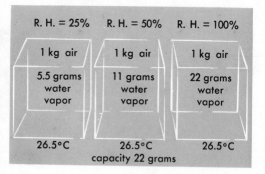

R. H. = 25%   R. H. = 50%   R. H. = 100%

1 kg air	1 kg air	1 kg air
5.5 grams water vapor	11 grams water vapor	22 grams water vapor
26.5°C	26.5°C	26.5°C

capacity 22 grams

Weather scientists need to know how near to capacity the air is. This information is the relative humidity. **Relative humidity** compares *the amount of water vapor in the air with the air's capacity* at that temperature.

Relative humidity is usually stated as a percent. It can be figured by dividing the specific humidity by the capacity. The result is multiplied by 100 to express the answer as a percent.

For example, air at a temperature of 26.5° C has a *capacity* of 22 grams. If its *specific humidity* at a particular time is 11 grams, its *relative humidity* is 50 percent.

$$\frac{11}{22} \times 100 = 50$$

Saturated air (specific humidity equals capacity) has a relative humidity of 100 percent.

Finding Relative Humidity 6.

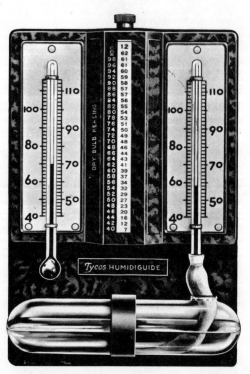

Instruments used to measure relative humidity are called hygrometers (hy GROM uh ters). In the *hair hygrometer* the relative humidity is read directly as a percent. The hygrograph (HY gruh graf) makes a continuous record of the relative humidity.

Another form of hygrometer is the **psychrometer** (sy KROM uh ter). It works on the principle that evaporation causes cooling.

A psychrometer consists of two identical thermometers. One, the "wet-bulb" thermometer, has a water-soaked wick wrapped around its bulb. The other is the "dry-bulb" thermometer. Air is forced past the two bulbs by fanning or by whirling the thermometers. The dry-bulb thermometer simply shows the air temperature. The wet-bulb thermometer usually shows a lower temperature. Why? As water evaporates from the wick, heat is taken from its bulb. *The drier the air, the faster the evaporation, and the lower the reading.*

The instrument shows nothing but two thermometer readings. These readings give signs of how dry the air is, but do not tell relative

The dry-bulb thermometer is on the left. The wet-bulb thermometer is on the right. Evaporation of water from the wet-bulb's wick has lowered the thermometer's reading 12° below the air temperature.

Atmospheric Science

humidity. With the thermometer readings, however, the relative humidity can be found in a table. The table has been worked out by actual experiment. Its percents are more accurate than those of a hair hygrometer.

TABLE: FINDING RELATIVE HUMIDITY IN PER CENT

Difference in degrees between wet-bulb and dry-bulb thermometers.

Air Temp.	1	2	3	4	5	6	7	8	9	10	11	12	13	14	15	16	17	18	19	20	21	22	23	24	25	26	27	28	29	30
30°	89	78	68	57	47	37	27	17	8																					
32°	90	79	69	60	50	41	31	22	13	4																				
34°	90	81	72	62	53	44	35	27	18	9	1																			
36°	91	82	73	65	56	48	39	31	23	14	6																			
38°	91	83	75	67	59	51	43	35	27	19	12	4																		
40°	92	84	76	68	61	53	46	38	31	23	16	9	2																	
42°	92	85	77	70	62	55	48	41	34	28	21	14	7																	
44°	93	85	78	71	64	57	51	44	37	31	24	18	12	5																
46°	93	86	79	72	65	59	53	46	40	34	28	22	16	10	4															
48°	93	87	80	73	67	60	54	48	42	36	31	25	19	14	8	3														
50°	93	87	81	74	68	62	56	50	44	39	33	28	22	17	12	7	2													
52°	94	88	81	75	69	63	58	52	46	41	36	30	25	20	15	10	6													
54°	94	88	82	76	70	65	59	54	48	43	38	33	28	23	18	14	9	5												
56°	94	88	82	77	71	66	61	55	50	45	40	35	31	26	21	17	12	8	4											
58°	94	89	83	77	72	67	62	57	52	47	42	38	33	28	24	20	15	11	7	3										
60°	94	89	84	78	73	68	63	58	53	49	44	40	35	31	27	22	18	14	10	6	2									
62°	94	89	84	79	74	69	64	60	55	50	46	41	37	33	29	25	21	17	13	9	6	2								
64°	95	90	85	79	75	70	66	61	56	52	48	43	39	35	31	27	23	20	16	12	9	5	2							
66°	95	90	85	80	76	71	66	62	58	53	49	45	41	37	33	29	26	22	18	15	11	8	5	1						
68°	95	90	85	81	76	72	67	63	59	55	51	47	43	39	35	31	28	24	21	17	14	11	8	4	1					
70°	95	90	86	81	77	72	68	64	60	56	52	48	44	40	37	33	30	26	23	20	17	13	10	7	4	1				
72°	95	91	86	82	78	73	69	65	61	57	53	49	46	42	39	35	32	28	25	22	19	16	13	10	7	4	1			
74°	95	91	86	82	78	74	70	66	62	58	54	51	47	44	40	37	34	30	27	24	21	18	15	12	9	6	4	1		
76°	96	91	87	83	78	74	70	67	63	59	55	52	48	45	42	38	35	32	29	26	23	20	17	14	12	9	6	4	1	
78°	96	91	87	83	79	75	71	67	64	60	57	53	50	46	43	40	37	34	31	28	25	22	19	16	13	11	8	6	4	
80°	96	91	87	83	79	76	72	68	64	61	57	54	51	47	44	41	38	35	32	29	27	24	21	18	15	13	10	8	6	4
82°	96	91	87	83	79	76	72	69	65	62	58	55	52	49	46	43	40	37	34	31	28	25	23	20	17	15	12	10	8	6
84°	96	92	88	84	80	77	73	70	66	63	59	56	53	50	47	44	41	38	35	32	30	27	25	22	20	17	15	12	10	8
86°	95	92	88	84	80	77	73	70	66	63	60	57	54	51	48	45	42	39	37	34	31	29	26	24	21	19	17	14	12	10
88°	96	92	88	85	81	78	74	71	67	64	61	58	55	52	49	46	43	41	38	35	33	30	28	25	23	21	18	16	14	12
90°	96	92	88	85	81	78	74	71	68	64	61	58	56	53	50	47	44	42	39	37	34	32	29	27	24	22	20	18	16	14

Air Temperature (reading of dry-bulb thermometer) in degrees Fahrenheit

A section of a table used with the psychrometer appears above. (Its temperatures are in Fahrenheit degrees.) Assume the dry-bulb reading is 70°F and the wet-bulb reading is 63°F—seven degrees lower. First find 70°F in the "Air Temperature" column. Then find 7 in the "Wet-bulb Depression" line. At the intersection of 70° and 7 number 68 is the relative humidity, which is stated as a percent.

If both wet-bulb and dry-bulb thermometers read the same, it means the air is saturated. The relative humidity at saturation is 100 percent.

The change from water vapor to water or ice is called **condensation.** It is the opposite of evaporation. When water evaporates, it takes heat from its surroundings. When water vapor condenses, it returns an equal amount of heat.

How does condensation usually happen in the atmosphere? Consider this example. It is a sunny spring afternoon. The air temperature is 15.5°C and the specific humidity is 8 grams. The air's capacity at this temperature is 11 grams, so it is not saturated. That night the air cools rapidly. When its temperature reaches 10°C, its capacity is only 8 grams. Since 8 grams is the specific humidity, the air has become saturated.

What happens if the temperature drops below 10°C? The air releases (condenses) all the water vapor over its capacity. Suppose the temperature drops to 4.5°C, where the air's capacity is 6 grams. Each kilogram of air releases 2 grams of water vapor. This condenses into dew on the grass, mist over the ground, or droplets in a cloud.

The specific humidity (S. H.) at each temperature is 8 grams. The capacity (cap.) drops as the temperature drops. Below the dew point, the air can hold only 6 grams of water. But, it had 8 grams! So, 2 grams come out as dew.

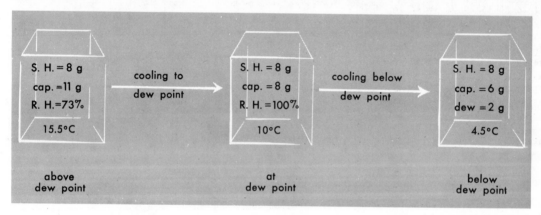

The temperature at which saturation occurs is called the **dew point.** In the example we just gave, it was 10°C. But the dew point may be any temperature. It depends on how much water vapor the air starts with. The more water it starts with, the higher its dew point. The dew point is an important temperature to weather scientists. *When air is cooled below the dew point, condensation of water vapor begins.*

How is the dew point found? A simple method is described in Student Activity 2 at the end of this chapter. The diagram here illustrates it.

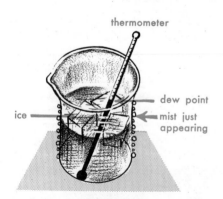

Cool the water with ice. The instant mist appears on the outside of the glass, read the thermometer. This is the dew point.

For water vapor to condense, air must be cooled below its dew point. This cooling can happen in four different ways. Air may lose heat by (1) contact with a colder surface, (2) radiation, (3) mixing with colder air, (4) expansion when it rises. The last process is most important in making rain and snow. Each of these processes will be discussed in what follows.

Even when air is cooled below its dew point, condensation may not occur. The air becomes supersaturated. Tiny particles called **condensation nuclei** are needed for water vapor to condense on. These are usually water-attracting substances such as common salt or sulfur trioxide. The salt gets into the air when fine sea spray evaporates. The sulfur trioxide is formed by the burning of fuels. Condensation nuclei are so tiny that even a handful of smoke contains millions of them. Ionized particles of air and meteorite dust may also be sources of condensation nuclei.

Forms of Condensation

9. Dew and Frost from Contact

Condensation usually happens when air is cooled below its dew point. When the cooling is by contact with a colder surface, water vapor condenses directly on that surface. If the temperature is above 0°C, drops of water called **dew** will form. Dew may form on the ground, on grass, on auto tops, and on other surfaces. At night these objects become cooler than the air because they lose heat more rapidly. The air reaches its dew point only where it touches the objects. The clearer the night, the greater the cooling and the heavier the dew.

If the temperature at condensation is below 0°C, white crystals of **frost** form. When temperatures near the ground drop below −2°C, plant-cell liquids in some plants may freeze. This bursts the cell walls and kills the plants. These *killing frosts* do not involve atmospheric moisture.

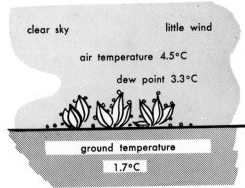

clear sky   little wind

air temperature 4.5°C

dew point 3.3°C

ground temperature
1.7°C

Both dew and frost form when the ground temperature is below the dew point. Above, the dew point is above 0° C. So, dew forms. At the left, the dew point is below 0° C. So, frost forms.

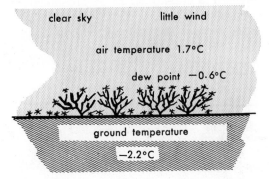

clear sky   little wind

air temperature 1.7°C

dew point −0.6°C

ground temperature
−2.2°C

421

It often happens that a few hundred feet of air near the surface is cooled below the dew point. Then water vapor condenses throughout the entire layer. When this happens, tiny droplets fill the air and form a **fog.** (If the temperature is below 0°C, the droplets will be ice.) Each droplet is centered about a condensation nucleus. The droplets are so small, that they fall slowly. The lightest air movement keeps them up.

Radiation fogs, or *ground fogs,* form under conditions similar to those that form dew. The nighttime sky is clear and the ground loses heat rapidly by radiation. Light winds mix the cold bottom air with the air a short way up. A whole layer of air is cooled below the dew point, and fog forms in it.

Radiation fogs are common in humid valleys near rivers or lakes. They are most frequent in the fall of the year. These fogs are thickest in the early morning. They are "burnt away" by the morning rays of the sun. The bottom air in this fog is colder than the air above it. This is, of course, a temperature inversion.

Advection fogs result when warm, moist air blows over cool surfaces. In the northern United States or southern Canada, they form when warm, moist southerly winds blow over snow-covered ground. The famous fogs of Newfoundland form when warm, moist Gulf Stream air blows over the cold Labrador Current. Summer fogs in coastal California form when warm ocean air strikes upwelling cold coastal waters. Winter fogs form along the Gulf coast. They occur when cold Mississippi River waters chill the warm Gulf air at the river's mouth.

The Origin of Clouds 11.

Clouds are simply high fogs. Fogs touch the ground; clouds do not.

Clouds form when air *above the surface* cools below its dew point. The shape of a cloud depends on the air movement that forms it. If air movement is mainly horizontal, clouds form in layers. They are called **stratiform.** If air movement is mainly vertical, clouds grow upward in great piles. These are called **cumuliform.**

Air movements that are mainly horizontal make layered stratiform clouds. Vertical movements make fluffy cumuliform clouds.

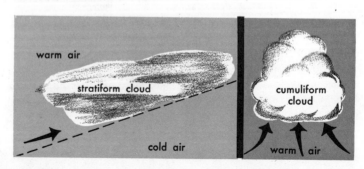

At temperatures above freezing, clouds are made entirely of water droplets. Below freezing, clouds are usually mixtures of snow crystals and **supercooled water.** (Supercooled water is water that has cooled below 0°C without freezing. When supercooled droplets are "disturbed," as by an airplane, they freeze instantly.) Below about −18°C, clouds are almost entirely snow and ice crystals.

12. Classification of Clouds

The drawing on the following page and table below show the four families of clouds. The "average height range" given in the table is for middle latitudes. The heights are measured above the surface, not above sea level. Cloud heights are greater in equatorial areas and less in polar areas.

Classification of Clouds

Family	Average Height Range	Types	Symbol
High clouds	7000 to 13,000 meters	Cirrus	Ci
		Cirrostratus	Cs
		Cirrocumulus	Cc
Middle clouds	2000 to 7000 meters	Altostratus	As
		Altocumulus	Ac
Low clouds	500 to 2000 meters	Stratocumulus	Sc
		Stratus	St
		Nimbostratus	Ns
Vertical development	500 to 13,000 meters	Cumulus	Cu
		Cumulonimbus	Cb

13. Cloud Names and Their Meaning

The cloud names in the table include three simple names—cirrus, stratus, and cumulus. These three names represent the three main cloud types. All the others are combinations or variations.

Cirrus (curl) clouds are thin, feathery, or tufted. They are so high that they are always made of ice crystals. All of the "high" family of clouds are of the cirrus type. *Stratus (spread)* clouds are low sheets or layers of cloud. *Cumulus (heap)* clouds are formed by vertically rising air currents. They are piled in thick, fleecy masses.

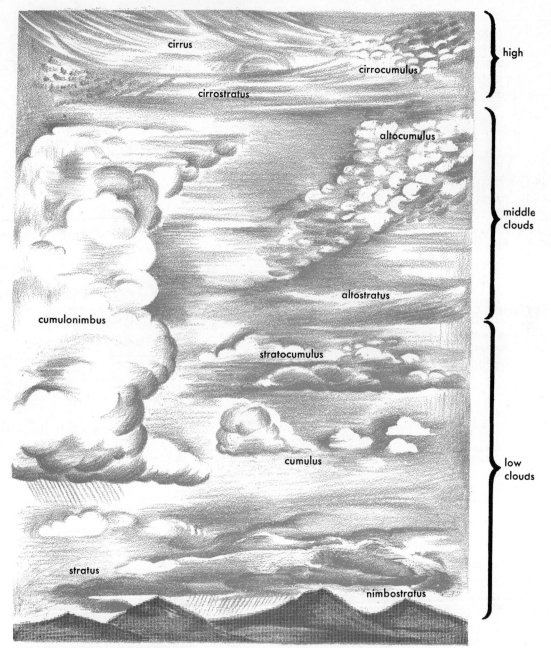

cirrus

cirrocumulus

cirrostratus

altocumulus

middle clouds

altostratus

cumulonimbus

stratocumulus

cumulus

low clouds

stratus

nimbostratus

All these clouds would not occur in the same sky at once, but this is a handy way to picture them.

Cirrostratus clouds are high, thin, feathery sheets or "veils" of ice-crystal clouds. They sometimes cause halos, or "rings," that appear to be around the moon and sun. This may mean the approach of rain or snow. *Stratocumulus* clouds are layers made up of round

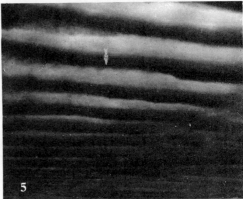

1. **Cirrus clouds**
2. **Cirrostratus clouds**
   (showing halo)
3. **Altocumulus clouds**
4. **Altostratus clouds**
5. **Stratocumulus clouds**

masses. They often cover the whole sky, especially in winter. *Cirro-cumulus* clouds are patches of small globular ice-crystal clouds.

The prefix *alto* (high) and the word *nimbus* (rain cloud) are used in cloud names. *Altocumulus* clouds look like higher, thinner, strato-cumulus clouds in smaller masses. *Altostratus* clouds look like thick cirrostratus at lower altitudes. They are gray or bluish in color. *Nim-bostratus* clouds are dark gray low layers. Steady rain or snow may develop from them.

14. Cumulus and Cumulonimbus

Rising air currents form **cumulus** clouds. These clouds often appear in the late morning or early afternoon of bright sunny days. They have flat bases and billowy tops. The flat base shows where the water

Evaporation and Condensation   **425**

Cumulus clouds

**Cumulonimbus clouds
(thunderhead)**

vapor began its condensation. The billowy top shows the height where condensation died out.

The stronger the rise in the air, or convection, the thicker and taller the cloud. Air rises most strongly on hot days when the air is very humid. Under these conditions, the cumulus clouds grow rapidly to mountainous heights. They become **cumulonimbus** clouds, or *thunderheads*. From them come lightning, thunder, and heavy showers of rain. Such storms are called *thunderstorms*. In violent thunderstorms, hailstones may fall.

Rising Cools Air; Sinking Warms Air 15.

When air *rises*, it reaches levels of lower air pressure. It therefore *expands* by itself. Some of its own heat energy is used to push aside the surrounding air. As a result, its temperature drops. *For every 100 meters that dry air rises, it cools about 1°C.* This is known as the *dry-adiabatic* (add ee uh BAT ik) *lapse rate.* It is much more than the normal lapse rate of 1°C per 160 meters. (Chapter 24, Topic 8.)

The word *adiabatic* describes a temperature change within a substance itself. The change is caused by its own expansion or compression. No heat is taken or added by anything outside. Adiabatic cooling can be felt in the expanding air escaping from an automobile tire.

As air sinks in the troposphere, it reaches levels of greater air pressure and is compressed. Energy is being added to it. This shows itself as a rise in temperature. The change for dry air is at the same rate of 1°C per 100 meters. Warming by compression can be felt in air just pumped into a bicycle tire. In nature, air warmed by compression often causes hot dry weather.

16. Condensation Level

Suppose the temperature and dew point of air at the ground are known. Then the height at which clouds will form in rising air can be found. The rate of cooling by expansion is 1°C per 100 meters. As air rises, however, its dew point also drops 0.2°C per 100 meters. This is because the expanding air contains less water vapor per unit volume than it had at the surface.

Here is an example: At the surface, air temperature is 20°C, dew point is 12°C; the difference between them is 8°C. One hundred meters higher, the air temperature is 19°C and the dew point is 12.2°C. The difference is only 7.2°C. The two temperatures continue to approach each other at a rate of 0.8°C for each 100 meters rise.

To find where the dew point will reach the air temperature, you divide eight (the difference between the air temperature at ground level and the dew point) by 0.8 (which is always the rate at which the dew point approaches the air temperature). Eight divided by 0.8 is 10, which is the number of hundreds of meters rise (1000 meters) necessary for the beginning of condensation. This level is known as the **lifting condensation level.** It is of great importance in weather forecasting.

For every 100 meters you go up, subtract 1 degree from the ground temperature and 0.2 degrees from the ground dew point. Where these two numbers are equal, clouds start to form.

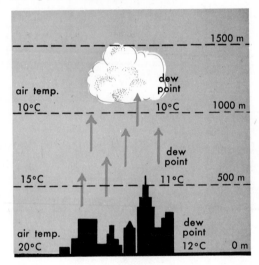

17. Lapse Rate in a Cloud

The rising air in a cloud cools more slowly than in clear air. Heat is given off by the water vapor that condenses in the cloud. On the average, the cooling rate changes from 1°C per 100 meters to 0.6°C per 100 meters.

Take the example given in Topic 16. What happens if the air in the cloud rises from 1000 to 1500 meters? It will cool only 0.6°C × 5 = 3.0°C. Below the cloud, the air had cooled 5°C in the same distance.

Weather scientists call this "cooling rate in rising *saturated* air" the **moist-adiabatic lapse rate.**

Clouds on the Weather Map 18.

Our weather maps give detailed information about clouds in the sky. The amount of sky covered by clouds is shown by shading in the station circle. Ten symbols are used by the U. S. Weather Service to show this *sky coverage*. Newspaper weather maps use only three symbols. The following terms are also used:

These symbols are used on weather maps. They show how much of the sky is covered by clouds.

sky cover 0.1 to 0.5 = scattered clouds;
0.6 to 0.9 = broken clouds;
more than 0.9 = overcast

SYMBOLS SHOWING PERCENTAGE OF CLOUDINESS											
tenths of sky covered	0	1	2	3	4	5	6	7	8	9	10
U. S. Weather Bureau maps	○	◐	◔	◕	◑	◑	◒	◕	◑	◑	●
newspaper maps		○				◑			●		

The weather map also shows the *type of cloud* at each level; the *height of the cloud base;* and the *amount of sky covered by the low clouds.* Arrows show the directions in which the clouds are moving.

Air Pollution 19.

Air pollution has become an important problem of cities all over the world. The chief pollutants are smoke from furnaces and power plants, chemical fumes, and automobile exhaust gases. Under certain atmospheric conditions, such pollutants can become concentrated enough to be a serious danger to health.

What are the conditions that cause an "air pollution crisis"? Ordinarily, pollutants are carried into the upper air by winds and air currents. When the lower air does not move, however, the poisonous gases remain close to the surface. Lower air is most likely to stay still when there is a temperature inversion. The warm air layer high above the surface traps the cool air at the ground. The cool air cannot "escape" by convection until it gets warmer than the air above it. Some inversions may last for many days.

As we saw in Topic 10, fogs often form in inversions. This makes matters even worse. The pollutants combine with the fog particles. The result is a poisonous fog called *smog* (smoke + fog). Smogs have resulted in death and sickness for many people in such cities as London, New York, Los Angeles, and Mexico City.

How can we prevent smog? We cannot prevent atmospheric inversions. We must, therefore, prevent the pollution of our atmosphere. Some of the ways this is being done now include:

1. use of low-sulfur fuels in furnaces;
2. use of lead-free fuels and anti-pollution devices in automobiles; and
3. use of anti-pollution devices to treat fumes from chemical plants and power plants.

At the left is a steel plant in normal operation. Note the thick smoke. At the right is the same plant during an air pollution crisis. Operations have been cut back.

Each topic question refers to the topic of the same number within this chapter.

TOPIC QUESTIONS

1. **(a)** In what forms does water exist in the atmosphere? Give examples. **(b)** Explain the terms melting, freezing, evaporation, and condensation.

2. **(a)** What are the sources of water vapor in the atmosphere? **(b)** How is water vapor spread throughout the troposphere? Why is there very little in the stratosphere?

3. **(a)** Why does water evaporate more rapidly as temperature rises? **(b)** Why is evaporation a cooling process?

4. **(a)** How are capacity and temperature related? **(b)** What is specific humidity? **(c)** When is air saturated?

5. **(a)** Define relative humidity and explain how it can be found.

6. **(a)** What is a hygrometer? **(b)** What is the psychrometer? What is the principle of its operation? **(c)** How is the psychrometer used in finding relative humidity?

7. **(a)** Define condensation. **(b)** Explain how condensation usually occurs in the atmosphere. **(c)** Define dew point. **(d)** When does condensation occur? **(e)** What does the dew point depend on?

8. **(a)** Name four ways by which the atmosphere may lose heat. **(b)** What are condensation nuclei? What are they made of? How do they originate?

9. **(a)** Explain the formation of dew and frost.

10. (a) Explain how fog forms and how it stays up. (b) How do radiation fogs form? (c) How do advection fogs form? Give examples.

11. (a) How are clouds formed? (b) When are clouds stratiform? cumuliform? (c) When do clouds consist only of water? only of snow and ice? a mixture of both? (d) What is supercooled water?

12. Briefly classify clouds into four families.

13. Explain the meanings of cloud names.

14. (a) How is a cumulus cloud formed? (b) What is a cumulonimbus cloud?

15. (a) Why does rising air become cooler? At what rate? What is this rate called? (b) Why does descending air become warmer?

16. (a) What is meant by the "lifting condensation level"? (b) Give the formula for finding it.

17. What is the moist-adiabatic lapse rate? Why is it less than the dry-adiabatic lapse rate?

18. What information about clouds is shown on the weather map?

19. (a) What are the chief pollutants of air? (b) When are the pollutants most likely to stay in the air? Why? (c) What is smog? Why is it so dangerous? (d) How can smogs be prevented?

1. Which contains more water vapor, air at 26.5° C with a relative humidity of 50 per cent or saturated air at 5° C? Why? (See Topics 4 and 5.)

2. Why should a psychrometer be fanned or whirled to get an accurate reading?

3. How can a single thermometer be used to obtain the relative humidity?

4. How many degrees must a sample of air be cooled in order that dew may form? (Suppose that its temperature is 26.5° C and its relative humidity is 50 per cent).

5. How may spraying an orchard with water help to prevent frost formation?

6. In distance and altitude contests glider pilots always try to go beneath cumulus clouds. Why?

1. Make a simple chemical hygrometer: Soak a piece of filter paper in a strong solution of cobalt chloride and let it dry. The paper will be blue in dry air. It will turn pink in humid air.

2. Find the dew point of the air in your room by this method: (a) Half fill a shiny metal container (or a clean glass) with water at room temperature. (b) Place a thermometer in the water. (c) Add cracked ice or ice cubes, a little at a time, while stirring. Watch the outside surface of the container closely for the first appearance of mist. Read the temperature immediately. (d) Wait until the mist just disappears. Note the temperature again. (e) Average the temperatures noted in c and d. This is the dew point.

3. Find the relative humidity with a psychrometer, as explained in Topic 6. Do this both indoors and outdoors. Compare your results.

28

Raindrops grow from cloud droplets by "coalescence" (Topic 1). To demonstrate coalescence, try this experiment. Take a piece of wax paper about 20 centimeters square. Using a medicine dropper, glass rod, or even your fingertip, place about 10 drops of water at different points on the paper. Now wiggle the paper until all the drops merge into one drop. What forces would cause similar coalescence of cloud droplets?

Precipitation

From Clouds to Rain

How Raindrops Form

Precipitation is the falling of any form of water from the air to the earth's surface. It happens when cloud droplets grow into drops heavy enough to fall to earth. Oddly enough, there is still some mystery as to just how this happens.

A cloud is composed mainly of billions of tiny droplets, all about the same size. They are controlled by air currents. When they fall, they fall together. When rising currents raise them, they rise together. They do not collide. How then do they ever unite to become large raindrops? (One raindrop equals about one million cloud droplets!)

As large droplets fall through the clouds, they capture thousands of tiny droplets. Soon they are heavy enough to fall to the ground as raindrops.

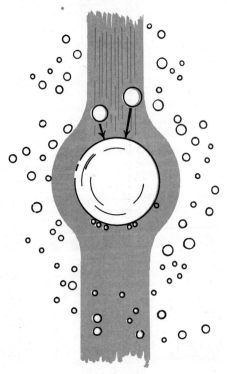

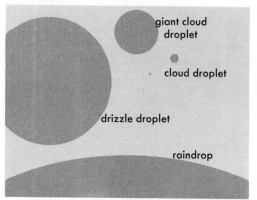

giant cloud droplet

cloud droplet

drizzle droplet

raindrop

While a large raindrop is about 0.25 centimeters across, the tiny droplets that form clouds are a hundred times as small in diameter and a million times as small in volume.

Here is one theory about how raindrops fall. Suppose that a cloud contains some "extra-large droplets." These will fall faster than the others. They will collide with the small droplets and capture them. They will capture others by suction as they fall. By these processes—collision and suction—the extra-large droplets will grow to raindrop size. If enough of them are scattered through the cloud, rain will fall.

But where will the extra-large droplets come from? Weather scientists think there are two ways in which they form. The first way is simply by condensing around extra-large salt crystals. (The salt crystals are the "condensation nuclei.") Scientists find this kind of extra-large droplet in warm water clouds.

The second way that extra-large droplets may form is from ice crystals. This happens in the upper levels of tall thick clouds. The temperature is below freezing. Both ice crystals and supercooled droplets are present. Supercooled water evaporates faster than ice does. The water vapor condenses on the ice crystals. Soon the crystals grow to extra-large droplet size. Then they, too, can get heavy enough to fall. If there are enough of them, precipitation will take place.

In summer, snow and ice crystals melt as they fall. They reach the ground as rain.

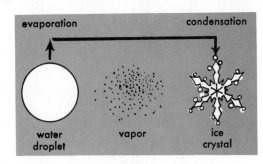

Supercooled water droplets evaporate and the water vapor condenses on already present ice crystals.

2. Rainmaking

Nowadays you can hire weather scientists to "make rain." Are they successful? The results are uncertain. When they do make rain, it is hard to prove that the same amount of rain would not have fallen naturally. Furthermore, they must always work with "promising" clouds.

What methods do rainmakers use? In general, they work only with supercooled clouds. In one method, the cloud is "seeded" with pellets of dry ice (frozen carbon dioxide) dropped from an airplane. The very cold dry ice makes ice crystals form in the cloud. The ice crystals cause some rainfall, leaving a "hole" in the cloud. But this method seems better for clearing fog than for making rain.

A second method seeds supercooled clouds with crystals of silver iodide. These are very much like ice crystals in shape. When water vapor condenses on the silver iodide, ice crystals may form. These, in turn, may cause some rain to fall. Smoke generators are used to make billions of tiny silver iodide crystals. The generators may be used on the ground or in airplanes.

3. Forms of Precipitation

Precipitation comes in many forms. **Drizzle** consists of very fine drops, very close together, falling very slowly. **Raindrops** are larger, farther apart, and fall much faster. A raindrop may have a diameter up to 0.25 centimeter. Larger raindrops may form, but are torn apart as they fall.

Snow usually falls as six-sided crystals or stars. At very low temperatures, fine ice needles form. When snowflakes fall into warm air, they melt together to form sticky wet snow. If they melt completely, they come down as rain.

All the forms of snowflakes have six sides except for ice needles formed at very low temperatures.

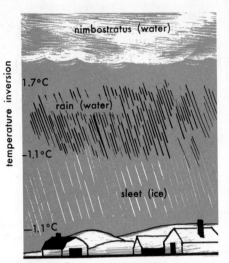

temperature inversion

nimbostratus (water)

1.7°C

rain (water)

−1.1°C

sleet (ice)

−1.1°C

Sleet is frozen rain. For it to form, there must be cold air near the ground and warmer air above it. This situation is, of course, a temperature inversion.

When supercooled rain hits trees or other objects that are below freezing, the rain freezes instantly. Then layers of ice begin to form. These can be heavy enough to knock down limbs or whole trees.

Note the many layers of ice and snow that form this large hailstone.

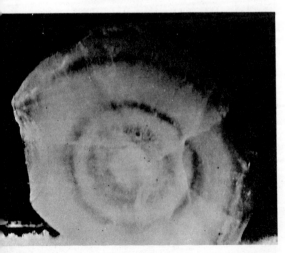

Sometimes in winter, warm rain clouds lie above a layer of freezing air. (This is, of course, an inversion.) When the raindrops fall through the freezing air, they turn into pellets of ice. This *frozen rain* is called **sleet.**

How do winter *ice storms* happen? Supercooled rain freezes when it hits ground surfaces that are below freezing. **Sheet ice,** or *glaze,* forms on sidewalks, trees, roofs, and power lines. If the ice becomes heavy enough, trees and power lines may break under its weight.

Hail forms only in thunderclouds. A **hailstone** begins as a large raindrop. The powerful rising currents called *updrafts* in the thundercloud carry it up to freezing levels. It freezes, falls, and picks up more water at warmer levels. Then updrafts carry it again to freezing levels. The more often this happens, the larger the hailstone becomes. Finally it gets so heavy that it falls to earth.

Hailstones resemble onions in structure, because of their many layers of ice. Hailstones are as small as buckshot or as large as baseballs. The largest hailstone on record fell at Coffeyville, Kansas, on September 3, 1970. It was as large as a softball.

The United States National Weather Service reports rainfall in hundredths of an inch. The rainfall is measured by an instrument called a **rain gauge.** The measurement represents the thickness of water that the rain would leave on a perfectly level impermeable surface.

In the standard rain gauge, a funnel guides the rain into a narrow tube. The mouth of the funnel has ten times the area of the mouth of the tube. The tube therefore gets ten times as much rain as it would receive it if were in the rain alone. This larger amount must be divided by ten to give the actual rainfall. But it is easier to read. A marked stick is dipped into the tube to get the reading. The *tipping bucket rain gauge* and the *weighing rain gauge* can automatically record both the time and the amount of the rainfall.

Snowfall is measured in inches and tenths of an inch. A simple measuring stick is used. The measurement is usually taken in as open a location as possible. The rain equivalent of the snowfall is determined by melting a definite depth of the snow. Dry snows pile up much higher than equal weights of wet snow. On the average, ten inches of snow equal one inch of rain. This ratio, however, may range from as little as five inches of snow to as much as thirty inches. Why?

The diagram here shows the symbols used on weather maps to show the kind of precipitation happening.

Here a standard rain gauge is taken apart to show its components.

These symbols are used on weather maps to show precipitation and storms.

NAME	drizzle	rain	shower	snow	sleet	fog	hail	thunderstorm
USNWS symbol	⸴	●	▽	✳	△	☰	◈	⊼⸜
Newspaper maps		Ⓡ		Ⓢ		Ⓕ	◖	hurricane

Where and When It Rains

Precipitation—rain, sleet, hail, or snow—occurs in every part of the world. But in some locations, such as parts of the desert of Peru, it may not rain for years at a time. In other places, such as the Amazon Valley, it may rain almost every day. Parts of Death Valley, California, average about one inch of rain a year. Cherrapunji in India averages 457 inches a year. What accounts for such differences?

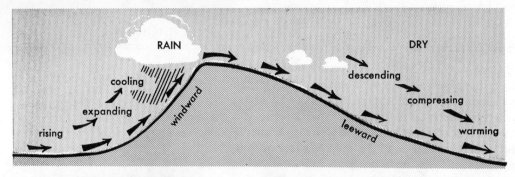

Rain and snow are usually heavy on the windward side of a tall mountain range, and very light on the leeward.

Wherever air rises high enough and in large enough quantities, precipitation will occur. The warmer the air, the more moisture it may contain. Also, the higher the air rises, the more moisture it can drop.

It follows, therefore, that the *rainy areas of the earth will be those where air often rises in large quantities*. The more often this happens, the more often it rains. Such areas are:

1. the *doldrums belt* of warm, humid, rising air. This has giant cumulonimbus clouds and almost daily thunderstorms. It includes the dense tropical forests of the Amazon, the Congo, and Indonesia;

2. the *windward sides of mountain ranges*, where prevailing winds are forced to climb to great heights. Examples are the rainy western slopes of the Cascade Mountains in the northwestern United States, and the rainy eastern slopes of the mountains of Central America in the trade-wind belt;

3. *storm areas* of all kinds, such as hurricanes, typhoons, cyclones, fronts, thunderstorms, and tornadoes. In all of these there are great masses of moist rising air. Storm areas will be described in Chapters 29 and 30.

Where Does It Not Rain? 6.

The answer to this question is almost the exact opposite of the answer to "Where does it rain?" *In areas of sinking air the air is being warmed by compression. So no precipitation can occur.* Sinking air may become so warm and dry that it creates desert conditions. Large masses of sinking air are found

1. in the two *horse-latitude belts,*
2. on the *leeward sides of mountains,*
3. in the middle-latitude *highs* (described in Chapter 30), and
4. in the great *polar highs.*

Now let us examine briefly the rainfall patterns of low, middle, and high latitudes.

7. Precipitation in the Tropics

Precipitation follows a fairly simple pattern in the tropics. Rising air in the moist, hot doldrums belt brings almost daily thundershowers. Yearly rainfall is high in the equatorial belt around the world.

Just the reverse is true in the horse-latitude high-pressure belts. Sinking air brings desert conditions to the latitudes of 30° to 35° in both hemispheres. But lands lying between the rainy doldrums and the dry horse-latitudes have changing rainy and dry seasons. These are caused by the shifting of the wind belts with the seasons.

Most places in the tropics get their rains when the doldrums belt arrives. Some places, however, get their rains because they are on the eastern sides of coastal mountains. Since the trade winds blow from the east, these are the rainy windward sides. For this reason, the east coasts of South America, Central America, and Africa get heavy rains. In India and Burma, the heavy monsoon rains are of similar origin. Here the hooked southwest trades drop their rains as they climb the Himalaya highlands. Very little of the tropics' rain comes from traveling storms. Now and then, however, typhoons drop heavy rains on islands and coastal areas.

8. Precipitation in Middle Latitudes

The middle latitudes reach from 35° latitude to about 65° in both hemispheres. They are covered for most of the year by the prevailing westerly winds. In these latitudes, there are no world-circling belts such as the "all wet" doldrums or the "all dry" horse-latitudes. Instead, the chief causes of raininess or dryness are mountain ranges, distance from the ocean, and storms.

The rainiest places are the windward slopes of high coastal mountains. The western slopes of the Olympic Mountains in northwest Washington are one example. The driest places are those lands lying leeward of high mountain ranges. The Mohave Desert of the southwestern United States is an example. It lies on the dry eastern side of the Sierra Nevada Mountains. It is in the "rain shadow" of the Sierras.

The western interior of North America and the eastern interior of Asia are dry for two reasons. One is distance from the ocean. The second is the effect of high mountains in keeping out moist ocean air. They are saved from total dryness, however, by occasional rain-bearing storms. These middle latitudes storms come mostly in summer.

As the east and south coasts of both North America and Asia are approached, rainfall increases. Semiarid conditions give way to much rainfall, as in the eastern United States and southwestern China.

There are two reasons for this increase in rainfall. One is a larger number of storms. The second is the higher moisture content of the air blowing in from the oceans that are east of the continents. In summer the "monsoon effect" helps to bring moist air from the cool oceans.

Precipitation in High Latitudes 9.

The high latitudes reach from about 65° to the poles in both hemispheres. They are covered most of the year by the polar easterlies or the polar highs. The very cold air has little capacity for holding water vapor. Precipitation is light in all seasons. It comes almost entirely from traveling storms. Yearly precipitation is rarely more than 10 or 15 inches. Very little water evaporates from the surface, however, because of the low temperatures.

This map shows the average yearly rainfall for all parts of the world.

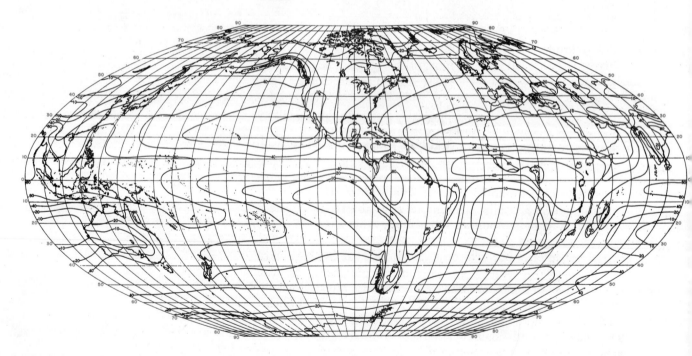

Each topic question refers to the topic of the same number within this chapter.

1. (a) Explain why cloud droplets of uniform size are unlikely to grow larger. (b) Explain how large droplets grow into raindrops. (c) How do large droplets form in warm water clouds? (d) How do large droplets form in supercooled clouds?

2. Describe two methods used for rainmaking.

3. (a) Describe drizzle, raindrops, and snow. (b) How does sleet form? sheet ice? (c) How do hailstones form?

4. (a) What is a rain gauge? Describe one. (b) In what units are snow and rain measured? Explain. (c) Draw and label some of the symbols used for precipitation.

5. (a) Where will precipitation happen? (b) Name the three kinds of areas in which rising air causes rain. Explain why the air rises in two of them. Name some places located in them.

6. (a) Why are areas of sinking air dry? (b) Name four areas of sinking air and explain why the air sinks in two of them.

7. (a) Describe the rainfall pattern of (1) the doldrums, (2) the horse latitudes, (3) the areas between them. (b) When do the trade winds bring rainfall to the tropics?

8. (a) What factors are important in determining raininess or dryness in middle latitudes? (b) Which are the rainiest regions in the United States and Canada? the driest regions? (c) How does any rain come to the dry interiors of North America and Asia?

9. Describe the rainfall pattern of high latitudes.

1. How may dry-ice seeding be of value at airports?

2. Why are winter hailstorms rather rare?

3. Why should average annual precipitation be greater in Mississippi than in Maine?

4. Why should average annual precipitation be greater in Massachusetts than in Minnesota?

Make a rain gauge similar to the standard weather bureau type described in Topic 4. Use a large-diameter container to collect the water and a tall narrow container as the gauge. To calibrate the gauge, simply fill the larger container with water to a depth of 1 inch; then pour this water into the long narrow tube. Now dip a slender measuring stick or ruler into the tube. Mark the height reached by the water, and label it "1 inch." Use this as a scale for further calibration of the "gauge."

29

An air mass (Topic 1) is a vast section of the atmosphere. Some air masses are cold. Others are warm. The boundary surface between two air masses is called a "front" (Topic 6).

To get some idea of how a front forms, set up a model using water instead of air. Get a rectangular aquarium tank. Place a stiff watertight divider (wood or plastic) across the width of the tank. It should divide the tank into two halves. It should be easily removable. Make a strong solution of salt water, enough to nearly fill half the tank. Color it with ink or food color so it is easily seen. This dense solution will represent a cold air mass. Warm tap water will represent a warm air mass.

*Now fill one side of the tank with your "cold air mass." Fill the other side with your "warm air mass." Get ready for a **quick** observation. Slide out the divider as smoothly as you can. Describe the "front" that formed (a) in the first few seconds, (b) after that. Can you explain why this happened?*

Air Masses and Fronts

Air Masses

An **air mass** is a huge section of the lower troposphere. It may be thousands of kilometers in diameter and several kilometers high. Two or three air masses can cover all of the continental United States.

Each air mass has its own kind of weather. In each air mass, *temperature and humidity are nearly the same at any given level.*

How does a huge section of the troposphere become an air mass? It has to "sit" for days or even weeks on a large uniform surface. Sitting on the Gulf of Mexico, for example, would make it warm and humid. Sitting on the Sahara Desert would make it hot and dry. Sitting on the Great Plains of Canada in winter would make it cold and dry.

Air masses originate in parts of wind belts where winds are light. These are mainly in the pressure belts south and north of the prevailing westerlies.

When you hear a television weatherman speak of an Arctic air mass, picture this map.

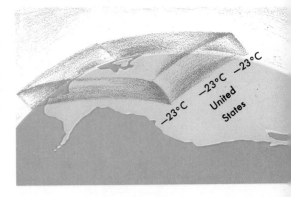

2. Kinds, Sources, and Paths

The *temperature* of an air mass depends on whether it comes from the tropics or the polar regions. The *humidity* of an air mass depends on whether it comes from land or sea.

Four kinds of air masses are possible. A **maritime tropical** (abbreviated **mT**) air mass comes from tropical seas. It is warm and humid. A **continental tropical** (abbreviated **cT**) air mass comes from tropical land areas. It is hot and dry. Both of these are carried into the latitudes of the United States by the prevailing southwesterlies. In general they move northward and eastward.

A **maritime polar** (abbreviated **mP**) air mass comes from cold ocean waters. It is cold and humid. A **continental polar** (abbreviated **cP**) air mass comes from land areas in high latitudes. It is cold and dry. Polar air masses are carried to the latitudes of the United States by the polar northeasterlies. In general, they move southward.

The air masses that reach the continental United States come mainly from these sources:

- **mT** Gulf of Mexico, Caribbean Sea, middle Atlantic Ocean
- **cT** desert region of the southwestern United States
- **mP** North Atlantic Ocean, North Pacific Ocean
- **cP** central and northern Canada

(Very cold air masses from ice-covered arctic regions may be called cA.)

The map below shows where North America's air masses come from, and what paths they follow.

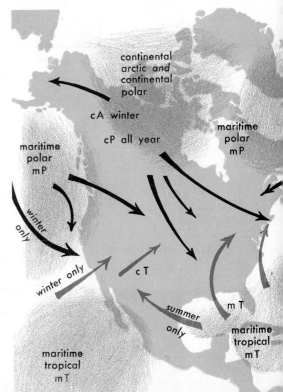

441

Weather in an Air Mass 3.

Air masses take many days to pass a given place. During this time the weather of the place comes from the air mass. In winter, cP air is usually an icy, clear, cold wave. It may reach as far south as Florida. In summer, cP air is felt as a cool spell.

When mP air comes in from the northern oceans, it brings cool, humid weather. The mT air masses bring mild, humid weather in winter. In summer, they bring hot, humid spells to the central and the eastern United States. Maritime tropical air also brings frequent thunderstorms and occasional tornadoes. Continental tropical air masses bring very hot dry weather.

As one air mass after another passes over a place, its weather changes. It may go from polar to tropical, from humid to dry, over and over again. This is why the weather in most of the United States is so variable.

Skies in an Air Mass 4.

Air masses change when they leave their source areas. Polar air masses eventually get warmer. Tropical air masses eventually get cooler. Dry air masses may become more humid and vice versa. Clear skies may become cloudy.

What kinds of clouds do air masses have? Is their weather fair or rainy, windy or calm? Let us see.

Weather scientists have found that the "skies" in an air mass depend mainly on one thing. Is the surface the air mass rests on warmer or colder than the air mass? *If the ground surface is colder, it cools the bottom layer* of the air mass, with these results:

1. Condensation of water vapor occurs. This may form dew, fogs, stratiform clouds, drizzle, or light rain.
2. Inversions form. Smoke, dust, and gases do not rise. Visibility is poor. Smog may form.

In the fall, as mT air moves over land that is colder than the air, clouds and fog may result.

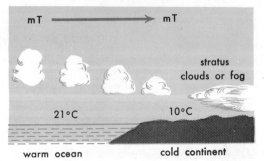

mT → mT

stratus clouds or fog

21°C   10°C

warm ocean   cold continent

In summer, when the land is warmer than the sea, mT air often brings thunderstorms.

In winter, cool Canadian air comes down the Great Plains, which causes clear, cold days with cumulus clouds.

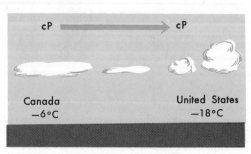

cP → cP

Canada −6°C   United States −18°C

Great Plains in winter

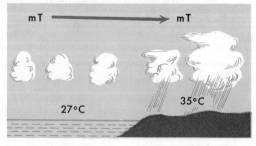

mT → mT

27°C   35°C

warm ocean   warmer land

If the ground surface is warmer, it warms the bottom layer of the air mass, with these results:

1. Warming causes convection and winds. Cumulus clouds form. Visibility is good.
2. If the air mass is a dry one—such as cP—the weather stays fair. If the air mass is humid, or the warm surface is water (lake or sea), showers may form. This is because the cumulus clouds grow into cumulonimbus (thunderheads).

5. Observing an Air Mass

How do weather scientists observe the temperature and humidity high up in an air mass? They use a clever tool called a **radiosonde**. Radiosonde observations are made twice daily at the same time at weather stations all over the world.

The radiosonde is a tiny combination of thermometer, barometer, hygrometer, and radio transmitter. The transmitter sends out signals that tell the temperature, air pressure, and relative humidity. An automatic radio receiver at the weather station records the signals. A balloon carries the radiosonde more than 30 kilometers high.

Tracking equipment is used to follow the flight of the radiosonde. From this, the speed and direction of the upper-air winds are found.

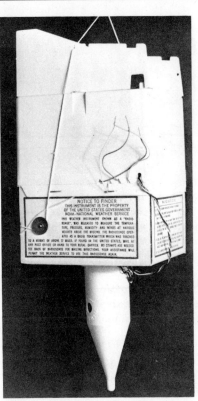

Above, the package carried by a radiosonde balloon. It broadcasts information about the upper atmosphere to the ground.

At the left, a radiosonde is released. The radio signals enable the position of the balloon to be noted as well as providing data.

443

Fronts

What Is a Front? 6.

At any moment several different air masses cover the United States. The boundary between any two air masses is called a **front**. A front may be several thousand kilometers long.

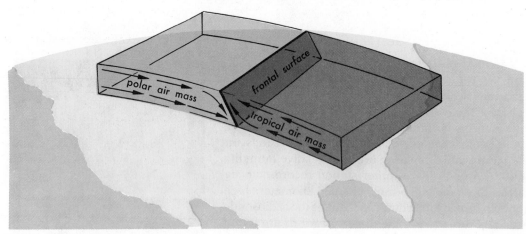

At a front, the warmer air always rises over the colder air (because the colder air is heavier). Thus, fronts always slope upwards toward the colder air mass.

This diagram of an "average" front's surface shows a rise of one kilometer in every 100.

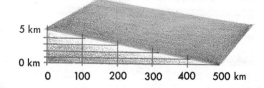

What is the shape of a front? Let us take an example. Suppose the front is the boundary between a polar air mass and a tropical air mass. Both are moving eastward. At the boundary, the heavier polar air slides like a wedge under the lighter tropical air. The tropical air is forced to rise high above the cold air mass. This makes the front a sloping surface. The air in two different air masses is always of two different densities. Thus, the surface of a front always slopes.

Observations show fronts to be very gentle in slope. The average rise is about one kilometer in 100. "Steep" fronts may rise as much as one kilometer in 40. "Gentle" slopes may rise as little as one kilometer in 200.

The front itself is not a very sharp boundary. Actually, it is a "mixing zone" about 30 kilometers thick.

Why Are Fronts Important? 7.

A front is important because it separates two different kinds of weather. When a front approaches a place, it means a change in the weather. The greater the difference between the air masses, the sharper the weather change. Suppose an mT air mass is replaced by a cP air mass. A warm humid spell will end, and a cool dry one will begin.

Another feature of a front is very important. Fronts almost always bring precipitation. Why? At the frontal surface, warm air is rising high into the troposphere. Rising air means cooling, condensation of water vapor, and then precipitation.

8. Kinds of Fronts

There are three main kinds of fronts. In a *cold front*, cold air is advancing and displacing warmer air. In a *warm front*, warm air is pushing ahead and displacing colder air. If neither air mass is being displaced, the front stays in one place. Then it is a *stationary front*.

The diagram here shows the symbols used for fronts on weather maps. The triangles and half-circles "show the way" the front is moving.

These are U.S.N.W.S. standard symbols.

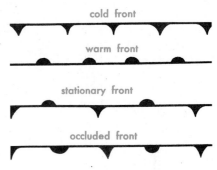

9. Warm-Front Weather

At a warm front, warm air is pushing cold air ahead of it. The slope is very gentle. The warm air may travel 1000 kilometers before rising five kilometers. As the warm air rises, a vast system of *stratiform*

Follow what happens as a warm front moves across the countryside.

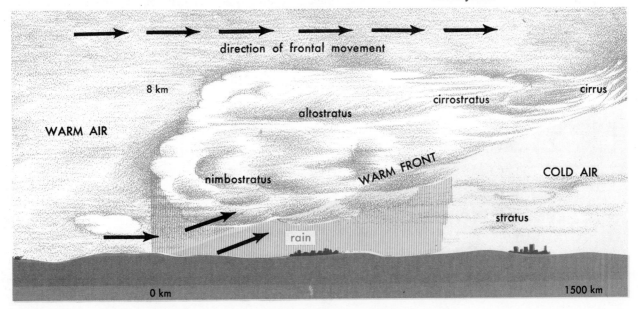

Air Masses and Fronts **445**

clouds forms in it. The clouds may stretch 1500 kilometers ahead of the front on the ground.

Thin icy cirrus clouds at great heights lead the way. Behind them come cirrostratus clouds that may make halos around the sun and moon. Then follow thick altostratus clouds that almost screen out the sun and moon. Finally, heavy low nimbostratus clouds arrive and steady rain or snow begins. This stretches hundreds of kilometers *ahead* of the front on the ground. Thunderstorms may form, but they are not typical of warm fronts.

Stationary fronts have the same kind of weather as warm fronts.

Cold-Front Weather

At a cold front, cold air is pushing warm air ahead. Cold fronts are steeper than warm fronts. This is because the advancing cold air winds move faster at higher levels. The slope averages about one kilometer in 80. Cold fronts also move faster than warm fronts.

Again, clouds form in the rising warm air. In cold fronts, however, the slope is steep enough to cause the air to rise fairly fast. As a result, the clouds are *cumuliform*. The steeper cloud system usually covers only from 300 to 500 kilometers. It *stretches both before and behind* the front at the ground.

Rain falls from cumulonimbus clouds. The clouds arrive rather suddenly, and precipitation is showery, heavy, and usually short. Thunderstorms are common.

When a cold front passes, sharp changes of weather occur. Temperatures fall fast as the cold air arrives. The wind rises in speed,

When a cold front passes, the weather changes more quickly than when a warm front moves in.

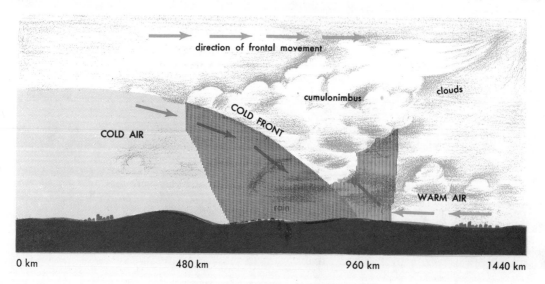

direction of frontal movement

COLD AIR

COLD FRONT

cumulonimbus

clouds

WARM AIR

0 km   480 km   960 km   1440 km

Sometimes you can see the weather change. Here a Kansas dust storm, caused by a fast-moving cold front, moves across the plain.

The photo below was taken from a weather satellite. It shows a top view of a cold front's "squall line" edge.

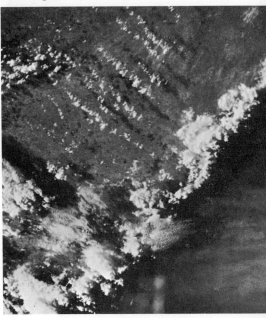

often blowing a gale. It usually shifts suddenly from a southerly direction to a northerly one. The rain ends shortly after the front passes.

Sometimes very humid mT air is being pushed forward at a cold front. In such cases, a whole line of thunderstorms may form at the front. This *squall line* may be hundreds of kilometers long.

Each topic question refers to the topic of the same number within this chapter.

TOPIC QUESTIONS

1. **(a)** Define air mass and explain your definition **(b)** How does an air mass acquire uniform temperature? uniform humidity?

2. **(a)** Name each of the following air masses, state its characteristics, and explain why it has these characteristics: cP, mP, cT, mT. **(b)** Where in the United States does each of these air masses come from? **(c)** In what direction do air masses move? Why?

3. Give a brief description of the weather in each of the following air masses in summer and winter: cP, mP, mT.

4. **(a)** What is the chief factor that determines what kind of skies an air mass has? **(b)** Describe the sky conditions of an air mass resting on (1) a colder surface; (2) a warmer surface.

5. Describe the radiosonde: **(a)** What three weather elements does it measure? **(b)** What does tracking equipment tell us?

6. **(a)** Explain what a front is. **(b)** Describe the average slopes and relative positions of warm and cold air in a front.

7. (a) Explain why precipitation almost always comes with a front. (b) Why does the passing of a front mean changes in weather?

8. (a) Define or explain three kinds of fronts. (b) Draw the symbols for each.

9. Describe the slope, cloud system, and precipitation in a warm front. Use a diagram as part of your explanation.

10. Describe the slope, cloud system, precipitation, and weather changes associated with a cold front. Use a diagram as part of your explanation.

GENERAL QUESTIONS

1. In what directions would polar and tropical air masses move in the Southern Hemisphere? Why?

2. What kind of thermometer is the radiosonde likely to carry? what kind of barometer? hygrometer? Why?

3. Why should the radiosonde balloon burst at very high altitudes? What determines how high it goes before bursting?

4. What kind of air-mass weather is likely to follow the passing of a warm front? of a cold front?

5. Why should there be small cumulus clouds in the cold air in Topic 10's diagram of a cold front?

6. Why should there be stratus clouds in the warm air behind the warm front in Topic 9's diagram?

STUDENT ACTIVITIES

1. Make a three-dimensional model of a warm-front or a cold-front cloud system, using a framework of wire or other material and hospital cotton for clouds.

2. Observe the temperature, barometer reading, relative humidity, wind direction, and wind speed during a period of cool, dry weather apparently caused by a continental polar air mass. Make the same observations during a warm, humid period caused by a maritime tropical air mass. Compare the two sets of observations.

30

HOW DO YOU KNOW THAT...?

Keep a daily record, in column form, of weather observations. These should include temperature, state of sky (per cent of cloudiness), cloud types, kind of precipitation, wind direction. If a barometer is available, record air pressure, too. Make your observations at the same time each day. See what relationships you can find among the weather elements you observe.

Storms and Weather Forecasts

Middle Latitude Lows

The *polar front* is the boundary between the polar easterlies and the prevailing westerlies. Polar air masses form north of the polar front. Tropical air masses form south of it.

In general, the polar front is a stationary front circling the earth. From time to time, however, wave motion develops along the polar front. The wave moves from west to east. It travels like a wave passing through a stage curtain shaken at one end. The wave ripples the polar front. Where the ripple bulges southward, polar air pushes tropical air ahead of it. This makes a southward-moving **cold front.** Where the ripple bulges northward, tropical air pushes polar air ahead of it. This makes a northward-moving **warm front.**

Both the cold front and the warm front also move eastward. Between them is a large amount of warm tropical air. The warm air bulges into the heavier polar air to form a region of low air pressure. The entire system of cold front, warm front, and "warm sector" is called a **low.** The system is the typical large-scale storm of middle latitudes. The isobars of the low are roughly oval or circular. Winds whirl about the center of the low in a counterclockwise direction (in the Northern Hemisphere).

The diagram shows this *wave theory of "low" development.* Stage (a) shows the polar front still stationary. Stage (b) shows the wave well on its way. Stage (c) shows the low fully developed.

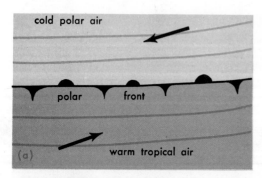

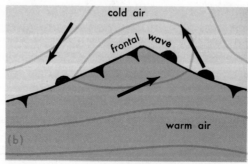

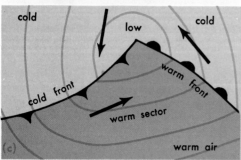

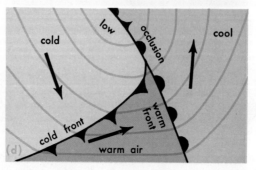

These four diagrams show one way that a low may develop.

As the low moves eastward, its cold front overtakes the slower warm front. The front formed where the cold front and warm front merge is called an **occluded front.** Occlusion (meaning "closing in") continues until both fronts merge completely. The "warm sector" between the two fronts is lifted completely off the ground.

When the warm air and cold air are thoroughly mixed, the low dies out. The polar front becomes stationary again until a new wave develops. Stage (d) illustrates the start of the occlusion process.

The development from stage (a) to (c) takes only 12 to 24 hours. From (c) to complete occlusion usually takes three days or more.

2. Winds and Weather in a Low

Since winds blow from high pressure to low pressure, they blow towards the center of a low. As you saw in Chapter 25, the Coriolis force turns them away from the center. In the Northern Hemisphere, the winds are deflected to the right of the pressure gradient direction. This results in a counterclockwise whirl of winds around the center of the low. In the Southern Hemisphere where deflection is to the left, the whirl is clockwise.

The diagram shows a vertical section through a typical low. As the diagram shows, these weather changes take place when a low passes any locality:

1. a long period of steady rains carried by the low's warm front.
2. clearing and warmer weather.
3. a short period of heavy showery rains carried by the low's cold front.
4. clearing and colder weather.

The black arrows show the way air moves in a typical low.

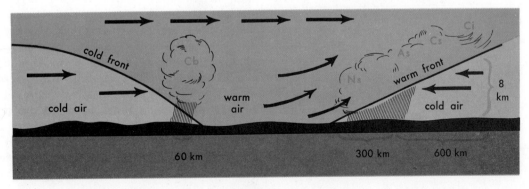

The Energy in Lows

The waves at the polar front are probably started by the blowing of the winds at the front. Soon, however, a vast new source of energy becomes available. Condensation of water vapor begins at the low's warm front and cold front. This releases heat energy. As explained in Chapter 27, when water vapor condenses, more than 540 calories of heat are released for every gram of water.

This energy heats the air in the low. It makes its low pressure lower. It increases the strength of its winds. It makes lows "heat engines" that grow and keep themselves running as long as condensation continues.

Lows in the United States

The lows that cross the United States come mainly from the northwest, the southwest, and the southeast. Almost all lows move toward the northeast and New England. In winter, lows are better developed and move faster. They are more frequent than in summer. Their rate of movement in winter is about 1100 kilometers a day. In summer it is about 800 kilometers a day. Lows have diameters of from 800 to 1600 kilometers. A single large low may cover nearly half of the country.

Tropical Storms

Hurricanes 5.

A hurricane is a **tropical storm.** A United States National Weather Service pamphlet describes hurricanes as "large revolving storms accompanied by violent destructive winds, heavy rains, and high waves and tides." In some ways a tropical storm is like our own middle-latitude lows. Both of them are storm areas of low air pressure. Winds spiral into their centers in the same general patterns. As a rule there are areas of heavy precipitation in both of them.

In many ways, however, the hurricane differs from the middle-latitude low. A hurricane is a much more intense storm. Its average diameter is only 300 to 600 kilometers. Its pressure changes very sharply from the surrounding air. Its central air pressure may go as low as 892.3 millibars (recorded as 26.35 inches at Key West, Florida, in 1935).

A hurricane has no fronts. It has a central area of sinking air currents, known as the **"eye of the storm."** The eye is usually from 15 to 50 kilometers in diameter. Here the sky is clear, there is no rain, and almost no wind.

But all around the eye the winds whirl violently. Their highest speeds may exceed 240 kilometers per hour. The area of destructive winds may have a diameter as large as 800 kilometers. It may cover a path more than 1600 kilometers long during the storm's life history. The storm area moves very slowly through the tropics. It speeds up when it enters middle latitudes.

The rains of a hurricane are almost always very heavy. They increase in amount toward the center. There the rain comes down in torrents, except in the dry eye. The world's record for a 24-hour rainfall is 46 inches. It fell during a tropical storm in the Philippines in 1911.

Tropical storms are known by various names. In the West Indies they are called *hurricanes*, in the Indian Ocean *cyclones*, in the China Sea *typhoons*, in the Philippine Islands *baguios* (bah gee OHS) and in the Pacific near Australia *willy-willies*.

The giant sea waves blown up by them do great damage along coastal areas. This is especially so when they come at the time of high tides. The famous Galveston, Texas, hurricane of September 8, 1900, took the lives of over 6,000 people. Many of them were drowned by great waves.

When winds of over two hundred kilometers per hour strike, trees may be blown over and houses destroyed. Such winds occur often in hurricanes and other tropical storms.

All tropical storms originate on the western sides of the oceans in the doldrums. They are most likely to develop when the doldrums are farthest north or south of the Equator.

After forming in the doldrums, these storms move westward and away from the Equator. They go through the tradewind belts at a slow, drifting pace of from 10 to 20 kilometers per hour. Still moving slowly, they pass through the horse latitudes and into the belt of prevailing westerlies. Here they speed up and turn eastward. But as their rate of movement increases, their wind speeds usually decrease. Eventually they "blow themselves out" at sea and vanish.

Hurricanes that form near the West Indies are most frequent in late summer and early fall. Many of them strike Florida and the southeastern United States before heading out to the Atlantic Ocean on the normal hurricane track.

Around the world, tropical storms are called by different names. They come at different times of the year in different places.

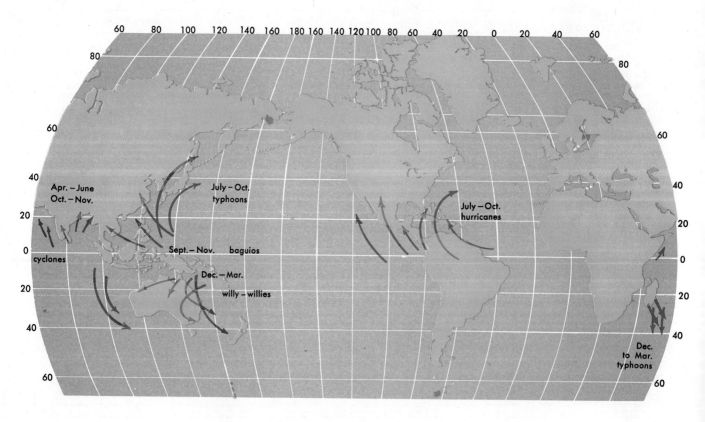

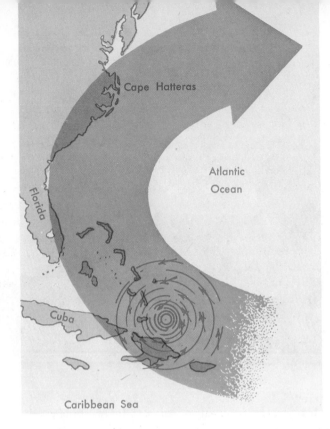

The normal track of a West Indian hurricane takes it out to sea at Cape Hatteras, North Carolina, as shown here. The most destructive storms, however, are those that leave the normal track and strike inland.

7. Hurricanes in the Northeast

Occasionally a hurricane in the North Atlantic fails to follow the "normal track" which takes it out to the Atlantic Ocean at Cape Hatteras, North Carolina. Instead, it continues northward along the coast and into the interior. It sometimes goes as far north as New England and southern Canada. Such a storm becomes greatly changed as it travels through the prevailing westerlies. But it may still be far more violent than any ordinary middle-latitude low.

In 1960 Hurricane Donna struck Florida and the Atlantic Coast as far north as the Gulf of St. Lawrence. It destroyed more than one billion dollars worth of property.

8. Naming and Forecasting Hurricanes

The practice of identifying hurricanes by giving them feminine names began in 1953. In 1960 the United States Weather Bureau introduced the use of four lists of names. Each list is alphabetical. One list is used

Today the origin and track of tropical storms all over the world can be followed in satellite photographs (right) or on radar (below).

each year and the entire set is to be used over again at the end of a four-year cycle. Some persons object to the use of feminine names. They point out that the identification of violent storms with women's names is unfair to both men and women.

Early hurricane forecasts are important in protecting life and property. Close watch is kept on each hurricane as it grows and moves. *Weather reconnaissance planes* fly around hurricanes to observe them. *Weather detection radar equipment* can determine the location of rain areas in storms within its range. *Weather satellites* discover storms by transmitting television pictures of the atmosphere to stations at the earth's surface.

Tornadoes and Thunderstorms Described

Tornadoes 9.

Tornadoes (twisters) are the smallest, briefest, and most violent of all storms. They are much more frequent in the United States than anywhere else. Most U.S. tornadoes occur in the Mississippi Valley and the eastern half of the Great Plains.

Tornadoes are narrow, funnel-shaped, spiral whirls. Their diameters average less than half a kilometer. Their paths are twisting and unpredictable. They usually travel at rates of from 40 to 65 kilometers an hour. They pass any point in a few seconds with a thunderous roar. Their life spans are measured in hours. Their paths of destruction are usually less than 25 kilometers long.

A Nebraska tornado comes across the plains bringing death and destruction. This one took six lives and caused great property losses over a 50 kilometer path.

The air pressure of a tornado may be one-third lower than normal atmospheric pressure. Its wind speeds may reach 800 kilometers per hour.

Air rushing into the low-pressure funnel of a tornado cools by expansion. A dense water cloud forms that is blackened by the dust and debris that blow into it. The tornado cloud hangs low from the thundercloud with which it always comes. Every now and then it dips onto the ground with destructive effects. Lightning and thunder, hail, and heavy rains from the thundercloud almost always accompany the tornado.

When a tornado passes over a body of water, it causes one kind of *waterspout*.

10. Tornadoes: Origin, Warnings, Frequency

What atmospheric conditions bring about the formation of tornadoes? Warm, moist air from the Gulf of Mexico moves northward into the Mississippi Valley and Great Plains. It reaches upward into the atmosphere about three kilometers. At the same time cool, dry air moves eastward over the Rocky Mountains. It rides over the air from the Gulf. Then the cold air sinks under the warm air and causes it to rise. A line of thunderstorms—a squall line—is likely to form. Tornadoes may be born with the thunderstorms.

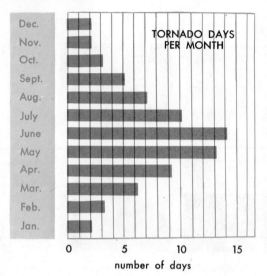

TORNADO DAYS PER MONTH

Dec.
Nov.
Oct.
Sept.
Aug.
July
June
May
Apr.
Mar.
Feb.
Jan.

0   5   10   15

number of days

Tornado experts work in the United States National Severe Storms Forecast Center at Kansas City, Missouri. They issue a **tornado watch** or **tornado warning** whenever necessary. Tornado watches and warnings are broadcast by radio and television.

A tornado watch gives the area covered by the watch. It also gives the period in which tornado probabilities will be dangerously high.

A tornado warning is issued when a tornado has actually been sighted in an area or has been detected by radar. It gives the location of the tornado when detected, the area in which it is likely to move, and the period of time during which it is expected to move.

Tornadoes are most frequent during spring and early summer. They are most likely to occur in the late afternoon. Tornadoes in the United States have killed an average of about 120 persons yearly since 1953.

The chart, which covers the whole United States for a typical year, shows that tornadoes occur most often in the spring and summer. Note, however, that tornadoes also occur throughout the year.

Where Thunderstorms Form

Thunderstorms are small-area storms formed by the strong upward movement of warm, moist air. It is estimated that 44,000 thunderstorms occur every day across the surface of the earth.

Thunderstorms are usually classified into two types according to their origin. **Air-mass thunderstorms** occur within an air mass. Warm, moist air is heated strongly at the earth's surface and powerful convection currents are developed. These thunderstorms are usually widely scattered. They may form over either land or water. They are most likely to occur in summer—over land by day, and over water by night. Air-mass thunderstorms may also develop on the *windward side of a mountain range.* Such storms are common in the northern Rockies when winds from the Pacific blow eastward over the mountains.

Frontal thunderstorms occur when warm, moist air is forced to rise at frontal surfaces. They too are most likely to occur in summer. However, they may occur in any season. In warm fronts, with their gentle slopes, thunderstorms are usually few. In steep cold fronts, on the other hand, a line of thunderstorms may stretch several hundred kilometers.

Lightning and Thunder

12. Electricity in the Thunderstorm

A thunderstorm is also, of course, a lightning storm. **Lightning** is the discharge of electricity from the thundercloud to the ground or to another cloud.

The temperature inside the channel of a lightning flash is believed to reach about 28,000°C. At this high temperature, the air expands almost explosively. This is how it produces the tremendous sound wave we call **thunder.** Light travels at a speed of 300,000 kilometers per second, so lightning is seen almost instantly. But the sound waves from lightning take about three seconds to travel a kilometer in the lower air.

If the lightning stroke covers a long distance, sound waves arrive for several seconds, and the thunder rumbles. Rumbling also happens when thunder echoes from mountainsides. The greatest distance at which it is ordinarily possible for thunder to be heard is about 16 kilometers.

Heat lightning is the glow of a distant lightning flash so far off that its thunder cannot be heard.

13. Lightning Danger and Protection

Lightning is beautiful, but it can be very dangerous. Every year lightning in the United States causes thousands of forest fires and electrocutes about 200 people.

When lightning strikes, it is likely to go from the cloud base to the nearest point projecting from the ground. Hence, it often strikes tall objects such as trees, church steeples, and the tops of skyscrapers. Benjamin Franklin's invention of the **lightning rod** was based on this fact. The lightning rod projects above the house roof. It is connected to the ground by a good conductor. When lightning strikes the rod, the electricity is conducted harmlessly to the ground. Otherwise it might strike some part of the house and set the house on fire.

Where should one take shelter in a lightning storm? The best shelter is a house. If you are driving and visibility is poor, pull off the road, but stay in the car. It, too, will protect you from lightning. Bathers and boaters should seek shelter as soon as a storm threatens. A tree or group of trees in an open field should be avoided. They "attract" lightning. It is better to stay in the open and get wet than to take refuge under a tree.

Spectacular lightning displays can accompany thunderstorms.

Weather in a High 14.

Highs, or *anticyclones,* usually appear on weather maps as a series of smooth circular isobars. Unlike a low, *a high represents a single air mass.* Its diameter may be more than 1500 kilometers. Since the air pressure is highest at its center, the winds of a high blow outward. It forms a whirl that is clockwise in the Northern Hemisphere and counterclockwise in the Southern Hemisphere. Isobars are generally farther apart than in lows, so winds are weaker.

Bright, clear weather is usually present throughout a high. Sinking dry air at the high center explains its fair weather. Heavy dew, frost, and radiation fogs may form at night in its quiet lower air. Occasionally rain, drizzle, and cloudy skies develop in the southwestern and western sectors of highs.

Making the Weather Map 15.

Weather map data are gathered in about 600 official Weather Service stations in the United States. Reports are also received from countries in all parts of the Northern Hemisphere and from ships at sea. **Weather maps** are prepared at the United States National Weather Service every three hours, starting with 1 A.M.

Observations are also transmitted immediately by teletype, telegraph, telephone, or radio to other forecast centers. There, weather maps can be drawn up and local forecasts made.

Official maps and general forecasts for the United States are drawn up at the National Meteorological Center at Suitland, Maryland (near Washington, D.C.). They are sent by wire to all forecast centers, and by radio to ships at sea. Only the map showing 7 A.M. weather is distributed in printed form. Maps for other times may be printed in simplified form in newspapers.

The Station Model 16.

About 20 different weather observations may be plotted next to each station on the weather map. The Weather Service arranges this information around the station in a form called the **station model.** Where possible, direct readings are given. In all other cases codes are used. Both station model and codes are based on those of the World Meteorological Organization. They can be read by meteorologists of any country. So can the coded information sent by wire or radio.

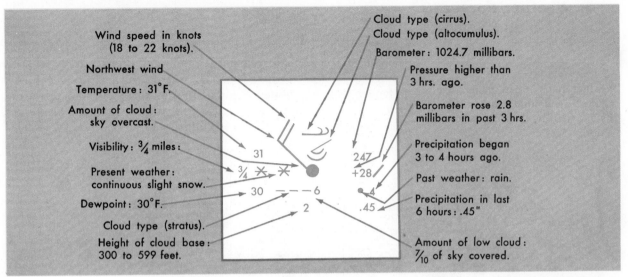

Wind speed in knots (18 to 22 knots).

Northwest wind

Temperature: 31° F.

Amount of cloud: sky overcast.

Visibility: ¾ miles:

Present weather: continuous slight snow.

Dewpoint: 30° F.

Cloud type (stratus).

Height of cloud base: 300 to 599 feet.

Cloud type (cirrus).

Cloud type (altocumulus).

Barometer: 1024.7 millibars.

Pressure higher than 3 hrs. ago.

Barometer rose 2.8 millibars in past 3 hrs.

Precipitation began 3 to 4 hours ago.

Past weather: rain.

Precipitation in last 6 hours: .45"

Amount of low cloud: 7/10 of sky covered.

A weather-map maker receives coded data from stations across the United States. The data often come as strings of numbers and letters. He or she translates this code into information on wind speed, temperature, cloud cover, and so forth. Then it is recoded into the standard form shown in the diagram and placed on the map.

A simplified weather map can tell you a lot if you know the code. It's partly cloudy in New Orleans, but the visibility is 10 miles. The temperature is 75° F; the dew point is 70° F. The wind is from the south. Its speed is 8 to 12 knots.

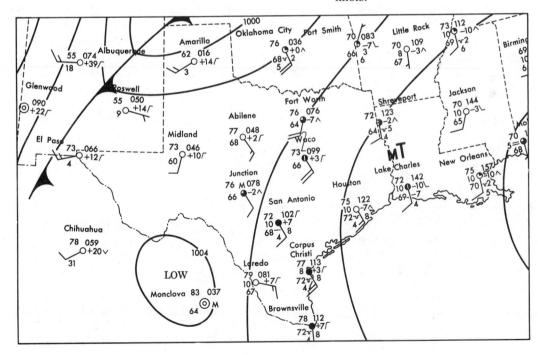

Weather maps in newspapers use a simpler code that is based on the one used by the U.S. National Weather Service.

Forecasters at each forecasting center may prepare daily weather forecasts for their own regions. These are forecasts for 36 hours in advance. They are issued at about 10 A.M. through radio, television, telephone, and the press. If necessary, they are revised at about 5 P.M., 11 P.M., and 5 A.M. the next day.

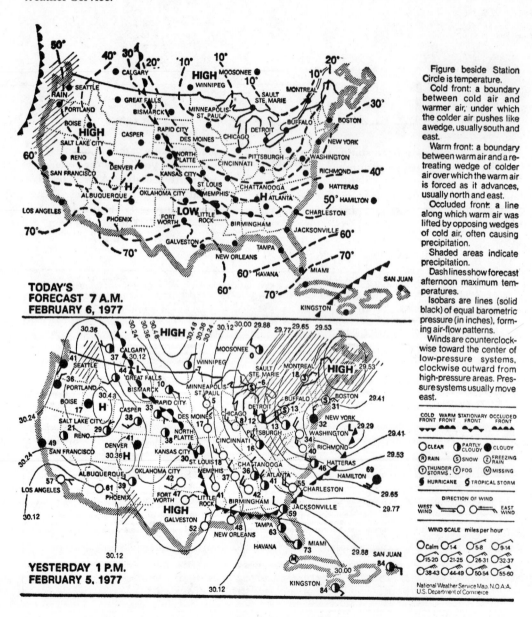

TODAY'S FORECAST 7 A.M. FEBRUARY 6, 1977

YESTERDAY 1 P.M. FEBRUARY 5, 1977

Figure beside Station Circle is temperature.

Cold front: a boundary between cold air and warmer air, under which the colder air pushes like a wedge, usually south and east.

Warm front: a boundary between warm air and a retreating wedge of colder air over which the warm air is forced as it advances, usually north and east.

Occluded front: a line along which warm air was lifted by opposing wedges of cold air, often causing precipitation.

Shaded areas indicate precipitation.

Dash lines show forecast afternoon maximum temperatures.

Isobars are lines (solid black) of equal barometric pressure (in inches), forming air-flow patterns.

Winds are counterclockwise toward the center of low-pressure systems, clockwise outward from high-pressure areas. Pressure systems usually move east.

National Weather Service Map. N.O.A.A.
U.S. Department of Commerce

The Weather Service's Extended Forecast Branch prepares "forecasts and outlooks" for intervals of from 5 to 30 days. A weekly weather and crop bulletin, and a daily Mississippi River stages and forecast bulletin are published throughout the year. All of these are available by subscription.

The National Severe Storms Forecast Center in Kansas City, Missouri, prepares special forecasts of severe thunderstorms and tornadoes. The Hurricane Warning Service in Miami, Florida, coordinates all services relating to hurricanes. Other services include the River and Flood Forecasting Service, the Fire-Weather Warning Service, the Fruit-Frost Service, the Marine Meteorological Service, and Aviation Forecasts.

All of the Armed Forces have their own weather services.

18. Modern Weather Forecasting

Before World War I the daily weather map showed the weather at the earth's surface only. Very little was known about the upper atmosphere. Weather forecasts were based almost entirely on surface observations. Forecasts were made by individual "experts," and little use was made of mathematics.

Today's weather forecasts are made by teams of forecast specialists. Mathematical formulas and computers are used. Upper air data are obtained by modern equipment such as the radiosonde, radar, weather balloons, and weather satellites. Together with surface data, the upper air data give a three-dimensional picture of the atmosphere. From these, highly accurate forecasts can be made.

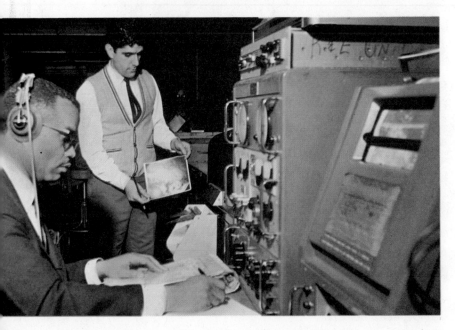

While modern meteorologists use data from all over the world and have access to computer forecasts, most of them also look at the sky just before they make a prediction.

The lower panel shows satellite photos of storm clouds reaching from north of Japan to eastern United States. The upper picture is a weather map of the same area, with the clouds sketched in.

How is radar used in weather observation? Radar waves are reflected as *radar echoes* from the water droplets and ice crystals in clouds, rain, and other forms of precipitation. Radar echoes form images like television pictures on the radarscope. These images show the surfaces from which they are reflected. Thus "pictures" may be seen of

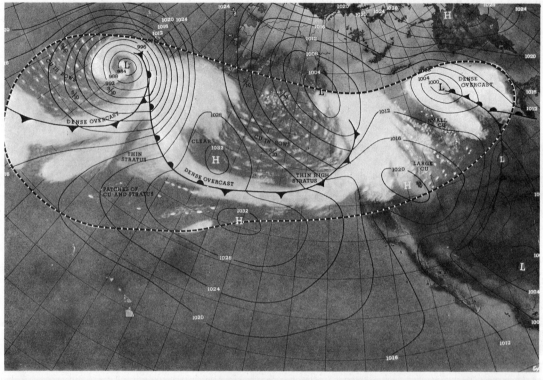

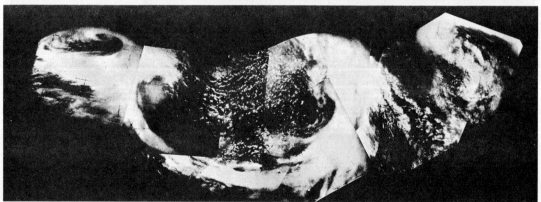

thunderstorms, hurricanes, and other areas of heavy precipitation. Ground-based radar can detect and track such storms within a radius of about 300 kilometers. U.S. Navy "hurricane hunter" planes also use radar in their search for hurricanes.

Radar echoes are sometimes useful in measuring the rate of rainfall and in distinguishing between snow and rain or between ice clouds and water clouds.

Weather satellites revolve around the earth in nearly circular orbits every 100 minutes at an altitude of about 720 kilometers. Two television cameras take pictures of the earth on command from the earth during each daytime orbit. They store the pictures on magnetic tape, and then transmit them automatically or on command to ground "readout" stations. A cloud map is made from these pictures. It provides valuable information about the location and origin of storms, especially in ocean areas not easily observed.

Each topic question refers to the topic of the same number within this chapter.

1. **(a)** Explain how waves on the polar front are related to warm fronts and cold fronts. **(b)** What is a "low"? **(c)** What is an occluded front? How does it form?

2. **(a)** What weather changes take place as a middle-latitudes low passes a station? **(b)** Describe the direction of its winds in each hemisphere. **(c)** What kind of weather does the passage of an occluded front bring?

3. **(a)** Explain how condensation provides a low with energy. **(b)** What is the effect of this energy on the low?

4. **(a)** Where do our lows originate? **(b)** Where do they move to? **(c)** How fast do they move? **(d)** How large are they?

5. **(a)** How do tropical storms resemble lows in middle latitudes? **(b)** How do tropical storms differ from lows in middle latitudes? **(c)** What is the "eye of the storm"?

6. **(a)** Where do tropical storms originate? **(b)** What general path do they follow? At what speeds do these storms travel? **(c)** When are hurricanes most likely to reach the United States? Why?

7. What paths are followed by hurricanes that go north of the regular track?

8. Describe the "forecasting" of hurricanes by the United States National Weather Service.

9. **(a)** Where do tornadoes occur? **(b)** Describe the appearance and weather elements of a tornado.

10. **(a)** Describe the atmospheric conditions that favor the formation of tornadoes. **(b)** Who issues tornado watches and tornado warnings? How do these differ? **(c)** When do most tornadoes occur in the United States?

11. Explain the difference in origin between air-mass thunderstorms and frontal thunderstorms.

12. (a) What is lightning? (b) How is thunder explained? (c) How can the distance to a lightning flash be calculated? (d) What causes thunder to rumble? (e) What is heat lightning?

13. (a) How does a lightning rod protect a building from lightning? (b) Where should shelter be sought during a lightning storm?

14. (a) Describe the direction and strength of winds in a high. (b) What kind of weather does a high have? Why?

15. Describe the making and distribution of the daily weather map.

16. What is the station model? List 10 weather items it shows.

17. (a) Where is the daily weather forecast prepared? How is it publicized? (Where are tornadoes forecast? hurricanes?)

18. Compare modern weather observations and forecasting with that done before World War I.

19. (a) How does radar "observe" the weather? (b) How do weather satellites provide useful weather information?

GENERAL QUESTIONS

1. What is the meaning, in terms of air masses, of the fact that hurricanes have no fronts?

2. What accounts for the heavy precipitation in tropical cyclones?

3. How does a tornado pluck a chicken's feathers?

4. If thunder is heard 12 seconds after lightning is seen, how far away is the storm?

5. Why should heavy frosts, dew, and fogs be associated with highs?

6. In what kind of air mass are air-mass thunderstorms most likely to develop? Why?

STUDENT ACTIVITIES

Form a school weather bureau. Build a shelter for the maximum and minimum thermometers and a psychrometer. Set up a standard rain gauge, an anemometer, and a wind vane. Make daily observations of temperature, air pressure, relative humidity, wind direction, wind speed, state of sky, types of clouds, and any precipitation. Record your observations daily on prepared mimeographed forms and post them on school bulletin boards.

31

HOW DO YOU KNOW THAT...?

If two places have the same average yearly temperature, are their climates the same? The first illustration in this chapter is a graph showing the average temperature for each month of the year in Peking, China, and Valdivia, Chile. Which month is warmest in Peking? What is its average temperature? Which month is coldest? What is its average temperature? How much is the range of temperature for Peking? Which month is warmest in Valdivia? What is its average temperature? Which month is coldest? What is its average temperature? How much is its temperature range? Why does Peking have its warmest weather when Valdivia is having its coldest weather and vice versa? Why are their temperature ranges so different? (See Topics 6, 7.)

Factors that Control Climate

Climate and Temperature Controls

Average Temperature;
Temperature Range 1.

Average temperatures are obtained, like any averages, by adding together two or more observations. The sum is then divided by the number of observations. The **average daily temperature** is usually obtained by averaging the highest and lowest temperatures of a day. (For example, a day with a high of 30°C and a low of 20°C has an average of 25°C.) The **average monthly temperature** is the average of all the daily averages of the month. The **average yearly temperature** is usually obtained by averaging the twelve monthly averages.

The **daily temperature range** is the difference between the highest and lowest temperatures of the day. The **yearly temperature range** is the difference between the average of the warmest month and that of the coldest month.

Is Climate
Average Weather? 2.

Valdivia and Peking have the same average yearly temperature.

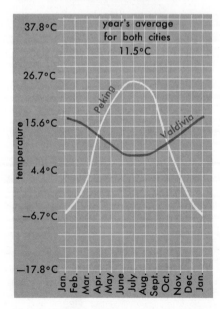

We might define climate simply by calling it "average weather." It is true that the climate of a region is made up of its temperature, moisture, winds, storms, cloudiness, and other weather elements. But averages alone may give a misleading picture of a place's climate. Let us look at two examples that illustrate this point.

Peking, China, and Valdivia, Chile, have almost identical yearly average temperatures of 12°C. But a year in Peking includes an icy January averaging −4°C and a hot July averaging 26°C. Compare this with Valdivia's mild 8°C and 17°C averages for its coldest and warmest months. In Peking the annual range in temperature is 30°C. In Valdivia it is only 9°C. Certainly their climates are not the same. Similar contrasts exist in the United States between east-coast and west-coast cities, such as New York City and Portland, Oregon.

Now take a second example. Bombay, India, has a yearly rainfall of about 188 centimeters. Mobile, Alabama, has almost as much rain, about 173 centimeters. But almost all of Bombay's rain falls in a monsoon season of four summer months. In Mobile, the rain is spread through the year. No month averages less than 7.6 centimeters of rain.

In these illustrations climate is not the same as average weather. No climate can be described accurately without going into details.

3. Climatic Controls

The two main features of a place's climate are its temperature and its rainfall. These depend on a whole set of conditions called **climatic controls.** The main climatic controls are:

1. latitude
2. altitude
3. prevailing winds
4. topography
5. distance from the sea or large lakes
6. nearby ocean currents.

In this chapter you will see how climatic controls work.

4. How Latitude Controls Temperature

The latitude of a place is its distance in degrees from the Equator. The average yearly temperature of a place depends mainly on its latitude. So do its daily and yearly temperature ranges. Let us take a few illustrations.

Suppose you live within 5 degrees or 10 degrees of the Equator. This might be Panama or the Congo or northern Brazil. Every day of the year the sun shines for about 12 hours. Every night is about 12 hours long. At noon the sun is never very far from vertical. The climate is hot all year. The average temperature is very high, perhaps about 27°C. There are no "summers and winters." There are only rainy seasons and dry seasons. The yearly range of temperature is only 3 or 4 degrees. Afternoons are very hot. But the rather long 12-hour nights are cool by contrast. The daily temperature range is large enough to make nighttime "the winter of the tropics."

Now move to a middle latitude—40 degrees or 45 degrees from the Equator. This might be Chicago or New York City or Montreal. In July you enjoy 15 or 16 hours of strong sunshine daily. Nights are only 8 or 9 hours long. But six months later a weak sun shines only 8 or 9 hours a day. For 15 or 16 hours each night no heat is received. On the average, the yearly temperature is far lower than near the Equator. The annual range of temperature is very large. It may be as much as 30°C.

Now move to the polar regions—to Greenland or Baffinland or Antarctica. Here most of the sunshine comes in a "day" that lasts for many months. The winter includes an equally long night. In summer the weak sun is never high in the sky. It goes completely *around* the sky each day but does not dip below the horizon. Temperatures hardly change for days at a time. The summer is comparatively mild. But when the long winter night comes, the weather turns fearfully cold. In these high latitudes, then, the average annual temperature is very low. The annual temperature range is very large, but the daily temperature range is very small.

Summarizing the relationship between latitude and temperature: *the higher the latitude, the lower the average yearly temperature and the larger the yearly temperature range.*

Altitude and Temperature 5.

Altitude is height above sea level. Its effect on temperature is somewhat like that of latitude. On the average, temperatures drop about 1°C for every 160 meters of altitude. *The higher the altitude, the lower the average yearly temperature.*

Here is an example. Vera Cruz and Mexico City have the same latitude but very different climates. Vera Cruz, at sea level in the tropics, is hot and humid. Mexico City, 2300 meters above sea level, is pleasantly cool even in summer.

Land, Sea, and Temperature 6.

Westerlies bring a marine climate to the west coast. In the interior and most of the east coast, the climate is continental.

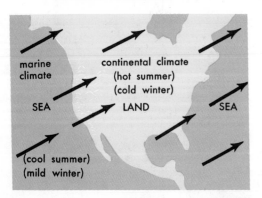

Land gains and loses heat much more quickly than water. Land areas tend to have hot summers and cold winters. Sea areas have cooler summers and milder winters. Small islands have climates like those of their surrounding waters. These climates are known as **marine climates.**

The interiors of continents, on the other hand, have greater extremes of temperature. This is especially so in middle latitudes. They are said to have **continental climates.** Reykjavik, Iceland, 64°N, and Verkhoyansk, Siberia, 68°N, are in nearly the same latitude. Reykjavik is on the south coast of Iceland. Its marine climate has an annual temperature range of only 11°C. Verkhoyansk is deep in the interior of the great Asian land mass. It has a continental climate with an annual range of almost 67°C.

Summarizing, *ocean areas have marine climates with a small yearly temperature range. Continental interiors have continental climates with a large yearly temperature range.*

Only small islands can have true marine climates. But many coastal areas have what is known as a *marine west-coast climate*. This near-marine climate is found in middle latitudes. The prevailing westerlies blow over these latitudes. When they come from the ocean, they carry maritime air masses onto the *west coasts* of continents and large islands. Air masses from the Pacific Ocean are carried over the west coasts of North America, South America, and New Zealand. Air masses from the Atlantic Ocean are carried over the west coasts of the British Isles and Europe. Portland, Oregon and London, England have marine west-coast climates.

How far inland does a marine west-coast climate reach? It depends chiefly on the topography. Usually it goes no farther than the first high mountain range. Beyond the mountains, continental interiors have continental climates.

East coasts in middle latitudes do not have marine climates. Most of the air masses that come to east coasts are brought by the prevailing westerlies. That means that they come from the interiors of the continents. As a result, east coasts have continental climates. Boston and New York, for example, are on the Atlantic coast. Nevertheless, their summers and winters are nearly as extreme as the interior's.

To sum up: In the belts of prevailing westerlies, west coasts have marine climates with cool summers and mild winters. East coasts have continental climates with hot summers and cold winters.

Mountain ranges may keep out winds that could affect an area's temperature. For example, the marine climate of the western United States reaches no farther inland than the Coast Ranges. The Sacramento Valley of California lies just east of the Coast Ranges. It is not far from the Pacific Ocean. Nevertheless, it has intensely hot summers and cold winters.

Southern Italy has a mild climate. This is partly because the Alps keep out cold winds from the north. On the Great Plains of Canada and the United States we see just the opposite. The Plains have no mountain range running across them to stop winds from the north. In winter cold waves, icy winds from the Arctic may come all the way to the Gulf of Mexico.

Ocean Currents and Temperature

Ocean currents may be considerably warmer or colder than the normal for their latitudes. When they are, they have a great effect on the places they pass. Their effect is greatest when the prevailing winds blow from them to the land. In one famous example, the prevailing westerlies blow from the warm Gulf Stream to the shores of Iceland, the British Isles, and Scandinavia. They make these regions as warm as places many hundreds of miles closer to the Equator. London, England, is about 1100 kilometers nearer the North Pole than Cleveland, Ohio. Nevertheless, its average annual temperature is higher than Cleveland's.

Cold currents also affect the temperature. Northern Labrador is chilled by the Labrador Current. Its yearly average temperature is more than 11°C lower than that of Stockholm, Sweden, in the same latitude! (See the isothermal maps of the world in Chapter 24 for many more illustrations of the effects of ocean currents on temperature.)

Current meters stand on the deck of a Woods Hole research ship.

Factors that Control Rainfall

Latitude and Rainfall 10.

The climate of a place includes its total yearly rainfall. The climate also includes the seasonal spread of the rainfall. Both of these are affected by a place's latitude. Latitude determines what wind belts the place is in. The doldrums, for example, are very rainy belts. The horse latitudes are dry belts. The trade wind belts are dry except where the winds climb high mountains. The westerlies have variable rainfall patterns.

Places located between the doldrums and the horse latitudes are likely to have both wet and dry seasons. This is because of the shifting of the wind belts. The nearer the places are to the Equator, the longer the wet seasons. The nearer they are to the horse latitudes, the longer the dry seasons.

Rising air makes the windward sides of high mountains rainy. Sinking air makes the leeward sides dry. In the trade wind belts, the rainy windward sides are as follows:

    Northern Hemisphere: northern slopes, eastern slopes
    Southern Hemisphere: southern slopes, eastern slopes
    Himalaya Mountains: southern slopes, western slopes

In the prevailing westerlies, the rainy windward sides of mountains are:

    Northern Hemisphere: southern slopes, western slopes
    Southern Hemisphere: northern slopes, western slopes

Eastern slopes, in general, will be very dry. So will the lands extending eastward from them. The heaviest rains of the United States fall on the western slopes of the Coast and Cascade ranges in Washington and Oregon. The least rain falls in the Great American Desert of the Southwest, east of the Sierra Nevada Mountains.

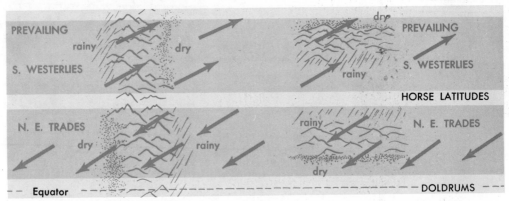

Winds going down the leeward slopes of mountains are heated by compression. They warm up at the rate of about 1°C per 100 meters. A drop of 2000 meters will raise the temperature about 20°C. Warm dry winds formed in this way often blow down the eastern slopes of the Rockies. In Europe, similar winds blow down the northern slopes of the Swiss Alps. These "snow-eating" winds are called **chinooks** in the Rockies. In Europe they are called *foehns* (FERNS).

When chinooks arrive suddenly, they can raise the temperature 20°C in 15 minutes. They make winters milder and springs earlier. They clear pastures for cattle grazing and fields for planting. But they may also cause snow to avalanche. And if they blow too long, houses and fields get dry as tinder. Then, a careful guard must be kept against fire.

Windward sides of mountains are rainy. Leeward sides are dry. Which side this is—north, south, east or west—depends on both the wind direction and the mountain position.

Nearness to the sea is no guarantee of rainfall. The great desert of Peru, for example, is alongside the Pacific Ocean. Even so, it is one of the driest places in the world. There are two reasons for this. First, its southeast trade winds come from the dry interior. Second, it is on the leeward (western) side of the great Andes Mountains.

Where winds do blow from the sea, rains are likely to be heaviest nearest the ocean. They are also usually heavier near warmer parts of the oceans. In the eastern United States, total yearly rainfall is greatest along the coast. Rainfall gets less inland and northward.

Continental interiors are likely to have more precipitation in summer than in winter. One reason is that warm summer winds can carry more moisture. A second reason is that thundershowers happen more often in summer.

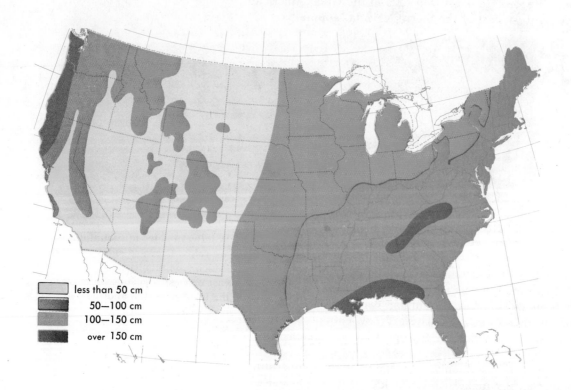

less than 50 cm
50—100 cm
100—150 cm
over 150 cm

The map shows annual rainfall. In the Far West, rainfall is controlled mainly by mountain ranges. Eastward from there, rainfall increases as you get closer to the Atlantic Ocean and the Gulf of Mexico. But note also the effect of the Appalachian Mountains.

Ocean currents make heavy fogs along coastal areas. The frequent winter fogs of England and Scotland are one example. These form when warm moist air from the Gulf Stream blows over the cold land.

The summer fogs of the New England coast are another example. They form when warm south winds are cooled over New England's cold coastal waters. The fogs of Newfoundland form when warm Gulf Stream air blows over the icy Labrador Current. The summer fogs of the Pacific coasts of the United States, Peru, and northern Chile are also examples. They form when warm ocean winds blow over cold upwelling coastal waters.

In general, fogs will form where ocean currents are much warmer or much colder than the adjoining land or water.

Each topic question refers to the topic of the same number within this chapter.

TOPIC QUESTIONS

1. (a) Explain how a city's average daily temperature, average monthly temperature, and average yearly temperature are calculated. (b) Define daily temperature range. (c) Define yearly temperature range.

2. (a) Show that two cities may have the same average temperatures but very different climates. (b) Show that two cities may have nearly the same yearly rainfall but very different climates.

3. Name six important climatic controls.

4. Explain the relationship between a place's latitude and its average yearly temperature, its yearly range in temperature, and its daily range in temperature. Give examples.

5. How does altitude affect temperature? Give examples.

6. How do marine climates differ from continental ones in temperature? Why?

7. (a) How do prevailing winds determine whether a climate is marine or continental? (b) How do the climates of the east and west coasts of the United States differ in temperature?

8. How may topography affect temperature? Give examples.

9. Give examples to show the temperature effects of the Gulf Stream and the Labrador Current.

10. (a) How does latitude determine a place's rainfall? (b) Why do some places have rains throughout the year? (c) Why are some places dry all year? (d) Why do some places have wet and dry seasons?

11. **(a)** Which are the rainy sides of mountains in the trade-wind belts? in the westerlies? (Use compass directions.) **(b)** Which are the dry sides? (Use compass directions.) **(c)** What are chinook winds? Describe their effects.

12. **(a)** Why is closeness to the sea no guarantee of rain? **(b)** How is closeness to the sea usually related to rainfall? **(c)** Why do interiors usually have more rain in summer than in winter?

13. What is the principal moisture effect of ocean currents? Illustrate.

GENERAL QUESTIONS

1. Why is the daily temperature range likely to be greater in mountain regions than at sea level?

2. How does the climate of an equatorial mountain differ from that of a mountain in middle latitudes?

3. In the doldrums belt temperature ranges are small in the interior as well as in coastal areas. Why is the effect of land or sea less important here than in higher latitudes?

4. Why does the Gulf Stream have little effect on the temperatures of the eastern United States? Why does the Labrador Current have so great an effect on the temperatures of Labrador?

5. Why should the rains of the western slopes of the Coast and Cascade ranges be so much heavier than those of the Rocky and Appalachian mountains?

6. Why does the chinook become much warmer as it blows down mountain slopes? (Look up the moist-adiabatic lapse rate in Chapter 27, Topic 17.)

32

HOW DO YOU KNOW THAT... ?

1. Look through recent issues of your local newspaper for stories related to pollution of air, soil, rivers, lakes, or the ocean. Cut out the stories and use them to start a scrapbook on people's effects on the environment. Make a list of the pollutants mentioned in each case. Include ways suggested in the stories to fix the problem.

2. Try the following method for collecting some of the dust blown about in your local air. Get a roll of masking tape at least 5 centimeters wide. Fasten a strip of this tape—sticky side out—completely around the outside of a jar or can. Leave the tape outdoors in the air and wind for about a week. It works best on a pole or other support above the ground and away from building walls.

   At the end of the week take off the tape and study it. From which direction did most dust come? Why? Examine the tape with a hand magnifier or low-power microscope. Can you recognize any of the dust particles? Are most of the particles about the same size? Why?

A Matter of Ecology

Ecology and Ecosystems 1.

Ecology is an old word with a new-found fame. It is the "relationship between organisms and their environment." The ecologist speaks of ecosystems. An **ecosystem** is any "unit consisting of all the living organisms in a given area interacting with the physical environment." A lake, the human and animal population surrounding it, and all the organisms in its waters make up an ecosystem. And each one of us is part of a "local ecosystem" consisting of his or her own community and its environment.

The interaction of a "community" of living things with its environment may be good for the living things. Animals need plants to live—for food and oxygen. And the plants may use animals for transport of seeds, or they may grow better because of animal wastes. In a balanced aquarium, for example, the fish, the snails, and the water plants thrive in their water environment. The plants would not do so well alone, neither would the fish or snails.

Now and in the past, one living thing may harm the environment for others. People have sometimes harmed the life-giving resources of this planet. More recently, however, this has happened more often. The chemical industry has expanded. Cities have grown larger and more numerous. The use of automobiles has increased many times. Some of this growth has caused serious damage to our air, our waters, and our soil. Let us see what some of this damage is.

Look at the litter washed up on this shore.

Parts of the Hydrosphere 2.

The **hydrosphere** is defined as the water part of the earth. There are four "parts" of the hydrosphere—ground water, running water, lakes, and oceans. They are all connected by what we call the *water cycle*. Some of the ground water seeps into streams and rivers and lakes. Streams and rivers drain into lakes, inland seas, and the ocean.

It is possible that pollutants entering the ground water will reach rivers and lakes. Pollutants entering rivers will reach lakes and seas. They also seep into ground water in regions where the water table is low. And pollutants may also be dumped directly into lakes and the ocean.

Which pollutants can find their way into the waters of the hydrosphere? Untreated or poorly treated sewage may be discharged by city sewage systems into rivers, lakes, and the sea. Sewage from inefficient cesspools may drain into the ground and enter the ground water. Insecticides, pesticides, and fertilizers may be washed by rains from the soils and plants on which they were used.

Poisonous wastes from industrial plants may be dumped into rivers, lakes, and the sea. Water may be taken from rivers and lakes for cooling processes in industrial plants. This water is often returned to its source at a higher temperature, changing the local ecosystem.

Oil pours into the sea when tankers run aground or offshore oil wells leak. Waste oil is sometimes deliberately dumped from ships at sea.

Radioactive wastes may come from uranium mining and milling, from nuclear plants, and from the testing of nuclear weapons.

Some of the poisons that pour into rivers and lakes—and even the oceans—become concentrated in fish in percentages that make the fish unfit to eat. They may kill waterfowl that feed upon the fish. These poisons include insecticides, lead, mercury, and by-products of industry. Insecticides have been responsible for fish kills in rivers.

Mercury, for example, has been concentrated in some swordfish and tuna. The concentration takes place through a "food chain." The chain begins when bacteria change metallic mercury into methyl mercury. This substance is absorbed by the tiny sea plants and animals called plankton. Small fish feed on the plankton. The small fish are eaten by larger fish such as tuna and swordfish. At each link of the chain, mercury is concentrated more. A person who eats tuna or swordfish almost every day can concentrate the mercury further.

Harmful germs from sewage may contaminate shellfish beds and cause such diseases as typhoid and hepatitis. Sewage has caused the closing of beach resorts because of fears that swimmers might develop diseases.

Sewage may also contain quantities of laundry detergents. Some detergents, especially the phosphate detergents, are not "biodegradable." This means that they are not broken down by bacteria into harmless simpler substances. In communities where sewage goes into cesspools, phosphates may seep into the wells. It can then reappear in the kitchen as foam in the drinking water.

Thermal pollution is heating caused by hot water wastes. It can kill fish in two ways. It makes the river or lake water too warm for them. It drives oxygen out of the water.

Oil spills may foul beaches. The oil is poisonous to some living things; it clogs the breathing passages of others; and it gets on birds' feathers, preventing them from swimming or flying.

High school students are cleaning up the beach and saving birds threatened by an oil spill.

Eutrophication: How a Lake Dies 5.

In relation to geological time spans, a lake is a "temporary" feature of the landscape. Streams carry sediments into a lake and make it shallower. Plants grow in the shallow waters and creep in on the lake. The lake gets smaller. Eventually it becomes a swamp. This destruction of a lake is called **eutrophication** (YOU truh fi KAY shun).

When eutrophication happens naturally, it is a fairly slow process. In a fairly large lake, it might take thousands of years. But when such a lake becomes polluted, it can be destroyed in dozens of years.

How do pollutants speed up eutrophication? The pollutants that do this are not poisons. They are chemicals that act as plant fertilizers. They allow algae (simple water weeds) to grow like wildfire. In warm weather, mats of foul-smelling green slime cover large areas of the lake. When these algae die, decay bacteria attack them. The decay process uses up the dissolved oxygen in the water. When this happens, fish can no longer survive, and the lake is "dead."

There are many chemicals that "fertilize" lake waters. These include phosphates from laundry detergents, crop fertilizers, and organic wastes in sewage. They may be washed into the lake by rain and streams. They may seep in through the ground. But however they enter a lake, they speed up its destruction.

6. Controlling Water Pollution

The cure for water pollution is obvious. Sewage treatment plants must eliminate harmful wastes from sewage. Industrial wastes must be made harmless before they are released into bodies of water. Chemical fertilizers must be used sparingly. Heated liquids must be allowed to cool. Radioactive wastes must be disposed of away from bodies of water.

Measures are being taken to reduce pollution from insecticides and pesticides. The use of DDT and other long-lasting poisons has been greatly cut by federal laws in the United States. As a result, fewer fish and birds are dying from these poisons. The use of phosphates in detergents has been greatly reduced by the manufacturers. Such measures may revive "dead" lakes and reduce eutrophication. They should also reduce pollution of such rivers as the Hudson and the lower Mississippi.

The above picture shows the connection between pollution in this river and loss of life. At the left, the river foams heavily because of detergent pollution.

A Matter of Ecology **481**

The prevention of oil spills is a more difficult problem. Federal regulation of offshore oil drilling procedures has been tightened. But the policing of ships that discharge oil wastes at seas requires international cooperation. Improved construction of giant tankers can reduce the risk of spillage. Oil spills can be partly cleaned up by chemical foams and absorbent materials.

What Pollutes the Atmosphere? 7.

Most atmospheric pollutants are either solids or gases. The main solids found in the air are soot, dust from soil, and plant pollens. Soot gets into the air mainly from the smoke of coal-burning or oil-burning furnaces. Most of the "dust" that plagues housekeepers is soot mixed with dust blown up from the soil. Soot is greasy and smudges easily. It is by far the more annoying part of household dust. Plant pollens are disturbing to hay fever sufferers. Ragweed pollen is probably the principal cause of hay fever.

The principal gas pollutants in the air are sulfur dioxide, carbon monoxide, oxides of nitrogen, and hydrocarbons. Sulfur dioxide comes mainly from the burning of coal and fuel oil. It is a very poisonous gas that is highly irritating to the nose and throat. When it combines with droplets of water in the air it forms a harmful acid. The other gas pollutants come mainly from the burning of gasoline in automobile engines. (In addition, poisonous lead compounds enter the air when leaded gasoline is burned.)

All gasoline exhaust gases are poisonous. In a closed garage, or in a closed car with leaking exhaust pipes, exhaust gases can cause death. The nitrogen oxides and hydrocarbon gases are also smog formers. They are the main cause of the smogs of Los Angeles.

Aircraft pollute the upper air with the fumes from their engine exhausts.

Air Pollution: Danger and Controls 8.

Air pollutants are a serious menace to health. They are believed to be a factor in causing many respiratory diseases. These include pneumonia, bronchitis, emphysema, tuberculosis, and lung cancer.

Recently, some scientists have stated that they believe that air pollution can affect the weather. Also, it has been shown that propellants often used in spray cans could destroy the ozone layer of the atmosphere. (The ozone layer protects us from too much ultra-violet radiation.) If this happens, there will almost surely be a rise in the rate of skin cancer.

Many measures must be taken to control air pollution. Pollution from sulfur dioxide can be reduced by burning low sulfur fuels. These are more expensive than coals and oils high in sulfur. Chemical plants must use devices to eliminate soot and poisonous gases from their smoke. An example of a city that cleaned up its air is Pittsburgh. It was once known as the Smoky City. Now it is a model for the successful use of air pollution controls.

Control of automobile pollution is more difficult. Progress is being made, however. Lead compounds are being eliminated by the use of unleaded gasolines. Devices are being used to change exhaust gases into harmless substances.

Pollutants are also removed from the air by natural processes. They can be washed out by rains. They can be blown away by winds. They can be carried into the upper air by convection. But natural cleansing processes can no longer keep pace with pollution of the atmosphere.

Pittsburgh found ways to decrease smog. At the top is a view of downtown Pittsburgh before smoke control. Below is the same view afterward.

Each topic question refers to the topic of the same number within this chapter.

TOPIC QUESTIONS

1. What is ecology? What is an ecosystem? What are the main parts of your local ecosystem?

2. What are the parts of the hydrosphere? How are they connected?

3. Give examples showing how each part of the hydrosphere may become polluted.

4. Give examples of the harm done by pollutants to (a) the sea, (b) local water supply. What is thermal pollution? What are its harmful effects?

5. What is eutrophication? Explain how certain pollutants hasten eutrophication. How does eutrophication make a lake "die"?

6. How can water pollution be controlled? How can oil spills be prevented or reduced?

7. What solids pollute the atmosphere? What gases pollute the atmosphere? Where do such gases come from?

8. What are the harmful effects of air pollution? How can air pollution from factories be controlled? How can air pollution from automobiles be reduced? What natural processes help to remove pollutants from the air?

A Matter of Ecology **483**

unit seven

Have you ever seen an
animal like the one whose shape is
shown in the photograph of a rock on the
opposite page? Not unless you lived more than
200 million years ago! This shape was left in the rock
by an ancient trilobite. The trilobites were once extremely
plentiful, and the rock record abounds with their fossils. But
they are no more.

Over the face of the earth there are many traces of what life on earth
was like in the distant past. Hairy creatures similar to elephants have
been found frozen in ice where they have been preserved for ten
thousand years. Impressions of the leaves of strange trees are common in
coal. Bones of creatures that died a million years ago can be found in a
cave in Africa. The shapes of ancient insects are preserved in amber.
Footprints of giant lizards are preserved in stone. And the trilobites lived
and died before any of the others mentioned here.

What do these evidences of ancient life mean? Why are they important
to the earth scientists? Finding out about the earth and the life on it long
ago is like a mystery story. Scientists have discovered clues that
suggest what may have been and what may have happened.

As part of the story, scientists make use of kinds of plants and
animals that lived at different times to tell us when and
where there were hot climates, cold climates, wet climates, or dry climates. They tell us about ancient
ice ages and draw maps showing
ancient continents with strange
outlines.

33

Most fossils found in rocks are not the original remains of prehistoric plants and animals. In most cases, the fossils are imprints. *These are molds or casts left in rock after the original remains have disappeared.*

Make a "fossil" mold. Flatten a small block of modeling clay to represent a layer of sediment. Use any object—a coin, a leaf—as your prehistoric organism. To keep the object from sticking in the clay, rub a little petroleum jelly on the object. Press the object firmly into the clay until a clear print is made. Remove the object and examine your "fossil" mold.

Now make a thick mixture of plaster of Paris and water. Rub a thin layer of petroleum jelly into all parts of the mold you have just made in the modeling clay. Pour the plaster into the mold. When the plaster hardens, remove it. You now have a "fossil" cast.

The Rock Record

Geologic Timetable

Era	Period	Epoch	(Millions of Years Ago) Began	(Millions of Years) Duration	Characteristic Life	Physical Events
CENOZOIC "Age of Mammals"	Quaternary	Recent	—	(11,000 yrs.)	Man dominant. Domestic animals develop.	West Coast uplift continues in U.S. Great Lakes form.
		Pleistocene	2	2	Primitive man appears, develops. Elephants flourish in N. America, then die out.	Ice Age. Raising of mountains and plateaus in western U.S.
	Tertiary	Pliocene	6	4	Modern horse, camel, elephant develop. Sequoias decline; tropical trees driven south.	N. America joined to S. America. Sierras and Appalachians re-elevated.
		Miocene	25	19	Horse migrates to Asia, elephant to America. Grasses, grazing animals thrive.	N. America joined to Asia. Vulcanism in northwest United States, Columbia Plateau.
		Oligocene	38	13	Mammals progress. Elephants in Africa. Monkeys die out in N. America.	Alps and Himalayas forming. Vulcanism in western United States.
		Eocene	53	15	Pygmy ancestors of modern horse, other mammals. Diatoms, flowering plants thrive.	Coal forming in western U.S.
		Paleocene	65	12	Many new mammals appear.	Uplift in western U.S. continues.
MESOZOIC "Age of Reptiles"	Cretaceous		136	71	Dinosaurs, ammonites die out. Mammals, birds advance. Flowering plants, hardwoods rise.	Uplift of Rockies begins. Colorado Plateau raised. Coal swamps in western U.S.
	Jurassic		190	54	Giant dinosaurs. First birds, more mammals. Conifers and cycads abundant.	Rise of Sierra Nevadas, West Coast mountains, Basin and Range mountains.
	Triassic		225	35	Reptiles thrive. First mammals. Forests of conifers and cycads.	Vulcanism in New England, New Jersey. Palisades of Hudson formed.
PALEOZOIC "Age of Amphibians"	Permian		280	55	Trilobites, seed ferns, scale trees die out. Corals abundant.	"Ancestral Appalachians" formed. Ice Age in South America. Salt-forming deserts in western U.S.
	Pennsylvanian		320	40	First reptiles. Many giant insects. Spore-bearing plants, amphibians flourish.	Great coal-forming swamps in North America and Europe.
	Mississippian		345	25	Amphibians and crinoids flourish. Ferns, conifers abundant.	Extensive submergence of continents.
"Age of Fishes"	Devonian		400	55	First amphibians; fishes abound. First land plants, forests.	Mountain building in New England and Canada. White Mountains raised.
"Age of Invertebrates"	Silurian		440	40	First land animals (spiders, scorpions). Fish develop; marine invertebrates thrive.	Salt-and-gypsum-forming deserts in eastern U.S.
	Ordovician		500	60	First vertebrates (fish). Marine invertebrates thrive: mollusks, trilobites, graptolites.	Taconic and Green Mts. form. Half of N. America submerged.
	Cambrian		570	70	Many marine invertebrates (trilobites, brachiopods, snails, sponges). Many seaweeds.	Extensive deposition of sediments in inland seas.
PROTEROZOIC			1530	960	No life on land. Simple marine plants (algae, fungi) and marine worms. Others probably existed, but fossil evidence is lacking.	Great volcanic activity, lava flows, metamorphism of rocks. Formation of iron, copper, and nickel ores.
ARCHEOZOIC			2400	870	?	?

Eras, Periods, and Fossils

The Geologic Timetable $1_\circ$

The main happenings in the earth's history have been put together in a **geologic timetable.** It puts the earth's history into five great *eras* and 12 shorter time divisions called *periods.* Within two of the periods there are divisions called *epochs.*

An era of earth history lasts many millions of years. it includes many geologic events. The purpose of Topic 2 is to describe the events that take place in a "typical" era. This description will help you to understand how geologists can "read" earth history.

A Sample of Earth History $2_\circ$

The time is hundreds of millions of years ago. Weathering and erosion continuously attack the surface of the continents. Rock fragments are carried from highlands to lowlands by erosion. Rivers drop their sediments on flood plains, lake floors, and continental shelves. The sediments form horizontal layers of gravels, sands, and clays. Layers of lime sediments also form on the continental shelves.

Plants and animals live on the land and in the waters. When they die, many of them are buried in the layers of sediment. When the sediments form rock, the buried plants and animals are preserved as fossils.

Erosion and deposition continue for millions of years. More sediments are deposited. More layers of rock are formed. The oldest layers are at the bottom. The most recent ones are at the top. In geosynclines, the sediments are thousands of meters in thickness. The shallow areas of the ocean are being filled in. The mountains and highlands of the continents are being worn down.

Then slowly a change begins. This change continues for millions of years. Volcanism becomes more active. As tectonic plates collide, large areas are built high above their former levels. Geosynclines are raised. Great mountain ranges are created. Horizontal rock layers are folded, tilted, faulted, and intruded by lava. Rocks are metamorphosed. The climate changes, and many forms of life die out. An era of earth history comes to an end.

Now a new era begins. The new highlands are attacked by weathering and erosion. Again, long intervals of time pass. New sediments are deposited on the older rocks.

The new sediments obviously do not belong to the same era in earth history as the rocks beneath them. The new sediments are in horizontal layers. The rocks beneath, however, may be folded or

An unconformity is an erosion surface that separates two different ages of earth history. See Topic 2.

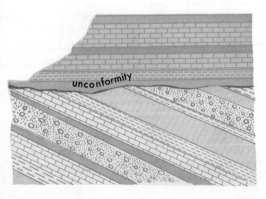

unconformity

tilted. They may be metamorphosed or intruded by lava. They contain different fossils. They do not "conform" or fit in with the younger rocks resting on them. Their surfaces may be weathered and eroded. This surface separates the rocks of two different ages of earth history. This surface is called an **unconformity.**

Notice how the unconformity in paleozoic strata shows where one set of processes stopped and another began.

3. Which Rocks Are Oldest?

Which sedimentary rocks *in any one place* are older or newer is easily told. The oldest layer of undisturbed sedimentary rocks is always at the bottom. The youngest layer of undisturbed sedimentary rocks is always at the top. Any igneous intrusions found in these rocks—dikes, sills, or laccoliths—must be younger. They must have entered after the rocks they cut into were formed.

In volcanic regions, lava flows and volcanic cones may lie above other rocks. These lavas must also be younger than the rocks on which they rest. The top layers of lava are the youngest ones. Which sedimentary rocks *in different areas* are older or newer can usually be told by the fossils they contain.

Metamorphic rocks—such as those of the Piedmont and New England mountain areas—are generally older than sedimentary rocks. In fact, some metamorphic rocks are the oldest surface rocks of the earth.

As noted above, in a sequence of *undisturbed* sedimentary rocks, the younger rocks will always be on top of the older rocks. This rule is

The relative ages of the rocks here are given by numbers. The surface that separates layers 1 and 3 is an unconformity.

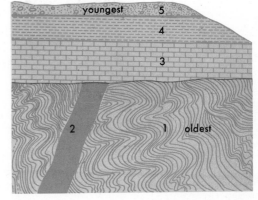

The Rock Record **489**

the **law of superposition.** But older rocks do sometimes lie on top of younger rocks. This happens in mountain regions where folding has overturned the rock layers. In such cases, also, fossils help to show the relative ages of the rocks.

Why Five Eras? 4.

What evidence tells historical geologists that one era has ended and another begun? They look for these signs in the rocks:
1. unconformities
2. different rock formations
3. marked differences in fossils.

The most important of these is the third. Different fossils mean that great changes have caused many forms of life to die out.

These "signs" lead the geologist to divide earth history into five eras. Each era has a Greek name that suggests the kind of life that lived then.

The oldest era is the **Archeozoic** (beginning life) era. Its rocks contain no fossils. But scientists believe the simplest forms of life existed then in ocean waters.

Then came the **Proterozoic** (earlier life) era. Simple plants and worms lived in the ocean. But there was still no life on land.

The **Paleozoic** (ancient life) era followed. Its rocks contain many fossils of both plants and animals. These lived on land as well as in the oceans.

Then came the **Mesozoic** (middle life) era, also known as the Age of Reptiles.

Today you live in the **Cenozoic** (recent life) era. It is also known as the Age of Mammals.

Periods and Epochs 5.

The Paleozoic, Mesozoic, and Cenozoic eras have been divided into **periods.** Like eras, periods differ from one another in important ways. They differ in climate. They differ in the level of the sea. Most important, they differ in plant and animal life. But the differences between periods are less than between the eras. Like eras, periods may be ended by times of volcanism and mountain formation.

The rock record of the Cenozoic era also shows divisions we call **epochs.** Epochs are shorter and less distinct than periods. We are now living in the *Recent epoch.* The Recent epoch began when the Ice Age ended about 11,000 years ago. The Ice Age itself occurred during the *Pleistocene epoch.*

How can geologists tell us what living things existed in past ages? They have found their fossils in the rocks. **Fossils** *are any evidence of the existence of life preserved in the rocks.* With this record, geologists can trace how life has changed in the past. Fossils also give clues to the climates of the past. They also help to show how the rocks they are in were formed.

Fossils are formed in four main ways:

(a) Original remains. In rare cases, fossils represent the actual remains of plants or animals.

Brontosaurus vertebrae have been found in the rocks of Wyoming. The hammer is shown to give some idea of the size.

The woolly mammoths were large elephantlike creatures of the Pleistocene epoch. Whole mammoths have been found preserved in the frozen earth in Siberia. They were trapped in glacial moraines when the Ice Age ended.

Other examples of original remains are the teeth of sharks and the shells of shellfish. Sharks' teeth are preserved in deep sea deposits. Shells are preserved in fossil limestones.

(b) Replaced remains. Many fossils no longer contain the original materials of which they were made. Ground water sometimes replaced the lime of shells and bones with other minerals. Ground water sometimes replaced the decaying wood of buried trees with mineral grains. This formed "petrified" trees.

Trapped insects leave molds in amber. These molds show insects that were trapped about 35 million years ago.

A child examines a footprint left by a brontosaurus.

(c) Molds and casts. Sometimes a fossil shell or bone is dissolved out of the rock in which it was preserved. This leaves a hollow *mold*. The mold shows only what the shape of the fossil had been. When new mineral material fills the mold, it forms a *cast* of the original fossil. Molds and casts of shellfish are common fossils. The molds of ferns, leaves, and fish are also found in many rocks.

Molds of prehistoric insects have been found in hardened resin. Resin is the "gum" that forms on trees. The resin oozed from pine trees on which the insects had crawled. This hardened resin is what we call *amber*. Most amber comes from the shores of the Baltic Sea in Europe.

(d) Impressions. Prehistoric animals left footprints on ancient flood plains and deltas. These were preserved when the muds and sands became rock. In such shales and sandstones, geologists have found the footprints of dinosaurs and the trails of ancient worms.

What Are Index Fossils? 7.

Some fossils are typical of a particular period of earth history. They are very useful to historical geologists. Suppose geologists find one of these fossils in a layer of rock. It may be in any part of the world. The fossil immediately tells them the geological age of the rock. Such fossils are called **index fossils,** or guide fossils. Index fossils help to match rocks of different parts of the world.

Index fossils are a great aid to oil geologists. Suppose they know that oil is found in the rocks of a particular period. In seeking new oil deposits, they look for rock formations with the same index fossils.

An animal called the trilobite is often used as an index fossil. Trilobites were scorpionlike animals. They lived in the oceans during the Paleozoic era. At the end of that era they became extinct. Fossil trilobites are plentiful and world-wide. Any trilobite immediately identifies its rocks as of the Paleozoic era. Some trilobite species lived during only a part of the era. This makes them even better index fossils because they specify time more closely.

The fossil formation consists of molds and casts of trilobites.

Measuring Geological Time

 Deposition, Erosion, and Salt

How do geologists calculate the numbers of years in the geological timetable? In some cases the numbers are in billions. In other cases they are in millions. At the top of the table on page 487, where the Recent period begins, the figure is only a few thousand years. How are such measurements made?

Modern methods of measuring geologic time are based largely on radioactivity. These methods are regarded as highly accurate. But geologic time was estimated before radioactive methods came into use. These estimates were made as follows:

(a) Rate of deposition. Geologists have studied the rates at which sediments are deposited on continental shelves. Rates of deposition vary widely. On the average, it takes about 20,000 years to form a layer of sedimentary rock one meter thick.

Suppose the total thickness of rock formed in a single geological period was 2,000 meters. This would mean that deposition had been going on for 2,000 × 20,000 years, or 40,000,000 years.

(b) Rate of erosion. The rate of erosion varies even more than the rate of deposition. Suppose that studies of the Colorado River show a rate of erosion of one meter in 3,000 years. Using this figure, geologists calculate the time taken by the Colorado River to erode its canyon 2,000 meters deep. Multiplying 2,000 by 3,000 years, they get a total of 6,000,000 years.

(c) Salt in the ocean. Geologists have estimated the age of the ocean. First they calculated how much salt there is in the entire ocean. Then they estimated how much salt is carried into the ocean

The Rock Record **493**

by rivers each year. From these figures they calculated how long it took the ocean to get its salt. But this method gives no exact answer. The rate of salt buildup must have varied widely through the ages. Using a rate near today's, we get an age of about 500,000,000 years.

The above methods depend on estimates and average rates. Now let us see how methods that use radioactivity work.

Radioactive Elements and Radioactivity 9.

What is a **radioactive element?** It is an element whose atoms give off radiations from their nuclei.

There are three kinds of radiations, called alpha, beta, and gamma rays. *Gamma rays* are rays like X rays. *Beta rays* are actually particles—electrons traveling at high speed. *Alpha rays* are also particles. Each alpha ray is a bundle of two protons and two neutrons. It is the same as a helium nucleus.

Each time an alpha ray is shot out of an atomic nucleus, the atom changes to a new lighter element. The alpha ray (also called an alpha particle) becomes helium gas. If the new element is also radioactive, radiation will again take place. Radiation will continue until an element is formed that is not radioactive.

Let us take an illustration. The most common isotope of uranium has an atomic weight of 238. It is radioactive. When this atom emits an alpha ray, it becomes an atom of thorium, also radioactive. The alpha particle becomes helium gas. The reaction is written as follows:

$$^{238}U \rightarrow {}^{4}He + {}^{234}Th$$

Radiation continues with alpha, beta, and gamma rays being emitted, until finally an element is formed that is not radioactive. This is the isotope of lead (symbol Pb), whose atomic weight is 206. In the process, eight alpha rays in all are emitted. This can be written as follows:

$$^{238}U \rightarrow 8({}^{4}He) + {}^{206}Pb$$

One uranium atom has become transformed into eight atoms of helium and one atom of lead 206.

Radioactive elements produce three different types of radiation. When an alpha ray is emitted, the atom changes to a different element.

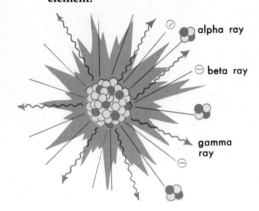

- alpha ray
- beta ray
- gamma ray

What Is Half-Life? 10.

How can radioactivity be used to measure time? The answer lies in a remarkable fact. *Radioactive disintegration takes place at an absolutely constant rate.* It is not affected by conditions that change the speed of ordinary chemical reactions. We can assume that its rate has not changed throughout earth history.

Radioactivity can be detected by instruments such as the Geiger counter. With these, scientists can find the rate at which a radioactive element "decays" into its nonradioactive end product. The time it takes for half of its atoms to do this is called its **half-life.**

Each radioactive isotope has its own rate of decay and half-life. Half-lives range from fractions of seconds to billions of years. The element protactinium has a half-life of about one minute. The half-life of ^{238}U is 4.5 billion years.

To clarify the idea of half-life, let us take an example. Thorium 234 has a half-life of about 24 days. This means that *every 24 days* a sample of this element will lose half of the thorium atoms with which it began that period. An original sample of 16 grams of thorium 234 will decay as follows:

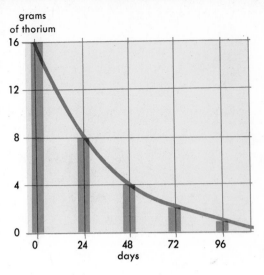

grams
of thorium

days

The graph shows the radioactive decay of thorium 234.

After 24 days, 8 grams of ^{234}Th are left $\qquad$ ($\frac{1}{2} \times 16$)

After 48 days, 4 grams of ^{234}Th are left $\qquad$ ($\frac{1}{2} \times 8$)

After 72 days, 2 grams of ^{234}Th are left $\qquad$ ($\frac{1}{2} \times 4$)

11. Measuring Age by Radioactivity

The geologic timetable gives in years the age of each era, period, and epoch. These figures are based on the decay rate of radioactive minerals in the rocks. Let us see how geologists use decay rates to tell the ages of the rocks.

(a) The **uranium-lead method.** Uranium 238 is one element used in measuring long periods of geologic time. Its half-life is about 4.5 billion years! In one year, one gram of uranium 238 forms only $\frac{1}{7,600,000,000}$ gram of lead 206.

How do the scientists use this knowledge? First, they find rocks that contain uranium minerals formed when the rock itself originated. Igneous rocks are such rocks. Then they measure the amounts of uranium and lead in the rock. The greater the percentage of lead present, the older the rock. To determine the actual age, the geologists use a formula based on the rate of decay. The age is the weight of the lead divided by the weight of the uranium times 7,600,000,000.

Let us take a specific example. Suppose the ratio of lead to uranium in a uraninite crystal from an igneous rock is 0.10. Then the age is 0.10 times 7,600,000,000, or 760,000,000 years.

The uranium-lead clock cannot always be used. "Original" uranium minerals are rarely found in sedimentary or metamorphic rocks. Neither are they found in all igneous rocks. Furthermore, the rate of uranium-lead decay is very slow. Because of its slowness, it does not give reliable results in rocks less than 10 million years old!

(b) The **rubidium-strontium method.** Another radioactive element used in measuring the age of rocks is rubidium 87. Its half-life is about 49 billion years! It decays into the element strontium. Rubidium occurs in the feldspars and micas of igneous rocks. Sometimes both rubidium 87 and uranium 238 occur in the same rock. Then one age measurement can be checked against the other.

(c) The **potassium-argon method.** A third radioactive element used to date rocks is potassium 40. It decays into the element argon. The half-life of potassium 40 is about 1.3 billion years. The potassium-argon method has many advantages. Potassium, unlike uranium and rubidium, is a very common element. It is part of potash feldspar and black mica. Suitable minerals for use with this method are found in metamorphic rocks as well as in igneous rocks. This makes possible the dating of many rocks that cannot be dated by uranium or rubidium. In some cases this method can date rocks as "young" as 50,000 years.

Measuring Ages of Thousands of Years 12.

In 1947 Dr. Willard F. Libby developed **radiocarbon dating.** This makes it possible to measure ages from about 1000 to 40,000 years.

All plant and animal cells contain carbon. A *tiny* percentage of this carbon is a radioactive isotope called *radiocarbon.* Ordinary carbon's atomic weight is 12. Radiocarbon's atomic weight is 14. Its half-life is about 5700 years.

Libby made a remarkable discovery. As long as an animal or a plant stays alive, the percentage of radiocarbon in its cells remains the same. But as soon as it dies, its radiocarbon decreases at a rate set by the half-life of radiocarbon.

Suppose scientists want to measure the age of wooden tools used by prehistoric man. They measure the ratio of radiocarbon to ordinary carbon in the wood. From this they can calculate how long ago the tree (from which the wood came) died.

Scientists have found plant and animal materials buried in late Ice Age deposits. By radiocarbon dating, they fixed the close of the last Ice Age at about 11,000 years ago.

Ice Age Dating by Varves 13.

A botanist can tell the age of a tree by counting the annual rings in its trunk. Geologists have used similar methods to date the melting of Ice Age glaciers. They have counted layers of sediment deposited each year by the retreating glacier. How were these layers recognized?

Wherever lakes formed at the ice front, streams from the melting ice carried sediment into the lakes. In summer, the ice melted rapidly and the streams ran fast. They carried a mixture of sands, silts, and clays into the lakes. The sands and silts settled to the bottom in a light-colored layer. But the fine clays remained in suspension. They were kept from settling by the motion of currents created by the wind.

When winter came, the streams slowed or stopped as they froze. The lakes, also, froze over. Winds were unable to reach and stir the water. The clays settled to the bottom to form a layer of fine dark sediment. Thus each year two distinct layers of sediment were deposited. There was a light-colored sandy layer in summer and a dark-colored clay layer in winter.

The layers of sediment are called **varves.** Each pair of layers is one varve. It represents the deposits of a single year.

Counting varves tells how long the glacier front was near a particular lake.

Varves can be used to determine how long a glacier was in a particular place even after it has disappeared.

14. Age of Niagara Falls

The age of Niagara Falls has been estimated in the following way. The falls are known to have first existed at Lewiston, New York. From there they have moved about 11 kilometers to their present position. Geologists know how fast Niagara is moving back today. The geologists then *assume* an average rate of movement since its origin. From this they can calculate how long it took to recede eleven kilometers.

This calculation can also be used to date the last Ice Age ending. Niagara Falls is known to have formed during the close of the Ice Age. If the average rate of moving back is 1.2 meters a year, the age is found by dividing 11 kilometers, or 11,000 meters, by 1.2 meters per year. This is about 9,000 years.

Clues to Ancient Climates 15.

The earth's bedrock holds many clues to the climates of past ages. Corals grow only in warm climates. Coal was formed from ancient plants. When coral limestone and coal beds are found in Antarctica, we know its climate was not always glacial.

Similarly, when we find ancient glacial deposits in equatorial Africa, we know its climate was once very cold.

The rocks also hold clues to the rainfall history of a region. Wherever we find beds of rock salt and gypsum, we believe the climate was once very dry. This is because such deposits are probably formed by long continued evaporation. Beds of peat and coal were formed in swamps. Wherever such beds are found, they probably indicate a former humid climate.

Paleogeography 16.

The oceans have risen and fallen in the past. How can scientists tell what the outlines of the continents were in prehistoric time? How can they tell where there were highlands, lowlands, rivers, lakes? This study is called *paleogeography* (*paleo*, ancient; *geography*, earth drawing).

Suppose **paleogeographers** wish to draw a map of North America at the close of the Paleozoic era. Here are some problems that they must work out:

1. *Where were the continental shelves and inland seas at that time?* There should be sedimentary rocks—with marine fossils of late Paleozoic age—in those places. They find outcrops of such rocks. Then they must determine; (a) how far these rocks extend below the surface; (b) how much surface rock was removed by erosion.

2. Were there any large inland fresh-water lakes on the continent? The procedure is the same as the one before. But now they must find lake deposits and fresh-water fossils.

3. What kind of topography did the area have? Some of the answers can be found by studying the rocks formed at that time. Conglomerates and coarse sandstones consist of coarse sediments. These must have been carried by swift young streams. And these streams must have run down steep slopes—hills or mountains—close to the sea.

   Fine sandstones or shales, similarly, must mean slower streams, gentle slopes, and broad lowlands. Pure limestones may mean an origin far from shore—away from sand and mud.

Each topic question refers to the topic of the same number within this chapter.

1. What is the geologic timetable?

2. Summarize the geological events in the history of an era. What is an unconformity?

3. (a) How do you determine which sedimentary and igneous rocks are older or younger in a particular area? (b) How do you determine which rocks are older or younger in different areas? (c) What is the law of superposition? How do exceptions to this law occur?

4. (a) How do we know there were five eras of earth history? (b) What does the name of each era mean?

5. (a) Explain how eras are divided into periods. (b) What is an epoch? (c) Why is the Cenozoic era divided into epochs as well as periods?

6. (a) What is a fossil? (b) How do fossils form? (c) Give a brief explanation of the four principal kinds of fossils.

7. (a) What is an index fossil? (b) What use do geologists make of index fossils?

8. Describe three "older" methods used to determine the duration of geological time.

9. (a) Describe the radiations given off by radioactive elements. (b) Describe the radioactive decay of uranium 238.

10. (a) Why is radioactivity more reliable for measuring time than rates of erosion and deposition? (b) What is meant by the half-life of an element? Use thorium 234 to illustrate your answer.

11. (a) Explain the uranium-lead method for measuring geological time. When can't it be used? (b) Give brief descriptions of: 1) the rubidium-strontium method; 2) the potassium-argon method.

12. Explain how radiocarbon is used in measuring short periods of time.

13. (a) Explain what varves are. (b) How are they used in studying glacier recession?

14. Describe a method of calculating the age of Niagara Falls.

15. Describe the evidences that provide clues to the climates of the past.

16. Explain how a paleogeographer can draw maps of what the earth was like in past ages.

1. Why are metamorphic rocks likely to be older than sedimentary rocks?

2. What factors would cause variations during a geological era in the rates of deposition? of erosion?

3. Why is radioactivity less useful for finding the ages of sedimentary or metamorphic rocks than for igneous rocks?

4. What factors may have caused the rate of salt accumulation in the ocean to vary through the ages?

5. Summer varves are usually reddish or brownish in color because of greater weathering by oxygen. Explain this.

6. Fall-winter varves are usually blackish because they contain more organic matter than spring-summer varves. Why?

7. Geologists believe that there were four glacial periods during the Pleistocene epoch. What evidences might indicate this?

8. Flakes of graphite are found in Archeozoic schists and gneisses. Why are they possible indicators that life existed in that era?

STUDENT ACTIVITIES

1. Visit the nearest museum or college geology department where you can study an exhibit of fossils of different types and different geological ages.

2. Refer to a textbook on historical geology for more information on types of unconformities. Then make models to represent these types.

3. Make "fossil" impressions, molds, and casts of leaves, shells, etc. Use modeling clay and plaster of Paris.

4. Make a diorama to represent the life of any selected prehistoric period.

34

Study a sample of limestone that contains fossils. Test for lime (calcite) by the acid test. Since it is limestone, a drop of dilute hydrochloric acid on the rock will fizz.

Limestone is almost always formed in shallow seas. What forms of shellfish can you identify in the rock? Are the fossils molds, casts, or both? Use a magnifying glass to study the details of the shells. With the help of your teacher, find out the era and period in which the rock was formed.

Precambrian
Through Paleozoic

Precambrian Time

What Does Precambrian Mean?

1.

Look back for a moment to the geologic timetable. The Cambrian is the first period in the Paleozoic era. (Read from the bottom up, as if periods were layers of rock. Oldest is at the bottom, youngest at the top.)

The Cambrian rocks date back over half a billion years. Beginning with them, the rocks have many fossils. From these fossils we read how life developed on the earth.

In Archeozoic and Proterozoic rocks, things are very different. The Archeozoic rocks have no fossils at all. Even the Proterozoic rocks have few distinct fossils. So geologists call these rocks **Precambrian** (before Cambrian) to emphasize their lack of a fossil record. They also speak of the Archeozoic and Proterozoic eras as Precambrian time.

What Life Existed in Precambrian Times?

2.

Archeozoic rocks are all highly metamorphosed. That's why they have no fossils at all.

Proterozoic rocks have almost no fossils. Even in Proterozoic sedimentary rocks fossils are rare. Plant fossils that do exist include algae and simple fungi. Animal fossils include jellyfish, soft corals, and marine worms. All of these lived in the ocean. There are no signs of life on land.

When the earth was young, after oceans had developed but before there was life, it might have looked like this.

Why are Precambrian fossils so scarce? Most of the simple organisms of those times were tiny. They had no shell or bone to be preserved as fossils. But large amounts of carbon are found in Precambrian rocks. Carbon is found in such rocks as black shales, black slates, and graphite deposits. The carbon may be the remains of buried plants and animals.

3. Precambrian Shields

Precambrian time covers several billion years. It included many periods of volcanism and crustal movement, erosion and deposition. Mountains and highlands were created, worn down, and partly covered by younger sediments. Even so, Precambrian rocks still form about one-fifth of the continents' surface rocks.

Each continent has a large area in which Precambrian rock is at the surface. Geologists call these areas **shields.** They are the remains

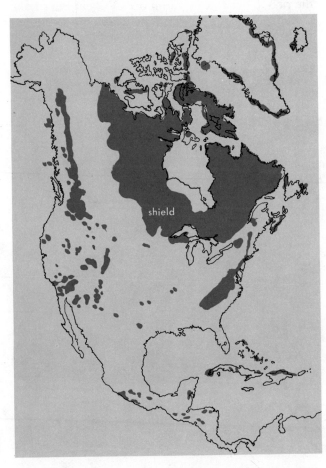

shield

The oldest rocks on earth were formed in Precambrian times. The dark areas on this map show where Precambrian rocks outcrop in North America today. The very large area in Canada is called the Canadian Shield.

of the mountains and highlands of Precambrian time. They are billions of years old. The largest is the African Shield that lies south of the Sahara Desert. The second largest is the Canadian Shield in eastern and central Canada. In Europe, much of Scandinavia and Finland are part of a Precambrian shield. In the United States, Precambrian rocks are found in the Lake Superior area, the Adirondacks, and the Piedmont. In New York City, the bedrock called Fordham gneiss is Precambrian.

Precambrian Mineral Deposits 4.

Some of the world's great mineral deposits were formed in Precambrian rocks. In North America these include the great nickel deposits of Sudbury, Ontario; the great iron deposits of the Lake Superior region of Minnesota and Canada; the iron ores of the Adirondacks; the rich copper ores of the Keeweenaw Peninsula of Michigan; and the rich deposit of uranium ore at Great Bear Lake in northwestern Canada. In South Africa they include the world-famous gold ores of the Transvaal.

The iron ores of the Mesabi Range in Minnesota formed in Precambrian time.

The Paleozoic Era

Paleozoic "firsts." The **Paleozoic** (ancient life) **era** began about 570 million years ago. It ended about 225 million years ago. Great changes in life took place during this era. It went from the Age of Invertebrates to the Age of Fishes to the Age of Amphibians. Invertebrates are animals without backbones, such as worms and shellfish. Amphibians are animals that usually live part of their lives in water and part on land, such as frogs, toads, and salamanders.

Among the "firsts" of the Paleozoic era were the first vertebrates (animals with backbones), the first land animals, the first insects, the first land plants, the first forests, and the first seed plants.

Paleozoic climates. The Paleozoic era was also marked by the variety of its climates. There were periods of warm, dry climate when great salt deposits were formed. There were periods of warm, humid climate in which coal-forming swamp plants thrived. There were periods of very cold climate and great ice ages.

Paleozoic geography in North America. At various times during the Paleozoic era large inland seas existed. These were formed when rising ocean waters flooded interior areas of North America. At other

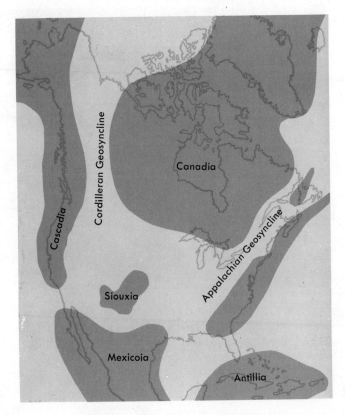

This map shows North America in Late Cambrian time. The dark areas are land. The light areas are seas. Note the two geosynclines.

505

times uplifts occurred, the seas receded, and mountains formed. The three largest inland seas of the era occupied broad shallow depressions. These were called the Appalachian Trough, the Cordilleran Trough, and the Ouachita (WASH ih tah) Trough. The Appalachian Trough was located roughly where the Appalachian Mountains are today. The Cordilleran Trough occupied the Rocky Mountains area. The Ouachita Trough stretched across Oklahoma, Texas, and New Mexico.

The Paleozoic era is usually divided into seven periods. Let us see what the highlights of each period were.

Cambrian Period: Trilobites and Brachiopods

The **Cambrian period** is the first period of the Paleozoic era. Its rocks are the first to have many fossils. But they are fossils of marine life only. No trace of land animals is found in Cambrian rocks. Its plants included many seaweeds and other algae. Its animals included almost all the kinds of invertebrate (without backbone) sea animals known today. Many of them had shells that were fossilized when they died.

The picture at the right shows fossil algae found at Saratoga Springs, New York.

In the picture below you can easily see the three parts of a trilobite.

The most common animals of Cambrian seas were the *trilobites* (*tri* = three; *lobite* = parts; the pronunciation is TRY lo bites). There were thousands of different kinds of these crablike animals. Most were less than 10 centimeters long.

The second most common animal of Cambrian time was the *brachiopod* (BRAY kee uh pod). This was a tiny "shellfish" that looked like a clam. Very few species of brachiopods exist today. Sponges and small snails also lived in the Cambrian seas.

7. Ordovician Period: First Vertebrates

A large part of North America was flooded by salt water during the Ordovician period. It is believed that at one time, about one half of the continent was covered by inland seas. A lot of sediment was deposited in these seas. Later the sediments hardened into sedimentary rocks with millions of fossils.

The seas teemed with trilobites and brachiopods. *Gastropods* (snails), *cephalopods* (like the nautilus of today), and *graptolites* were also abundant. Graptolites are extinct marine animals. Their carbonized remains look like thick pencil lines on the shales in which they are found. *Pelecypods* (clams) and corals appeared for the first time.

The earth's first vertebrates (animals with backbones) appeared in this period. They were primitive fishes called *ostracoderms* (OSS truh koh derms). Fossils of ostracoderms have been found in Colorado and Wyoming.

There was a good deal of mountain formation in this period. Among the mountains formed were the Green Mountains of Vermont and the Taconics of western New England.

A fossil of a cephalopod looks much like a modern-day nautilus.

8. Silurian Period: First Land Animals

In the Silurian period there were many volcanoes in eastern Maine and Quebec. The climate was warm and dry. Corals built reefs in the ocean waters as far north as northern Greenland.

The seas swarmed with trilobites, brachiopods, cephalopods, graptolites, sponges, snails, and clams. Primitive fishes were increasing in number. In Late Silurian time ancient sea scorpions called *eurypterids* (you RIP tuh rids) appeared. They reached lengths of nearly three meters.

An eurypterid (sea scorpion) from the Silurian period is attacking its prey.

Land animals appeared for the first time. They included such invertebrates as spiders, millipedes, and scorpions. Simple land plants, such as mosses and lichens, probably grew on bare rock surfaces. However, there are no fossils to prove this.

In Late Silurian time the climate of what is now the northern United States became very dry. Shallow seas in eastern North America evaporated continuously. Thick beds of rock salt and gypsum were left from central New York to Lake Michigan. The salt deposits near Detroit, Michigan, and Syracuse, New York, are in this belt. The famous Lockport dolomite, cap rock of Niagara Falls, also formed during this period.

This photograph shows a chunk of fossilized Silurian chain coral.

Devonian Period: Age of Fishes

Here is a model of a lobe-finned fish, the ancestor of the amphibian.

Inland seas in the Devonian formed mainly in the Appalachian, Cordilleran, and Ouachita troughs. Invertebrates of all kinds, especially brachiopods, still filled the seas. Vertebrates included more freshwater fishes, marine fishes, and sharks. The *armored fishes* were the giants of these Devonian seas. They reached lengths of 9 meters. This period is called the *Age of Fishes*.

One newcomer was the *lungfish*. This fish could breathe air outside the water. (Lungfishes still exist today.) Before the Devonian period ended, an important development took place. A group of fishes similar to the lungfish had developed very strong fins. With these fins, they could crawl out of the water and live briefly on land. These "lobe-finned" fishes gave rise to the first *amphibians*. (Recall that amphibians are land-and-water animals, such as today's frogs and salamanders.) The first amphibians were large-headed crawling animals resembling giant salamanders.

In the plant world important things also happened. Plants were now growing on land. There were true (spore-bearing) ferns, seed-bearing ferns, and giant rushes (horsetails). There were scale trees with scaly bark resembling snakeskin. There were *Cordaites* (primitive conifers resembling our cone-bearing pines and fir trees).

The Devonian landscape included plants, but our familiar flowering plants had not arrived on the scene.

Mountain building reached its peak in the middle of the Devonian period. Uplift of the continent was greatest in the northeastern part of North America. Mountains were raised from Newfoundland to the Appalachian region. Igneous intrusions helped to build the White Mountains of New Hampshire.

10. Mississippian Period: Foraminifera; Sea Lilies

Advances in the evolution of life were not so striking in this period as in earlier periods. Fresh-water lakes, great inland seas, and ocean waters still teemed with invertebrates and fishes. Amphibians became more numerous. Tiny shell-forming protozoans called *Foraminifera* thrived in the ocean waters.

Among the larger invertebrates the **crinoids** (CRY noyds) became important. Crinoids are related to the starfish. Unlike the starfish, however, crinoids spend most of their lives attached to the sea floor. Because of their petal-like arms, they are called *sea lilies*. But they are animals, not plants.

Plant life did not undergo any great changes, but many new species developed.

Here are fossils of two kinds of crinoid. These were found near La Grande, Iowa.

During this period the interior basins of what is now the eastern United States were almost always under water. When they were below sea level, the basins held inland seas. When they were above sea level, they became fresh-water swamps.

The climate was warm and rainy most of the time. Trees, ferns, and rushes filled swamps and forests. In the swamps, the dead trees and ferns slowly changed to peat. In time the peat changed to coal. Today these deposits form the rich coal fields of Pennsylvania, Ohio, West Virginia, Indiana, and Illinois.

When inland seas covered the interior basins, no coal was formed. Instead of trees, there were deposits of sand, mud, and lime. In time, these deposits became the layers of sandstone, shale, and limestone that now separate coal beds.

What was happening in the animal world? The first reptiles appeared. These reptiles resembled today's lizards. They were the first true land vertebrates. (Amphibians lay their eggs in water. Reptiles lay their eggs on land. Reptiles can live their entire life cycles without entering water.) They could spread into areas where amphibians could not live.

Insects had already appeared in the Devonian period. In the Pennsylvanian period, however, they flourished. There were many new kinds in a wide range of sizes. The largest were giant dragonflies with a wingspread of almost one meter. Cockroaches abounded and reached lengths of 10 centimeters. Some scientists have called this period the Age of Cockroaches.

The swampy forests of the Pennsylvanian period became a major source of coal for the United States.

510

The Permian period is noted for its long desert climate. Sea water filled shallow inland seas and evaporated steadily. Great deposits of sea minerals were formed in many parts of the earth.

A fin-backed flesh-eating Dimetrodon has long, spearlike teeth. In the background is a Edaphosaurus, which looks similar but eats plants.

In the United States, Permian beds of rock salt and gypsum are widespread. They run through Nebraska, Kansas, Oklahoma, and Texas. (Oklahoma is nicknamed the Gypsum State.) In Germany, the world-famous potash deposits of Stassfurt are Permian beds.

Crowds walk through the giant salt quarries of Syracusa, Italy. Many such beds of rock salt were formed during the Permian period.

511

Corals thrived in the warm waters of the ocean and the deeper inland seas. Large coral reefs of Permian age are found in the Guadalupe Mountains of west Texas.

During the Permian period a great ice age took place, mostly in the southern hemisphere. The areas covered by ice were in South America, Australia, South Africa, and India.

The Paleozoic Era Closes 13.

The Paleozoic era covered about 350 million years of earth history. Many forms of life appeared in this great span of time. Most of these survived and moved into the next era. Some became extinct. Let us see which these were.

Some forms of life disappear. In the world of animals, the main losses were among the marine invertebrates. Graptolites died out in the Mississippian period. Eurypterids and trilobites became extinct in the Permian period. Among the land plants, too, there were losses. The seed ferns, scale trees, and Cordaites had flourished in Mississippian and Pennsylvanian time. They were very important in the formation of coal beds. But by the end of the Permian period they were almost extinct.

Most forms of life survive. Many individual *species* of plants and animals became extinct. But most *groups* of living things continued into the Mesozoic era. The reptiles made the greatest advances during the Permian period. By the end of the period there were reptiles resembling modern alligators. Insects made great progress too. Beetles, wasps, May flies, and other new forms appeared before the period closed.

Paleozoic Mountains 14.

Large parts of the North American continent were raised during the Paleozoic era. However, most of this took place in the east. Mountains were formed from Nova Scotia through New England and from New York to Alabama. These were the original Appalachian Mountains. In some areas, mountain formation folded and metamorphosed the rock layers. In Pennsylvania, this changed soft coals into hard coals (anthracites).

In Arkansas, the Ouachita Mountains were formed. In parts of the western United States and Mexico, volcanism helped to build small mountain areas.

Each topic question refers to the topic of the same number within this chapter.

1. Why does the geologist often speak of both the Archeozoic and Proterozoic eras as Precambrian?

2. (a) Describe the life of Precambrian time. (b) Why are the Precambrian fossils so scarce? (c) What do Precambrian carbon deposits tell us about Precambrian life?

3. (a) What is a "Precambrian shield"? (b) Where are there Precambrian outcrops in North America?

4. Name and locate some important mineral deposits of Precambrian time.

5. (a) What are some Paleozoic "firsts"? (b) Describe the variety of Paleozoic climates. (c) Name and locate the three great Paleozoic seas in North America.

6. Describe the chief plants and animals of Cambrian time.

7. (a) Describe the flooding of North America in Ordovician time. (b) What animals lived in this period? (c) What mountains were formed?

8. Describe (a) the marine life of Silurian time, (b) the land animals of Silurian time, (c) the origin of Silurian salt and gypsum deposits.

9. (a) What were the highlights in the Devonian animal world? Why were the lobe-finned fishes so important? (b) What were the highlights in the Devonian plant world? (c) What mountains were formed in this period?

10. What were the highlights of the Mississippian period? What were the crinoids?

11. (a) Explain how Pennsylvanian coal was formed. (b) How do reptiles differ from amphibians? (c) Describe Pennsylvanian insects.

12. (a) Describe the Permian deposits of gypsum and salt. (b) Describe the Permian ice age.

13. (a) What forms of life died out by the close of the Paleozoic era? (b) What forms of life survived?

14. Which mountains were formed in North America in the Paleozoic era?

1. Compare the locations of the salt and gypsum deposits of Silurian and Permian time. How can Silurian salt beds be distinguished from Permian beds?

2. Trace the changes in animal life as it developed through the entire Paleozoic era.

3. Trace the changes in plant life from the beginning to the end of the Paleozoic era.

See list at end of Chapter 33.

35

Coquina is a common bedrock in Florida. It is a limestone that formed in relatively recent times. Look at a sample. What kind of shellfish formed its shells? Are they original remains, or are they molds and casts? How can you tell? Use the acid test on it—a drop of dilute hydrochloric acid. What does the reaction tell you about the coquina? Compare coquina with the more ancient fossil-containing limestone of Chapter 34. In what ways does coquina seem more recent?

Mesozoic
Through Cenozoic

The Mesozoic Era: Age of Reptiles

1. Highlights of the Mesozoic Era

The **Mesozoic era** lasted about 160 million years. It was an era of dinosaurs, flying reptiles, and birds with teeth. Flowering plants appeared. Hardwood trees appeared too, and joined the evergreens in the forests. Mammals also appeared for the first time.

New mountains were raised in what is now the United States. This took place mainly in the west. In the east the land was being eroded steadily.

The Mesozoic era had three periods: Triassic, Jurassic, and Cretaceous.

2. Triassic Period: Evergreen Forests, Reptiles

Physical events. Large inland seas in what is now the United States existed only in the far west. Throughout the Triassic period these seas received deposits of marine sediments. Meanwhile, nonmarine sediments were being deposited by winds and rivers in the western deserts. Some of these sediments became sandstones. These sandstones were red because they contained bits of red iron oxide, or hematite. Today, these desert sandstones are found in Wyoming, Utah, Colorado, Arizona, and New Mexico. Many of them also contain ores of uranium.

In the east of what is now the United States, the Appalachian Mountains were being eroded and worn down. Faulting split parts of the Appalachians into block mountains. Between the block mountains lay great north-south basins. One basin ran through Massachusetts and Connecticut. Another reached from southeastern New York across New Jersey and Pennsylvania into Virginia.

Mountain streams carried coarse sediments into the basins. As in the west, these formed red sandstones. In the Connecticut Valley, these *Triassic sandstones* are famous for their dinosaur footprints.

At times, flows of lava interrupted the process of depositing sediments. Then the lavas were covered by more sediments. Lava also intruded the sediments to form sills and dikes. Before the Triassic period ended, the Appalachians were once more raised to mountain heights. Some of the buried flows and sills were later exposed by erosion. These formed the Watchung Ridges (lava flows) and the Palisades (a lava sill) in New Jersey.

The Petrified Forest consists of fossil tree trunks whose wood has been replaced by minerals.

Plant life. Triassic plant life began with survivors from the Paleozoic era. These included tree ferns, spore-bearing ferns, rushes, and conifers. New plants included new evergreens such as our pines, yews, and cypresses. There were also ginkgo trees and a kind of palm. The famous Petrified Forest of Arizona was formed in this period. Trees that fell into a shallow lake were buried in sediments. They were then petrified by minerals from ground water.

Marine animals. Most Paleozoic invertebrates had become extinct. New invertebrates included corals, snails, clams and lobsters. The most common were shellfish called *ammonites* and *belemnites*. Ammonites resembled our "chambered nautilus." Belemnites were related to squids. Marine vertebrates included many species of fish and amphibians. *Ichthyosaurs* were reptiles that looked like swordfish and lived mainly in the sea.

The fossil of an ammonite looks something like a horn. In fact, the ammonites are named after "the horn of Ammon." Ammon was an Egyptian god whose sign was a ram's horn.

Land animals. New arrivals included insects that could "meta-morphose" their bodies (example, caterpillar to moth). But the most important event from our point of view was the appearance of the first tiny primitive mammals.

The most common land vertebrates were reptiles. These included turtles and the first dinosaurs. The Triassic dinosaurs lived on land. They left many footprints in the sands of river flood plains.

Jurassic Period: Great Dinosaurs, Toothed Birds

Physical events. In eastern North America no new mountains were formed. The Appalachians were steadily eroded and worn down. In western North America, inland seas were even larger than in Triassic times. Both marine and nonmarine sediments were deposited. Some of the nonmarine beds formed uranium-bearing sandstones. In Wyoming and Utah, nonmarine beds became the rocks of the famous Morrison formation. Its sandstones and shales are one of the world's richest sources of dinosaur fossils.

Volcanism and the folding of the earth's crust took place in the Far West through much of the Jurassic period. By the end of the period, a great chain of mountains reached from British Columbia to California. These include the Sierra Nevadas, the Coast Ranges, and the Basin Ranges. In California, lava intrusions formed rich veins of gold in quartz.

Zion National Park in Utah is in the heart of a rock formation famous for its fossils of dinosaurs.

The Double Arch in Arches National Monument, Utah, is made of Jurassic red sandstone.

Sea life in the Jurassic period also included many shellfish.

Giant reptiles thrived in the Jurassic seas. The long-necked plesiosaurs were fish eaters. The fish-shaped ichthyosaurs fed mainly on squids.

Marine animals. Sea life included many invertebrates. Among them were clams, brachiopods, ammonites, belemnites, and a new arrival, shrimps. Sea reptiles were true sea monsters. Ichthyosaurs, or "fish lizards," reached lengths of eight meters. *Plesiosaurs*—snakelike sea reptiles—were up to 15 meters long. They fed on fish, squids, and other marine animals. (Plesiosaur means "near lizard.")

Land animals. New insects included flies, termites, moths, and grasshoppers. Mammals were still small and primitive, but were more developed than in the Triassic period. Reptiles included flying types called *pterosaurs* ("winged lizards") and many more dinosaurs.

The first bird that we know about appeared in this period. It is called *Archeopteryx* (are key OP tuh rix). The name means "ancient wing". Like most reptiles, this bird had teeth and laid eggs. But it also had feathers on its wings and tail. Its wings ended in claws!

Land plants. Jurassic forests were very much like Triassic forests. The most common trees were conifers and a kind of palm.

These photos of Archeopteryx show the fossil as it was found in rock and its "restoration" by paleontologists.

518

Dinosaurs first appeared in the Triassic period. The word *sauros* is Greek and means *lizard*. Dinosaurs are "terrible lizards". The largest Triassic dinosaurs were about four or five meters long. In the next two periods, however, great "monsters" developed. What were these "terrible lizards" like?

Flesh eaters (carnivores). Dinosaurs were either flesh eaters (carnivores) or plant eaters (herbivores). The most famous of the meat eaters was *Tyrannosaurus rex*, the largest tyrannosaur. At full growth it was about 15 meters long and weighed many tons. It stood about six meters high on its hind legs. Its razor-edged teeth stood out 15 centimeters beyond its gums.

Carnivorous dinosaurs lived during all the Mesozoic era. Tyrannosaurs, however, did not appear until the Cretaceous period. *Allosaurus*, another famous flesh eater, lived in the Jurassic period.

Tyrannosaurus rex, "King of the dinosaurs," attacking the horned dinosaur Triceratops.

Stegosaurus was a plant-eating armored dinosaur of Jurassic time.

Plant eaters (herbivores.) There were four types of plant-eating dinosaurs: armored dinosaurs, sauropods, horned dinosaurs, and duck-billed dinosaurs.

One famous *armored dinosaur* was the 10-meter long *Stegosaurus*. Its "armor" included two long rows of bony plates. These stretched down its back from its tiny head to its spiked tail.

The *sauropods* (lizard foot) were the largest land animals that ever lived. Among them were *Apatosaurus*, *Diplodocus*, and *Brachiosaurus*. *Apatosaurus* was a Brontosaur, or "thunder lizard." It was more than 20 meters long. It stood about six meters high on all four legs. It weighed about 30 metric tons. *Diplodocus* had a neck so long that its total length reached about 27 meters. *Brachiosaurus* was the heaviest of all dinosaurs. It weighed about 45 metric tons!

Stegosaurus, *Apatosaurus*, *Diplodocus*, and *Brachiosaurus* lived in both the Jurassic and Cretaceous periods.

The *horned dinosaurs* included the famous three-horned *Triceratops*. Its neck was protected by a large bony plate. On each side of the plate, a long horn stretched forward. A third smaller horn protruded above its nose. It was several times as large and heavy as a modern elephant.

The *duck-billed dinosaurs* included the strange *Trachodon*. It walked on hind legs just as *Tyrannosaurus* did. *Triceratops* and *Trachodon* lived in Cretaceous time.

Not all of the dinosaurs were giants. The smallest adult dinosaurs were only a few centimeters long. But large or small, dinosaurs had tiny brains. *Triceratops*, for example, had a brain the size of a walnut!

Trachodon, one of the duck-billed dinosaurs, walked on its hind legs.

Physical Events. Midway in this period a great inland sea split North America into two unequal "halves." It reached from the Arctic Ocean to the Gulf of Mexico. The sea covered about the area now covered by the Rocky Mountains.

In this period the famous Dakota sandstone, artesian aquifer of the Great Plains, was deposited. (In Europe, chalk beds were formed from the microscopic shells of tiny marine animals. These were later uplifted and eroded to become the famous chalk cliffs of England and France.)

In the western United States peat bogs formed in great swamps. These later became the Cretaceous coal beds of California, Montana, Wyoming, Utah, and New Mexico. In Arkansas and Louisiana, large salt deposits were formed.

Intense folding, faulting, and volcanism brought the Mesozoic era to an end. The entire length of the two Americas from Alaska to Cape Horn was involved. In North America the floor of the great inland sea was uplifted. From its folded and faulted rock layers, the Rocky Mountains were born.

Marine life. Plant and animal life of the seas continued to develop new types. The invertebrates included the tiny protozoans with chalk-forming shells *(Foraminifera)*. They also included sponges, corals, starfish, mollusks (clams, snails, cephalopods), and crabs. Among the vertebrates there were many kinds of sharks and bony fishes. The great swimming reptiles of earlier periods—ichthyosaurs and plesiosaurs—abounded. So did the greatest "sea serpents" of all time, the *mosasaurs*. These ferocious creatures made their first appearance in Cretaceous time.

Giant sea lizards, turtles, and flying reptiles abounded in the late Cretaceous period.

By the close of the Cretaceous period, some forms of marine life had died out. These included all of the great swimming reptiles—ichthyosaurs, plesiosaurs, and mosasaurs—and the invertebrate ammonites and belemnites.

Plant life on land. Plant life made its greatest progress in this period when *flowering plants* appeared. Chief among these were the deciduous trees. (Deciduous trees are broad-leaved trees that shed their leaves in the fall. They are the hardwood trees. Their "opposites" are the evergreen trees, which are known as softwoods.) The deciduous trees appeared early in the Cretaceous period. They developed rapidly until they crowded the forests. First came magnolia, sassafras, fig, willow, laurel, and the tulip tree. Later came oak, maple, beech, birch, walnut, chestnut, and other present trees. Evergreen conifers continued in existence. The *sequoia*, ancestor of California's giant redwoods, made its first appearance.

Animal life on land. Insects continued to thrive and to develop throughout the period. There were relatively few amphibians, but many reptiles. Dinosaurs dominated the animal life of the period. Giant pterosaurs, turtles, crocodiles, and the first snakes were also present. Birds and mammals made important advances. The most highly developed mammal of Late Cretaceous time was the *insectivore* or *anteater*.

When the Cretaceous period ended, dinosaurs and pterosaurs had become extinct.

Dinosaurs vanish. We do not know why dinosaurs became extinct. Many reasons have been suggested. Here are some of them:

1. Uplift of the land wiped out most of the great swamps where dinosaurs lived.
2. The climate became too cool or too dry for dinosaurs.
3. Mammals ate the dinosaurs' eggs.
4. They were wiped out by disease.
5. They starved when flowering plants displaced the plants they had always eaten.
6. They didn't become extinct. The birds that abound today are simply dinosaurs with feathers.

These famous dozen fossilized dinosaur eggs were found in the Gobi desert. Most dinosaurs laid eggs.

The Cenozoic Era: Age of Mammals

6. Divisions of the Cenozoic Era

Early geologists divided the *Cenozoic* era into two periods. The first, covering the time before the Ice Age, was called the *Tertiary*. The second, from the Ice Age to the present, was named the *Quaternary*.

Geologists now recognize seven epochs of the Cenozoic era. The first five—Paleocene, Eocene, Oligocene, Miocene, and Pliocene—are all included in the Tertiary period. The last two epochs, the Pleistocene and the Recent, are included in the Quaternary period.

7. Crustal Activity in the Cenozoic Era

When the Cenozoic era opened, North America looked much as it does today. Only the Atlantic and Gulf Coastal Plains, and part of California, were submerged. They were covered and uncovered by sea waters several times during the Cenozoic era.

Both the Appalachian Mountains and the Rocky Mountains were worn down and raised again in this era. The Colorado Plateau was raised a number of times. During its last uplift, its Colorado River carved out the famous Grand Canyon. Also in the Southwest, faulting created the block mountains of the Basin Ranges and Sierra Nevadas.

Volcanism was also active during this era. Lava flows built up the Columbia Plateau in what is now Washington, Oregon, Idaho, and California. Erupting volcanoes studded the landscape from the Cascade Mountains to the southwest. In the Yellowstone National Park area, lava and ash buried whole forests of trees. Later these trees were "petrified" by ground water.

Mountain building took place in other continents besides North America. In Asia, the world's highest mountains, the Himalayas, were created. In Europe, the Alps were formed. In South America, the Andes Mountains were already in existence. They were raised higher, however, in late Cenozoic time.

Bryce Canyon is cut through Eocene rock.

8. Cenozoic Climates; The Great Ice Age

Early in the Cenozoic era, North America was warm and humid. Then temperatures began to fall. By the Pleistocene epoch, the climate had become very cold. Ice sheets formed from northern Canada into the United States. Ice sheets also formed in northern Europe, Siberia, Greenland, and Antarctica. Alpine glaciers formed in most of the earth's high mountains. Altogether, about one-fourth of all the land was covered by ice.

Many modern trees had developed in the Cretaceous period. Most of them still exist in the present. Often, however, they grow in new locations.

At the beginning of the Cenozoic era the climate was warm. Tropical plants grew even in the northern United States. These included palm trees, ferns, fig trees, and camphor trees. Cypress, laurel, and sequoia grew as far north as Greenland.

Late in the era climates cooled off. All tropical plants were forced southward. By the end of the era, they had disappeared from western North America. Sequoia trees remained, but they were reduced to only two species. These are the "Big Trees" of California's Sierras and the redwoods of coastal California and Oregon.

Grasses arrived about the middle of the Cenozoic era. With this rich new food, grazing animals thrived. Domestic animals such as the cow, sheep, goat, and horse developed. Some grasses became grains. These included wheat, corn, barley, rye, oats, rice, and others.

Diatoms (DIE uh toms) teemed in the seas and lakes of the era. Diatoms are one-celled water plants. They have microscopic shells of snow-white silica. When they died in the Cenozoic waters, their shells piled up. From them came thick layers of a lightweight white rock called *diatomite*, or *diatomaceous earth.*

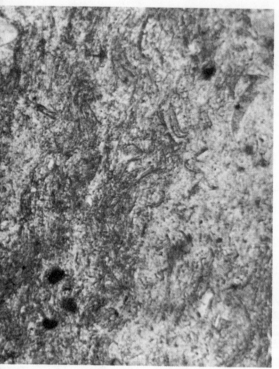

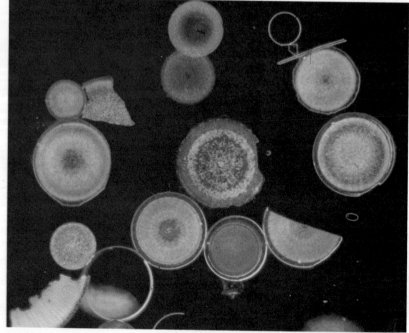

Diatoms, such as the fossil marine diatoms shown at the left as they appear through a microscope, leave the fossil diatomaceous earth, as shown above. You may be familiar with the use of diatomaceous earth in swimming-pool filters.

Throughout the Cenozoic era the waters had nearly the same invertebrate animals as we have today. *Foraminifera* are single-celled protozoans that form tiny shells of lime. They were very abundant in the early half of the era. Sponges, corals, starfish, sea urchins, and sand dollars were fairly common then, as today. Brachiopods and cephalopods were rare. *Mollusks*—clams, oysters, mussels, and snails—thrived throughout the era. Crabs and barnacles were common too.

On land, the spiders, centipedes, scorpions, and insects continued to thrive. Insects included butterflies, moths, bees, wasps, ants, beetles, and many others. The famous fossil "insects in amber" were formed in the Oligocene epoch.

11. **Cenozoic Fishes, Amphibians, Reptiles, Birds**

Most Cenozoic fishes were like those of late Mesozoic time. Sharks and rays (flat fish related to sharks) were abundant and gigantic. Some sharks were 20 meters long, with jaws nearly two meters wide.

Amphibians—frogs, toads, and salamanders—were about as common as today. The reptiles—turtles, lizards, snakes, and crocodiles—were like those of today.

Birds developed into those we have today. Early in the era, however, there were many ostrich-like types. Some were three meters tall. None of them could fly.

These ostrich-like giant moas were great flightless birds that developed early in the Cenozoic period.

525

Rise of the Mammals 12.

In the Cenozoic era, mammals became common. **Mammals** are warm-blooded animals. They nurse their young. Their skin is covered with fur or hair.

Primitive mammals had first appeared in the Triassic period. Through the entire Mesozoic era they made little progress. When the Cenozoic era opened, most mammals were small animals that resembled woodchucks. There were also small monkey-like mammals called *lemuroids*. Monkeys are probably related to them.

At this time the mammals were not a very impressive group. Let us see how they developed through the Cenozoic era.

Paleocene Epoch: Many New Mammals 13.

Many new mammals appeared in this epoch. There were tiny rodents that resembled modern mice and squirrels. There were small flesh-eating animals called *creodonts*. Some creodonts resembled our modern cats. Others looked like modern dogs. There were also new plant eaters called *amblypods*. All of these were in addition to the anteaters, lemuroids, and opossum-like and woodchuck-like animals that already existed.

Most Paleocene mammals were small. The largest was about the size of a small bear.

Eocene Epoch: Preview of Modern Mammals 14.

Many of today's mammals appeared in Eocene time in pygmy sizes. One of these was *Eohippus,* the first "horse." It was about as large as a large cat. Other pygmies included rodents, lemurs, monkeys, and rhinoceroses. Small camels appeared in North America.

Among the new mammals were some who could live in the sea. They were the ancestors of our modern whales and porpoises. Other new mammals could fly. From them in time came our modern bats.

Oligocene Epoch: Mammals Get Larger 15.

In this epoch, the Eocene pygmies "grew up." Camels, horses, and rhinoceroses developed much larger species. In Europe, apes resembling gibbons developed. In North America, however, monkeys mysteriously died out.

Brontotherium, largest of the titanotheres, was nearly three meters tall at the shoulders.

New mammals included small pigs, dogs, cats, beavers, rabbits, and squirrels. Small mastodons (a kind of elephant) appeared in Africa.

Many strange mammals that no longer exist also lived at this time. Among them were the *titanotheres* (giant beasts). They were related to the rhinoceros. The largest titanothere was called **Brontotherium**. It was a slender-legged creature with the body of an elephant and the horned head of a rhinoceros. **Oreodons** were grazing animals about as large as sheep. They were like modern deer and hogs.

Titanotheres and creodonts became extinct in the Oligocene epoch. Oreodons lived into the next epoch.

16. Miocene Epoch: Grazing Animals Thrive

During this epoch grasses covered the plains and the prairies. Grazing animals thrived in North America. Camels were as tall as giraffes. Horses continued to grow in size. But they had developed to the size of ponies only.

North America and Asia were joined by a "land bridge" between Alaska and Siberia. Two-way traffic took place. Horses, until now only in North America, spread to Asia. Mastodons from Asia moved into North America. (Mastodons had spread from Africa to Europe and Asia.)

Monkeys continued to develop. Apes were numerous in Europe and Asia. The dog family evolved into wolves, foxes, raccoons, and (in Europe only) bears. The cat family evolved into leopards, lynxes, and saber-toothed cats (now extinct). The rhinoceroses developed into the giant **Baluchitherium,** the largest land mammal of all time. (The name comes from Baluchistan in West Pakistan, Asia.) This creature was nearly twice as large as our largest elephants today.

Baluchitherium, a hornless rhinoceros, was the largest land mammal of all time.

Pliocene Epoch: A One-Toed Horse 17.

Mammals of the Miocene epoch continued to develop. The first one-toed horse, *Pliohippus*, appeared. (Earlier horses had feet with four, three, or two toes. Modern horses have only one toe. This means that the foot is not divided.)

Until now, North America and South America had been separate continents. Near the close of the epoch, an uplift of the ocean floor connected them. We now call this land bridge the Isthmus of Panama.

Again, animals spread from one continent to another. To North America came the giant armadillo *Glyptodont* and the great sloth *Megatherium.* To South America went camels, horses, mastodons, and wild pigs. In time, more than 20 mammal families had members in both continents.

Before the epoch closed, *mammoths,* or true elephants, appeared. Also, *Equus,* or modern horse, developed from earlier one-toed horses.

The teleoceras is a Pliocene North American ancestor of the rhinoceros.

18. Pleistocene Epoch: Great Elephants in North America

This was the time of the great Ice Age. In North America, elephants reached their peak and then died out. The great "elephants" of the epoch included the mastodons, the imperial mammoths, and the woolly mammoths.

Bodies of woolly mammoths were found almost perfectly preserved in the frozen soil of Siberia in the year 1900. This was thousands of years after they had died.

The woolly mammoth inhabited Europe, Asia, and North America in the Pleistocene epoch. It often wandered close to the Pleistocene ice sheets.

Animals coming to drink from Pleistocene water holes were sometimes trapped in underlying asphalt pits, such as those at Rancho La Brea in Los Angeles.

Many other mammals became extinct in Pleistocene time. Among them were the dire wolf, the giant ground sloth, the giant armadillo, and the great saber-toothed cat. Remains of these animals have been found in the natural tar pits of Rancho La Brea in Los Angeles.

Great herds of horses, camels, and bison lived in North America in this epoch. By the close of the epoch, however, horses and camels had become extinct in North America. Eventually horses returned to North America. But they were horses brought from Europe by early Spanish explorers.

Some scientists believe that the people living in North America at that time caused the mass extinctions of large mammals. There is evidence that these people hunted mastodons and horses, for instance.

Recent Epoch: The Past 11,000 Years. 19.

The Pleistocene epoch came to an end when its last ice sheets disappeared. About 11,000 years have passed since then. These years—including our own times—are the beginning of the **Recent epoch.**

In the Recent epoch, people have definitely become the main cause for the extinction of animal species. Within the past 400 years the Great Auk, the passenger pigeon, the Dodo, and the Moa have become extinct. The American bison was nearly wiped out. The great whales are in danger of becoming extinct. So are many more "endangered species" such as the golden eagle, the whooping crane, the American alligator, and the rhinoceros.

What part do people play in this story? The principal "villains" are greedy and short-sighted commercial hunters. But civilization itself is also to blame. As people fill swamps and cut down forests, they destroy the breeding grounds of many animals.

How can "endangered species" be saved? Conservation groups all over the world have been formed to protect these species. At their urging, many governments have adopted protective programs for both animals and plants. Wildlife sanctuaries have been created. Attempts are being made to regulate commercial hunting, fishing, and whaling. But conservation is everyone's responsibility!

TOPIC QUESTIONS

Each topic question refers to the topic of the same number within this chapter.

1. Briefly state the highlights of the Mesozoic era. Name its three periods.

2. Describe the Triassic period with respect to (a) important physical events, (b) plant life, (c) marine life, (d) land life.

3. Describe the Jurassic period with respect to (a) physical events and rocks, (b) marine life, (c) land animals and plants.

4. Classify and describe some of the great dinosaurs of the Mesozoic era.

5. (a) Describe the principal physical events of the Cretaceous period and some of its important minerals. (b) Describe its marine life. (c) Describe its land plants. (d) Describe its land animals. (e) What reasons have been given for the extinction of the dinosaurs?

6. Explain how the Cenozoic era is divided.

7. Describe the principal crustal activities of the Cenozoic era. What mountains were formed during this era?

8. Describe the coming of the Ice Age in the Cenozoic era.

9. Describe Cenozoic trees, grasses, and diatoms.

10. Describe the invertebrates of the Cenozoic era (a) in the sea, (b) on land.

11. Describe the Cenozoic fishes, amphibians, reptiles, and birds.

12. (a) What are mammals? (b) When did mammals first appear? (c) What were the first Cenozoic mammals like?

13. Describe the mammals of the Paleocene era.

14. Which modern mammals appeared in Eocene time?

15. (a) Which modern mammals appeared in Oligocene time? (b) What kind of animal was *Brontotherium?* (c) What were the oreodons? (d) Which mammals became extinct in Oligocene time?

16. (a) Why did grazing animals thrive in North America during the Miocene epoch? (b) What new modern mammals developed? (c) What were the effects of the land bridge between Asia and North America? (d) Describe *Baluchitherium.*

17. **(a)** In what way did horses develop in Pliocene time? **(b)** What were the effects of the land bridge between North and South America?

18. **(a)** Name the principal mammals that lived in North America during the Pleistocene epoch. **(b)** Which mammals became extinct at the close of the epoch?

19. **(a)** What is the Recent epoch? **(b)** In what ways may people cause animals to become extinct? **(c)** Name some animals that man has made extinct or has "endangered."

GENERAL QUESTIONS

1. Summarize the changes in plant life that took place through the Mesozoic era.

2. Continue the summary of the development of plant life through the Cenozoic era.

3. Trace the development of animal life through the Mesozoic era.

4. Trace the development of animal life through the Cenozoic era.

STUDENT ACTIVITIES

See list at end of Chapter 33.

Appendix

Topographic Maps

1. Mapmakers Have Problems

*A **map** shows all or part of the earth's surface on a plane* (a plane is a flat surface). Since the earth is a sphere, its surface is like the skin of an orange or the cover of a basketball. Therefore, making a map of half the earth is like making the skin of half an orange fit the flat surface of a table. The orange skin will be distorted (torn or stretched out of shape). Making a single map of the whole earth is even more difficult and requires more distortion. On the other hand, if a small section of an orange skin is taken, it can be flattened with less distortion. *The smaller the area mapped, the less distortion is required.*

2. How Map Projections Are Used

Mapmakers have suggested many ways for showing the curved earth on a flat surface. They are called **map projections.** The ideal map would show *shapes, distances,* and *directions* correctly. But no map projection can do all of these things. Some projections show true shapes while distorting distances and directions. Maps of small areas, however, can be made with very little distortion in any respect.

There are many useful map projections, but only three will be mentioned here. The **Mercator projection** shows the whole world (except the extreme polar regions) on one continuous map. It *shows true directions by straight lines.* The chief fault of the Mercator projection is its tremendous exaggeration of distances in high latitudes.

On the **gnomonic** (noh MON ik) **projection,** a straight line between two points shows the shortest route (great-circle route: see Chapter 23) between those points. This is used in planning long voyages or flights. But its directions and distances are not true, so other maps must be used with it.

For small areas, the **polyconic projection** is nearly correct in all respects. It is therefore well suited to the making of topographic maps. The topographic maps of the United States Geological Survey use this projection. (They also still use feet and miles.)

In the left-hand map, Greenland and South America are shown in about their true relative size. In the right-hand map which is a Mercator projection, Greenland appears larger than South America.

In polar-view maps, north (or south) is toward the center. East and west are merely opposite directions around the concentric circles.

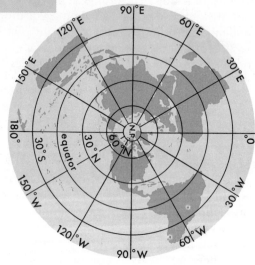

Which Way Is North?

On any map, directions are shown by parallels and meridians. (See Chapter 23 for a fuller explanation.) North or south on a map is found simply by finding and following any meridian. East or west is found by following any parallel. Most of us are used to maps in which north is at the top, south at the bottom, east to the right, and west to the left. But in many projections this does not hold true.

What the Scale Means 4.

*A **map scale** is the ratio of distance on the map to distance on the earth. This ratio may be shown on the map verbally,* as a simple statement, such as "1 inch to 100 miles." Or it may be shown *graphically,* by a line segment divided into equal parts. The parts are then marked in miles or other units of length.

Often a scale is shown *numerically.* Usually this is done by writing a fraction to show what part of the *true* distances the *map* distances really are. For example, the scale $\frac{1}{1,000,000}$ (also written 1:1,000,000) means that any distance on the map is one-millionth of its true length on the earth.

5. Showing Elevation

In order to show land forms, maps must show the relief of the earth's surface. This can be done in many ways, such as shading, coloring, or even minature sketching of land forms. The most accurate way for large-scale maps, however, is with *contour lines.* Use modeling clay to make an irregular cone-shaped "mountain" about 8 to 10 centimeters high. Its base should fit easily into a transparent plastic or glass box. Make the cone steeper on one side. Mark the outside of the box with short horizontal lines every half inch, starting at the bottom.

Put the mountain in the box. Pour in water until the first marker is reached. Draw a line all around the mountain showing the exact level of the water. Repeat this process for each marker to the top of the mountain. Each line drawn is a **contour line.**

Fasten a transparent cover (glass plate, plastic cover, or plastic sheet) securely to the top of the box. Tape a sheet of tracing paper to the cover. Look straight down through the cover. Copy each contour line as accurately as possible. The result is a *contour map* of your mountain.

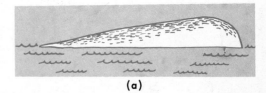

(a)

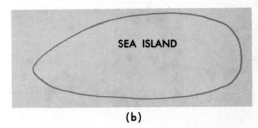

SEA ISLAND

(b)

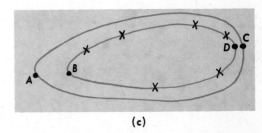

(c)

Figure (a) is a sketch of an island in the sea. This island is 6 miles long, 3 miles wide, oval-shaped, and 113 feet high at its highest point. In an ordinary map the island would look as shown in Figure (b). The shoreline shows the shape of the island at *sea level.* But the map gives no information about the height of the island, the steepness of its surface, or its shape above sea level. Figure (c) is a contour map. *A contour line is drawn through points at the same height above sea level.* Every point on this line is 20 feet higher than the shoreline. The shoreline is also a contour line. It joins points all of which are at zero or sea level.

The distance along the ground between any two points is still found by use of the map scale! **Using the scale in (d), we see that between *A* and *B* the island reached the 20-foot elevation in one mile. Between *C* and *D* the same height is reached in only one-fourth of a mile. The island is steeper between *C* and *D.* Where contour lines are close together, the slope of the ground is comparatively steep. *Where contour lines are far apart, the slope of the ground is comparatively gentle.***

Now the mapmakers draw additional contour lines showing where the island reaches the 40-foot, 60-foot, 80-foot, and 100-foot elevations respectively, shown in (d). They are using a 20-foot *contour interval.*

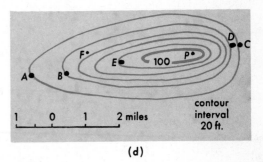

(d)

contour interval 20 ft.

A **contour interval** is the *difference in elevation between two consecutive contour lines.* (Do not confuse the contour interval, which is difference in height, with distance along the ground. The horizontal distance between any two points is measured with the map scale.)

The contour interval differs according to the relief of the land. Suppose the land to be mapped is high and steep. Mapmakers use a large contour interval such as 50 feet or 100 feet. Suppose it slopes gently or is nearly level. Mapmakers use a small contour interval such as 10 feet, 5 feet, or even 1 foot. For moderately rough land, a 20-foot contour interval is used.

To make the reading of contour lines easier, every fifth line is made heavier. The elevation is also marked on it. The other contour lines are not numbered. The contour interval is stated at the bottom of the map.

Depression Contours 6.

Up to now, we have been assuming that the farther you go from sea level, the higher the land becomes. This is not always true. In climbing a volcano, for example, the highest point is reached when you come to the rim of the crater. If you go on from there, you go *down*, not up. To show this we use **depression contours.** These are drawn like contours but are marked on the inside.

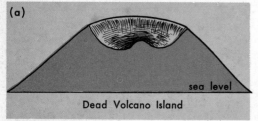

(a) sea level

Dead Volcano Island

At the top is a sketch of an island volcano. The contour map at the right shows the volcano's crater by depression contours.

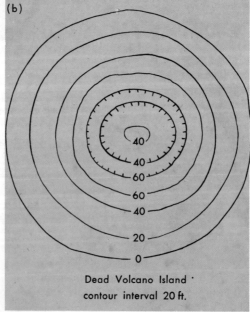

(b)

40
40
60
60
40
20
0

Dead Volcano Island
contour interval 20 ft.

In reading depression contours, the first one is read *at the same altitude as the ordinary contour* that encloses or precedes it. (Similarly, a regular contour has the same altitude as the depression contour that encloses it.) Thereafter, each depression contour is *lower* than the one that encloses it (and each regular contour is higher) by an amount equal to the contour interval of the map.

7. Bench Marks and Spot Elevations

In a map-making survey, surveyors determine the *exact elevation* of many points in the map area. These may be shown on the map in a number of ways. **Bench mark** points are points whose exact elevation is inscribed on a brass or aluminum plate. This is permanently set into the ground at the point of survey. Bench mark points are shown on the map by the letters *BM.* Numbers give the elevation to the nearest foot. A survey point for which there is no bench mark is shown on the map by a triangle and the elevation.

Spot elevations are the elevations of road forks, hilltops, lake surfaces, and other points of special interest. These points are usually located on the map by a small cross. Numbers giving elevations checked by surveyors are printed in *black.* Unchecked elevations are printed in *brown.* Water elevations are shown in *blue.*

A bench mark is used by surveyors as a starting point.

8. U.S.G.S. Contour Maps

The United States Geological Survey issues contour maps in two main series.

The 15-minute quadrangle series. These represent "quadrangles" that cover one-fourth degree of latitude (15 minutes) and one-fourth degree of longitude. Each map, or *sheet,* is named for a part of the quadrangle. Examples are the Brooklyn Sheet, the Shasta Sheet, and the Delaware Water Gap Sheet. The area covered by each sheet in the 15-minute series is about 18 miles (north to south) by 13 miles (east to west). The scale used on most of these sheets is 1:62,500. This means that one inch on the map represents 62,500 inches (nearly a mile) on the surface of the earth. (The exact number of inches in a

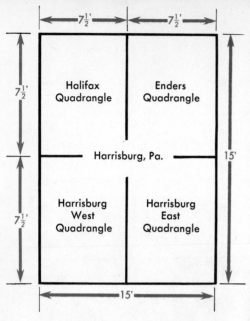

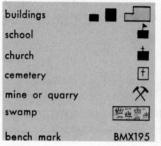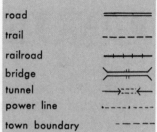

mile is 63,360, but the number 62,500 is used to simplify calculations.) The contour interval found most often on these sheets is 20 feet.

The 7 1/2-minute quadrangle series. These use a scale of 1:24,000 (one inch = 24,000 inches, or exactly 2,000 feet). This scale is more than twice as large as the 1:62,500 scale. It gives much greater detail. Each map sheet shows an area 7 1/2 minutes from north to south, and 7 1/2 minutes from east to west.

Use of color. The features of the contour map are shown in three colors. Contour lines are always printed in brown. Roads, railroads, and other works of man are printed in black. Water features—such as rivers, lakes, and swamps—are shown in blue. Many maps also show woodland areas in green and highways in red. A complete key to all symbols is obtainable from the United States Geological Survey.

Four 7 1/2-minute quadrangles fit on one 15-minute quadrangle.

buildings	■ ■	road	
school		trail	
church		railroad	Many symbols on topographic maps are easily read.
cemetery	†	bridge	
mine or quarry	⚒	tunnel	
swamp		power line	
bench mark	BMX195	town boundary	

Reading the Contour Map

Direction. As explained in Topic 3, directions are found by following meridians and parallels. If a map shows no meridians or parallels, it should have an arrow pointing to true north. U.S.G.S. topographic maps also show the *magnetic declination*, or *variation*, of the compass from true north in each map region.

Distance. If the scale of a map is given verbally, distances on the map may be measured with a ruler. When a graphic scale is printed on the map, the distance between two points can be marked off with any straightedge, such as the edge of a sheet of paper. A piece of string may also be used. The marked straightedge is held directly against the scale for reading. Zigzag distances along roads, rivers, etc., may be marked off in succession on the edge of a sheet of paper before measuring against the graphic scale.

Elevation. When a point is *on* a contour line, its *exact* elevation is known. When a point is between two contour lines, its elevation is estimated. For example, a point may be halfway between the 20-foot and 40-foot contour lines. Its elevation is estimated at about 30 feet.

When the exact elevation of a hilltop is known, it is shown on the map. Any point between two contour lines is higher than the last

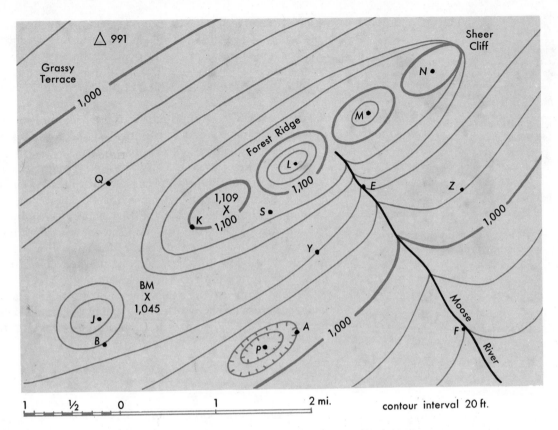

contour interval 20 ft.

contour line, but lower than the next contour line. For example, a point between the 100 feet line and the 120 feet line may be anything from 101 feet to 119 feet.

Each elevation given on a contour map is *height above sea level*. Only those contour maps that include a sea coast will start from sea level. To determine the elevation of any point, one should start from the marked contour line that is nearest to it.

To find the elevation of point Q, we begin from the marked, 1,000-foot contour line. We count *up* in 20-foot "rises," since the contour interval of the map is 20 feet. Point Q is therefore 1,040 feet above sea level. (We count *up* rather than *down* because we are approaching the top of the ridge.)

10. Landforms on Contour Maps

Level land. If a large part of a contour map shows no contour lines, it means that the land is comparatively level. In the diagram on this page, for example, Grassy Terrace (in the northwest) has no contour lines on it and must be fairly level.

Cliffs. Where contour lines run very close together, the land is very steep. If contour lines coincide, it means that the higher ground

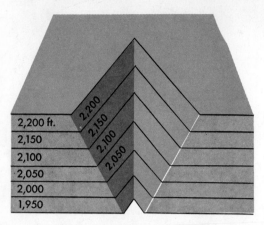

2,200 ft.	2,200
2,150	2,150
2,100	2,100
2,050	2,050
2,000	
1,950	

Contour lines bend upstream where they cross river valleys.

is directly above the lower ground. The contour lines therefore indicate a cliff. An example of this is shown at Sheer Cliff.

Hilltops. Closed circles or ovals at the end of a rising series of contours show the tops of hills or mountains, as at *J, K, L, M,* and *N* in the diagram. The exact elevation of the top of a hill may be indicated, as at *K.*

Ridges. Hills or mountains that are long and narrow are called ridges. They may include a number of peaks. Ridges are shown by long oval contour lines, as at Forest Ridge.

River valleys. Where a river has cut a valley through the land, contour lines plainly show the carved-out valley. As each contour line approaches the valley, it can stay at the elevation it represents *only by bending* in the direction of the high land from which the river is running down. This rule may be used to determine the direction in which a river flows. The direction of the river flow can also be determined by noticing the elevations of marked contour lines. A river must flow from higher to lower elevations.

The **steepness of a river** is shown by the closeness of the contour lines that cross it. The **width of the valley** is approximately shown by the width of the "V" made by a contour line where it crosses a river.

The Average Slope 11.

The average slope, or gradient, between any two points of a hill, mountain, river, trail, or road is easily determined from a contour map. If we know how many feet our hill drops in a given distance, we have

$$\text{Average Slope} = \frac{\text{Drop in Altitude (ft.)}}{\text{Distance (mi.)}}$$

Both drop in altitude and mileage between two points can easily be read from a contour map. Let us calculate the average slope of a trail from the 1,060-feet line, to the 960-feet line. If the *distance* between them, measured with the scale, is 4 miles, then:

$$\text{Average Slope} = \frac{1060 - 960 \text{ (ft.)}}{4 \text{ (mi.)}} = \frac{100 \text{ ft.}}{4 \text{ mi.}} = 25 \text{ ft./mi.}$$

Profiles from Contour Maps 12.

A **profile,** which shows the ups and downs of a line across any part of a contour map, is easily made. Wherever the line meets a contour, we know the exact height above sea level. If we plot this on some definite vertical scale, we get our profile.

A profile is done most easily by placing the bottom edge of a sheet of paper on top of the line we wish to follow. Then we mark on the paper each point where our path crosses a contour. At each point we record the height of the point. When all points are marked, we use our vertical scale to raise each point to its proper height. We keep them as far apart as they were on the map, of course. Then we join the elevated points and have our profile.

(Vertical scales may be 1/8 inch = 20 feet, or whatever you may wish. Plotting is easier if you use graph or cross-section paper.)

Making a profile from a contour map is just the reverse process of making the map. Compare this with the map of the clay "mountain" described on pages 535–36.

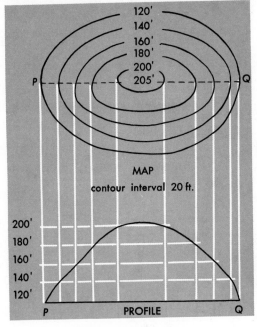

Each topic question refers to the topic of the same number with this chapter.

TOPIC QUESTIONS

1. (a) What is a map? (b) Why is mapmaking a problem? (c) Why can a map of a small area be made with less distortion than a map of a large area?

2. What is a map projection? What three features do all maps show? Name three map projections and describe the feature that makes each one useful.

3. How are north and south found on any map? east and west?

4. (a) Explain what a map scale is. (b) Describe three ways to express a map scale. Give examples. (c) Distinguish between a large-scale map and a small-scale map.

5 (a) What is a contour line? How are contour lines drawn on maps? (b) How does a contour map show whether a slope is gentle or steep? (c) Define *contour interval*. Give examples of large and small contour intervals and their uses. (d) Distinguish between the use of the contour interval and the scale. (e) How are contour lines drawn on maps to make them easier to read?

6. Explain the meaning, use, and rules for drawing and reading depression contours.

7. (a) What is a bench mark? (b) How is a bench mark point shown on the map? (c) What are spot elevations? How are they shown?

8. (a) Describe the following features of a U.S.G.S. 15-minute topographic sheet: Area, scale, contour interval. (b) Describe the use of color on U.S.G.S. topographic maps.

9. (a) How is direction found on a contour map. (b) How is distance measured on a contour map? (c) How is the elevation of a point determined on a contour map? Of a hilltop? When the map does not show sea level?

10. How does a contour map show: (a) level areas, (b) cliffs, (c) hilltops, (d) ridges, (e) river valleys, (f) the steepness of a river, (g) the width of a valley?

11. Explain what a "profile" is and how one is made from a contour map.

The Metric System and SI Units

Some Basic Units of Measurement in the SI (International System of Units)

Quantity	Name	Symbol
length	meter	m
mass	kilogram	kg
time	second	s

Metric System Prefixes

Prefix	Symbol	Multiples
kilo	k	1000
hecto	h	100
deka	da	10
		Divisions
deci	d	0.1 $(\frac{1}{10})$
centi	c	0.01 $(\frac{1}{100})$
milli	m	0.001 $(\frac{1}{1000})$

Examples Using the Meter

Name	Symbol	Equivalent
kilometer	km	1000 m
hectometer	hm	100 m
dekameter	dam	10 m
meter	m	1 m
decimeter	dm	0.1 m
centimeter	cm	0.01 m
millimeter	mm	0.001 m

Metric and English Equivalents in the SI (International System)

Length

1 meter = 39.37 in
= 3.280 ft
= 1.093 yd
= 0.00062 mi

1 cm = 0.393 in
1 km = 0.62 mi

1 inch = 0.0254 m or 2.54 cm
1 foot = 0.3048 m or 30.48 cm
1 yard = 0.9144 m or 91.44 cm
1 mile = 1,609 m or 1.609 km

Area

1 square meter = 1550.0 sq in
= 10.76 sq ft
= 1.19 sq yd

1 sq in. = 0.000645 sq m or 6.45 sq cm
1 sq ft = 0.09290 sq m
1 sq yd = 0.8361 sq m
1 sq mi = 2,589,900 sq m or 2.589 sq km

Volume

1 cubic meter = 61,023 cu in
= 35.314 cu ft
= 1.308 cu yd

1 cu in. = 0.000016 cu m or 16.38 cu cm
1 cu ft = 0.02832 cu m
1 cu yd = 0.7646 cu m

Capacity

1 liter = 1.06 qt
= 33.9 oz
1 kiloliter = 265 gal

1 quart = 0.95 l
1 pint = 0.47 l
1 gallon = 3.8 l

1 cu meter = 265 gal
= 113.51 pecks
= 28.38 bushels

Mass

1 kilogram = 2.204 lb
= 35.374 oz

1 pound = 0.4536 kg
= 453.6 g

1 ounce = 0.2835 kg
= 28.35 g

The Chemical Elements

Element	Symbol	Atomic Number	Atomic Weight	Element	Symbol	Atomic Number	Atomic Weight
Hydrogen	H	1	1.0079	Iodine	I	53	126.90
Helium	He	2	4.003	Xenon	Xe	54	131.30
Lithium	Li	3	6.939	Cesium	Cs	55	132.91
Beryllium	Be	4	9.012	Barium	Ba	56	137.34
Boron	B	5	10.811	Lanthanum	La	57	138.91
Carbon	C	6	12.01	Cerium	Ce	58	140.12
Nitrogen	N	7	14.007	Praseodymium	Pr	59	140.91
Oxygen	O	8	15.999	Neodymium	Nd	60	144.24
Fluorine	F	9	18.999	Promethium	Pm	61	(147)
Neon	Ne	10	20.183	Samarium	Sm	62	150.35
Sodium	Na	11	22.99	Europium	Eu	63	151.96
Magnesium	Mg	12	24.32	Gadolinium	Gd	64	157.25
Aluminum	Al	13	26.98	Terbium	Tb	65	158.92
Silicon	Si	14	28.01	Dysprosium	Dy	66	162.50
Phosphorus	P	15	30.97	Holmium	Ho	67	164.93
Sulfur	S	16	32.064	Erbium	Er	68	167.26
Chlorine	Cl	17	35.453	Thulium	Tm	69	168.93
Argon	Ar	18	39.948	Ytterbium	Yb	70	173.04
Potassium	K	19	39.102	Lutetium	Lu	71	174.97
Calcium	Ca	20	40.08	Hafnium	Hf	72	178.49
Scandium	Sc	21	44.96	Tantalum	Ta	73	180.95
Titanium	Ti	22	47.90	Tungsten	W	74	183.85
Vanadium	V	23	50.94	Rhenium	Re	75	186.2
Chromium	Cr	24	52.00	Osmium	Os	76	190.2
Manganese	Mn	25	54.94	Iridium	Ir	77	192.2
Iron	Fe	26	55.85	Platinum	Pt	78	195.09
Cobalt	Co	27	58.93	Gold	Au	79	196.97
Nickel	Ni	28	58.71	Mercury	Hg	80	200.59
Copper	Cu	29	63.54	Thallium	Tl	81	204.37
Zinc	Zn	30	65.37	Lead	Pb	82	207.19
Gallium	Ga	31	69.72	Bismuth	Bi	83	208.98
Germanium	Ge	32	72.59	Polonium	Po	84	(210)
Arsenic	As	33	74.92	Astatine	At	85	(210)
Selenium	Se	34	78.96	Radon	Rn	86	(222)
Bromine	Br	35	79.91	Francium	Fa	87	(223)
Krypton	Kr	36	83.80	Radium	Ra	88	(226)
Rubidium	Rb	37	85.47	Actinium	Ac	89	(227)
Strontium	Sr	38	87.62	Thorium	Th	90	232.04
Yttrium	Y	39	88.91	Protactinium	Pa	91	(231)
Zirconium	Zr	40	91.22	Uranium	U	92	238.03
Niobium	Nb	41	92.91	Neptunium	Np	93	(237)
Molybdenum	Mo	42	95.94	Plutonium	Pu	94	(242)
Technetium	Tc	43	(99)	Americium	Am	95	(243)
Ruthenium	Ru	44	101.1	Curium	Cm	96	(247)
Rhodium	Rh	45	102.90	Berkelium	Bk	97	(247)
Palladium	Pd	46	106.4	Californium	Cf	98	(249)
Silver	Ag	47	107.87	Einsteinium	Es	99	(254)
Cadmium	Cd	48	112.40	Fermium	Fm	100	(253)
Indium	In	49	114.82	Mendelevium	Md	101	(256)
Tin	Sn	50	118.69	Nobelium	No	102	(256)
Antimony	Sb	51	121.75	Lawrencium	Lw	103	(257)
Tellurium	Te	52	127.60				

Properties of Some Common Minerals

The minerals are arranged alphabetically, and the most useful properties in identification are printed in italic type. Most minerals can be identified by means of two or three of the properties listed below. In some minerals, color is important; in others, cleavage is characteristic; and in others, the crystal shape identifies the mineral.

Name and Chemical Composition	Hard-ness	Color	Streak	Type of Cleavage	Remarks
Amphibole (complex ferromagnesian silicate)	5–6	*Dark green to black*	Greenish black	Two directions at angles of 56° and 124°	Vitreous luster. Hornblende is the common variety. Long, slender, six-sided crystals. *Black with shiny cleavage surfaces at 56° and 124°.*
Apatite (calcium fluophosphate)	5	Green, brown, red, variegated	White	Indistinct	Crystals are common as are granular masses; vitreous luster.
Beryl (beryllium silicate)	8	*Greenish*	colorless	None	*Hardness, greenish color, six-sided crystals.* Aquamarine and emerald are gem varieties. Nonmetallic luster.
Biotite mica (complex silicate)	2.5–3	Black, brown, dark green	Colorless	*Excellent in one direction*	*Thin elastic films peel off easily.* Nonmetallic luster.
Calcite (CaCO₃)	3	Varies	Colorless	*Excellent, three directions, not at 90° angles*	*Fizzes in dilute hydrochloric acid. Hardness.* Nonmetallic luster.
Chalcopyrite (CuFeS₂)	3.5–4	*Golden yellow*	Greenish black	None	*Hardness and color distinguish from pyrite.* Metallic luster.
Copper (Cu)	2.5–3	*Copper red*	Red	None	*Metallic luster on fresh surface. Ductile and malleable. Sp. gr. 8.5 to 9.*
Corundum (Al₂O₃)	8	Dark grays or browns common	Colorless	Parting resembles cleavage	*Barrel-shaped, six-sided crystals with flat ends.*
Diamond (C)	10	Colorless to black	Colorless	Excellent, four directions	Hardest of all minerals.
Chlorite (complex silicate)	1–2.5	*Greenish*	Colorless	Excellent, one direction	*Nonelastic flakes, scaly, micaceous.*
Dolomite (CaMg(CO₃)₂)	3.5–4	Varies	Colorless	*Good, three directions, not at 90°*	*Scratched surface fizzes in dilute hydrochloric acid. Cleavage surfaces curved.*
Feldspar (Potassium variety) (silicate)	6	*Flesh, pink, and red are diagnostic;* may be white and light gray	Colorless	*Good, two directions, 90° intersection*	*Hardness, color, and cleavage.*
Feldspar (sodium plagioclase variety) (silicate)	6	*White to light gray*	Colorless	*Good, two directions, about 90°*	*If striations are visible, they are diagnostic.* Nonmetallic luster.
Feldspar (calcium plagioclase variety) (silicate)	6	*Gray to dark gray*	Colorless	*Good, two directions, about 90°*	*Striations commonly visible;* may show iridescence. Associated with augite, whereas other feldspars are associated with hornblende. Nonmetallic luster.
Fluorite (CₐF₂)	4	Varies	Colorless	*Excellent, four directions*	Nonmetallic luster. In cubes or octahedrons as crystals and in cleavable masses.
Galena (PbS)	2+	*Bluish lead gray*	Lead gray	Excellent, three directions, intersect 90°	*Metallic luster.* Occurs as crystals and cleavable masses. *Very heavy.*
Gold (Au)	2.5–	*Gold*	Gold	None	Malleable, ductile, *heavy.* Metallic luster.

Properties of Some Common Minerals *(cont.)*

Name and Chemical Composition	Hard-ness	Color	Streak	Type of Cleavage	Remarks
Graphite (C)	1-2	*Silver gray to black*	Grayish black	Good, one direction	Metallic or earthy luster. *Foliated, scaly masses common. Greasy feel, marks paper.* This is the "lead" in a pencil (mixed with clay).
Gypsum (hydrous calcium sulfate)	2	White, yellowish, reddish	Colorless	*Very good in one direction*	Vitreous luster. *Can be scratched easily by fingernail.*
Halite (NaCl)	2-2.5	Colorless and various colors	Colorless	*Excellent, three directions intersect at 90°*	*Taste, cleavage, hardness.*
Hematite (Fe_2O_3)	5-6 (may appear softer)	*Reddish*	*Reddish*	None	Sp. gr. 5.3. Metallic luster (also earthy).
Kaolinite (hydrous aluminum silicate)	2-2.5	White	Colorless	None (without a microscope)	Dull, earthy luster. Claylike masses.
Limonite (group of hydrous iron oxides)	1-5.5	*Yellowish brown*	*Yellowish brown*	None	Earthy, granular. Rust stains.
Magnetite (Fe_3O_4)	5.5-6.5	*Black*	Black	None	Metallic luster. Occurs in eight-sided crystals and granular masses. *Magnetic. Sp. gr. 5.2.*
Muscovite mica (complex silicate)	2-2.5	Colorless in thin films; yellow, red, green, and brown in thicker pieces	Colorless	*Excellent, one direction*	*Thin elastic films peel off readily.* Nonmetallic luster.
Olivine (iron magnesium silicate)	6.5-7	*Yellowish and greenish*	*White to light green*	None	*Green, glassy, granular.*
Opal (hydrous silica)	5-6.5	Varies	Colorless	None	*Glassy and pearly lusters, conchoidal fracture.*
Pyrite (FeS_2)	6-6.5	*Brass yellow*	Greenish black	None	*Cubic crystals and granular masses. Metallic luster. Crystals may be striated. Hardness important.*
Pyroxene (complex silicate)	5-6	Greenish black	Greenish gray	*Two, nearly at 90°*	*Stubby eight-sided crystals and cleavable masses. Augite is common variety.* Non-metallic.
Quartz (SiO_2)	7	Varies from white to black	Colorless	None	Vitreous luster. *Conchoidal fracture.* Six-sided crystals common. Many varieties. Very common mineral. *Hardness.*
Serpentine (hydrous magnesium silicate)	2.5-4	*Greenish (variegated)*	Colorless	Indistinct	*Luster resinous to greasy. Conchoidal fracture.* The most common kind of asbestos is a variety of serpentine.
Sphalerite (ZnS)	3.5-4	Yellowish brown to black	White to yellow	*Good, six directions*	*Color, hardness, cleavage, and resinous luster.*
Sulfur (S)	1.5-2.5	*Yellow*	White to yellow	Indistinct	Granular, earthy.
Talc (hydrous magnesium silicate)	1+	White, green, gray	Colorless	Good, one direction	Nonelastic flakes, *greasy feel. Soft.* Nonmetallic luster.
Topaz (complex silicate)	8	Varies	Colorless	*One distinct (basal)*	Vitreous. *Crystals commonly striated lengthwise.*
Tourmaline (complex silicate)	7-7.5	Varies; *black* is common	Colorless	Indistinct	*Elongated, striated crystals with triangular-shaped cross sections are common.*

Simplified Mineral Identification Key

The minerals are subdivided into three main groups on the basis of luster (metallic or nonmetallic) and color (light or dark). Further subdivision is based upon the presence or absence of cleavage. In the last column on the right, the minerals are arranged in order of decreasing hardness. A few minerals are listed in more than one place: e.g., some specimens of a certain mineral may be light, whereas others are dark colored; some specimens of another mineral may have a metallic luster, whereas others do not. You should not expect to detect relatively small differences in hardness: e.g., the difference between 3.5 and 4; but you should easily distinguish between 5 and 7 or 2 and 4.

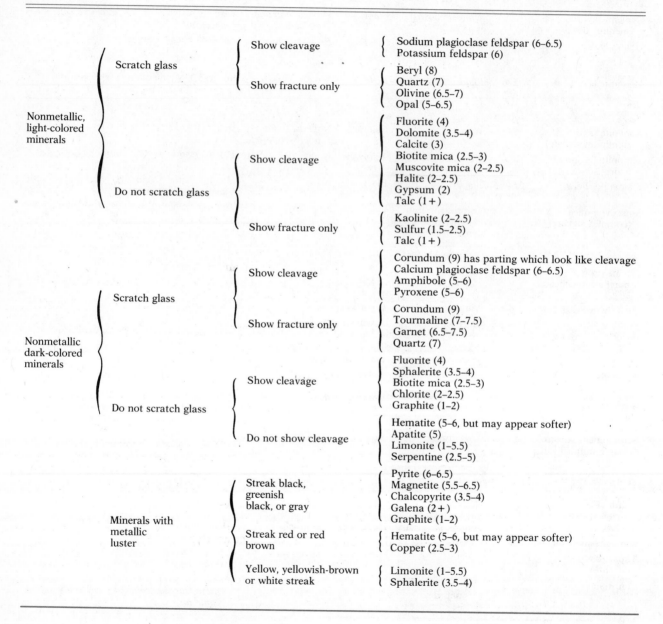

Nonmetallic, light-colored minerals

Scratch glass
- Show cleavage
  - Sodium plagioclase feldspar (6–6.5)
  - Potassium feldspar (6)
- Show fracture only
  - Beryl (8)
  - Quartz (7)
  - Olivine (6.5–7)
  - Opal (5–6.5)

Do not scratch glass
- Show cleavage
  - Fluorite (4)
  - Dolomite (3.5–4)
  - Calcite (3)
  - Biotite mica (2.5–3)
  - Muscovite mica (2–2.5)
  - Halite (2–2.5)
  - Gypsum (2)
  - Talc (1+)
- Show fracture only
  - Kaolinite (2–2.5)
  - Sulfur (1.5–2.5)
  - Talc (1+)

Nonmetallic dark-colored minerals

Scratch glass
- Show cleavage
  - Corundum (9) has parting which look like cleavage
  - Calcium plagioclase feldspar (6–6.5)
  - Amphibole (5–6)
  - Pyroxene (5–6)
- Show fracture only
  - Corundum (9)
  - Tourmaline (7–7.5)
  - Garnet (6.5–7.5)
  - Quartz (7)

Do not scratch glass
- Show cleavage
  - Fluorite (4)
  - Sphalerite (3.5–4)
  - Biotite mica (2.5–3)
  - Chlorite (2–2.5)
  - Graphite (1–2)
- Do not show cleavage
  - Hematite (5–6, but may appear softer)
  - Apatite (5)
  - Limonite (1–5.5)
  - Serpentine (2.5–5)

Minerals with metallic luster

- Streak black, greenish black, or gray
  - Pyrite (6–6.5)
  - Magnetite (5.5–6.5)
  - Chalcopyrite (3.5–4)
  - Galena (2+)
  - Graphite (1–2)
- Streak red or red brown
  - Hematite (5–6, but may appear softer)
  - Copper (2.5–3)
- Yellow, yellowish-brown or white streak
  - Limonite (1–5.5)
  - Sphalerite (3.5–4)

Glossary

Aa. Hawaiian name for lava flows with a rough, jagged surface.

Abrasion. Wearing away of rock by grinding action.

Abyssal plains. The nearly level areas in the deeper ocean basins.

Adiabatic change. A temperature change within a substance caused only by its own expansion or compression.

Advection fog. Type of fog formed when warm, moist air moves horizontally over a cooler surface.

Air mass. Large section of the troposphere in which temperature and humidity are fairly uniform at any given level.

Alluvial fan. Deposit of a stream where it emerges from a steep mountain valley upon open level land.

Altimeter. An instrument used to measure altitude.

Altitude. Height above sea level.

Altitude of a star. Angle between the star and the horizon.

Amber. Fossil resin from ancient conifers.

Ammonites. Extinct shell animals resembling today's chambered pearly nautilus.

Amphibian. Land-and-water animal like present-day frogs and salamanders.

Anemometer. An instrument that measures the speed of the wind.

Aneroid barometer. A nonliquid barometer.

Antarctic circle. The parallel of latitude 66½°S of the Equator.

Anticline. Upfold of rock layers.

Anticyclone. *See* High.

Aphelion. Point in orbit farthest from the sun.

Apogee. Point farthest from the earth in the orbit of an earth satellite.

Aquifer. Water-bearing layer of rock.

Archeopteryx. First bird, closely resembling a reptile. Appeared in Jurassic period.

Archeozoic era. The oldest era in earth history for which there is a rock record. Early Precambrian time.

Arctic circle. The parallel of latitude 66½°N of the Equator.

Arête. Narrow, sharp divide between two glacial cirques.

Artesian well. Well in which the water comes from an aquifer below an impervious layer.

Asteroids (planetoids). "Minor planets" revolving around the sun, mainly between Mars and Jupiter.

Asthenosphere. Partly melted layer of the mantle that underlies the lithosphere.

Astronomical unit. Average distance between earth and sun: about 150,000,000 kilometers.

Atoll. Ring-shaped island, usually of coral limestone, nearly encircling a lagoon.

Atomic number. Number of protons in the nucleus of an atom.

Atomic weight. Number of protons and neutrons in an atom.

Aurora. Glow in nighttime sky, produced in the upper atmosphere by solar radiations.

Badlands. Areas of deeply gullied clay deposits.

Baguio. A tropical storm in the Philippines.

Barchan. Crescent-shaped sand dune.

Barograph. A recording barometer.

Barometer. An instrument that measures atmospheric pressure.

Barrier beach. Beach separated from the mainland by a lagoon or marsh.

Base level. Level of the body of water into which a stream flows.

Batholith. Great mass of intrusive igneous rock of unknown depth.

Baymouth bar. Bar extending across the mouth of a bay.

Beach. Part of shoreline that lies between high tide and low tide.

Bedding plane. The surface which separates one rock layer from another.

Belemnite. Mesozoic shell animal with a cone-shaped chambered shell. Related to present-day squids.

Bench mark. Marker in the ground indicating exact elevation above sea level.

Binary star. A pair of stars that revolve around a common center of gravity.

Block mountains. Mountains formed by faulting and tilting.

Brachiopods. Small marine shellfish abundant in Paleozoic seas, also known as "lamp-shells."

Butte. In western United States, a flat-topped steep-sided hill smaller than a mesa.

Calcareous. Made mainly of lime or calcite.

Caldera. A very broad volcanic crater.

Calving. Blocks of ice breaking off from glaciers to form icebergs.

Cancer (Tropic of). Parallel which marks the farthest north position of the vertical rays of the sun, 23½°N.

Capacity. Maximum weight of water vapor a given quantity of air can hold at a given temperature.

Capricorn (Tropic of). Parallel that marks the farthest south position of the sun's vertical rays, 23½°S.

Cap rock. An impermeable top layer of rock, usually shale or clay.

Carbonation. Chemical weathering in which minerals are altered to carbonates by carbonic acid.

Celestial navigation. Determining position from observations of the sun, moon, planets, or stars.

Celsius scale. Scale on which the fixed points of freezing and boiling of water are 0° and 100° respectively (same as centigrade).

Cenozoic era. Most recent of the eras of earth history.

Cepheid variable. Pulsating star whose distance can be determined from its period of pulsation.

Chinook wind. Warm, dry wind resulting from compressional movement of air down the eastern slope of the Rocky Mountains.

Chromosphere. The layer of the sun's atmosphere just above the photosphere.

Chronometer. Very accurate ship's clock used in determining longitude.

Cinder cone. Steep-sided volcanic cone composed largely of loose volcanic cinder or ash.

Cirque. Steep-walled basin at the head of a glacial valley.

Cirrus clouds. Feathery, wispy clouds of ice crystals at high altitudes.

Cleavage. Tendency of a mineral to split easily along planes parallel to the crystal faces, leaving smooth flat surfaces in one or more directions.

Cold front. Leading edge of mass of relatively cold air.

Comet. A mass of rock, ice, dust, and gas revolving around the sun in a highly eccentric orbit.

Composite cone. Large volcanic cone built of alternating layers of lava and cinders.

Condensation. Process by which water vapor changes into liquid water or solid ice crystals.

Condensation nuclei. Microscopic chemical particles on which water vapor condenses in forming cloud droplets.

Contact metamorphism. Metamorphism caused by contact with hot lava.

Continental air mass. Air mass that originates over a continental (land) area and in general is relatively dry.

Continental climate. One of great extremes of temperature; hot summers, cold winters.

Continental rise. Gently sloping ocean floor reaching from the continental slope to the abyssal plain.

Continental shelf. Gently sloping extension of a coastal plain under the sea.

Continental slope. Relatively steep slope leading from the outer edge of the continental shelf to the deep ocean basin.

Contour interval. Difference in elevation between two consecutive contour lines.

Contour line. Line drawn through points at the same height above sea level.

Cordaites. Primitive conifers of the Paleozoic era, resembling modern cone-bearing pines and firs.

Core (inner). A sphere about 2575 kilometers in diameter, largely nickel and iron.

Core (outer). Zone of earth's interior extending 2175 kilometers from mantle to inner core. Dense nickel-iron, probably liquid.

Coriolis force. An effect of the earth's rotation that causes deflection of moving objects everywhere except at the Equator.

Corona. The sun's outer atmosphere above the chromosphere.

Countercurrent. One flowing in a direction opposite to that of a particular current.

Crater. Cuplike depressions, as at the top of a volcano or on the lunar surface.

Creep. Slow, invisible, downhill movement of soil.

Crevasse. Deep fissure in a glacier.

Cumuliform clouds. Clouds having dome-shaped upper surfaces with horizontal bases.

Cyclone. Tropical storm in the China Sea.

Daylight time. Standard time advanced one hour.

Dead reckoning. Determining position by knowing speed, time, and direction of travel.

Declination of the sun. Number of degrees the sun's vertical ray is north or south of the Equator.

Deflation basin. Shallow basin formed by wind erosion.

Delta. Level, fan-shaped deposit formed at the mouth of stream entering quiet body of water.

Density current. A subsurface current heavier (denser) than the surrounding water.

Depression contour. Contour line joining points of equal elevation within a depression.

Desert pavement. Pebble and boulder surface resulting from removal of sand and clay by wind.

Destructional forces. Forces that wear down the earth's surface (weathering and erosion).

Dew point. Temperature at which air becomes saturated with water vapor.

Diatom. Single-celled water plant that forms tiny shell of white silica.

Diffuse nebula. A cloud of cosmic dust and gas.

Dike. Intrusion of magna into vertical or nearly vertical fissures in bedrock.

Dip. The angle a rock layer makes with the horizontal.

Divide. Higher land separating two adjacent drainage basins.

Doldrums. Rainy equatorial belt of low air pressure and rising air.

Doppler effect. An apparent change in the wavelength of a radiation where there is relative motion between the source of radiation and the receiver.

Drainage basin. Land drained by a river system.

Drift. (1) Material deposited by a glacier. (2) One of the slower movements of oceanic circulation.

Drift bottles. Dated floats which drift with ocean currents.

Drizzle. Precipitation in the form of very fine drops of water falling very slowly.

Drumlin. Smooth, oval, or elongated hill or ridge of glacial drift.

Dry-adiabatic lapse rate. The rate—1°C per 100 meters—at which rising air cools by expansion.

Dune. Hill or ridge formed by the wind from sand or other granular material.

Dwarf stars. Stars of absolute magnitude +1 or less.

Earthshine. Light reflected on the moon from the earth. Best seen at new and old crescent.

Echo sounder. Device for measuring depth of water by means of sound waves.

Ecology. The study of the relations between organisms and their environment.

Ecosystem. Any unit made up of all the organisms in a given area interacting with the physical environment.

Electron. Negatively charged particle which spins around the nucleus of an atom.

Element. A substance that cannot be broken down into simpler substances by ordinary chemical or physical means.

Emergence. Process by which part of a sea or lake floor becomes dry land.

Entrenched meander. Canyon with meandering form, resulting from uplift or rejuvenation of a meandering river.

Epicenter. Point on the earth's surface vertically above the origin (focus) of an earthquake.

Epoch. Subdivision of a geological period of earth history.

Equinox. Time of year (usually March 21, September 23) when day and night are everywhere equal on the earth, and sun's vertical rays are on the Equator.

Era. A major division of geological time.

Erosion. Process of breaking up and removing rock materials by such moving forces as streams, wind, glaciers, waves, and ground water.

Erratic. Glacially transported boulder, different from the bedrock on which it rests.

Escape velocity. Minimum speed needed for an object to escape from any other body to which it is held by gravitation.

Esker. Long, winding ridge of sand and gravel, deposited by a stream flowing beneath a glacier.

Eutrophication. The process of a lake becoming a swamp as sediments and plants fill it in.

Evapotranspiration. Loss of moisture as water vapor from the ground and from plant leaves.

Exfoliation. Peeling of outer layers of bare rock.

Exfoliation domes. Mountain tops rounded by large-scale exfoliation.

Extrusive (eruptive) rocks. Igneous rocks formed by hardening of magma after it reaches the earth's surface.

Eye of storm. Calm, clear center of a tropical low.

Fahrenheit scale. Scale on which the fixed points of freezing and boiling of water are 32° and 212° respectively.

Fall equinox. The beginning of fall in the north temperate zone, about September 23.

Fall zone. Series of falls and rapids occurring where streams flow from harder rock of the Piedmont Upland to softer sediments on the Atlantic Coastal Plain.

Fault. Deep fracture in rock, along which vertical or horizontal displacement has occured.

Faulting. Movement of bedrock along a fault.

Fetch. Length of open water over which the wind blows steadily.

Fiord. Narrow, deep, steep-walled inlet of the sea formed by the partial submergence of a glaciated mountainous coast.

Fireball. An unusually bright meteor.

Firn. The granular snow or ice of a glacier.

Flood plain. Any plain that borders a stream and is covered by its water in time of flood.

Focus. (1) Point within the earth at which an earthquake originates. (2) Position of the sun inside the earth's elliptical orbit.

Foehn wind. *See* Chinook.

Folded mountains. Mountains formed as a result of lateral or sidewise pressure which folds the earth's crust.

Foliated. Refers to the arrangement of minerals in layerlike parallel bands, as in schist and gneiss.

Foraminifera. Tiny protozoans that form shells of lime.

Fossil. Remains, impressions, or any evidence of the former existence of life, as found in the rocks.

Fracture. Appearance of a mineral surface where it breaks along other than cleavage planes.

Fringing reef. A coral reef attached to the shore in places.

Front. Boundary between two adjacent air masses.

Frontal thunderstorm. Thunderstorm that occurs along a well-developed or fast-moving front, usually a cold front.

Fumarole. Hole or vent in volcanic region, from which steam or hot gases are emitted.

Galaxy. (1) A system of billions of stars, cosmic dust, and gas held together by gravitation. (2) Our own Milky Way galaxy.

Geosyncline. Great elongated downfold in the earth's crust, in which deposition and subsidence occur.

Geyser. Hot spring that erupts hot water and steam from time to time.

Geyserite. Deposits of silica formed around the openings of hot springs and geysers.

Glacial trough. U-shaped valley formed by glacier.

Glacier. Moving mass of ice and snow found all year round in a mountain valley or polar region.

Globigerina. One-celled animals whose shells form calcareous deep-sea ooze.

Great circle. Circle whose plane passes through the center of a sphere, or divides the sphere into halves.

Great-circle route. Shortest distance between two points on a sphere, following the great circle that joins them.

Greenhouse effect. Ability of the air to absorb long heat waves from the earth after allowing the sun's short waves to pass through it.

Gully. Miniature valley formed on a hillside by heavy rains.

Guyot. Deeply submerged volcanic cone with broad flat top.

Gyrocompass. A nonmagnetic device to show north.

Hail. Precipitation in the form of irregular balls or lumps made of concentric layers of ice and snow.

Half-life. Time required for a radioactive substance to lose half of its radioactivity.

Hanging trough. A hanging valley formed by glacial erosion.

Hanging valley. Tributary valley which enters the main valley some distance above the main valley floor.

Hanging wall. The face of the faulted block above the fault surface.

Hard water. Water which contains dissolved compounds of calcium, magnesium, or iron.

Hardness. Resistance to scratching.

Heat equator. A line on a world map connecting the hottest places in the world on the various meridians at any given time.

High. Area of high air pressure in which winds spiral away from the center—clockwise in the Northern Hemisphere, counterclockwise in the Southern Hemisphere.

Hook. Spit with a curved end.

Hooked trades. Winds that change their direction as they cross the Equator.

Horizon. Line where earth and sky seem to meet.

Horn (matterhorn). Sharp, hornlike or pyramid-shaped mountain peak.

Horse latitudes. Belts of high air pressure and very dry descending air, located at about 30°–35° latitudes both north and south of the Equator.

Humus. Decayed organic remains in soil.

Hurricanes. Tropical storms that develop over the oceans near the West Indies.

Hydration. Chemical union of water with a substance.

Hydrosphere. Water part of the earth, including surface and subsurface waters.

Hygrometer. Instrument that measures relative humidity.

Ichthyosaurs. Sea-going fishlike reptiles of the Mesozoic era, now extinct.

Igneous rocks. Those formed by the solidification of hot molten rock material called magma.

Index (guide) fossils. Those that are typical of a particular period or epoch of earth history.

Insolation. The solar energy that reaches the earth.

International date line. Imaginary line through the Pacific Ocean, roughly following the 180th meridian. Ships crossing westward advance the date. Ships crossing eastward set the date back.

Intrusive (plutonic) rocks. Igneous rocks formed by hardening of magma below the earth's surface.

Ion. An atom or group of atoms that is electrically charged.

Ionosphere. The part of the earth's atmosphere, from about 65 kilometers to 500 kilometers above the surface, in which layers rich in electrified particles exist.

Iron. Meteorite made mostly of iron and nickel.

Island arc. Chain of volcanic islands parallel to an ocean trench.

Isobar. Line on a map connecting places of the same atmospheric pressure at the same time.

Isotherm. Line draw on a map through places having the same atmospheric temperature at a given time.

Isotopes. Atoms of the same chemical element with different atomic weights.

Jet stream. A narrow band of very strong westerly winds at high levels in middle latitudes. Usually at heights of 6,000 to 12,000 meters.

Joint. A large fracture or crack in the bedrock.

Kame. Small cone-shaped hill or partly stratified sand and gravel deposited by glacial streams.

Karst topography. Surface of area containing sinks, sink hole lakes, disappearing streams, and streamless valleys underlain by limestone.

Kepler's Law of Equal Areas. Each planet revolves so that the line joining it to the sun sweeps over equal areas in equal intervals of time.

Kettle (kettle hole). Depression in the terminal moraine or outwash plain formed when buried blocks of ice melted.

Knot. Speed of one nautical mile per hour.

Laccolith. Dome-shaped intruded mass of igneous rock.

Lagoon. Area of quiet, shallow water between a bar and the mainland.

Lapse rate. Rate at which atmospheric temperature changes with altitude.

Latitude. Distance in degrees north or south of the Equator.

Lava. (1) Molten rock that reaches the earth's surface. (2) The same material after it has solidified.

Lava cone. Broad, gently sloping volcanic cone composed chiefly of solidified lava.

Law of Equal Areas. *See* Kepler.

Leeward side. Side opposite to that from which the wind blows. The sheltered side.

Levee. Bank confining a stream channel, either natural or artificial.

Lichen. Simple plant combination that grows on rocks and clings to them.

Light-year. Distance light travels in one year: about 9.5 million million kilometers.

Line squall. *See* Squall line.

Lithosphere. Outer solid shell of the earth that extends 70 kilometers or more down to the asthenosphere.

Local noon. Moment when the sun crosses the meridian of a particular locality.

Loess. Yellowish unstratified silt deposited by wind.

Longitude. Distance in degrees east or west of the prime meridian.

Longshore current. A current which flows parallel to the shore.

Loran. Long range navigation that uses radio beams.

Low. Area of low pressure in which winds spiral into the center—counterclockwise in the Northern Hemisphere, clockwise in the Southern Hemisphere.

Lunar month. Time from new moon to new moon—29½ days.

Luster. Shine of a mineral surface.

Magma. Hot liquid rock beneath the earth's surface.

Magnetic variation or declination. Angle by which the compass needle varies from true north.

Magnitude (absolute). Apparent magnitude at a distance of 32.6 light-years.

Magnitude (apparent). Brightness of a star as observed by the eye or telescope.

Mantle. Zone of rock extending from crust downward 2,900 kilometers.

Map scale. Ratio of distance on the map to distance on the earth.

Mare. Latin word for *sea*. An extensive dark area on the moon.

Marine climate. Oceanic or equable type of climate, with small temperature range.

Maritime air mass. Air mass that originates over water areas and is relatively moist.

Meander. One of a series of broad looping bends in a stream.

Mediterranean climate. Warm, dry summers and mild, rainy winters.

Meridian. (1) Line on the earth extending from N Pole to S Pole. (2) North-south line on a map. (3) A north-south line on the ground or through the sky.

Mesa. Isolated, broad, flat-topped hill with steep sides.

Mesosphere. The layer of the earth's atmosphere between the stratosphere and the thermosphere.

Mesozoic era. The second most recent era in earth history. Also known as the Age of Reptiles.

Metamorphic rocks. Those formed by the effect of heat, pressure, and chemical action on other rocks.

Meteor. Light produced when a meteoroid streaks through the earth's atmosphere.

Meteorite. A meteor that reaches the earth's surface.

Meteoroid. Rock fragment traveling in space.

Meteorology. Science of the atmosphere.

Meteor shower. A fall of many meteors.

Micrometeor. A tiny meteor or bit of meteoric dust.

Milky Way. The galaxy to which our sun belongs.

Millibar. Unit used by meteorologists to measure air pressure; 34 millibars equal 1 inch of mercury.

Mohorovicic discontinuity (Moho). Boundary between the earth's crust and the mantle.

Moist-adiabatic lapse rate. Rate at which *saturated* air cools when it rises (usually 0.6°C per 100 meters).

Molecule. The smallest part of a substance that retains the composition and properties of the substance and can exist free.

Monsoon. Wind that changes its direction with a change of season, particularly in Asia.

Moraine. (1) Rock material carried by a glacier. (2) Rock material deposited directly by glacial melting, therefore unassorted and unstratified.

Mosasaur. Extinct giant sea reptile of the Cretaceous period.

Mudflow. Rapid movement of large masses of mud and other rock debris.

Nansen bottle. Bottle used to get samples of sea water at different depths.

Nautical mile. One minute of latitude; about $1\frac{1}{16}$ ordinary miles.

Neap tide. A tide of small range occurring at quarter phase of the moon.

Nebula. Great cloud of interstellar dust and gas.

Neck. Land separating the ends of a stream meander. Also, the core of a volcano.

Neutron. One of the three basic atomic particles; weighs slightly more than the proton and has no electric charge.

Normal fault. A fault in which the overhanging block of rock has slid down. A gravity fault.

Normal lapse rate. Average rate of change of temperature with elevation in the troposphere. It is equal to a drop of 1°C for a rise in elevation of 160 meters.

Nova. A star that has flared into intense brightness.

Nucleus. Inner core of the atom consisting of neutrons and protons tightly locked together.

Nunatak. Mountain peak which projects through a continental glacier.

Oblate spheroid. A sphere which is flattened at its poles and bulges at its equator.

Occluded front. Front formed when a cold front overtakes a warm front.

Offshore bar. Sand bar running parallel to coast line.

Ooze. Fine lime or silica mud, found on deep ocean floor.

Orbit. Path of a revolving body, like that of the earth around the sun.

Ostracoderms. Primitive fishes believed to be the first vertebrate animals.

Outwash plain. Broad, stratified, gently sloping deposit formed beyond the terminal moraine by streams from a melting glacier.

Oxbow lake. Crescent-shaped lake remaining after a meandering river has formed a cut-off and the ends of the original bend have been silted up.

Ozonosphere or ozone layer. The part of the earth's atmosphere richest in ozone, reaching from 15 to 45 kilometers above the surface.

Pahoehoe. Hawaiian name for lava flows with a smooth and ropelike surface.

Paleozoic era. The era of earth history which followed Precambrian time.

Parallelism of axis. Each position of the earth's axis is parallel to every other position during revolution.

Parallels. East-west circles around the earth parallel to the Equator.

Peat. Dark brown decomposed plant material representing first stage in coal formation.

Pedalfers. Soils whose B-horizon is rich in iron oxides and clays.

Pedocal. Soils rich in lime, especially in the B-horizon.

Penumbra. Part of shadow that is partly illuminated. Partial shadow.

Perigee. Point nearest the earth in the orbit of an earth satellite.

Perihelion. Point in orbit nearest the sun.

Period. Subdivision of a geological era of earth history.

Period (of a revolving body). Time taken to complete one orbit or revolution.

Period (of a wave). The time needed for one full wavelength to pass a given point.

Permeable rock. Rock which transmits fluids, such as ground water.

Photosphere. The yellow surface of the sun.

Pillow lava. Basaltic lava that has a pillowlike structure.

Plankton. Microscopic sea plants and animals.

Plate. A large block of lithosphere, topped by continental or oceanic crust, that moves slowly on the asthenosphere.

Plate tectonics. A hypothesis suggesting that the surface of the earth is covered by a number of thick blocks, or plates, of rock that move with respect to one another.

Plesiosaurs. Giant sea-going reptiles of the Mesozoic era.

Plunge pool. Large depression formed at the base of a waterfall.

Polar creep. Slow movement of cold water along the ocean bottom from the Poles to the Equator.

Polar easterlies. Winds that blow out of the polar highs toward the subpolar lows.

Polar front. Permanent front between the prevailing westerlies and the polar easterlies.

Porphyry. Rock containing large crystals embedded in a fine-grained groundmass.

Pothole. Circular hole in the bed of a stream, formed by the grinding action of rock material.

Precambrian. Time preceding the Cambrian, such as the Archeozoic and Proterozoic eras.

Pressure gradient. Rate at which air pressure changes on the shortest path between two isobars.

Pressure gradient direction. The direction at right angles to the isobars.

Prevailing westerlies. Winds that originate in the horse latitude highs and blow toward the subpolar lows.

Prime meridian. Zero meridian, which passes through Greenwich, England, and from which longitude is measured.

Prominence. A flamelike cloud of gas above the sun's chromosphere.

Promontory (headland). A long, narrow projection of a coastline.

Proterozoic era. The second and later era of Precambrian time.

Protocontinent. In the theory of continental drift, a single continent that preceded all our present continents.

Proton. A positively charged particle in the nucleus of an atom.

Psychrometer. An instrument that measures relative humidity by using wet-bulb and dry-bulb thermometers.

Pterosaur. Flying reptile of the Mesozoic era.

Pulsar. A distant heavenly object that emits rapid pulses of light and radio waves.

Quasars. Very distant intense radio sources that resemble stars, but are far larger, more luminous, and more massive. Also called *quasi-stellar radio sources.*

Radarscope. A screen, similar to a television screen, on which objects located by radar are pictured.

Radiation (ground) fog. Fog that occurs during calm, clear nights when moist air near the surface is cooled by radiation.

Radiocarbon. Radioactive isotope of carbon; atomic weight, 14.

Radio compass. A device for determining north from the direction of radio waves from known sources.

Radiolaria. One-celled animals whose shells form siliceous deep-sea ooze.

Radiosonde. Weather radio carried aloft by balloon to determine relative humidity, temperature, and pressure of the upper air.

Radio telescope. An instrument that picks up radio waves emitted by bodies in space.

Rain gauge. Instrument for measuring amount of precipitation.

Red clay. Deep ocean ooze containing less than 30 percent shell material.

Red shift. Doppler shift toward the red end of the spectrum, caused by relative motion of source and receiver away from each other.

Reflector or reflecting telescope. Telescope that uses a concave mirror as its objective.

Refraction. Bending of light rays when passing from one transparent substance to another of different density.

Refractor or refracting telescope. Telescope that uses a convex lens as its objective.

Regolith. Lunar "soil."

Relative humidity. The extent to which air is saturated with water vapor. Expressed in percent.

Residual soil. Soil that remains where it was formed.

Reverse fault. A fault in which the overhanging block of rock has been raised.

Rip current. A strong surface current that flows away from the beach in a narrow channel through incoming breakers.

Roches moutonnées. Outcrops of bedrock, smoothed and striated by glacial action and resembling sheep's backs.

Rock flour. Mixture of fine sand and silt formed by the crushing of unweathered rock under a glacier.

Rotation. Turning of an object on its axis.

Saltation. Moving in short jumps and bounces.

Satellite. Smaller body revolving around a larger body.

Schmidt telescope. A reflecting telescope with a wide field of view, especially suited to photography.

Seamount. A submerged, steep-sloped peak rising from the ocean floor. Flat-topped peaks are called guyots.

Seismograph. Instrument that detects and records earthquake shocks.

Sextant. Instrument used to measure the altitude of the sun, stars, and other heavenly bodies.

Shield. Large area of Precambrian rock.

Shield volcano. Volcano whose cone is broad, gently sloping, and nearly all lava.

Silica tetrahedrons. Grouping of one silicon ion and four oxygen ions that forms the building blocks of silicate minerals.

Siliceous. Consisting mainly of silica.

Sill. Sheet of igneous rock forced between sedimentary rock layers.

Sink (sinkhole). A surface depression in a region of soluble bedrock such as limestone.

Slack water. Short period of time in which there is no movement of the water between changing tides.

Sleet. Frozen raindrops.

Smog. Mixture of smoke (or other chemical fumes) and fog.

Snow line. Level above which snow exists all the year.

Solar flare. A great eruption of glowing gas into the photosphere.

Solar wind. Streams of protons and electrons that are blown out from the sun in all directions.

Solstice. The time of year when the sun's vertical rays reach farthest north (June 21) or south (Dec. 21) of the Equator.

Sounding. Method of determining depth of water.

Specific gravity. Ratio of the weight of a substance to the weight of an equal volume of water.

Specific humidity. Number of grams of water vapor in one kilogram of air.

Spectrograph. A spectroscope used as a camera.

Spectroscope. An instrument that can disperse a beam of light into a spectrum of its component wavelengths.

Spectrum. The band of colors formed when light is split into its separate wavelengths.

Spit. Bar built across a bay with one end attached to the land.

Spring equinox. Beginning of spring in north temperate zone, about March 21.

Spring tide. A tide of large range occurring at new moon and full moon.

Squall line. A line of thunderstorms at or ahead of a fast-moving cold front.

Stalactite. Iciclelike deposit of mineral (usually calcite) hanging from a cavern roof.

Stalagmite. Blunt, rounded deposit of mineral (usually calcite) grown upward from the floor of a cavern.

Standard time. Time based on one particular meridian but used over a belt of about 15 degrees longitude.

Stationary front. Boundary between two air masses that are not moving.

Stock. A large igneous intrusion similar to a batholith, but with smaller exposed surface area.

Stone. Meteorite made mostly of rock material.

Stratification. Arrangement of rock beds in visible layers.

Stratiform clouds. Those which are arranged in unbroken, horizontal layers or sheets.

Stratopause. Boundary between the stratosphere and the mesosphere.

Stratosphere. The layer of the earth's atmosphere that extends from the troposphere to the mesosphere.

Streak. Color of a mineral when powdered or rubbed on a streak plate.

Streak plate. Unglazed piece of porcelain or tile used to obtain the streak of a mineral.

Stream piracy (capture). Diversion of the upper part of one stream by the headward growth of another stream.

Striations. (1) Fine parallel lines common on plagioclase feldspars. (2) Scratches on rocks and bedrock due to glacier movement.

Strike-slip fault. Displacement of rock in a horizontal direction only.

Subpolar lows. Stormy belts of low air pressure located at about 60°–65° latitudes in both hemispheres.

Subtropical highs. The horse latitudes.

Summer solstice. Beginning of summer in north temperate zone, about June 21.

Sunspot. A dark area on the sun's photosphere.

Superposition, Law of. In historical geology the general rule that younger rocks lie on top of older rocks.

Syncline. Downfold of rock strata.

Talus. Fallen rock material at the foot of a steep hillside or cliff.

Temperature gradient. Rate of change of temperature between two places.

Temperature inversion. Increase in temperature with increase in altitude.

Thermocline. Transitional layer between warm surface waters and cold bottom waters in oceans or lakes.

Thermograph. A recording thermometer.

Thrust fault. A reverse fault with dip of less than 45°.

Tidal range. Vertical distance between low and high tide.

Till. Unstratified glacial deposits, chiefly clay, gravel, and boulders.

Time meridians. The 24 meridians, each of which is the approximate center of a standard time zone. They begin at the prime meridian, and are 15 degrees apart.

Tornado. Small, violent, twisting storm occurring over level land areas.

Torrid Zone. Forty-seven-degree wide belt between the Tropics over which the vertical rays of the sun pass.

Trade winds. Winds that originate in the horse latitudes and blow toward the doldrums.

Transit. Passage of Mercury or Venus across the face of the sun. Also, the passage of a celestial body across the meridian.

Travertine. Ground water deposit composed of calcite.

Trenches. Long, narrow depressions forming the deepest parts of the ocean floor.

Trilobites. Crablike marine animals, now extinct. They were abundant all through the Paleozoic.

Tropopause. Boundary between the troposphere and the stratosphere.

Troposphere. Convective region of the atmosphere that extends from the earth's surface to the stratosphere. Its height ranges from 5 miles at the poles to 11 miles at the Equator.

Tsunami. Gigantic waves that result from earthquakes or landslides on the sea floor.

Tuff. Rock formed of volcanic fragments.

Turbidity current. Currents carrying mud down continental slopes. Believed to have carved out some submarine canyons.

Twilight circle. Boundary line around the earth between its day and night halves.

Typhoon. A tropical storm in the Indian Ocean.

Umbra. Darkest part of the shadow of the moon or earth.

Unconformity. A surface that separates the rocks of two different ages of earth history.

Uniformitarianism. The concept that the present is the key to the past.

Valley train. A long narrow body of sediment deposited by the stream flowing out of a valley glacier.

Varve. Pair of layers of clay deposited in a glacial lake in one year.

Ventifact. Wind abraded pebble with one or more flat sides.

Volcanic neck. The solidified lava filling the central vent of an extinct volcano.

Volcanism. Movements of liquid rock inside or outside of the earth's crust.

Volcano. Opening in the earth's crust through which an eruption takes place.

Waning. The decreasing of the moon's visible illuminated surface, from full moon to new moon.

Warm front. Leading edge of a mass of relatively warm air.

Water gap. Pass in a mountain ridge through which a stream flows.

Watershed. The entire area drained by a stream and its tributaries.

Water table. Surface below which the ground is saturated with water.

Wave height. Vertical distance from trough to crest.

Wavelength. Distance between two successive wave crests.

Wave period. Time between two successive wave crests at a given point.

Waxing. The increasing of the moon's visible illuminated surface, from new moon to full moon.

Weathering. Process in which rocks are broken up by the action of the atmosphere and organisms.

Willy-willy. A tropical storm in the Pacific near Australia.

Wind gap. Water gap no longer occupied by a stream.

Windward side. Side from which the wind blows.

Winter solstice. Beginning of winter in the north temperate zone, about December 21.

Yazoo stream. Tributary stream which flows parallel to the main stream for some distance through its flood plain.

Zenith. Point in the sky directly above the observer.

Zenith distance. Angle between the sun or star and the zenith.

Zone of aeration. Unsaturated area above the water table.

Zone of saturation. The area beneath the earth's surface which is saturated with water.

Index

Aa lava, *184*
Abrasion, water, 111; wind, *153*
Absolute magnitude, 279–80
Abyssal hills, 237
Abyssal plain, *158*, 237, 339
Acid test, 42
Adiabatic, *426*
Adirondacks, 504
Advection, 378
Advection fogs, 422
Agassiz, Louis, 131
Air masses, 441–43
Air pollution, 428, *429*
Alaska current, 259
Alluvial fan, *124*
Alpha Centauri, 277
Alpha ray, 494
Altimeter, 391
Altitude and air pressure, 378
Altitude and temperature, 470
Altocumulus, 423
Altostratus, 423
Amber, *492*
Amblypods, 526
Amethyst, *44*
Ammonite, *516*
Amphibians, 525
Andromeda galaxy, *287*
Anemometer, 398
Aneroid barometer, *391*
Anthracite, 63, *68*
Anticline, 213
Anticyclone, 460
Aphelion, 304
Apogee, 338
Appalachian Mountains, 506, 523
Appalachian Plateau, 216
Apparent magnitude, 279
Aquifer, 99–100, 521
Archeopteryx, *518*
Archeozoic era, 490
Arête, 140
Arecibo, 270
Armored dinosaurs, 520
Artesian formations, 99–100
Asthenosphere, *181*, 373
Asteroids, 313

Atmosphere, 8, 373–87, 390–400;
  temperature layers, 374, *375*,
  376–77
Atoll, *175*
Atom, *26*
Atomic number, 27–28
Atomic weight, 28
Augite, *46*
Auroras, 299–300

Back swamp, 125
Badlands, *116*
Baluchitherium, 528
Barchan, 155
Barograph, 391
Barometer, aneroid, *391;* mercury,
  390; and weather, 392
Barrier beach, 170, *171*
Barringer meteor crater, 317
Basalt, 53, *54*, 57, 58
Basin Ranges, 523
Batholith, *194*
Bathythermograph, 233
Baymouth bar, 170
Bay of Fundy, 342–43
Beach, 165, 166, 171
Bedding Planes, 65, 214
Bed load, *113*
Bedrock, 23, shaping, 139
Belemnite, 516
Beta ray, 494
Betelgeuse, 277
Big Dipper, 290–91, *361*
Big Bang hypothesis, 288
Biotite mica, *45*, 69
Biotite gneiss, *69*
Bituminous coal, *63*
Black Hills, 193
Body waves, earthquake, 200
Boulder field, 78
Boulders, 23
Brachiopod, 507, 525
Brachiosaurus, 520
Brahe, Tycho, 303
Breakers, *164*
Bright-line spectrum, *271, 273*

Brontotherium, 527
Buffon's hypothesis, *4*
Butte, 158

Calcareous oozes, 245
Calcite, 42, *43*, 48, 62–63
Caldera, 188, *191*
California current, 259
Calving (icebergs), 136
Cambrian period, 506–07
Canyon, 114–16; submarine, 238
Capacity, 417
Cap rock, 99
Carbonate minerals, 48
Carbonation, 81
Cascade Mountains, 523
Caverns, 104–07, *105*
Celestial navigation, 361–64
Celsius scale, 384
Centigrade scale, see Celsius
Cenozoic era, 490, 523–30
Cephalopod, *507*
Cepheid variables, 281
Ceres, 313
Challenger, *226*, 244
Chamberlain, 4–5
Chromosphere, 298
Chronometer, 363–64
Cinder cone, 188
Cinnabar, *37*
Circumference of earth, 17–18
Cirrostratus clouds, 424
Cirrus clouds, 423
Cirque, *140*
Cirque lake, 145
Clastic rocks, 59–60
Clay, red, 245, 246
Cleavage, mineral, 34, *39–40*
Cleopatra's Needle, 83
Climates, 468–75; glacial, 147
Cloudbursts and erosion, 116, *117*,
  422
Clouds, 422–29
Coastal Plains, 172, 237
Coal, *63*
Cold front, 446–47, 450

Colorado Plateau, 114, 216, 523
Columbia Plateau, *189*, 523
Comets, *315*, *316*, 317
Compass, 362
Compounds, 29–34
Composite volcano, *188*, 189
Conchoidal fracture, *40*
Concretions, *67*
Condensation, 416, 420–23
Conduction (heat), 377
Conglomerate, *24*, 60, *61*
Constellations, 290–93
Continental climate, 470
Continental drift, 10–13
Continental glacier, 135
Continental rise, *237*, 239
Continental shelf, 59, 236–37
Continental slope, 236, *237*, *238*
Continents, origin, 9
Convection, 377–79
Copernicus, Nicolaus, 303
Coriolis force, 396–97
Coral, 174, *175*, 176
Coral reef, 174–75
Core of earth, 9
Corer, sediment, *243*, *247*
Corona, 298
Coronagraphs, 297
Cosmic dust and gas, 283
Countercurrent, 259, *260*
Crab nebula, *282*, 283
Craters, lunar, *328*, *329*
Craters, meteor, 317–18
Crater, volcanic, *185*
Crater Lake, *191*
Craters of the moon, 328–29
Creep, *86*
Creodont, 526
Cretaceous period, 521
Crevasse, *136*
Crinoids, *509*
Cromwell Current, 260
Cross-bedding, 65
Crust, 9; composition, 25,
    movement, 12–13, 211
Crystals, 32–34
Cumuliform clouds, 422
Cumulonimbus, 423, 425, *426*
Cumulus clouds, 234, 423, 425–26,
    426
Currents (ocean), 165–66, 252–60

Dakota sandstone, 99, 521
Dalton, John, 26

Dalton's atomic theory, 26
Dams, 126–27
Dark-line spectrum, 271, *273*
Dark nebulae, 293
Daylight time, 367
Dead reckoning, 364
Death Valley, *435*
Deep Sea Drilling Project, 244
Deflation, 153–54
Deflation basins, 154
Delta, *123*, *124*, 145
Density currents, 252–54
Desert pavement, *154*
Devonian period, 508–09
Dew, 421
Dew point, *420*
Diabase, *56*, *58*
Diameter of earth, 18
Diatom, 235, 246, *524*
Diffuse nebulae, 292–93
Dike, 192, *193*
Dinosaurs, 519–22
Dinosaur eggs, *522*
Diorite, *56*
Dip, *213*
Diplodocus, 520
Divide, 117
Doldrums, 229, 405, 408, *412*, 437
Dolomite, 48
Dome mountains, 79
Doppler effect, 272, *273*
Double refraction, 43
Drainage basin, 117
Drift, glacial, 142–45
Drift bottle, 259
Dripstone, 106
Drizzle, 433
Drowned valleys, 173
Drumlin, *143*
Dry regions, 474
Dunes, 154–57
Dust storm, 159
Dwarf stars, 281, 285
Dynamic metamorphism, 68–69

Earth, axis, 7; circumference, 17;
    composition, 8; core, 9; crust, 9;
    day and night, 349; dimensions,
    18; orbit, see solar system;
    rotation, 17, *292*, 347, *348*;
    shape, *16*; specific gravity, 19;
    temperatures below surface, 20
Earthshine, 336
Earthquakes, 198–206

Echo sounder, 241, *242*
Eclipse, lunar, 337–38; solar, 339
Eclipsing binary stars, 281
Ecology, 478
Ecosystems, 478
Einstein, Albert, 300
Electromagnetic spectrum, 268
Electrons, 26
Elements, 24–31; in crust, *25;* in
    stars, 278, 283–84
Ellipse, 302
Elliptical galaxies, 288
Entrenched meander, *122*
Eocene epoch, 526
Eohippus, 526
Epicenter, 200, *202*, *203*, *204*
Equator, 358
Equatorial Currents, 257, 259
Equinox, 352
Eratosthenes, 17–18
Erosion, 77, 152–58, 162–76
Erratic, *143*
Esker, *144*
Eurypterid, *507*
Eutrophication, 480
Evaporation, *416*, *417*
Evapotranspiration, 94
Evening star, 318–19
Exfoliation, 78–79
Extrusive rock, *52*

Fahrenheit scale, *384*
Fault, 199, 214–17
Fault-block mountains, 217
Fault plateau, 216
Feldspar, 24, *40*, *45*, *55*
Fetch, 162
Finger Lakes, 145
Fiord, 173
Firn, 134
Fissure eruptions, 189
Flood, flash, 126; prevention, 127
Flood basalt, 189
Flood plain, 121, 125–27
Flowering plants, 522, 524
Fluorescence, 43
Focus of earthquake, 200
Fogs, 422; and ocean currents, 475
Fold mountain, 212, *213*
Foliation, 68
Fool's gold, 39
Foraminifera, 525
Fossils, 65–66, 491–93
Foucault's pendulum, 348

Fracture, 40
Fronts, *444*, 445, *446*
Frost, 421; weathering by, 78
Fumarole, 102–03
Fusion reaction, 284, 300

Gabbro, 56, 58
Galaxies, 285–88
Galena, 29
Galileo, 323
Gamma ray, 494
Garnet, 47
Geminids, 318
Geode, *67*
Geologic timetable, 487, 488,
    493–98
Geosyncline, 218, *219*
Geyser, *102–03*, 107, 141
Giant stars, 280, 284–85
Glacial milk, 138
Glacial trough, 140
Glaciers, 131–48, 489–98
Globigerina, 245
Glomar Challenger, 244
Glyptodont, 528
Gneiss, *19*
Gold, 25
Grab samplers, 243
Grand Canyon of Colorado River,
    114, 523
Granite, *24*, *54*, 55–56, *57*
Graptolites, 507
Gravitation, 84–85
Great-circle route, 364
Great Lakes, 145
Great Red Spot, *311*
Greenhouse Effect, 376
Greenland glacier, 135
Greenwich time, 363
Ground water, 93
Gulf Stream, 252, 257, *258*
Gulf Stream Countercurrent, 260
Gullies, 116, 238
Gusts, 397
Guyot, *241*
Gypsum, *62*
Gyrocompass, 362

Hail, 434
Half-life, 494–95
Halite, 43, *62*
Hall, John, 218
Halley, Edmund, 316

Halley's Comet, 316–17
Hanging trough, *141*
Hard water, 103
Hardness of mineral, 41
Harmonic Law, 303–04
Hawaiian volcano, 190
Headland, 167
Heat equator, 384
Heating, atmosphere, *376*, 377–83
Helium, 27
Henry Mountains, Utah, 193
Highs, 394, 460
High tide, 340–41
Himalaya Mountains, 220
Hook, 170, *171*
Hooked trades, *409*, *412*
Horizon, soil, *88*
Horneblende, *46*
Horse latitudes, 405, 408, 413, *436*
Hot springs, *101*
Hubble, Edwin, *289*
Hudson River, *173*
Hudson River Canyon, 238
Humus, 87–89
Hurricane, 452–56, *456*
Hutton, James, *51*
Hydration, 80
Hydrogen atoms, 27
Hydrologic cycle, 93–100
Hydrosphere, 478–80
Hygrometer, *418*

Ice Age, 146–48
Icebergs, 136, *137*
Ice cap, 135
Ice front, 136
Icelandic volcano, 184, 188, 189
Iceland spar, *40*, *43*, 48
Ice sheet, 133, 135
Ice shelf, 137
Ichthyosaur, 516, 518, 521
Igneous rocks, 51–58
Index fossil, 492–93
Inner core, 9
Insectivore, 523
Insolation, 376
Interglacial period, 147
International date line, 367
Intrusive rocks, *52*
Ionosphere, 375
Ion, 30
Iron pyrite, 39
Irregular galaxies, 288
Island arcs, 183

Isobar, 392–93
Isotherm, 384–85
Isotopes, *28*

Japan Current, 259
Jeans, Sir James, 5
Jet stream, 407
Jeffries, Harold, 5
Jodrell Bank Observatory, *270*
Johnstown flood, 127
Joint, *214*
Jupiter, *311*, 312
Jurassic period, 517–18

Kame, 145
Kant, 6
Kaolin (ite), 47
Karst topography, 106–07
Kepler, Johannes, 303
Kepler's laws, 303–04
Kettle, 145
Kettle lake, 145
Kitt Peak National Observatory,
    267, *297*
Knot, 364
Krakatoa, 190
Kuroshio (Japan Current), 259

Labrador Current, 258
Laccolith, 193
Lagoon, 170
Lake George, 145
Lake Louise, 145
Lakes, 145
Land breeze, 411
Landslide, *84–85*
Laplace, 6
Lapse rate, dry adiabatic, 426;
    moist adiabatic, *427;* normal,
    378–79
Latitude, 358–60
Lava, 53, *181*, 183–85
Lava tunnel, 184
Law of Definite Proportions, 29
Law of Equal Areas, 303
Law of Original Horizontality, 212
Law of superposition, 490
Lemuroids, 526
Levee, artificial, *127;* natural, 125
Libby, Willard, 496
Lichens, *80*
Lick Observatory, 266

Lifting condensation level, 427
Lightning, *459*
Light year, 278
Lignite, 63
Limestone, 24, *62, 63*
Lithium, 27
Lithosphere, 13
Lobe-finned fishes, 508
Local Group, 286
Lodestone, 48
Loess, 157–58
Long Lake, 145
Long Island, 147
Longitude, 358–60
Longshore current, 165–66, *169*
Long waves (ocean), 167
Lost rivers, 106
Lows, 450–56, *453, 454, 455*
Low tide, 340–41
Lunar craters, 325–28
Lunar maria, 324–28
Lunar Orbiter, 329
Lunar spacecraft, 323, *332*
Lungfish, 508
Luster, 38

Magellanic Clouds, 286, *288*
Magma, 53, *181*, 183–84, 192–94
Magnetic storm, 299
Magnetism of earth, 361; of minerals, 43
Magnetite, 43, 48
Magnitude of star, 279–*280*; absolute magnitude, *280*
Malachite, *37*
Mammals, 526–30
Mammoths, 528–30
Manganese nodule, 248
Magnetic storms, 299
Mantle, 9
Marble, 68
Mare basalts, 331
Maria (lunar), 324–28
Mariana Trench, 225, 240
Marine climate, 231
Mars, *309, 310*
Mass movement, 84–86
Mastodons, 527–30
Matterhorn, *140*.
Mauna Loa, *187*, 190–91
Maury, Matthew, 225
Meander, *122*
Measuring precipitation, 435

Mediterranean current, 253
Megatherium, 528
Mercury (planet), 306, *307*, 319
Meridians, 358, 360
Mesa, 158
Mesosphere, 375
Mesozoic era, 490, 515–22
Metals, 30
Metamorphic rock, 52, 68–71
Metamorphism, dynamic, 68, *69;* rock cycle, *71*
Meteor, 317
Meteor Crater, 318
Meteorites, *317*
Meteoroids, 317
Meteor showers, 318
Mica, *38, 39,* 45
Mica schist, *69*
Mid-Atlantic Ridge, 12–13, 182, *240*
Mid-ocean ridges, 237, 240
Milky Way, 285–86
Millibar, 392
Minerals, 24–34, 37–48
Mineral springs, 103
Mineral tests, acid test, 42–43; color, 37–38; crystal shape, 39; luster, 38; specific gravity, *42;* double refraction, *43;* fluorescence, *43;* radioactivity, *43*
Miocene epoch, 527
Mississippian period, 509
Mixed layer of ocean, 232
Mixture, 29
Mosasaurs, 521
Mojave Desert, 437
Mohorovicic discontinuity or Moho, *206*
Mohs' scale of hardness, 41
Moist-adiabatic lapse rate, 427
Molecule, 29
Mollusks, 525
Monsoons, 255–56, 409–10
Monterey Canyon, 238
Moon, 323–43
Moraine, 137–38
Moraine-dammed lake, 145
Morning star, 306, *307*, 318
Moulton, 4–5
Mountain breeze, 411
Mountain glacier, 134
Mount Everest, *225*
Mount Lassen, 187
Mount Palomar Observatory, 267
Mount Pelée, 185, 190

Mountains, 210–20, 415
Mount Wilson Observatory, 265
Mud cracks, 66
Mudflow, 85
Mud volcano, 107
Muscovite mica, *45*

Nansen bottle, *228*, 233
Natural bridge, 104, *105*, 158, *159*
Natural levee, 125
Nautical mile, 359, 360
Nazca plate, 182
Neap tide, 341–42
Nebulae, 292, *293*
Nebular hypothesis, *6*
Neptune, 312
Neutrons, 26
Newton, Isaac, 340
Niagara Falls, *120, 121*, 497
Nimbostratus, 423
Nonmetals, 30
Normal fault, *215*
North, finding, 361–62
North Atlantic Deep Water, 254–55
North Atlantic Drift, 258
North Star, 292, 361
Nova, 282
Nova explosion hypothesis, *282*
Nucleus of atom, 26
Nunatak, 135

Oasis, 100
Oblate spheroid, 17, 305
Obsidian, *40, 54,* 57
Ocean, 8, 236–37; currents, 252–60, 472, 475; temperature, 232–33, 472
Octant, 362–63
Offshore bar, 170, *171*
Oil, see Petroleum
Oligocene epoch, 526–27
Olivine, *46*
Olympus Mons, 310
Oozes, 245
Ordovician period, 507
Oreodons, 527
Orionids, 318
Orthoclase feldspar, *45*
Ostracoderm, 507
Ouachita Mountains, 506, 512
Outcrops, 23
Outer core, 9

Outwash, 142
Outwash plain, 144
Oxbow lake, 122
Oxidation, 80
Oxygen in ocean, 231
Ozonosphere, 374

Pahoehoe, *184*
Paint pot, 101
Paleocene epoch, 526
Paleography, 498
Paleozoic era, 490, 505–12
Palisades, 193, 515
Pangaea, *10*
Parallelism of axis, 351
Parallels, 358–59
Parícutin, 186
Peat, 63
Pedalfer, 89
Pedocal, 89
Pelecypod, 507
Pennsylvanian period, 510
Penumbra, 337–39
Perigee, 338
Perihelion, 304
Period of wave, 163
Permafrost, 101
Permeability of rocks, *96–97*
Permian period, 511–12
Perseids, 318
Petroleum, 64
Petrified trees, 107
Phases of moon, 335–36
Phosphorescent, 43
Photography underwater, 248
Photosphere, *298*
Pillow lava, 184
Pilot balloon, 399
Phyllite, *69*
Plagioclase feldspar, *45*
Plane of the earth's orbit, 347
Plane of the ecliptic, 304
Planetesimal hypothesis, *4–5*
Planetoid, 7
Planets, 301–19
Plankton, 231
Plate tectonics, 12–13, 180–83,
    203–05, 219–20
Plateau, 216
Pleistocene epoch, 490
Pliohippus, 528
Plunge pool, 119
Pluto, 312
Polar creep, 233, 254

Polar easterlies, 408, 413
Polar front, 404
Polar high, 405, 408
Polaris, *291*
Pollution, environmental, 479, *480,
    481, 482, 483*
Porosity of rock, 61, *96*
Porphyry, *55*
Potassium-argon dating, 496
Pothole, 119
Precambrian time, 502–04
Precambrian shields, 503–04
Pressure gradient, 395
Prevailing westerlies, 408, 410, 413
Primary highs and lows, 395
Prime meridian, 360
Proterozoic era, 490, 502
Protons, 26
Protoplanet hypothesis, 7
Psychrometer, *418*, 419
Pterosaur, 518
Pulsars, 283
Pulsating star, 281
Pumice, *57*
Pyrite, 39

Quartz, 24, *38, 44*, 58
Quartzite, 68, 70
Quasars, 282
Quaternary period, 523, 529–31

Radar in weather, 464, 465
Radiation fogs, 422
Radiation (heat), 377
Radioactivity, 43, 494–96
Radio astronomy, 269
Radiocarbon dating, 496
Radio compass, 362
Radiolaria, 246
Radiosonde, *443*
Radio telescope, *270*
Rainbow Natural Bridge, 159
Raindrops, *432, 433*
Rainfall, 472–74
Rain gauge, 435
Rainmaking, 431, *432, 433*
Rancho La Brea, 530
Recent epoch, 490, 530
Red clays, 245
Red shift, 273
Reef, barrier, 170–71; coral,
    174–75; fringing, 175
Reflecting telescope, *267*

Refracting telescope, *266–67*
Refraction of ocean waves, *166,
    167*
Regolith, 331–32
Relative humidity, *418*, 418–20
Relief, 216
Reptiles, 525
Return wells, 100
Reverse fault, *215*
Rhyolite, *55, 58*
Richter scale, 203
Rift valley, ocean, 240
Rilles, 330
Rings of Saturn and Uranus,
    314–15
Rip current, 165
Ripple marks, 66
Roches moutonnées, 139
Rock cycle, 71
Rock flour, 138
Rock gypsum, *62*
Rocks, 24, 51–71; lunar, 331
Rock salt, *62*, 508
Rocky Mountains, 506
Ross ice shelf, 137
Rotation of the earth, 347–48
Rubidium-strontium dating, 496

Salinity of sea, 227–30
Salinometer, 228–29
Saltation, 153
San Andreas fault, 205, 211
Sand bars, 169–71
Sandstone, *61, 66*, 156
Sargasso Sea, 257, *258*
Satellites (natural) of planets,
    313–14
Saturated air, 417
Saturn, 312, 314–15
Schist, *69*
Schmidt telescope, 268
Sea arch, 169
Sea breeze, 411
Sea cave, 169, *210*
Sea cliff, 168
Sea floor spreading, 11–12
Sea lily, *509*
Seamount, 237, *241*
Seasons, *254*
Sea stack, *169*
Sedimentary rocks, 50, 51, 59–67
Sediment corer, *243, 244*
Seismogram, 201
Seismograph, 201

Seismologist, 200
Sequoia, 522, 524
Sextant, 362, *363*
Shale, *61*
Sharks, 521
Shield volcano, *187*, 188
Shiprock, 194
Shorelines, 169
Short-wave radiation, 268
Sierra Nevadas, 217, *218*, 523
Silica tetrahedron, *33*
Silicates, 33, 44–47
Siliceous oozes, 246
Sill, 192
Silt, 87–89
Silurian period, 507–08
Silver iodide, 433
Sink hole, 104
Sirius, 278–79
Slate, *69*
Sleet, 434
Smog, 428–29
Snow, *433*
Snow field, 132
Snow line, *133–34*
Sodium chloride, *30*
Soil profile, 87–*88*
Soils, 87–89; lunar, 331–32
Solar flare, 299
Solar prominences, 298
Solar system, 3–7, 300–19
Solar wind, 300
Solstices, 350–51, 353–54
Sounding, *241*, 242
Sphalerite, *38*
Specific gravity of earth, 19; of
    minerals, 34, *42*
Specific humidity, 417
Spectrograph, 271
Spectroscope, *270–73*
Spectrum, 272
Spectrum, absorption, 272; bright
    line, 271; continuous, 271; dark
    line, 272; electromagnetic, 268
Spiral galaxies, 287
Spit, 170
Springs, 99
Springs, hot, *101*
Springs, mineral, 103
Spring tide, 341–42
Squall line, 447
Stable state (stars), 284
Stalactite, 106
Stalagmite, 106
Standard time, 365, *366*, 367

Star characteristics, 276–83
Station model, 460
Stegosaurus, 520
Steno, Nicolaus, 212
Stock, 194
Stone Mountain, 79
Storms, *450*, 451
Stratification, 64, *65*
Stratiform clouds, 422
Stratocumulus, 423
Stratopause, 374
Stratosphere, 374
Stratus clouds, 423
Streak, mineral, 39
Stream piracy, *117*
Striations, 139
Strike, 215
Strike-slip fault, 215
Subglacial streams, 144
Submarine canyon, 232, 238, *239*
Subplates, 13
Subpolar low, 405, 408, 413
Sulfur, 25, *37*
Sun, 297–300
Sunspots, 298, *299*
Supercooled water, 423
Supergiant star, 280
Supernova, *282*
Supersaturated air, 417
Surf, *165*
Surf beats, 167
Surtsey, 186
Suspended load, 112–13
Swallow float, 259
Swells, 164
Syncline, 213

Taconic Mountains, 507
Talc, 47
Talus, *85*
Tarn, 145
Taurids, 318
Tectonics, plate, 12–13, 180–83,
    203–05, 219–20
Telescopes, 265–68
Temperature, atmospheric, 314,
    468–72
Temperature inversion, 381–82
Tertiary period, 523
Thermal metamorphism, 70
Thermocline, 232, *233*
Thermograph, *383*
Thermometers, 382–83
Thermosphere, 375

Thorium, 494–95
Thrust fault, 215
Thunderstorm, 458–59
Thunder, 459
Tidal hypothesis, *5*
Tidal wave, 160, 199–200
Tides, 340–43
Till, 142
Time, standard time belts, 366
Titanotheres, 527
Tornado, 456–58, *457*
Torricelli, 390
Torrid Zone, 354
Tower telescope, *297*
Trachodon, 520
Trade winds, 408, *412*
Transpiration, 93–94
Transported soils, 87
Trap rock, 58
Travertine, 107
Trench, ocean, 183, 225, 240
Triassic period, 515–17
Triceratops, 520
Trilobites, 506–07
Tropic of Cancer, 353
Tropic of Capricorn, 354
Tropical storms, 452–56
Tropopause, 374
Troposphere, 374
Trough of wave, 163
Tsunami, 160, 199, 200
Tuff, 185
Turbidity currents, 239, *252*
Typhoon, 452
Tyrannosaur, 519

Umbra, 337–39
Unconformity, *488*, *489*
Undertow, 165
Uniformitarianism, 51
Universe, origin, 288
Upwelling, 254–55
Uranium, 27
Uranus, 312, 315
Ursa Major, 290

Valley breeze, 411
Valley, drowned, 173
Valley glacier, 132
Valleys and canyons, *114*, *115*, *116*
Variable stars, 281
Varves, 496–97
Ventifact, *153*

Venus, *308*, 309, 318
Volcanic ash, *185*
Volcanic bombs, *185*
Volcanic neck, *194*
Volcanism, 181–94
Von Weizsacker, 7

Warm front, 450
Watchung Ridges, 515
Water, 93–127
Water budget, 94–95
Water cycle, 93–97, *94*
Waterfalls, *119–22*
Water gap, *118*
Water pollution, 479–82
Watershed, 117
Waterspout, 457

Water table, *96*, *98*, *99*
Wavelength, *163*
Waves (earthquake), 200
Waves (ocean), 162–67, 252
Weather forecasts, *462*, 463
Weathering, 77–83
Weather map, 394, 395, 428, 435, 460, *461*
Weather satellites, 465
Weather services, 462–63
Wegener, Alfred, 10–11
Weizsacker, von, 7
Wells, 99–100, 460
West Wind Drifts, 257
Wet-bulb thermometer, *461*
Whipple, F. L., 315
Whitecaps, 163–64
White dwarf stars, 281

Willy-willies, 452
Wind erosion, *152*, *153*, 154, 155
Wind gap, 118
Winds, 396–400, 403–13
Wind vane, 398
Woolly mammoth, *529*

Yazoo streams, 125
Yellowstone National Park, 107, 523
Yerkes Observatory, 266

Zenith, 353
Zone of aeration, 97
Zone of saturation, 97

Photo Credits

UNIT ONE: *1,* NASA

Chapter 2: *16,* NASA; *20,* Magnum by Dennis Stock.   **Chapter 3:** *25,* Ward's Natural Science Establishment, Inc.   **Chapter 4:** *37 left, right (top and bottom),* Jerome Wyckoff; *38 top, bottom (left and right),* Encyclopedia of Minerals by Roberts, 1974; *39,* Ward's Natural Science Establishment, Inc.; *40 top and bottom;,* Ward's Natural Science Establishment, Inc.; *43,* Jerome Wyckoff; *44 top (left and right), bottom (left and right),* Jerome Wyckoff; *45 top (left and right), bottom,* Jerome Wyckoff; *45 center,* Encyclopedia of Minerals, Roberts, 1974; *46 top (left and right), bottom,* Jerome Wyckoff; *47 top (left and right),* Ward's Natural Science Establishment, Inc.; *47 center and bottom,* Jerome Wyckoff.   **Chapter 5:** *51,* The Granger Collection; *54 top and bottom,* Jerome Wyckoff; *55 top (left and right), bottom,* Jerome Wyckoff; *56 top (left and right), bottom,* Jerome Wyckoff; *57 top,* Samuel Namowitz; *57 bottom,* Jerome Wyckoff; *58,* Jerome Wyckoff; *61 left, right (top and bottom),* Jerome Wyckoff; *62 top (left and right), bottom,* Jerome Wyckoff; *63 top left, bottom left,* Jerome Wyckoff; *63 right,* National Coal Assocation; *64,* Samuel Namowitz; *65,* Samuel Namowitz; *66 left,* Samuel Namowitz; *66 right,* Jerome Wyckoff; *67 top,* Jerome Wyckoff; *67 bottom,* Ward's Natural Science Establishment, Inc.; *68,* Jerome Wyckoff; *69 top right, center, bottom (left and right),* Jerome Wyckoff; *69 top left,* Specimen produced by Dr. Kurt Lowe.

UNIT TWO: *75,* Jerome Wyckoff

Chapter 6: *77,* Samuel Namowitz; *78,* Maurice Rosalsky; *79 top,* Maurice Rosalsky; *79 bottom,* Samuel Namowitz; *80,* Samuel Namowitz; *81,* Luray Caverns, Va.; *83,* June Lundborg; *85 top,* Ward's Natural Science Establishment, Inc.; *85 bottom,* Maurice Rosalsky; *88,* American Museum of Natural History.   **Chapter 7:** *98,* Jerome Wyckoff; *101,* Samuel Namowitz; *102 top,* Ray Seyd; *102 bottom,* Samuel Namowitz; *104 left and right,* Jerome Wyckoff; *105 top,* Jerome Wyckoff; *105 bottom,* Luray Caverns, Va.; *107,* Ray Seyd.   **Chapter 8:** *111,* Samuel Namowitz; *114,* Maurice Rosalsky; *115,* Samuel Namowitz; *116 top and bottom,* Jerome Wyckoff; *118,* Jerome Wyckoff; *119,* Jerome Wyckoff; *121* Niagara Falls; *122 top,* Jerome Wyckoff; *122 bottom,* Albert Corwin; *123,* U.S. Army, Corps of Engineers; *124,* Maurice Rosalsky; *126,* U.S. Air Force Photo; *127 top,* Woodfin Camp and Associates by Rod Hanna; *127 bottom,* Maurice Rosalsky.   **Chapter 9:** *132,* Jerome Wyckoff; *133,* Fred Tickner; *135 top and bottom,* Samuel Namowitz; *136,* Samuel Namowitz; *137,* Maurice Rosalsky; *138 top,* U.S. Forest Service; *138 bottom,* Maurice Rosalsky; *139 left and right,* Jerome Wyckoff; *140,* Maurice Rosalsky; *141,* Ward's Natural Science Establishment, Inc.; *142,* Jerome Wyckoff; *143 top and bottom,* Ward's Natural Science Establishment, Inc.; *144* and *147,* Ward's Natural Science Establishment, Inc.   **Chapter 10:** *152,* Soil Conservation Service; *153,* Campbell, U.S. Geological Survey; *154 top,* U.S. Geological Survey; *154 bottom,* Soil Conservation Service; *155,* Gilbert, U.S. Geological Survey; *156* Museum of Natural History; *157 top,* Gregory, U.S. Geological Survey; *157 bottom,* Shaw, U.S. Geological Survey; *159 left,* Darton, U.S. Geological Survey; *159 right,* Gregory, U.S. Geological Survey; **Chapter 11:** *162,* Black Star; *165,* Steve Wilkings (Focus on Sports); *167,* Southern Pacific Photo; *171,* Fairchld Aerial Surveys; *173 top,* Fairchild Aerial Surveys; *173 bottom,* Norwegian National Travel Office; *174,* Stose, U.S. Geological Survey; *175,* Ward's Science Establishment, Inc.; *176,* U.S. Air Force Photo.

UNIT THREE: *179,* Icelandic National Tourist Office

Chapter 12: *184 left,* Soil Conservation Service; *184 right,* Mendenhall, U.S. Geological Survey; *185 top,* Stearns, U.S. Geological Survey; *185 bottom,* painting by Charles R. Knight, American Museum of Natural History; *186,* Ward's Natural Science Establishment, Inc.; *187,* U.S. Air Force Photo; *188,* American Museum of Natural History; *189,* Carl B. Lewis; *190,* UPI; *191,* U.S. Air Force; *192 top,* Stose, U.S. Geological Survey; *193 center,* R. L. Christie, Geological Survey of Canada; *193 bottom,* Darton, U.S. Geological Survey; *194* Dutton, U.S. Geological Survey.   **Chapter 13:** *198,* NOAA; *203,* ESSA.   **Chapter 14:** *210,* U.S. Geological Survey; *212,* Darton, U.S. Geological Survey; *213,* Keith, U.S. Geological Survey; *214,* Russell, U.S. Geological Survey; *215 left and right,* Ward's Natural Science Establishment, Inc.; *216,* Jerome Wyckoff; *218,* Jerome Wyckoff.

UNIT FOUR: *223,* Editorial Photo Color Archives, Inc.

Chapter 15: *226 top and bottom,* The Granger Collection;, *227,* Woods Hole Oceanographic Institute; *228 top left,* Woods Hole Oceanographic Institute; *228 center (left and right),* John A. Kostecki, Lamont-Doherty Geological Observatory; *230 top and bottom,* Leslie Salt Co.,; *231 top,* Richard B. Hoover; *231 bottom,* Magnum by David Pilosof; *233,* John A. Kostecki, Lamont-Doherty Geological Observatory.   **Chapter 16:** *242 top and bottom,* Woods Hole Oceanographic Institute; *243,* John A. Kostecki, Lamont-Doherty Geological Observatory; *244 left and center,* NOAA; *244, top right,* John A. Kostecki; Lamont-Doherty Geological Observatory; *247,* Lamont-Doherty Geological Observatory.   **Chapter 17:** *259,* John A. Kostecki, Lamont-Doherty Geological Observatory.

UNIT FIVE: *263,* Mount Wilson and Palomar Observatories

Chapter 18: *265,* Mount Wilson and Palomar Observatories; *266,* Lick Observatory; *267,* Lick Observatory; *270, left,* Central Office of Information; *270 right,* Commonwealth of Puerto Rico; *271,* Lick Observatory; *273,* Lick Observatory.   **Chapter 19:** *282 top left,* Mount Wilson and Palomar Observatories; *282 center,* Lick Observatory; *286,* American Museum of Natural History; *287 top,* Lick Observatory; *287 bottom,* Mount Wilson and Palomar Observatories; *288,* Yerkes Observatory; *289,* Mount Wilson and Palomar Observatories; *292,* Lick Observatory; *293 left,* Lick Observatory; *293 right,* Mount Wilson and Palomar Observatories.   **Chapter 20:** *297,* NSF Photo; *298 left,* Perkin-Elmer Corporation; *298 right,* Mount Wilson and Palomar Observatories; *299 left and right,* Mount Wilson and Palomar Observatories; *307 left and right,* NASA; *308,* NASA; *309,* NASA; *310,* Lowell Observatory; *311,* NASA; *312,* Lick Observatory; *313,* NASA; *314,* Mount Wilson and Palomar Observatories; *316,* Mount Wilson and Palomar Observatories; *317,* American Museum of Natural History; *319,* U.S. Navy Photo.   **Chapter 21:** *323,* NASA; *324,* NASA; *327,* Mount Wilson and Palomar Observatories; *328 left,* Lick Observatory; *328 right,* Mount Wilson and Palomar Observatories; *329 top,* Mount Wilson and Palomar Observatories; *329 bottom,* NASA; *330 left,* NASA; *330 right,* NASA; *331,* NASA; *332 top,* NASA; *332 bottom,* NASA; *336,* Yerkes Observatory; *339,* Lick Observatory.   **Chapter 22:** *352,* National Film Board of Canada.   **Chapter 23:** *363,* U.S. Navy Photo.

UNIT SIX: *371,* World Wide Photo

Chapter 24: *283,* Taylor Instrument Co.   **Chapter 25:** *391 left and right,* Taylor Instrument Co.; *398,* U.S. National Weather Service; *399,* Photo Researchers, Inc. by Russ Kinne.   **Chapter 27:** *418,* Taylor Instrument Co.; *425,* U.S. National Weather Service; *426 left and right,* U.S. National Weather Service; *429,* World Wide Photo.   **Chapter 28:** *433,* American Museum of Natural History; *434 top and bottom,* U.S. National Weather Service; *435,* U.S. National Weather Service.   **Chapter 29:** *443 left and right,* NOAA *447 right,* NASA.   **Chapter 30:** *453,* Magnum by Leonard Freed; *456 left,* NOAA; *456 right,* UPI; *457,* Mrs. Ray Homer, U.S. National Weather Service; *459,* Ward's Natural Science Establishment, Inc.; *462,* The New York Times; *463,* NOAA; *464,* NOAA.   **Chapter 31:** *472,* Woods Hole Oceanographic Institute.   **Chapter 32:** *478,* Magnum by Arthur Tress; *480 left and right* Magnum by Paul Fusco; *481 left,* Magnum by James H. Kareles; *481 right,* Magnum by Dave Healey; *482,* Magnum by Dave Healey; *483,* UPI.

UNIT SEVEN *485,* American Museum of Natural History

Chapter 33: *489,* Jerome Wyckoff; *491,* American Museum of Natural History; *492 top,* Ward's Natural Science Establishment, Inc.; *492 left,* American Museum of Natural History; *493,* Ward's Natural Science Establishment, Inc.; *497,* Ward's Natural Science Establishment, Inc.   **Chapter 34:** *502,* Field Museum of Natural History; *504,* Maurice Rosalsky; *506 left,* Ward's Natural Science Establishment, Inc.; *506 right,* American Museum of Natural History by Bruce Hunter; *507 top,* Ward's Natural Science Establishment, Inc.; *507 bottom,* American Museum of Natural History; *508 top,* Ward's Natural Science Establishment, Inc.; *508 bottom,* American Museum of Natural History; *509 top,* American Museum of Natural History; *509 bottom,* Ward's Natural Science Establishment, Inc.; *510,* American Museum of Natural History; *511 top,* American Museum of Natural History; *511 bottom,* Ray Seyd.   **Chapter 35:** *516 top (left and right),* National Park Service Photo by Fred Mang, Jr.; *516 bottom,* Ward's Natural Science Establishment, Inc.; *517 left,* Ray Seyd; *517 right,* Zion National Park; *518 top,* Field Museum of Natural History; *518 left center,* Ward's Natural Science Establishment, Inc.; *518 bottom (left and right),* American Museum of Natural History; *519,* Ward's Natural Science Establishment, Inc., Buffalo Museum, New York; *520 top and bottom,* American Museum of Natural History; *521,* Field Museum of Natural History; *522,* American Museum of Natural History; *523,* Samuel Namowitz; *524 left,* Ward's Natural Science Establishment, Inc.; *524 right,* Richard B. Hoover; *525,* Field Museum of Natural History; *527,* Field Museum of Natural History; *528,* American Museum of Natural History; *529 top,* American Museum of Natural History; *529 bottom,* Ward's Natural Science Establishment, Inc.; *530,* Field Museum of Natural History.

Appendix *537,* U.S. Geological Survey.